EX LIBRIS

THE MERRY ADVENTURES OF ROBIN HOOD

THE MERRY ADVENTURES OF ROBIN HOOD

HOWARD PYLE

ILLUSTRATED BY SCOTT McKOWEN

STERLING PUBLISHING CO., INC.

New York

LIBRARY OF CONGRESS CATALOGING-IN-PUBLICATION DATA AVAILABLE

2   4   6   8   10   9   7   5   3   1

BOOK DESIGN BY DEBORAH KERNER / DANCING BEARS DESIGN

Published in 2004 by Sterling Publishing Co., Inc.
387 Park Avenue South, New York, NY 10016
Editorial matter copyright © 2004 by Arthur Pober
Illustrations © 2004 by Scott McKowen
Distributed in Canada by Sterling Publishing
c/o Canadian Manda Group, 165 Dufferin Street
Toronto, Ontario, Canada M6K 3H6
Distributed in Great Britain and Europe by Chris Lloyd at Orca Book
Services, Stanley House, Fleets Lane, Poole BH15 3AJ, England
Distributed in Australia by Capricorn Link (Australia) Pty. Ltd.
P.O. Box 704, Windsor, NSW 2756, Australia

Sterling ISBN 1-4027-2207-9

CONTENTS

Part Third

Recounting three merry adventures that befell Robin Hood and certain others, by which he gained sore bones and three good merry men all in one day.
87

Part Fourth

In which it is told how Allan a Dale was brought to Robin Hood, who promised to help him in trouble. Also how Robin sought the curtal Friar of Fountain Abbey with that aim in view. Likewise it is recounted how Robin Hood brought two true lovers together that would else have been made unhappy all their lives.
125

Part Fifth

In which it is told how that Robin Hood met a sorrowful knight, and brought him to Sherwood. Also, how the Bishop of Hereford was more generous than he desired to be. Likewise it is told how Sir Richard of the Lea paid his debts in due season, both to the Prior of Emmet and to Robin Hood.
171

Contents

Part Sixth

*In which it is told how that Robin Hood and Little John turned,
the one a beggar and the other a strolling Friar, and went forth to
seek adventures. Likewise it is told how Little John prayed to some
purpose, and how Robin Hood drubbed four beggars and outwitted a corn engrosser.*
205

Part Seventh

*In which it is told how Queen Eleanor sent for Robin Hood to
come to the Court at famous London Town, and how Robin
Hood came at her bidding. Likewise, it is told how King Henry
chased Robin through the land, yet caught him not.*
241

Part Eighth

*In which it is told how Robin Hood met Guy of Gisbourne in
Sherwood Forest, and of the famous fight betwixt them. Also, how
Little John fell into the Sheriff's hands through saving the life of
three men. Likewise, it is told how good King Richard of the
Lion's Heart came to Nottinghamshire and visited Robin Hood in
Sherwood Forest.*
281

Epilogue

Telling how Robin Hood came back again to Sherwood Forest, and how Sir William Dale was sent against him to take him. Likewise it is told how Robin Hood died by the treachery of his cousin, the Prioress of the Nunnery of Kirklees.
319

THE MERRY ADVENTURES OF ROBIN HOOD

PREFACE
FROM THE AUTHOR TO THE READER

You who so plod amid serious things that you feel it shame to give yourself up even for a few short moments to mirth and joyousness in the land of Fancy; you who think that life hath nought to do with innocent laughter that can harm no one; these pages are not for you. Clap to the leaves and go no farther than this, for I tell you plainly that if you go farther you will be scandalized by seeing good, sober folks of real history so frisk and caper in gay colors and motley, that you would not know them but for the names tagged to them. Here is a stout, lusty fellow with a quick temper, yet none so ill for all that, who goes by the name of Henry II. Here is a fair, gentle lady before whom all the others bow and call her Queen Eleanor. Here is a fat rogue of a fellow, dressed up in rich robes of a clerical kind, that all the good folk call my Lord Bishop of Hereford. Here is a certain fellow with a sour temper and a grim look—the worshipful, the Sheriff of Nottingham. And here, above all, is a great, tall, merry fellow that roams the greenwood and joins in homely sports, and sits beside the Sheriff at merry feast, which same beareth the name of the proudest of the

Plantagenets—Richard of the Lion's Heart. Beside these there are a whole host of knights, priests, nobles, burghers, yeomen, pages, ladies, lasses, landlords, beggars, pedlers, and what not, all living the merriest of merry lives, and all bound by nothing but a few odd strands of certain old ballads (snipped and clipped and tied together again in a score of knots) which draw these jocund fellows here and there, singing as they go.

Here you will find a hundred dull, sober, jogging places, all tricked out with flowers and what not, till no one would know them in their fanciful dress. And here is a country bearing a well-known name, wherein no chill mists press upon our spirits, and no rain falls but what rolls off our backs like April showers off the backs of sleek drakes; where flowers bloom forever and birds are always singing; where every fellow hath a merry catch as he travels the roads, and ale and beer and wine (such as muddle no wits) flow like water in a brook.

This country is not Fairy-land. What is it? 'Tis the land of Fancy, and is of that pleasant kind that, when you tire of it,—whisk!—you clap the leaves of this book together and 'tis gone, and you are ready for every-day life, with no harm done.

And now I lift the curtain that hangs between here and No-man's-land. Will you come with me, sweet Reader? I thank you. Give me your hand.

PROLOGUE

Giving an account of Robin Hood and his adventure with the King's foresters. Also telling how his Band gathered around him; and of the merry adventure that gained him his good right-hand man, the famous Little John.

IN MERRY ENGLAND IN THE TIME OF OLD, WHEN GOOD KING HENRY THE Second ruled the land, there lived within the green glades of Sherwood Forest, near Nottingham Town, a famous outlaw whose name was Robin Hood. No archer ever lived that could speed a gray goose shaft with such skill and cunning as his, nor were there ever such yeomen as the sevenscore merry men that roamed with him through the greenwood shades. Right merrily they dwelt within the depths of Sherwood Forest, suffering neither care nor want, but passing the time in merry games of archery or bouts of cudgel play, living upon the King's venison, washed down with draughts of ale of October brewing.

Not only Robin himself but all the band were outlaws and dwelt apart from other men, yet they were beloved by the country people round about, for no one ever came to jolly Robin for help in time of need and went away again with an empty fist.

And now I will tell how it first came about that Robin Hood fell afoul of the law.

When Robin was a youth of eighteen, stout of sinew and bold of heart, the Sheriff of Nottingham proclaimed a shooting-match and offered a prize of a butt of ale to whomsoever should shoot the best shaft in Nottinghamshire. "Now," quoth Robin, "will I go too, for fain would I draw a string for the bright eyes of my lass, and a butt of good October brewing." So up he got and took his good stout yew bow and a score or more of broad clothyard arrows, and started off from Locksley Town through Sherwood Forest to Nottingham.

It was at the dawn of day in the merry May-time, when hedgerows are green and flowers bedeck the meadows; daisies pied and yellow cuckoo buds and fair primroses all along the briery hedges; when apple buds blossom and sweet birds sing, the lark at dawn of day, the throstle cock and cuckoo; when the lads and lasses look upon each other with sweet thoughts; when busy housewives spread their linen to bleach upon the bright green grass. Sweet was the greenwood as he walked along its paths, and bright the green and rustling leaves, amid which the little birds sang with might and main: and blithely Robin whistled as he trudged along, thinking of Maid Marian and her bright eyes, for at such times a youth's thoughts are wont to turn pleasantly upon the lass that he loves the best.

As thus he walked along with a brisk step and a merry whistle, he came suddenly upon some foresters seated beneath a great oak tree. Fifteen there were in all, making themselves merry with feasting and drinking as they sat around a huge pasty, to which each man helped himself, thrusting his hands into the pie, and washing down that which they ate with great horns of ale which they drew all foaming from a barrel that stood nigh. Each man was clad in Lincoln green, and a fine show they made, seated upon the sward beneath that fair, spreading tree. Then one of them, with his mouth full, called out to Robin,—

"Halloa, where goest thou, little lad, with thy one penny bow and thy farthing shafts?"

Then Robin grew angry, for no stripling likes to be taunted with his green years.

"Now," quoth he, "my bow and eke mine arrows are as good as thine; and moreover, I go to the shooting-match at Nottingham Town, which same has been proclaimed by our good Sheriff of Nottinghamshire; there I will shoot with other stout yeomen, for a prize has been offered of a fine butt of ale."

Then one who held a horn of ale in his hand, said, "Ho! listen to the lad! Why, boy, thy mother's milk is yet scarce dry upon thy lips, and yet thou pratest of standing up with good stout men at Nottingham butts, thou who art scarce able to draw one string of a two stone bow."

"I'll hold the best of you twenty marks," quoth bold Robin, "that I hit the clout at threescore rods, by the good help of Our Lady fair."

At this all laughed aloud, and one said, "Well boasted, thou fair infant, well boasted! and well thou knowest that no target is nigh to make good thy wager."

And another cried, "He will be taking ale with his milk next."

At this Robin grew right mad. "Hark ye," said he; "yonder, at the glade's end, I see a herd of deer, even more than threescore rods distant. I'll hold you twenty marks that, by leave of Our Lady, I cause the best hart among them to die."

"Now done!" cried he who had spoken first. "And here are twenty marks. I wager that thou causest no beast to die, with or without the aid of Our Lady."

Then Robin took his good yew bow in his hand, and placing the tip at his instep, he strung it right deftly; then he nocked a broad clothyard arrow, and, raising the bow, drew the gray goose-feather to his ear; the next moment the bowstring rang and the arrow sped down the glade as a sparrowhawk skims in a northern wind. High leaped the noblest hart of all the herd, only to fall dead, reddening the green path with his heart's blood.

"Ha!" cried Robin, "how likest thou that shot, good fellow? I wot the wager were mine, an it were three hundred pounds."

Then all the foresters were filled with rage, and he who had spoken the first and had lost the wager was more angry than all.

"Nay," cried he, "the wager is none of thine, and get thee gone, straightway, or, by all the saints of heaven, I'll baste thy sides until thou wilt ne'er be able to walk again."

"Knowest thou not," said another, "that thou hast killed the King's deer, and, by the laws of our gracious lord and sovereign, King Harry, thine ears should be shaven close to thy head?"

"Catch him!" cried a third.

"Nay," said a fourth, "let him e'en go because of his tender years."

Never a word said Robin Hood, but he looked at the foresters with a grim face; then, turning on his heel, strode away from them down the forest glade. But his heart was bitterly angry, for his blood was hot and youthful and prone to boil.

Now, well would it have been for him who had first spoken had he left Robin Hood alone; but his anger was hot, both because the youth had gotten the better of him and because of the deep draughts of ale that he had been quaffing. So, of a sudden, without any warning, he sprang to his feet, and seized upon his bow and fitted it to a shift. "Ay," cried he, "and I'll hurry thee anon;" and he sent the arrow whistling after Robin.

It was well for Robin Hood that the same forester's head was spinning with ale, or else he would never have taken another step; as it was, the arrow whistled within three inches of his head. Then he turned around and quickly drew his own bow, and sent an arrow back in return.

"Ye said I was no archer," cried he aloud, "but say so now again!"

The shaft flew straight; the archer fell forward with a cry, and lay on his face upon the ground, his arrows rattling about him from out of his quiver, the gray goose shaft wet with his heart's blood. Then, before the others could gather their wits about them, Robin Hood was gone into the depths of the greenwood. Some started after him, but not with much heart, for each feared to suffer the death of his fellow; so presently they all came and lifted the dead man up and bore him away to Nottingham Town.

Meanwhile Robin Hood ran through the greenwood. Gone was all the joy and brightness from everything, for his heart was sick within him, and it was borne in upon his soul that he had slain a man.

"Alas!" cried he, "thou hast found me an archer that will make thy wife to wring! I would that thou hadst ne'er said one word to me, or that I had never passed thy way, or e'en that my right forefinger had been stricken off ere that this had happened! In haste I smote, but grieve I sore at leisure!" And then, even in his trouble, he remembered the old saw that "What is done is done; and the egg cracked cannot be cured."

And so he came to dwell in the greenwood that was to be his home for many a year to come, never again to see the happy days with the lads and lasses of sweet Locksley Town; for he was outlawed, not only because he had killed a man, but also because he had poached upon the King's deer, and two hundred pounds were set upon his head, as a reward for whoever would bring him to the court of the King.

Now the Sheriff of Nottingham swore that he himself would bring this knave, Robin Hood, to justice, and for two reasons: first, because he wanted the two hundred pounds, and next, because the forester that Robin Hood had killed was of kin to him.

But Robin Hood lay hidden in Sherwood Forest for one year, and in that time there gathered around him many others like himself, cast out from other folk for this cause and for that. Some had shot deer in hungry winter time, when they could get no other food, and had been seen in the act by the foresters, but had escaped, thus saving their ears; some had been turned out of their inheritance, that their farms might be added to the King's lands in Sherwood Forest; some had been despoiled by a great baron or a rich abbot or a powerful esquire,—all, for one cause or another, had come to Sherwood to escape wrong and oppression.

So, in all that year, fivescore or more good stout yeomen gathered about Robin Hood, and chose him to be their leader and chief. Then they vowed that even as they themselves had been despoiled they would despoil their oppressors, whether baron, abbot, knight, or squire, and that from each they would take that which had been wrung from the poor by unjust taxes, or land rents, or in wrongful fines; but to the poor folk they would give a helping hand in need and trouble, and would return to them that which had been unjustly taken from them. Beside this, they swore never to harm a child nor to wrong a woman, be she maid, wife, or widow; so that, after a while, when the people began to find that no harm was meant to them, but that money or food came in time of want to many a poor family, they came to praise Robin and his merry men, and to tell many tales of him and of his doings in Sherwood Forest, for they felt him to be one of themselves.

Up rose Robin Hood one merry morn when all the birds were singing blithely among the leaves, and up rose all his merry men, each fellow washing his head and hands in the cold brown brook that leaped laughing from stone to stone. Then said Robin: "For fourteen days have we seen no sport, so now I will go abroad to seek adventures forthwith. But tarry ye, my merry men all, here in the greenwood; only see that ye mind well my call. Three blasts upon the bugle horn I will blow in my hour of need; then come quickly, for I shall want your aid."

So saying, he strode away through the leafy forest glades until he had come to the verge of Sherwood. There he wandered for a long time, through highway and byway, through dingly dell and forest skirts. Now he met a fair buxom lass in a shady lane, and each gave the other a merry word and passed their way; now he saw a fair lady upon an ambling pad, to whom he doffed his cap, and who bowed sedately in return to the fair youth; now he saw a fat monk on a pannier-laden ass; now a gallant knight, with spear and shield and armor that flashed brightly in the sunlight; now a page clad in crimson; and now a stout burgher from good Nottingham Town, pacing along with serious footsteps; all these sights he saw, but adventure found he none. At last he took a road by the forest skirts; a bypath that dipped toward a broad, pebbly stream spanned by a narrow bridge made of a log of wood. As he drew nigh this bridge he saw a tall stranger coming from the other side. Thereupon Robin quickened his pace, as did the stranger likewise; each thinking to cross first.

"Now stand thou back," quoth Robin, "and let the better man cross first."

"Nay," answered the stranger, "then stand back thine own self, for the better man, I wot, am I."

"That will we presently see," quoth Robin; "and meanwhile stand thou where thou art, or else, by the bright brow of Saint Ælfrida, I will show thee right good Nottingham play with a clothyard shaft betwixt thy ribs."

"Now," quoth the stranger, "I will tan thy hide till it be as many colors as a beggar's cloak, if thou darest so much as touch a string of that same bow that thou holdest in thy hands."

"Thou pratest like an ass," said Robin, "for I could send this shaft clean through thy proud heart before a curtal friar could say grace over a roast goose at Michaelmastide."

"And thou pratest like a coward," answered the stranger, "for thou standest there with a good yew bow to shoot at my heart, while I have nought in my hand but a plain blackthorn staff wherewith to meet thee."

"Now," quoth Robin, "by the faith of my heart, never have I had a coward's name in all my life before. I will lay by my trusty bow and eke my arrows, and if thou darest abide my coming, I will go and cut a cudgel to test thy manhood withal."

"Ay, marry, that will I abide thy coming, and joyously, too," quoth the stranger; whereupon he leaned sturdily upon his staff to await Robin.

Then Robin Hood stepped quickly to the coverside and cut a good staff of ground oak, straight, without flaw, and six feet in length, and came back trimming away the tender stems from it, while the stranger waited for him, leaning upon his staff, and whistling as he gazed round about. Robin observed him furtively as he trimmed his staff, measuring him from top to toe from out the corner of his eye, and thought that he had never seen a lustier or a stouter man. Tall was Robin, but taller was the stranger by a head and a neck, for he was seven feet in height. Broad was Robin across the shoulders, but broader was the stranger by twice the breadth of a palm, while he measured at least an ell around the waist.

"Nevertheless," said Robin to himself, "I will baste thy hide right merrily, my good fellow;" then, aloud, "Lo, here is my good staff, lusty and tough. Now wait my coming, an thou darest, and meet me, an thou fearest not; then we will fight until one or the other of us tumble into the stream by dint of blows."

"Marry, that meeteth my whole heart!" cried the stranger, twirling his staff above his head, betwixt his fingers and thumb, until it whistled again.

Never did the Knights of Arthur's Round Table meet in a stouter fight than did these two. In a moment Robin stepped quickly upon the bridge where the stranger stood; first he made a feint, and then delivered a blow at the stranger's head that, had it met its mark, would have tumbled him speedily into the water; but the stranger turned the blow right deftly, and in return gave one as stout, which Robin also turned as the stranger had done. So they stood, each in his place, neither moving a finger's breadth back, for one good hour, and many blows were given and received by each in that time, till here and there were sore bones and bumps, yet neither thought of crying "Enough," or seemed likely to fall from off the bridge. Now and then they stopped to rest, and each thought that he never had seen in all his life before such a hand at quarterstaff. At last Robin gave the stranger a blow upon the ribs that made his jacket smoke like a damp straw thatch in the sun. So shrewd was the stroke that the stranger came within a hair's breadth of falling off the bridge; but he regained himself right quickly, and, by a dexterous blow, gave Robin a crack on the crown that caused the blood to flow. Then Robin grew mad with anger, and smote with all his might at the other; but the stranger warded the blow, and once again thwacked Robin, and this time so fairly that he fell heels over head into the water, as the queen pin falls in a game of bowls.

"And where art thou now, good lad?" shouted the stranger, roaring with laughter.

"Oh, in the flood and floating adown with the tide," cried Robin; nor could he forbear laughing himself at his sorry plight. Then, gaining his feet, he waded to the bank, the little fish speeding hither and thither, all frightened at his splashing.

"Give me thy hand," cried he, when he had reached the bank. "I must needs own thou art a brave and a sturdy soul, and, withal, a good stout stroke with the cudgels. By this and by that, my head hummeth like to a hive of bees on a hot June day."

Then he clapped his horn to his lips, and winded a blast that went echoing sweetly down the forest paths. "Ay, marry," quoth he again, "thou art a tall lad, and eke a brave one, for ne'er, I trow, is there a man betwixt here and Canterbury Town could do the like to me that thou has done."

"And thou," quoth the stranger, laughing, "takest thy cudgelling like a brave heart and a stout yeoman."

But now the distant twigs and branches rustled with the coming of men, and suddenly a score or two of good stout yeomen, all clad in Lincoln green, burst from out the covert, with merry Will Stutely at their head.

"Good master," cried Will, "how is this? Truly thou art all wet from head to foot, and that to the very skin."

"Why, marry," answered jolly Robin, "yon stout fellow hath tumbled me neck and crop into the water, and hath given me a drubbing beside."

"Then shall he not go without a ducking and eke a drubbing himself!" cried Will Stutely. "Have at him, lads!"

Then Will and a score of yeomen leaped upon the stranger, but though they sprang quickly they found him ready and felt him strike right and left with his stout staff, so that, though he went down with press of numbers, some of them rubbed cracked crowns before he was overcome.

"Nay, forbear!" cried Robin, laughing until his sore sides ached again; "he is a right good man and true, and no harm shall befall him. Now hark ye, good youth, wilt thou stay with me and be one of my band? Three suits of Lincoln green shalt thou have each year, beside forty marks in fee, and share with us whatsoever good shall befall us. Thou shalt eat sweet venison and quaff the stoutest ale, and mine own good right-hand man shalt thou be, for never did I see such a cudgel-player in all my life before. Speak! wilt thou be one of my good merry men?"

"That know I not," quoth the stranger, surlily, for he was angry at being so tumbled about. "If ye handle yew bow and apple shaft no better than ye do oaken cudgel, I wot ye are not fit to be called yeomen in my country; but if there be any man here that can shoot a better shaft than I, then will I bethink me of joining with you."

"Now by my faith," said Robin, "thou art a right saucy varlet, sirrah; yet I will stoop to thee as I never stooped to man before. Good Stutely, cut thou a fair white piece of bark four fingers in breadth, and set it forescore yards distant on yonder oak. Now, stranger, hit that fairly with a gray goose shaft and call thyself an archer."

"Ay, marry, that will I," answered he. "Give me a good stout bow and fair broad arrow, and if I hit it not strip me and beat me blue with bow-strings."

Then he chose the stoutest bow amongst them all, next to Robin's own, and a straight gray goose shaft, well-feathered and smooth, and stepping the mark—while all the band, sitting or lying upon the greensward, watched to see him shoot—he drew the arrow to his cheek and loosed the shaft right deftly, sending it so straight down the path that it clove the mark in the very centre. "Aha!" cried he, "mend thou that if thou canst;" while even the yeomen clapped their hands at so fair a shot.

"That is a keen shot, indeed," quoth Robin, "mend it I cannot, but mar it I may, perhaps."

Then taking up his own good stout bow and nocking an arrow with care he shot with his very greatest skill. Straight flew the arrow, and so true that it lit fairly upon the stranger's shaft and split it into splinters. Then all the yeomen leaped to their feet and shouted for joy that their master had shot so well.

"Now by the lusty yew bow of good Saint Withold," cried the stranger, "that is a shot indeed, and never saw I the like in all my life before! Now truly will I be thy man henceforth and for aye. Good Adam Bell was a fair shot, but never shot he so!"

"Then have I gained a right good man this day," quoth jolly Robin. "What name goest thou by, good fellow."

"Men call me John Little whence I came," answered the stranger.

Then Will Stutely, who loved a good jest, spoke up. "Nay, fair little stranger," said he, "I like not thy name and fain would I have it otherwise. Little art thou indeed, and small of bone and sinew, therefore shalt thou be christened Little John, and I will be thy godfather."

Then Robin Hood and all his band laughed aloud until the stranger began to grow angry.

"An thou make a jest of me," quoth he to Will Stutely, "thou wilt have sore bones and little pay, and that in short season."

"Nay, good friend," said Robin Hood, "bottle thine anger for the name fitteth thee well. Little John shall thou be called henceforth, and Little John shall it be. So come, my merry men, and we will go and prepare a christening feast for this fair infant."

So turning their backs upon the stream, they plunged into the forest once more, through which they traced their steps till they reached the spot where they dwelt in the depths of the woodland. There had they built huts of bark and branches of trees, and made couches of sweet rushes spread over with skins of fallow deer. Here stood a great oak tree with branches spreading broadly around, beneath which was a seat of green moss where Robin Hood was wont to sit at feast and at merrymaking with his stout men about him. Here they found the rest of the band, some of whom had come in with a brace of fat does. Then they all built great fires and after a time roasted the does and broached a barrel of humming ale. Then when the feast was ready they all sat down, but Robin Hood placed Little John at his right hand, for he was henceforth to be the second in the band.

Then when the feast was done Will Stutely spoke up. "It is now time, I ween, to christen our bonny babe, is it not so, merry boys?" And "Aye! Aye!" cried all, laughing till the woods echoed with their mirth.

"Then seven sponsors shall we have," quoth Will Stutely; and hunting among all the band he chose the seven stoutest men of them all.

"Now by Saint Dunstan," cried Little John, springing to his feet, "more than one of you shall rue it an you lay finger upon me."

But without a word they all ran upon him at once, seizing him by his legs and arms and holding him tightly in spite of his struggles, and they bore him forth while all stood around to see the sport. Then one came forward who had been chosen to play the priest because he had a bald crown, and in his hand he carried a brimming pot of ale. "Now who bringeth this babe?" asked he right soberly.

"That do I," answered Will Stutely.

"And what name callest thou him?"

"Little John call I him."

"Now Little John," quoth the mock priest, "thou hast not lived heretofore, but only got thee along through the world, but henceforth thou wilt live indeed. When thou livedst not thou wast called John Little, but now that thou dost live indeed, Little John shalt thou be called, so christen I thee." And at these last words he emptied the pot of ale upon Little John's head.

Then all shouted with laughter as they saw the good brown ale stream over Little John's beard and trickle from his nose and chin, while his eyes blinked with the smart of it. At first he was of a mind to be angry, but found he could not because the others were so merry; so he, too, laughed with the rest. Then Robin took this sweet, pretty babe, clothed him all anew from top to toe in Lincoln green, and gave him a good stout bow, and so made him a member of the merry band.

And thus it was that Robin Hood became outlawed; thus a band of merry companions gathered about him, and thus he gained his right-hand man, Little John; and so the prologue ends. And now I will tell how the Sheriff of Nottingham three times sought to take Robin Hood, and how he failed each time.

PART FIRST

Telling how the Sheriff of Nottingham swore that he would deal dole to Robin Hood. Also, how he made three trials threat, but missed each time by a good bow's length.

1

ROBIN HOOD AND
THE TINKER

NOW IT WAS TOLD BEFORE HOW TWO HUNDRED POUNDS WERE set upon Robin Hood's head, and how the Sheriff of Nottingham swore that he himself would seize Robin, both because he would fain have the two hundred pounds and because the slain man was a kinsman of his own. Now the Sheriff did not yet know what a force Robin had about him in Sherwood, but thought that he might serve a warrant for his arrest as he could upon any other man that had broken the laws; therefore he offered fourscore golden angels to any one who would serve this warrant. But men of Nottingham Town knew more of Robin Hood and his doings than the Sheriff did, and many laughed to think of serving a warrant upon the bold outlaw, knowing well that all they would get for such service would be cracked crowns; so that no one came forward to take the matter in hand. Thus a fortnight passed, in which time none came forward to do the Sheriff's business. Then said he: "A right good reward have I offered to whomsoever would serve my warrant upon Robin Hood, and I marvel that no one has come to undertake the task."

Then one of his men who was near him said: "Good master, thou wottest not the force that Robin Hood has about him and how little he cares for warrant of king or sheriff. Truly, no one likes to go on this service, for fear of cracked crowns and broken bones."

"Then I hold all Nottingham men to be cowards," said the Sheriff. "And let me see the man in all Nottinghamshire that dare disobey the warrant of our sovereign lord, King Harry, for, by the shrine of Saint Edmund, I will hang him forty cubits high! But if no man in Nottingham dare win fourscore angels, I will send elsewhere, for there should be men of mettle somewhere in this land."

Then he called up a messenger in whom he placed great trust, and bade him saddle his horse and make ready to go to Lincoln Town to see whether he could find any one there that would do his bidding, and win the reward. So that same morning the messenger started forth upon his errand.

Bright shone the sun upon the dusty highway that led from Nottingham to Lincoln, stretching away all white over hill and dale. Dusty was the highway and dusty the throat of the messenger, so that his heart was glad when he saw before him the sign of the Blue Boar Inn, when somewhat more than half his journey was done. The inn looked fair to his eyes, and the shade of the oak trees that stood around it seemed cool and pleasant, so he alighted from his horse to rest himself for a time, calling for a pot of ale to refresh his thirsty throat.

There he saw a party of right jovial fellows seated beneath the spreading oak that shaded the greensward in front of the door. There was a tinker, two barefoot friars, and a party of six of the King's foresters all clad in Lincoln green, and all them were quaffing humming ale and singing merry ballads of the good old times. Loud laughed the foresters, as jests were bandied about between the singing, and louder laughed the friars, for they were lusty men with beards that curled like the wool of black rams; but loudest of all laughed the Tinker, and he sang more sweetly than any of the rest. His bag and his hammer hung upon a twig of the oak tree, and near by leaned his good stout cudgel, as thick as his wrist and knotted at the end.

"Come," cried one of the foresters to the tired messenger, "come join us for this shot. Ho, landlord! bring a fresh pot of ale for each man."

The messenger was glad enough to sit down along with the others who were there, for his limbs were weary and the ale was good.

"Now what news bearest thou so fast?" quoth one, "and wither ridest thou today?"

The messenger was a chatty soul and loved a bit of gossip dearly; beside the pot of ale warmed his heart; so that, settling himself in an easy corner of the inn bench, while the host leaned upon the doorway and the hostess stood with her hands beneath her apron, he unfolded his budget of news with great comfort. He told all from the very first: how Robin Hood had slain the forester, and how he had hidden in the greenwood to escape the law; how that he lived therein, all against the law, God wot, slaying his Majesty's deer and levying toll on fat abbot, knight, and esquire, so that none dare travel even on the broad Watling Street or the Foss Way for fear of him; how that the Sheriff, Heaven save his worship, who paid him, the messenger, sixpence every Saturday night, of good broad money stamped with the King's head, beside ale at Michaelmas and a fat goose at Christmas-tide, had a mind to serve the king's warrant upon this same rogue, though little would he mind either warrant of king or sheriff, for he was far from being a law-abiding man. Then he told how none could be found in all Nottingham Town to serve this warrant, for fear of cracked pates and broken bones, and how that he, the messenger, was now upon his way to Lincoln Town to find of what mettle the Lincoln men might be, and whether there were any there that dared serve this same warrant; wherefore was he now sitting among the prettiest lads he had ever known, and the ale was the best ale he had tasted in all his life.

To this discourse they listened with open mouths and eyes, for it was a fair piece of gossip to them. Then when the messenger had done the jolly Tinker broke silence.

"Now come I, forsooth, from good Banbury Town," said he, "and no one nigh Nottingham—nor Sherwood either, an that be the mark—can hold cudgel with my grip. Why lads, did I not meet that mad wag, Simon of Ely, even at the famous Fair at Hertford Town, and beat him in the ring at that place before Sir Robert of Leslie and his lady? This same Robin Hood, of whom, I wot, I never heard before, is a right merry blade, but gin he be strong, am not I stronger? and gin he be sly, am not I slyer? Now by the bright eyes of Nan o' the Mill, and by mine own name, and that's what o' the Crabstaff, and by mine own mother's son, and that's myself, will I, even I, Wat o' the Crabstaff, meet this same sturdy rogue, and gin he mind not the seal of our glorious sovereign, King Harry, and the warrant of the good Sheriff of Nottinghamshire, I will so bruise, beat, and bemaul his pate, that he shall never move finger or toe again! Hear ye that, bully boys? Come, let us have another bout."

"Now art thou the man for my farthing," cried the messenger. "And back thou goest with me to Nottingham Town."

"Nay," quoth the Tinker, shaking his head slowly from side to side. "Go I with no man gin it be not with mine own free will."

"Nay, nay," said the messenger, "no man is there in Nottinghamshire could make thee go against thy will, thou brave fellow."

"Ay, that be I brave," said the Tinker.

"Ay, marry," said the messenger, "thou art a brave lad; but our good Sheriff hath offered foursome angels of bright gold to whosoever shall serve the warrant upon Robin Hood; though little good will it do."

"Then I will go with thee, lad. Do but wait till I get my bag, and hammer, and my cudgel. Ay, let me but meet this same Robin Hood, and let me see whether he will not mind the King's warrant." So, after having paid their score, the messenger, with the Tinker striding beside his nag, started back to Nottingham again.

ONE BRIGHT MORNING SOON AFTER THIS TIME, ROBIN HOOD started off to Nottingham Town to find what was a-doing there, walking merrily along the roadside where the grass was sweet with daisies, his eyes wandering and his thoughts also. His bugle-horn hung at his hip and his bow and arrows at his back, while in his hand he bore a good stout oaken staff, which he twirled with his fingers as he strolled along.

As thus he walked down a shady lane he saw a tinker coming, trolling a merry song as he drew nigh. On his back hung his bag and his hammer, and in his hand he carried a right stout crabstaff full six feet long, and thus sang he:—

> *"In peascod time, when hound to horn*
> *Gives ear till buck be killed,*
> *And little lads with pipes of corn*
> *Sit keeping beasts afield"*—

"Halloa, good friend!" cried Robin.

> *"I went to gather strawberries"*—

"Halloa!" cried Robin again.

> *"By woods and groves full fair"*—

"Halloa! art thou deaf, man? Good friend, say I!"

"And who art thou dost so boldly check a fair song?" quoth the Tinker, stopping in his singing. "Halloa, thine own self, whether thou be good friend or no. But let me tell thee, thou stout fellow, gin thou be a good friend it were well for us both; but gin thou be no good friend it were ill for thee."

"Then let us be good friends," quoth jolly Robin, "for ill would it be to the ill, and ill like I thine oaken staff full well to make it but well, so good friends let us be."

"Ay, marry, then let us be," said the Tinker. "But, good youth, thy tongue runneth so nimbly that my poor and heavy wits can but ill follow it, so talk more plainly, I pray, for I am a plain man, forsooth."

"And whence comest thou, my lusty blade?" quoth Robin.

"I come from Banbury," answered the Tinker.

"Alas!" quoth Robin, "I hear there is sad news this merry morn."

"Ha! Is it indeed so?" cried the Tinker, eagerly. "Prythee tell it speedily, for I am a tinker by trade, as thou seest, and as I am in my trade I am greedy for news, even as a priest is greedy for farthings."

"Well, then," quoth Robin, "list thou and I will tell, but bear thyself up bravely, for the news is sad, I wot. Thus it is: I hear that two tinkers are in the stocks for drinking ale and beer!"

"Now a murrain seize thee and thy news, thou scurvy dog," quoth the Tinker, "for thou speakest but ill of good men. But sad news it is indeed, gin there be two stout fellows in the stocks."

"Nay," said Robin, "thou hast missed the mark and dost but weep for the wrong sow. The sadness of the news lieth in that there be but two in the stocks, for the others do roam the country at large."

"Now by the pewter platter of Saint Dunstan," cried the Tinker, "I have a good part of a mind to baste thy hide for thine ill jest. But gin men be put in the stocks for drinking ale and beer, I trow thou wouldst not lose thy part."

Loud laughed Robin and cried: "Now well taken, Tinker, well taken! Why, thy wits are like beer, and do froth up most when they grow sour! But right art thou, man, for I love ale and beer right well. Therefore come straightway with me hard by to the sign of the Blue Boar, and if thou drinkest as thou appearest,—and I wot thou wilt not belie thy looks,—I will drench thy throat with as good homebrewed as ever was tapped in all broad Nottinghamshire."

"Now by my faith," said the Tinker, "thou art a right good fellow in spite of thy scurvy jests. I love thee, my sweet chuck, and gin I go not with thee to that same Blue Boar thou mayst call me a heathen Jew."

"Tell me thy news, good friend, I Prythee," quoth Robin as they trudged along together, "for tinkers, I ween, are all as full of news as an egg of meat."

"Now I love thee as my brother, my bully blade," said the Tinker, "else I would not tell thee my news; for sly am I, man, and I have in hand a grave undertaking that doth call for all my wits, for I come to seek a bold outlaw that men, hereabouts, call Robin Hood. Within my pouch I have a warrant, all fairly written out on parchment, forsooth, with a great red seal for to make it lawful. Could I but meet this same Robin Hood I would serve it upon his dainty body, and if he minded it not I would beat him till every one of his ribs would cry Amen. But thou livest hereabouts, mayhap thou knowest Robin Hood thyself, good fellow."

"Ay, marry, that do I somewhat," quoth Robin, "and I have seen him this very morn. But, Tinker, men say that he is but a sad, sly thief. Thou hadst better watch thy warrant, man, or else he may steal it out of thy very pouch."

"Let him but try!" cried the Tinker. "Sly may he be, but sly am I, too. I would I had him here now, man to man!" And he made his heavy cudgel to spin again. "But what manner of man is he, lad?"

"Much like myself," said Robin, laughing, "and in height and build and age nigh the same; and he hath blue eyes, too, like mine."

"Nay," quoth the Tinker, "thou art but a green youth. I thought him to be a great bearded man, Nottingham men feared him so."

"Truly, he is not so old nor so stout as thou art," said Robin. "But men do call him a right deft hand at quarterstaff."

"That may be," said the Tinker, right sturdily; "but I am more deft than he, for did I not overcome Simon of Ely in a fair bout in the ring at Hertford Town? But if thou knowest him, my jolly blade, wilt thou go with me and bring me to him? Fourscore bright angels hath the Sheriff promised me if I serve the warrant upon the knave's body, and ten of them will I give to thee if thou showest me him."

"Ay, that will I," quoth Robin; "but show me thy warrant, man, until I see whether it be good or no."

"That will I not do, even to mine own brother," answered the Tinker. "No man shall see my warrant till I serve it upon yon fellow's own body."

"So be it," quoth Robin. "An thou show it not to me I know not to whom thou wilt show it. But here we are at the sign of the Blue Boar, so let us in and taste his brown October."

No sweeter inn could be found in all Nottinghamshire than that of the Blue Boar. None had such lovely trees standing around, or was so covered with trailing clematis and sweet woodbine; none had such good beer and such humming ale; nor, in winter time, when the north wind howled and snow drifted around the hedges, was there to be found, elsewhere, such a roaring fire as blazed upon the hearth of the Blue Boar. At such times might be found a goodly company of yeomen or country folk seated around the

25

blazing hearth, bandying merry jests, while roasted crabs bobbed in bowls of ale upon the hearthstone. Well known was the inn to Robin Hood and his band, for there had he and such merry companions as Little John or Will Stutely or young David of Doncaster often gathered when all the forest was filled with snow. As for mine host, he knew how to keep a still tongue in his head, and to swallow his words before they passed his teeth, for he knew very well which side of his bread was spread with butter, for Robin and his band were the best of customers, and paid their scores without having them chalked up behind the door. So now, when Robin Hood and the Tinker came thereto and called aloud for two great pots of ale, none would have known from look or speech that the host had ever set eyes upon the outlaw before.

"Bide thou here," quoth Robin to the Tinker, "while I go and see that mine host draweth ale from the right butt, for he hath good October, I know, and that brewed by Withold of Tamworth." So saying, he went within and whispered to the host to add a measure of Flemish strong waters to the good English ale; which the latter did and brought it to them.

"By Our Lady," said the Tinker, after a long draught of the ale, "yon same Withold of Tamworth—a right good Saxon name, too, I would have thee know—breweth the most humming ale that e'er passed the lips of Wat o' the Crabstaff."

"Drink, man, drink," cried Robin, only wetting his own lips meanwhile. "Ho, landlord! bring my friend another pot of the same. And now for a song, my jolly blade."

"Ay, that will I give thee a song, my lovely fellow," quoth the Tinker, "for I never tasted such ale in all my days before. By'r Lady, it doth make my head hum even now! Hey, Dame Hostess, come listen, an thou wouldst hear a song; and thou too, thou bonny lass, for never sing I so well as when bright eyes do look upon me the while."

Then he sang an ancient ballad of the time of good King Arthur, called the Marriage of Sir Gawaine, which you may some time read, yourself, in stout English of early times; and as he sang, all listened to that noble tale of noble knight and his sacrifice to his king. But long before the Tinker came to the last verse his tongue began to trip and his head to spin, because of the strong waters mixed with the ale. First his tongue tripped, then it grew thick of sound; then his head wagged from side to side, until at last he fell asleep as though he never would waken again.

Then Robin Hood laughed aloud, and quickly took the warrant from out the Tinker's pouch with his deft fingers. "Sly art thou, Tinker," quoth he, "but not yet, I trow, art thou as sly as that same sly thief, Robin Hood."

Then he called the host to him and said, "Here, good man, are ten broad shillings for the entertainment thou hast given us this day. See that thou takest good care of thy fair guest there, and when he wakes thou mayest again charge him ten shillings also, and if he hath it not, thou mayst take his bag and hammer, and even his coat, in payment. Thus do I punish those that come into the greenwood to deal dole to me. As for thine own self, never knew I landlord yet that would not charge twice as he could."

At this the host smiled slyly, as though saying to himself the rustic saw, "Teach a magpie to suck eggs."

The Tinker slept until the afternoon drew to a close and the shadows grew long beside the woodland edge, then he awoke. First he looked up, then he looked down, then he looked east, then he looked west, for he was gathering his wits together, like barley-straws blown apart by the wind. First he thought of his merry companion, but he was gone. Then he thought of his stout crabstaff, and that he had within his hand. Then of his warrant, and of the fourscore angels he was to gain for serving it upon Robin Hood. He thrust his hand into his pouch, but not a scrap nor a farthing was there. Then he sprang to his feet in a rage.

"Ho, landlord!" cried he, "whither hath that knave gone that was with me but now?"

"What knave meaneth your worship?" quoth the landlord, calling the Tinker worship to soothe him, as a man would pour oil upon angry water; "I saw no knave with your worship, for I swear no man would dare call that man knave so nigh to Sherwood Forest. A right stout yeoman I saw with your worship, but I thought that your worship knew him, for few there be about here that pass him by and know him not."

"Now, how should I, that ne'er have squealed in your sty, know all the swine therein? Who was he, then, as thou knowest him so well?"

"Why, yon same is a right stout fellow whom men hereabouts do call Robin Hood; which same"—

"Now, by'r Lady!" cried the Tinker hastily, and in a deep voice like an angry bull, "thou didst see me come into thine inn, I, a staunch, honest craftsman, and never told me who my company was, well knowing thine own self who he was. Now, I have a right round piece of mind to crack thy knave's pate for thee!" Then he took up his cudgel and looked at the landlord as though he would smite him where he stood.

"Nay," cried the host, throwing up his elbow, for he feared the blow, "how knew I that thou knewest him not?"

"Well and truly thankful mayst thou be," quoth the Tinker, "that I be a patient man, and so do spare thy bald crown, else wouldst thou ne'er cheat customer again. But as for this same knave, Robin Hood, I go straightway to seek him, and if I do not score his knave's pate, cut my staff into fagots and call me woman." So saying, he gathered himself together to depart.

"Nay," quoth the landlord, standing in front of him and holding out his arms like a gooseherd driving his flock, for money made him bold, "thou goest not till thou hast paid me my score."

"But did not he pay thee?"

"Not so much as one farthing; and ten good shillings' worth of ale have ye drunk this day. Nay, I say, thou goest not away without paying me, else shall our good sheriff know of it."

"But nought have I to pay thee with, good fellow," quoth the Tinker.

" 'Good fellow' not me," said the landlord. "Good fellow am I not when it cometh to lose ten shillings! Pay me that thou owest me in broad money, or else leave thy coat and bag and hammer; yet, I wot they are not worth ten shillings, and I shall lose thereby. Nay, an thou stirrest, I have a great dog within and I will loose him upon thee. Maken, open thou the door and let forth Brian if this fellow stirs one step."

"Nay," quoth the Tinker,—for, by roaming the country, he had learned what dogs were,—"take thou what thou wilt have, and let me depart in peace, and may a murrain go with thee. But oh, landlord! an I catch yon scurvy varlet, I swear he shall pay full with usury for that he hath had!"

So saying, he strode away toward the forest, talking to himself, while the landlord and his worthy dame and Maken stood looking after him, and laughed when he had fairly gone.

"Robin and I have stripped yon ass of his pack main neatly," quoth the landlord.

Now it happened about this time that Robin Hood was going through the forest to Foss Way, to see what was to be seen there, for the moon was full and the night gave promise of being bright. In his hand he carried his stout oaken staff, and at his side hung his bugle horn. As thus he walked up a forest path, whistling, down another path came the Tinker, muttering to himself and shaking his head like an angry bull; and so, at a sudden bend, they met sharply face to face. Each stood still for a time, and then Robin spoke:—

"Halloa, my sweet bird," said he, laughing merrily, "how likest thou thine ale? Wilt not sing to me another song?"

The Tinker said nothing at first, but stood looking at Robin with a grim face. "Now," quoth he at last, "I am right glad I have met thee, and if I do not rattle thy bones within thy hide this day, I give thee leave to put thy foot upon my neck."

"With all my heart," cried merry Robin; "rattle my bones, an thou canst." So saying, he gripped his staff and threw himself upon his guard. Then the Tinker spat upon his hands, and, grasping his staff, came straight at the other. He struck two or three blows, but soon found that he had met his match, for Robin warded and parried all of them, and, before the Tinker thought, he gave him a rap upon the ribs in return. At this Robin laughed aloud, and the Tinker grew more angry than ever, and smote again with all his might and main. Again Robin warded two of the strokes, but at the third, his staff broke beneath the mighty blows of the Tinker. "Now, ill betide thee, traitor staff," cried Robin, as it fell from his hands; "a foul stick art thou to serve me thus in mine hour of need."

"Now yield thee," quoth the Tinker, "for thou art my captive; and if thou do not, I will beat thy pate to a pudding."

To this Robin Hood made no answer, but, clapping his horn to his lips, he blew three blasts, loud and clear.

"Ay," quoth the Tinker, "blow thou mayest, but go thou must with me to Nottingham Town, for the Sheriff would fain see thee there. Now wilt thou yield thee, or shall I have to break thy pretty head?"

"An I must drink sour ale, I must," quoth Robin; "but never have I yielded me to man before, and that without wound or mark upon my body. Nor, when I bethink me, will I yield now. Ho, my merry men! come quickly!"

Then from out the forest leaped Little John and six stout yeomen clad in Lincoln green.

"How now, good master," cried Little John, "what need hast thou that thou dost wind thy horn so loudly?"

"There stands a tinker," quoth Robin, "that would fain take me to Nottingham, there to hang upon the gallows tree."

"Then shall he himself hang forthwith," cried Little John; and he and the others made at the Tinker, to seize him.

"Nay, touch him not," said Robin, "for a right stout man is he. A metal man he is by trade, and a mettled man by nature; moreover, he doth sing a lovely ballad. Say, good fellow, wilt thou join my merry men all? Three suits of Lincoln green shalt thou have a year, beside twenty marks in fee; thou shalt share all with us and lead a right merry life in the greenwood; for cares have we not and misfortune cometh not upon us within the sweet shades of Sherwood, where we shoot the dun deer, and feed upon venison and sweet oaten cakes, and curds and honey. Wilt thou come with me?"

"Ay, marry, will I join with you all," quoth the Tinker, "for I love a merry life, and I love thee, good master, though thou didst thwack my ribs and cheat me into the bargain. Fain am I to own thou art both a stouter and a slyer man than I; so I will obey thee and be thine own true servant."

So all turned their steps to the forest depths, where the Tinker was to live henceforth. For many a day he sang ballads to the band, until the famous Allan a Dale joined them, before whose sweet voice all others seemed as harsh as a raven's; but of him we will learn hereafter.

THE SHOOTING-MATCH AT NOTTINGHAM TOWN

THEN THE SHERIFF WAS VERY WROTH BECAUSE OF THIS FAILURE to take jolly Robin, for it came to his ears, as ill news always does, that the people laughed at him and made a jest of his thinking to serve a warrant upon such a one as the bold outlaw; and a man hates nothing so much as being made a jest of; so he said: "Our gracious Lord and Sovereign King himself shall know of this, and how his laws are perverted and despised by this band of rebel outlaws. As for yon traitor Tinker, him will I hang, if I catch him, upon the very highest gallows tree in all Nottinghamshire."

Then he bade all his servants and retainers to make ready to go to London Town, to see and speak with the King.

At this there was bustling at the Sheriff's castle and men ran hither and thither upon this business and upon that, while the forge fires of Nottingham glowed red far

into the night like twinkling stars, for all the smiths of the town were busy making or mending armor for the Sheriff's troop of escort. For two days this labor lasted, then, on the third, all was ready for the journey. So forth they started in the bright sunlight, from Nottingham Town to Fosse Way and thence to Watling Street; and so they journeyed for two days, until they saw at last the spires and towers of great London Town; and many folks stopped, as they journeyed along, and gazed at the show they made riding along the highways with their flashing armor and gay plumes and trappings.

In London King Henry and his fair Queen Elnor held their court, gay with ladies in silks and satins and velvets and cloth of gold, and also brave knights and gallant courtiers. Thither came the Sheriff and was shown into the King's presence.

"A boon, a boon," quoth he, as he knelt upon the ground.

"Now what wouldst thou have?" said the King. "Let us hear what may be thy desires."

"O good my Lord and Sovereign," spake the Sheriff, "in Sherwood Forest, in our own good shire of Nottingham, liveth a bold outlaw whose name is Robin Hood."

"In good sooth," said the King, "his doings have reached even our own royal ears. He is a saucy, rebellious varlet, yet, I am fain to own, a right merry soul withal."

"But hearken, O my most gracious Sovereign," said the Sheriff. "I sent a warrant to him with thine own royal seal attached, by a right lusty knave, but he beat the messenger and stole the warrant. And he killeth thy deer and robbeth thine own liege subjects even upon the great highways."

"Why, how now," quoth the King, wrathfully. "What wouldst thou have me do? Comest thou not to me with a great array of men-at-arms and retainers, and yet art not able to take a single band of lusty knaves without armor on breast, in thine own country! What wouldst thou have me do? Art thou not my Sheriff? Are not my laws in force in Nottinghamshire? Canst thou not take thine own course against those that break the laws or do an injury to thee or thine? Go, get thee gone, and think well; devise some plan of thine own but trouble me no further. But look well to it, master Sheriff, for I will have my laws obeyed by all men within my kingdom, and if thou art not able to enforce them thou art no sheriff for me. So look well to thyself, I say, or ill may befall thee as well as the thieving knaves in Nottinghamshire. When the flood cometh it sweepeth away grain as well as chaff."

Then the Sheriff turned away with a sore and troubled heart, and sadly he rued his fine show of retainers, for he saw that the King was angry because he had so many men about him and yet could not enforce the laws. So, as they all rode slowly back to Nottingham, the Sheriff was thoughtful and full of care. Not a word did he speak to any one, and no one of his men spoke to him, but all the time he was busy devising some plan to take Robin Hood.

"Aha!" cried he suddenly, smiting his hand upon his thigh, "I have it now! Ride on, my merry men all, and let us get back to Nottingham Town as speedily as we may. And mark well my words: before a fortnight is passed, that evil knave, Robin Hood, will be safely clapped into Nottingham gaol."

But what was the Sheriff's plan?

As a Jew takes each one of a bag of silver angels, feeling each coin to find whether it be clipped or not, so the Sheriff, as all rode slowly and sadly back toward Nottingham, took up thought after thought in turn, feeling around the edges of each but finding in every one some flaw. At last he thought of the daring soul of jolly Robin and how, as he the Sheriff knew, he often came even within the walls of Nottingham.

"Now," thought the Sheriff, "could I but persuade Robin nigh to Nottingham Town so that I could find him, I warrant I would lay hands upon him so stoutly that he would never get away again." Then of a sudden it came to him like a flash that were he to proclaim a great shooting-match and offer some grand prize, Robin Hood might be over-persuaded by his spirit to come to the butts; and it was this thought which caused him to cry "Aha!" and smite his palm upon his thigh.

So, as soon as he had returned safely to Nottingham, he sent messengers north and south, and east and west, to proclaim through town, hamlet, and countryside, this grand shooting-match, and every one was bidden that could draw a long bow, and the prize was to be an arrow of pure beaten gold.

33

When Robin Hood first heard the news of this he was in Lincoln Town, and hastening back to Sherwood Forest he soon called all his merry men about him and spoke to them thus:—

"Now hearken, my merry men all, to the news that I have brought from Lincoln Town today. Our friend the Sheriff of Nottingham hath proclaimed a shooting-match, and hath sent messengers to tell of it through all the country side, and the prize is to be a bright golden arrow. Now I fain would have one of us win it, both because of the fairness of the prize and because our sweet friend the Sheriff hath offered it. So we will take our bows and shafts and go there to shoot, for I know right well that merriment will be a-going. What say ye, lads?"

Then young David of Doncaster spoke up and said: "Now listen, I pray thee, good master, unto what I say. I have come straight from our friend Eadom o' the Blue Boar, and there I heard the full news of this same match. But, master, I know from him, and he got it from the Sheriff's man Ralph o' the Scar, that this same knavish Sheriff hath but laid a trap for thee in this shooting-match and wishes nothing so much as to see thee there. So go not, good master, for I know right well he doth seek to beguile thee, but stay within the greeenwood lest we all meet dole and woe."

"Now," quoth Robin, "thou art a wise lad and keepest thine ears open and thy mouth shut, as becometh a wise and crafty woodsman. But shall we let it be said that the Sheriff of Nottingham did cow bold Robin Hood and sevenscore as fair archers as are in all merry England? Nay, good David, what thou tellest me maketh me to desire the prize even more than I else should do. But what sayeth our good gossip Swanthold? is it not 'A hasty man burneth his mouth, and the fool that keepth his eyes shut falleth into the pit?' Thus he says, truly, therefore we must meet guile with guile. Now some of you clothe yourselves as curtal friars, and some as rustic peasants, and some as tinkers, or as beggars, but see that each man taketh a good bow or broadsword, in case need should arise. As for myself, I will shoot for this same golden arrow, and should I win it, we will hang it to the branches of our good greenwood tree for the joy of all the band. How like you the plan, my merry men all?"

Then, "good, good!" cried all the band right heartily.

A fair sight was Nottingham Town on the day of the shooting-match. All along upon the green meadow beneath the town wall stretched a row of benches, one above the other, which were for knight and lady, squire and dame, and rich burghers and their wives; for none but those of rank and quality were to sit there. At the end of the range, near the target, was a raised seat bedecked with ribbons and scarfs and garlands of flowers, for the Sheriff of Nottingham and his dame. The range was two score paces broad. At one end stood the target, at the other a tent of striped canvas, from the pole of which fluttered many-colored flags and streamers. In this booth were casks of ale, free to be broached by any of the archers who might wish to quench their thirst.

Across the range from where the seats for the better folk were raised was a railing to keep the poorer people from crowding in front of the target. Already, while it was early, the benches were beginning to fill with people of quality, who kept constantly arriving in little carts, or upon palfreys that curveted gayly to the merry tinkle of silver bells at bridle-reins; with these came also the poorer folk, who sat or lay upon the green grass near the railing that kept them from off the range. In the great tent the archers were gathering by twos and threes; some talking loudly of the fair shots each man had made in his day; some looking well to their bows, drawing a string betwixt the fingers to see that there was no fray upon it, or inspecting arrows, shutting one eye and peering down a shaft to see that it was not warped, but straight and true, for neither bow nor shaft should fail at such a time and for such a prize. And never were such a company of yeomen as were gathered at Nottingham Town that day, for the very best archers of merry England had come to this shooting-match. There was Gill o' the Red Cap, the Sheriff's own head archer, and Diccon Cruikshank of Lincoln Town, and Adam o' the Dell, a man of Tamworth, of threescore years and more, yet hale and lusty still, who in his time had shot in the famous match at Woodstock, and had there beaten that renowned archer, Clym o' the Clough. And many more famous men of the long bow were there, whose names have been handed down to us in goodly ballads of the olden time.

But now all the benches were filled with guests, lord and lady, burgher and dame, when at last the Sheriff himself came with his lady, he riding with stately mien upon his milk-white horse and she upon her brown filly. Upon his head he wore a purple velvet cap, and purple velvet was his robe, all trimmed about with rich ermine; his jerkin and hose were of sea-green silk, and his shoes of black velvet, the pointed toes fastened to his garters with golden chains. A golden chain hung about his neck, and at his collar was a great carbuncle set in red gold. His lady was dressed in blue velvet, all trimmed with swan's down. So they made a gallant sight as they rode along side by side, and all the people shouted from where they crowded across the space from the gentlefolk; so the Sheriff and his lady came to their place, where men-at-arms, with hauberk and spear, stood about, waiting for them.

Then when the Sheriff and his dame had sat down, he bade his herald wind upon his silver horn; who thereupon sounded three blasts that came echoing cheerily back from the gray walls of Nottingham. Then the archers stepped forth to their places, while all the folks shouted with a mighty voice, each man calling upon his favorite yeoman. "Red Cap!" cried some; "Cruikshank!" cried others; "Hey for William o' Leslie!" shouted others yet again; while ladies waved silken scarfs to urge each yeoman to do his best.

Then the herald stood forth and loudly proclaimed the rules of the game as follows:—

"Shoot each man from yon mark, which is sevenscore yards and ten from the target. One arrow shooteth each man first, and from all the archers shall the ten that shooteth the fairest shafts be chosen for to shoot again. Two arrows shooteth each man of these ten, then shall the three that shoot the fairest shafts be chosen for to shoot again. Three arrows shooteth each man of those three, and to him that shooteth the fairest shafts shall the prize be given."

Then the Sheriff leaned forward, looking keenly among the press of archers to find whether Robin Hood was amongst them; but no one was there clad in Lincoln green, such as was worn by Robin and his band. "Nevertheless," said the Sheriff to himself, "he may still be there, and I miss him among the crowd of other men. But let me see when but ten men shoot, for I wot he will be among the ten, or I know him not."

And now the archers shot, each man in turn, and the good folk never saw such archery as was done that day. Six arrows were within the clout, four within the black, and only two smote the outer ring; so that when the last arrow sped and struck the target, all the people shouted aloud, for it was noble shooting.

And now but ten men were left of all those that had shot before, and of these ten, six were famous throughout the land, and most of the folk gathered there knew them. These six men were Gilbert o' the Red Cap, Adam o' the Dell, Diccon Cruikshank, William o' Leslie, Hubert o' Cloud, and Swithin o' Hertford. Two others were yeomen of merry Yorkshire, another was a tall stranger in blue, who said he came from London Town, and the last was a tattered stranger in scarlet, who wore a patch over one eye.

"Now," quoth the Sheriff to a man-at-arms who stood near him, "seest thou Robin Hood amongst these ten?"

"Nay, that do I not, your worship," answered the man. "Six of them I know right well. Of those Yorkshire yeomen, one is too tall and the other too short for that bold knave. Robin's beard is as yellow as gold, while yon tattered beggar in scarlet hath a beard of brown, besides being blind of one eye. As for the stranger in blue, Robin's shoulders, I ween, are three inches broader than his."

"Then," quoth the Sheriff, smiting his thigh angrily, "yon knave is a coward as well as a rogue, and dares not show his face among good men and true."

Then, after they had rested a short time, those ten stout men stepped forth to shoot again. Each man shot two arrows, and as they shot, not a word was spoken, but all the crowd watched with scarce a breath of sound; but when the last had shot his arrow another great shout arose, while many cast their caps aloft for joy of such marvellous shooting.

"Now by our gracious Lady fair," quoth old Sir Amyas o' the Dell, who, bowed with fourscore year and more, sat near the Sheriff, "ne'er saw I such archery in all my life before, yet have I seen the best hands at the long bow for threescore years and more."

And now but three men were left of all those that had shot before. One was Gill o' the Red Cap, one the tattered stranger in scarlet, and one Adam o' the Dell of Tamworth Town. Then all the people called aloud, some crying, "Ho for Gilbert o' the Red Cap!" and some, "Hey for stout Adam o'

Tamworth!" but not a single man in the crowd called upon the stranger in scarlet.

"Now, shoot thou well, Gilbert," cried the Sheriff, "and if thine be the best shaft, fivescore broad silver pennies will I give to thee beside the prize."

"Truly I will do my best," quoth Gilbert, right sturdily. "A man cannot do aught but his best, but that will I strive to do this day." So saying, he drew forth a fair smooth arrow with a broad feather and fitted it deftly to the string, then drawing his bow with care he sped the shaft. Straight flew the arrow and lit fairly in the clout, a finger breadth from the centre. "A Gilbert, a Gilbert!" shouted all the crowd; and, "Now, by my faith," cried the Sheriff, smiting his hands together, "that is a shrewd shot."

Then the tattered stranger stepped forth, and all the people laughed as they saw a yellow patch that showed beneath his arm when he raised his elbow to shoot, and also to see him aim with but one eye. He drew the good yew bow quickly, and quickly loosed a shaft; so short was the time that no man could draw a breath betwixt the drawing and the shooting; yet his arrow lodged nearer the centre than the other by twice the length of a barleycorn.

"Now by all the saints in Paradise!" cried the Sheriff, "that is a lovely shaft in very truth!"

Then Adam o' the Dell shot, carefully and cautiously, and his arrow lodged close beside the stranger's. Then after a short space they all three shot again, and once more each arrow lodged within the clout, but this time Adam o' the Dell's was farthest from the centre, and again the tattered stranger's shot was the best. Then, after another time of rest, they all shot for the third time. This time Gilbert took great heed to his aim, keenly measuring the distance and shooting with shrewdest care. Straight flew the arrow, and all shouted till the very flags that waved in the breeze shook with the sound, and the rooks and daws flew clamoring about the roofs of the old gray tower, for the shaft had lodged close beside the spot that marked the very centre.

"Well done, Gilbert!" cried the Sheriff, right joyously. "Fain am I to believe the prize is thine, and right fairly won. Now, thou ragged knave, let me see thee shoot a better shaft than that."

Naught spake the stranger but took his place, while all was hushed, and no one spoke or even seemed to breathe, so great was the silence for wonder what he would do. Meanwhile, also, quite still stood the stranger holding his bow in his hand, while one could count five; then he drew his trusty yew, holding it drawn but a moment, then loosed the string. Straight flew the arrow, and so true that it smote a gray goose feather from off Gilbert's shaft, which fell fluttering through the sunlit air as the stranger's arrow lodged close beside his of the red cap, and in the very centre. No one spoke a word for a while and no one shouted, but each man looked into his neighbor's face amazedly.

"Nay," quoth old Adam o' the Dell presently, drawing a long breath and shaking his head as he spoke; "twoscore years and more have I shot shaft, and maybe not all times bad, but I shoot no more this day, for no man can match with yon stranger, whosoe'er he may be." Then he thrust his shaft into his quiver, rattling, and unstrung his bow without another word.

Then the Sheriff came down from his dais and drew near, in all his silks and velvets, to where the tattered stranger stood leaning upon his stout bow, whilst the good folk crowded around to see the man who shot so wondrously well. "Here, good fellow," quoth the Sheriff, "take thou the prize, and well and fairly hast thou won it, I trow. What may be thy name, and whence comest thou?"

"Men do call me Jock o' Teviotdale, and thence am I come," said the stranger.

"Then, by our Lady, Jock, thou art the fairest archer that e'er mine eyes beheld, and if thou wilt join my service I will clothe thee with a better coat than that thou hast upon thy back; thou shat eat and drink of the best, and at every Christmas-tide fourscore marks shall be thy wage. I trow thou drawest better bow than that same coward knave, Robin Hood, that dared not show his face here this day. Say, good fellow, wilt thou join my service?"

"Nay, that will I not," quoth the stranger, roughly. "I will be mine own, and no man in all merry England shall be my master."

"Then get thee gone, and murrain seize thee!" cried the Sheriff, and his voice trembled with anger. "And by my faith and troth I have a good part of a mind to have thee beaten for thine insolence!" Then he turned upon his heel and strode away.

It was a right motley company that gathered about the noble greenwood tree in Sherwood's depths that same day. A score and more of barefoot friars were there, and some that looked like tinkers, and some that seemed to be sturdy beggars and rustic hinds; and seated upon a mossy couch was one all clad in tattered scarlet, with a patch over one eye; and in his hand he held the golden arrow that was the prize of the great shooting-match. Then, amidst a noise of talking and laughter, he took the patch from off his eye and stripped away the scarlet rags from off his body and showed himself all clothed in fair Lincoln green, and quoth he: "Easy come these things away, but walnut stain cometh not so speedily from yellow hair." Then all laughed louder than before, for it was Robin Hood himself that had won the prize from the Sheriff's very hands.

Then all sat down to the woodland feast and talked amongst themselves of the merry jest that had been played upon the Sheriff, and of the adventures that had befallen each member of the band in his disguise. But when the feast was done, Robin Hood took Little John apart and said, "Truly am I vexed in my blood, for I heard the Sheriff say today, 'Thou shootest better than that coward knave, Robin Hood, that dared not show his face here this day.' I would fain let him know who it was who won the golden arrow from out his hand, and also that I am no coward such as he takes me to be."

Then Little John said, "Good master, take thou me and Will Stutely and we will send yon fat Sheriff news of all this by a messenger such as he doth not expect."

That day the Sheriff sat at meat in the great hall of his house at Nottingham Town. Long tables stood down the hall, at which sat men-at-arms and household servants and good stout villains, in all fourscore and more. There they talked of the day's shooting as they ate their meat and quaffed their ale. The Sheriff sat at the head of the table upon a raised seat under a canopy, and beside him sat his dame.

"By my troth," said he, "I did reckon full roundly that that knave, Robin Hood, would be at the game today. I did not think that he was such a coward. But who could that saucy knave be who answered me to my beard so bravely? I wonder that I did not have him beaten; but there was something about him that spoke of other things than rags and tatters."

Then, even as he finished speaking, something fell rattling among the dishes on the table, while those that sat near started up wondering what it might be. After a while one of the men-at-arms gathered courage enough to pick it up and bring it to the Sheriff. Then every one saw that it was a blunted gray goose shaft, with a fine scroll, about the thickness of a goose quill, tied near to its head. The Sheriff opened the scroll and glanced at it, while the veins upon his forehead swelled and his cheeks grew ruddy with rage as he read, for this was what he saw:—

> *"Now Heaven bless thy grace this day,*
> *Say all in sweet Sherwood,*
> *For thou didst give the prize away*
> *To merry Robin Hood."*

"Whence came this?" cried the Sheriff in a mighty voice.

"Even through the window, your worship," quoth the man who had handed the shaft to him.

3

WILL STUTELY RESCUED BY HIS GOOD COMPANIONS

NOW WHEN THE SHERIFF FOUND THAT NEITHER LAW NOR GUILE could overcome Robin Hood, he was much perplexed, and said to himself, "Fool that I am! Had I not told our King of Robin Hood, I would not have gotten myself into such a coil; but now I must either take him captive or have wrath visited upon my head from his most gracious Majesty. I have tried law, and I have tried guile, and I have failed in both; so I will try what may be done with might."

Thus communing within himself, he called his constables together and told them what was in his mind. "Now take ye each four men, all armed in proof," said he, "and get ye gone to the forest, at different points, and lay in wait for this same Robin Hood. But if any constable finds too many men against him, let him sound a horn, and then let each band within hearing come with all speed and join the party that calls them. Thus, I think, shall we take this green-clad knave. Furthermore, to him that first meeteth with Robin Hood shall one hundred pounds of silver money be given, if he be brought to me, dead or alive; and to him that meeteth with any of his band shall twoscore pounds be given, if such be brought to me dead or alive. So, be ye bold and be ye crafty."

So thus they went in threescore companies of five to Sherwood Forest, to take Robin Hood, each constable wishing that he might be the one to find the bold outlaw, or at least one of his band. For seven days and nights they hunted through the forest glades, but never saw so much as a single man in Lincoln green; for tidings of all this had been brought to Robin Hood by trusty Eadom o' the Blue Boar.

When he first heard the news, Robin said, "If the Sheriff dare send force to meet force, woe will it be for him and many a better man beside, for blood will flow, and there will be great trouble for all. But fain would I shun blood and battle, and fain would I not deal sorrow to women folk and wives because good stout yeomen lose their lives. Once I slew a man, and never do I wish to slay a man again, for it is bitter for the soul to think thereon. So now we will abide silently in Sherwood Forest, so that it may be well for all; but should we be forced to defend ourselves, or any of our band, then let each man draw bow and brand with might and main."

At this speech many of the band shook their heads, and said to themselves, "Now the Sheriff will think that we are cowards, and folk will scoff throughout the countryside, saying that we fear to meet these men." But they said nothing aloud, swallowing their words, and doing as Robin bade them.

Thus they hid in the depths of Sherwood Forest for seven days and seven nights, and never showed their faces abroad in all that time; but early in the morning of the eighth day Robin Hood called the band together and said, "Now who will go and find what the Sheriff's men are at by this time? for I know right well they will not bide forever within Sherwood shades."

At this a great shout arose, and each man waved his bow aloft and cried that he might be the one to go. Then Robin Hood's heart was proud when he looked around on his stout, brave fellows, and he said, "Brave and true are ye all, my merry men, and a right stout band of good fellows are ye; but ye cannot all go, so I will choose one from amongst you, and it shall be good Will Stutely, for he is as sly as e'er an old dog fox in Sherwood Forest."

Then Will Stutely leaped high aloft and laughed loudly, clapping his hands, for pure joy that he should have been chosen from amongst them all. "Now thanks, good master," quoth he, "and if I bring not news of those knaves to thee, call me no more thy sly Will Stutely."

Then he clad himself in a friar's gown, and underneath the robe he hung a good broadsword in such a place that he could easily lay hands upon it. Thus clad, he set forth upon his quest, until he came to the verge of the forest, and so to the highway. He saw two bands of the Sheriff's men, yet he turned neither to the right nor the left, but only drew his cowl the closer over his face, folding his hands as if in meditation. So at last he came to the Sign of the Blue Boar. "For," quoth he to himself, "our good friend Eadom will tell me all the news."

At the Sign of the Blue Boar he found a band of the Sheriff's men drinking right lustily; so, without speaking to any one, he sat down upon a distant bench, his staff in his hand, and his head bowed forward as though he were meditating. Thus he sat waiting until he might see the landlord apart, and Eadom did not know him, but thought him to be some poor tired friar, so he let him sit without saying a word to him or molesting him, though he liked not the cloth; "for," said he to himself, "it is a hard heart that kicks the lame dog from off the sill."

As Stutely sat thus, there came a great house cat and rubbed against his knee, raising his robe a palm's breadth high. Stutely pushed his robe quickly down again, but the constable who commanded the Sheriff's men saw what had passed, and saw also fair Lincoln green beneath the friar's robe. He said nothing at the time, but communed within himself in this wise: "Yon is no friar of orders gray, and also, I wot, no honest yeoman goeth about in priest's garb, nor doth a thief go so for naught. Now I think in good sooth that is one of Robin Hood's own men." So, presently, he said aloud:—

"O holy father, wilt thou not take a good pot of March beer to slake thy thirsty soul withal?" But Stutely shook his head silently, for he said to himself, "Maybe there be those here who know my voice."

Then the constable said again, "Whither goest thou, holy friar, upon this hot summer's day?"

"I go a pilgrim to Canterbury Town," answered Will Stutely, speaking gruffly, so that none might know his voice.

Then the constable said, for the third time, "Now tell me, holy father, do pilgrims to Canterbury wear good Lincoln green beneath their robes? Ha! by my faith, I take thee to be some lusty thief, and perhaps one of Robin Hood's own band! Now, by Our Lady's grace, if thou movest hand or foot, I will run thee through the body with my sword!"

Then he flashed forth his bright sword and leaped upon Will Stutely, thinking he would take him unaware; but Stutely had his own sword tightly held in his hand, beneath his robe, so he drew it forth before the constable came upon him. Then the stout constable struck a mighty blow; but he struck no more in all that fight, for Stutely, parrying the blow right deftly, smote the constable back again with all his might. Then he would have escaped, but could not, for the other, all dizzy with the wound and with the flowing blood, seized him by the knees with his arms even as he reeled and fell. Then the others rushed upon him, and Stutely struck again at another of the Sheriff's men, but the steel cap glanced the blow, and though the blade bit deep, it did not kill. Meanwhile, the constable, fainting as he was, drew Stutely downward, and the others, seeing the yeoman hampered so, rushed upon him again, and one smote him a blow upon the crown so that the blood ran down his face and blinded him. Then, staggering, he fell, and all sprang upon him, though he struggled so manfully that they could hardly hold him fast. Then they bound him with stout hempen cords so that he could not move either hand or foot, and thus they overcame him. But it was a doleful day's doings for two of that band; for the constable was sorely wounded, and the other, that Stutely smote upon the crown, lay sick for many a day ere he was the stout man that he had been before this famous fight.

Robin Hood stood under the greenwood tree, thinking of Will Stutely and how he might be faring, when suddenly he saw two of his stout yeomen come running down the forest path, and betwixt them ran buxom Maken of the Blue Boar. Then Robin's heart fell, for he knew they were the bearers of ill tidings.

"Will Stutely hath been taken," cried they, when they had come to where he stood.

"And is it thou that hast brought such doleful news?" said Robin to the lass.

"Ay, marry, for I saw it all," cried she, panting as the hare pants when it has escaped the hounds; "and I fear he is wounded sore, for one smote him main shrewdly i' the crown. They have bound him and taken him to Nottingham Town, and ere I left the Blue Boar I heard that he should be hanged tomorrow day."

"He shall not be hanged tomorrow day," cried Robin; "or, if he be, full many a one shall gnaw the sod, and many shall have cause to cry Alack-a-day!"

Then he clapped his horn to his lips and blew three blasts right loudly, and presently his good yeomen came running through the greenwood until sevenscore bold blades were gathered around him.

"Now hark you all!" cried Robin. "Our dear companion, Will Stutely, hath been taken by that vile Sheriff's men, therefore doth it behoove us to take bow and brand in hand to bring him off again; for I wot that we ought to risk life and limb for him, as he hath risked life and limb for us. Is it not so, my merry men all?" Then all cried, "Ay!" with a great voice.

"Now," quoth Robin again, "if there be any here that care not to risk life and limb, let them bide within Sherwood shades, for I constrain no man to my will; but tomorrow I will bring Will Stutely back or I will die with him."

Then up spake stout Little John. "Thinkest thou, good master," he said, "that there be one among us all that would not risk life and limb for fellow in trouble? If such there be, then do not I know every man in this company of stout yeomen. And, moreover, if there be such, I wot he should be stripped and beaten from out our merry woodlands. Is it not so, good friends?"

Then all cried, "Ay!" again, for there was not one man amongst them all that would not venture everything for a friend in need.

So the next day they all wended their way from Sherwood Forest, but by different paths, for it behooved them to be very crafty; so the band separated into parties of twos and threes, which were all to meet again in a tangled dell that lay near to Nottingham Town. Then, when they had all gathered together at the place of meeting, Robin spoke to them thus:—

"Now we will lie here in ambush until we can get news, for it doth behoove us to be cunning and wary if we would bring our friend, Will Stutely, off from the Sheriff's clutches."

So they lay hidden a long time, until the sun stood high in the sky. The day was warm and the dusty road was bare of travelers, except an aged palmer who walked slowly along the highroad that led close beside the gray castle wall of Nottingham Town. When Robin saw that no other wayfarer was within sight, he called young David of Doncaster, who was a shrewd man for his years, and said to him, "Now get thee forth, young David, and speak to yonder palmer that walks beside the town wall, for he hath come but now from Nottingham Town, and may tell thee news of good Stutely, perchance."

So David strode forth, and when he came up to the pilgrim, he saluted him and said: "Good morrow, holy father, and canst thou tell me when Will Stutely will be hanged upon the gallows tree? I fain would not miss the sight, for I have come from afar to see so sturdy a rogue hanged."

"Now, out upon thee, young man," cried the Palmer, "that thou shouldst speak so when a good stout man is to be hanged for nothing but guarding his own life!" and he struck his staff upon the ground in anger. "Alas, say I, that this thing should be! for even this day, toward evening, when the sun falleth low, he shall be hanged, fourscore rods from the great town gate of Nottingham, where three roads meet; for there the Sheriff sweareth he shall die as a warning to all outlaws in Nottinghamshire. But yet, I say again, Alas! for, though Robin Hood and his band may be outlaws, yet he taketh only from the rich and the strong and the dishonest man, while there is not a poor widow nor a peasant with many children, nigh to Sherwood, but has barley-flour enough all the year long through him. It grieves my heart to see one as gallant as this Stutely die, for I have been a good Saxon yeoman in my day, ere I turned palmer, and well I know a stout hand and one that smiteth shrewdly at a cruel Norman or a proud abbot with fat money-bags. Had good Stutely's master but known how his man was compassed about with perils, perchance he might send succor to bring him out of the hand of his enemies."

"Ay, marry, that is true," cried the young man. "If Robin and his men be nigh this place, I wot right well they will strive to bring him forth from his peril. But fare thee well, thou good old man, and believe me, that, if Will Stutely die, he shall be right well avenged."

Then he turned and strode rapidly away; but the Palmer looked after him, muttering, "I wot that youth is no country hind that hath come to see a good man die. Well, well, perchance Robin Hood is not so far away but that there will be stout doings this day." So he went upon his way, muttering to himself.

When David of Doncaster told Robin Hood what the Palmer had said to him, Robin called the band around him and spoke to them thus:

"Now let us get straightway into Nottingham Town, and mix ourselves with the people there; but keep ye one another in sight, pressing as near the prisoner and his guards as ye can, when they come outside the walls. Strike no man without need, for I would fain avoid bloodshed, but if ye do strike, strike hard, and see that there be no need to strike again. Then keep all together until we come again to Sherwood, and let no man leave his fellows."

The sun was low in the western sky when a bugle-note sounded from the castle wall. Then all was bustle in Nottingham Town and crowds filled the streets, for all knew that the famous Will Stutely was to be hanged that day. Presently the castle gates opened wide and a great array of men-at-arms came forth with noise and clatter, the Sheriff, all clad in shining mail of linked chain, riding at their head. In the midst of all the guard, in a cart, with a halter about his neck, rode Will Stutely. His face was pale with his wound and with loss of blood, like the moon in broad daylight, and his fair hair was clotted in points upon his forehead, where the blood had hardened. When he came forth from the castle he looked up and he looked down, but though he saw some faces that showed pity and some that showed friendliness, he saw none that he knew. Then his heart sank within him like a plummet of lead, but nevertheless he spoke up boldly.

"Give a sword into my hand, Sir Sheriff," said he, "and wounded man though I be, I will fight thee and all thy men till life and strength be gone."

"Nay, thou naughty varlet," quoth the Sheriff, turning his head and looking right grimly upon Will Stutely, "thou shalt have no sword but shall die a mean death, as beseemeth a vile thief like thee."

"Then do but untie my hands and I will fight thee and thy men with no weapon but only my naked fists. I crave no weapon, but let me not be meanly hanged this day."

Then the Sheriff laughed aloud. "Why, how now," quoth he, "is thy proud stomach quailing? Shrive thyself, thou vile knave, for I mean that thou shalt hang this day, and that where three roads meet, so that all men shall see thee hang, for carrion crows and daws to peck at."

"O thou dastard heart!" cried Will Stutely, gnashing his teeth at the Sheriff. "Thou coward hind! If ever my good master meet thee thou shalt pay dearly for this day's work! He doth scorn thee, and so do all brave hearts. Knowest thou not that thou and thy name are jests upon the lips of every brave yeoman? Such a one as thou art, thou wretched craven, will never be able to subdue bold Robin Hood."

"Ha!" cried the Sheriff, in a rage, "is it even so? Am I a jest with thy master, as thou callest him? Now I will make a jest of thee and a sorry jest withal, for I will quarter thee limb from limb, after thou art hanged." Then he spurred his horse forward, and said no more to Stutely.

At last they came to the great town gate, through which Stutely saw the fair country beyond, with hills and dales all clothed in verdure, and far away the dusky line of Sherwood's skirts. Then when he saw the slanting sunlight lying on field and fallow, shining redly here and there on cot and farmhouse, and when he heard the sweet birds singing their vespers, and the sheep bleating upon the hillside, and beheld the swallows flying in the bright air, there came a great fulness to his heart so that all things blurred to his sight through salt tears, and he bowed his head lest the folk should think him unmanly when they saw the tears in his eyes. Thus he kept his head bowed till they had passed through the gate and were outside the walls of the town. But when he looked up again he felt his heart leap within him and then stand still for pure joy, for he saw the face of one of his own dear companions of merry Sherwood; then glancing quickly around he saw well-known faces upon all sides of him, crowding closely upon the men-at-arms who were guarding him. Then of a sudden the blood sprang to his cheeks, for he saw for a moment his own good master in the press, and, seeing him, knew that Robn Hood and all his band were there. Yet betwixt him and them was a line of men-at-arms.

"Now, stand back!" cried the Sheriff in a mighty voice, for the crowd pressed around on all sides. "What mean ye, varlets, that ye push upon us so? Stand back, I say!"

Then came a bustle and a noise, and one strove to push between the men-at-arms so as to reach the cart, and Stutely saw that it was Little John that made all that stir.

"Now stand thou back!" cried one of the men-at-arms whom Little John pushed with his elbows.

"Now stand thou back thine own self," quoth Little John, and straightway smote the man a buffet beside his head that felled him as a butch fells an ox, and then he leaped to the cart where Stutely sat.

"I pray thee take leave of thy friends ere thou diest, Will," quoth he, "or maybe I will die with thee if thou must die, for I could never have better company." Then with one stroke he cut the bonds that bound the other's arms and legs, and Stutely leaped straightway from the cart.

"Now as I live," cried the Sheriff, "yon varlet I know right well is a sturdy rebel! Take him, I bid you all, and let him not go!"

So saying he spurred his horse upon Little John, and rising in his stirrups smote with might and main, but Little John ducked quickly underneath the horse's belly and the blow whistled harmlessly over his head.

"Nay, good Sir Sheriff," cried he, leaping up again when the blow had passed, "I must e'en borrow thy most worshipful sword." Thereupon he twitched the weapon deftly from out the Sheriff's hand. "Here, Stutely," he cried, "the Sheriff hath lent thee his sword! Back to back with me, man, and defend thyself, for help is nigh!"

"Down with them!" bellowed the Sheriff in a voice like an angry bull; and he spurred his horse upon the two who now stood back to back, forgetting in his rage that he had no weapon with which to defend himself.

"Stand back, Sheriff!" cried Little John; and even as he spoke, a bugle-horn sounded shrilly, and a clothyard shaft whistled within an inch of the

Sheriff's head. Then there came a swaying hither and thither and oaths and cries and groans and clashing of steel, and swords flashed in the setting sun, and a score of arrows whistled through the air: and some cried "Help, help!" and some, "A rescue, a rescue!"

"Treason!" cried the Sheriff in a loud voice. "Bear back! bear back! else we be all dead men!" Thereupon be reined his horse backward through the thickest of the crowd.

Now Robin Hood and his band might have slain half of the Sheriff's men had they desired to do so, but they let them push out of the press and get them gone, only sending bunch of arrows after them to hurry them in their fight.

"Oh stay!" shouted Will Stutely after the Sheriff. "Thou wilt never catch bold Robin Hood if thou dost not stand to meet him face to face." But the Sheriff, bowing along his horse's back, made no answer but only spurred the faster.

Then Will Stutely turned to Little John and looked him in the face till the tears ran down from his eyes and he wept aloud, and kissing his friend's cheeks, "O Little John!" quoth he, "mine own true friend, and he that I love better than man or woman in all the world beside! Little did I reckon to see thy face this day, or to meet thee this side Paradise." And Little John could make no answer, but wept also.

Then Robin Hood gathered his band together in a close rank, with Will Stutely in the midst, and thus they moved slowly away toward Sherwood, and were gone, as a storm-cloud moves away from the spot where a tempest has swept the land. But they left ten of the Sheriff's men lying along the ground wounded—some more, some less—yet no one knew who smote them down.

Thus the Sheriff of Nottingham tried thrice to take Robin Hood and failed each time; and the last time he was frightened, for he felt how near he had come to losing his life; so he said: "These men fear neither God nor man, nor King nor king's officers. I would sooner lose mine office than my life, so I will trouble them no more." So he kept close within his castle for many a day and dared not show his face outside of his own household, and all the time he was gloomy and would speak to no one, for he was ashamed of what had happened that day.

PART SECOND

In which shall be told how Robin Hood turned Butcher, and how he revenged himself upon the Sheriff. Also, of the famous adventures that befell Little John at the Nottingham Archery Match, and how he entered the Sheriff's service.

1

ROBIN HOOD TURNS BUTCHER

NOW AFTER ALL THESE THINGS HAD HAPPENED, AND IT BECAME known to Robin Hood how the Sheriff had tried three times to make him captive, he said to himself: "If I have the chance, I will make our worshipful Sheriff pay right well for that which he hath done to me. Maybe I may bring him some time into Sherwood Forest, and have him to a right merry feast with us." For when Robin Hood caught a baron or a squire, or a fat abbot or bishop, he brought them to the greenwood tree and feasted them before he lightened their purses.

But in the mean time Robin Hood and his band lived quietly in Sherwood Forest, without showing their faces abroad, for Robin knew that it would not be wise for him to be seen in the neighborhood of

Nottingham, those in authority being very wroth with him. But though they did not go abroad, they lived a merry life within the woodlands, spending the days in shooting at garlands hung upon a willow wand at the end of the glade, the leafy aisles ringing with merry jests and laughter: for whoever missed the garland was given a sound buffet, which, if delivered by Little John, never failed to topple over the unfortunate yeoman. Then they had bouts of wrestling and of cudgel play, so that every day they gained in skill and strength.

Thus they dwelt for nearly a year, and in that time Robin Hood often turned over in his mind many means of making an even score with the Sheriff. At last he began to fret at his confinement; so one day he took up his stout cudgel and set forth to seek adventure, strolling blithely along until he came to the edge of Sherwood. There, as he rambled along the sunlit road, he met a lusty young Butcher driving a fine mare, and riding in a stout new cart, all hung about with meat. Merrily whistled the Butcher as he jogged along, for he was going to the market, and the day was fresh and sweet, making his heart blithe within him.

"Good morrow to thee, jolly fellow," quoth Robin; "thou seemest happy this merry morn."

"Ay, that am I," quoth the jolly Butcher; "and why should I not be so? Am I not hale in wind and limb? Have I not the bonniest lass in all Nottinghamshire? And lastly, am I not to be married to her on Thursday next in sweet Locksley Town?"

"Ha," said Robin, "comest thou from Locksley Town? Well do I know that fair place for miles about, and well do I know each hedgerow and gentle pebbly stream, and even all the bright little fishes therein, for there I was born and bred. Now, where goest thou with thy meat, my fair friend?"

"I go to the market at Nottingham Town to sell my beef and my mutton," answered the Butcher. "But who art thou that comest from Locksley Town?"

"A yeoman am I, good friend, and men do call me Robin Hood."

"Now, by Our Lady's grace," cried the Butcher, "well do I know thy name, and many a time have I heard thy deeds both sung and spoken of. But Heaven forbid that thou shouldst take ought of me! An honest man am I, and have wronged neither man nor maid; so trouble me not, good master, as I have never troubled thee."

"Nay, Heaven forbid, indeed," quoth Robin, "that I should take from such as thee, jolly fellow! Not so much as one farthing would I take from thee, for I love a fair Saxon face like thine right well; more especially when it cometh from Locksley Town, and most especially when the man that owneth it is to marry a bonny lass on Thursday next. But come, tell me for what price thou wilt sell all thy meat and thy horse and cart."

"At four marks do I value meat, cart, and mare," quoth the Butcher; "but if I do not sell all my meat I will not have four marks in value."

Then Robin Hood plucked the purse from his girdle, and quoth he, "Here in this purse are six marks. Now, I would fain be a butcher for the day and sell my meat in Nottingham Town, wilt thou close a bargin with me and take six marks for thine outfit?"

"Now may the blessings of all the saints fall on thine honest head!" cried the Butcher right joyfully, as he leaped down from his cart and took the purse that Robin held out to him.

"Nay," quoth Robin, laughing loudly, "many do like me and wish me well, but few call me honest. Now get thee gone back to thy lass, and give her a sweet kiss from me." So saying, he donned the Butcher's apron, and, climbing into the cart, he took the reins in his hand, and drove off through the forest to Nottingham Town.

When he came to Nottingham, he entered that part of the market where butchers stood, and took up his inn in the best place he could find. Next, he opened his stall and spread his meat upon the bench, then, taking his cleaver and steel and clatting them together, he trolled aloud, in merry tones:—

> "Now come, ye lasses, and eke, ye dames,
> And buy your meat from me;
> For three pennyworths of meat I sell
> For the charge of one penny.

> "Lamb have I that hath fed upon nought
> But the dainty daisies pied,
> And the violet sweet, and the daffodil
> That grow fair streams beside.

> "And beef have I from the heathery wolds,
> And mutton from dales all green,
> And veal as white as a maiden's brow,
> With its mother's silk, I ween.

"Then come, ye lasses, and eke, ye dames,
Come, buy your meat from me;
For three pennyworths of meat I sell
For the charge of one penny."

Thus he sang blithely, while all who stood near listened amazedly; then, when he had finished, he clattered the steel and cleaver still more loudly, shouting lustily, "Now, who'll buy? who'll buy? Four fixed prices have I. Three pennyworths of meat I sell to a fat friar or priest for sixpence, for I want not their customs; stout aldermen I charge threepence, for it doth not matter to me whether they buy or not; to buxom dames I sell three pennyworths of meat for one penny, for I like their custom well; but to the bonny lass that hath a liking for a good tight butcher I charge nought but one fair kiss, for I like her custom the best of all."

Then all began to stare and wonder, and crowd around, laughing, for never was such selling heard of in all Nottingham Town; but when they came to buy they found it as he had said, for he gave good wife or dame as much meat for one penny as they could buy elsewhere for three, and when a widow or a poor woman came to him, he gave her flesh for nothing; but when a merry lass came and gave him a kiss, he charged not one penny for his meat; and many such came to his stall, for his eyes were as blue as the skies of June, and he laughed merrily, giving to each full measure. Thus he sold his meat so fast that no butcher that stood near him could sell anything.

Then they began to talk among themselves, and some said, "This must be some thief who has stolen cart, horse, and meat"; but others said, "Nay, when did ye ever see a thief parted with his goods so freely and merrily? This must be some prodigal who hath sold his father's land, and would fain live merrily while the money lasts." And these latter being the greater number, the others came round, one by one, to their way of thinking.

Then some of the butchers came to him to make his acquaintance. "Come, brother," quoth one who was the head of them all, "we be all of one trade, so wilt thou go dine with us? For this day the Sheriff hath asked all the Butcher Guild to feast with him at the Guild Hall. There will be stout fare and much to drink, and that thou likest, or I much mistake thee."

"Now, beshrew his heart," quoth jolly Robin, "that would deny a butcher. And, moreover, I will go dine with you all, my sweet lads, and that as fast as I can hie." Whereupon, having sold all his meat, he closed his stall, and went with them to the great Guild Hall.

There the Sheriff had already come in state, and with him many butchers. When Robin and those that were with him came in, all laughing at some merry jest he had been telling them, those that were near the Sheriff whispered to him, "Yon is a right mad blade, for he hath sold more meat for one penny this day than we could sell for three, and to whatsoever merry lass gave him a kiss he gave meat for nought." And other said, "He is some prodigal that hath sold his land for silver and gold, and meaneth to spend all right merrily."

Then the Sheriff called Robin to him, not knowing him in his butcher's dress, and made him sit close to him on his right hand, for he loved a rich young prodigal—especially when he thought that he might lighten that prodigal's pockets into his own most worshipful purse. So he made much of Robin, and laughed and talked with him more than with any of the others.

At last the dinner was ready to be served and the Sheriff bade Robin say grace, so Robin stood up and said: "Now Heaven bless us all and eke good meat and good sack within this house, and may all butchers be and remain as honest men as I am."

At this all laughed, the Sheriff loudest of all, for he said to himself, "Surely this is indeed some prodigal, and perchance I may empty his purse of some of the money that the fool throweth about so freely." Then he spake aloud to Robin, saying: "Thou art a jolly young blade, and I love thee mightily"; and he smote Robin upon the shoulder.

Then Robin laughed loudly too. "Yea," quoth he, "I know thou dost love a jolly blade, for didst thou not have jolly Robin Hood at thy shooting-match and didst thou not gladly give him a bright golden arrow for his own?"

At this the Sheriff looked grave and all the guild of butchers too, so that none laughed but Robin, only some winked slyly at each other.

"Come, fill us some sack!" cried Robin. "Let us e'er be merry while we may, for man is but dust, and he hath but a span to live here till the worm getteth him, as our good gossip Swanthold sayeth; so let life be merry while it lasts, say I. Nay, never look down i' the mouth, Sir Sheriff. Who knowest but that thou mayest catch Robin Hood yet if thou drinkest less good sack and Malmsey, and bringest down the fat about thy paunch and the dust from out thy brain. Be merry, man."

Then the Sheriff laughed again, but not as though he liked the jest, while the butchers said, one to another, "Before Heaven, never have we seen such a mad rollicking blade. Mayhap, though, he will make the Sheriff mad."

"How now, brothers," cried Robin, "be merry! nay, never count over your farthings, for by this and by that I will pay this shot myself, e'en though it cost two hundred pounds. So let no man draw up his lip, nor thrust his forefinger into his purse, for I swear that neither butcher nor Sheriff shall pay one penny for this feast."

"Now thou art a right merry soul," quoth the Sheriff, "and I wot thou must have many a head of horned beasts and many an acre of land, that thou dost spend thy money so freely."

"Ay, that have I," quoth Robin, laughing loudly again, "five hundred and more horned beasts have I and my brothers, and none of them have we been able to sell, else I might not have turned butcher. As for my land, I have never asked my steward how many acres I have."

At this the Sheriff's eyes twinkled, and he chuckled to himself. "Nay, good youth," quoth he, "if thou canst not sell thy cattle it may be I will find a man that will lift them from thy hands; perhaps that man may be myself, for I love a merry youth and would help such a one along the path of life. Now how much dost thou want for thy horned cattle?"

"Well," quoth Robin, "they are worth at least five hundred pounds."

"Nay," answered the Sheriff, slowly, and as if he were thinking within himself; "well do I love thee, and fain would I help thee along, but five hundred pounds in money is a good round sum; beside I have it not by me. Yet

I will give thee three hundred pounds for them all, and that in good hard silver and gold."

"Now thou old Jew!" quoth Robin; "well thou knowest that so many horned cattle are worth seven hundred pounds and more, and even that is but small for them, and yet thou, with thy gray hairs and one foot in the grave, wouldst trade upon the folly of a wild youth."

At this the Sheriff looked grimly at Robin. "Nay," quoth Robin, "look not on me as though thou hadst sour beer in thy mouth, man. I will take thine offer, for I and my brothers do need the money. We lead a merry life, and no one leads a merry life for a farthing, so I will close the bargain with thee. But mind that thou bringest a good three hundred pounds with thee, for I trust not one that driveth so shrewd a bargain."

"I will bring the money," said the Sheriff. "But what is thy name, good youth?"

"Men call me Robert o' Locksley," quoth bold Robin.

"Then, good Robert o' Locksley," quoth the Sheriff, "I will come this day to see thy horned beasts. But first my clerk shall draw up a paper in which thou shalt be bound to the sale, for thou gettest not my money without I get thy beasts in return."

Then Robin Hood laughed again. "So be it," he cried, smiting his palm upon the Sheriff's hand. "Truly my brothers will be thankful to thee for thy money."

Thus the bargain was closed; but many of the butchers talked among themselves of the Sheriff, saying that it was but a scurvy trick to beguile a poor spendthrift youth in this way.

The afternoon had come when the Sheriff mounted his horse and joined Robin Hood, who stood outside the gateway of the paved court waiting for him, for he had sold his horse and cart to a trader for two marks. Then they set forth upon their way, the Sheriff riding upon his horse and Robin running beside him. Thus they left Nottingham Town and travelled forward along the dusty highway, laughing and jesting together as though they had been old friends; but all the time the Sheriff said within himself, "Thy jest to me of Robin Hood shall cost thee dear, good fellow, even four hundred pounds, thou fool." For he thought he would make at least that much by his bargain.

So they journeyed onward till they came within the verge of Sherwood Forest, when presently the Sheriff looked up and down and to the right and to the left of him and then grew quiet and ceased his laughter. "Now," quoth he, "may Heaven and its saints preserve us this day from a rogue men call Robin Hood."

Then Robin laughed aloud. "Nay," said he, "thou mayest set thy mind at rest, for well do I know Robin Hood and well do I know that thou art in no more danger from him this day than thou art from me."

At this the Sheriff looked askance at Robin, saying to himself, "I like not that thou seemest so well acquainted with this bold outlaw, and I wish that I were well out of Sherwood Forest."

But still they travelled deeper into the forest shades, and the deeper they went the more quiet grew the Sheriff. At last they came to where the road took a sudden bend, and before them a herd of dun deer went tripping across the path. Then Robin Hood came close to the Sheriff and pointing his finger he said, "These are my horned beasts, good Master Sheriff. How dost thou like them? Are they not fat and fair to see?"

At this the Sheriff drew rein quickly. "Now fellow," quoth he, "I would I were well out of this forest, for I like not thy company. Go thou thine own path, good friend, and let me but go mine."

But Robin only laughed and caught the Sheriff's bridle rein. "Nay," cried he, "stay a while, for I would thou shouldst see my brothers who own these fair horned beasts with me." So saying he clapped his bugle to his mouth and winded three merry notes, and presently up the path came leaping fivescore good stout yeomen with Little John at their head.

"What wouldst thou have, good master?" quoth Little John.

"Why," answered Robin, "dost thou not see that I have brought goodly company to feast with us today? Fye, for shame! do you not see our good and worshipful master, the Sheriff of Nottingham? Take thou his bridle, Little John, for he has honored us today by coming to feast with us."

Then all doffed their hats humbly, without smiling, or seeming to be in jest, whilst Little John took the bridle rein and led the palfrey still deeper into the forest, all marching in order, with Robin Hood walking beside the Sheriff, hat in hand.

All this time the Sheriff said never a word but only looked about him like one suddenly awakened from sleep; but when he found himself going within the very depth of Sherwood his heart sank within him, for he thought, "Surely my three hundred pounds will be taken from me, even if they take not my life itself, for I have plotted against their lives more than once." But all seemed humble and meek and not a word was said of danger, either to life or money.

So at last they came to that part of Sherwood Forest where a noble oak spread its branches wide, and beneath it was a seat all made of moss, on which Robin sat down, placing the Sheriff at his right hand. "Now busk ye, my merry men all," quoth he, "and bring forth the best we have, both of meat and wine, for his worship, the Sheriff, hath feasted me in Nottingham Guild Hall today, and I would not have him go back empty."

All this time nothing had been said of the Sheriff's money, so presently he began to pluck up heart; "For," said he to himself, "maybe Robin Hood hath forgotten all about it."

Then, whilst beyond in the forest bright fires crackled and savory smells of sweetly roasting venison and fat capons filled the glade, and brown pasties warmed beside the blaze, did Robin Hood entertain the Sheriff right royally. First, several couples stood forth at quarterstaff, and so shrewd were they at the game, and so quickly did they give stroke and parry, that the Sheriff, who loved to watch all lusty sports of the kind, clapped his hands, forgetting where he was, and crying aloud, "Well struck! well struck, thou fellow with the black beard!" little knowing that the man he called upon was the Tinker that tried to serve his warrant upon Robin Hood.

Then the best archers of the band set up a fair garland of flowers at eightscore paces distance, and shot at it with the cunningest archery practice. But the Sheriff grew grave, for he did not like this so well, the famous meeting at the butts in Nottingham Town being still green in his memory, and the golden arrow that had been won there hanging close behind him. Then, when Robin saw what was in the Sheriff's mind, he stopped the sport, and calleth forth some of his band, who sang merry ballads, while others made music upon the harp.

When this was done, several yeomen came forward and spread cloths upon the green grass, and placed a royal feast; while others still broached barrels of sack and Malmsey and good stout ale, and set them in jars upon the cloth, with drinking-horns about them. Then all sat down and feasted and drank merrily together until the sun was low and the half-moon glimmered with a pale light betwixt the leaves of the trees overhead.

Then the Sheriff arose and said, "I thank you all, good yeomen, for the merry entertainment ye have given me this day. Right courteously have ye used me, showing therein that ye have much respect for our glorious King and his deputy in brave Nottinghamshire. But the shadows grow long, and I must away before darkness comes, lest I lose myself within the forest."

Then Robin Hood and all his merry men arose also, and Robin said to the Sheriff, "If thou must go, worshipful sir, go thou must; but thou hast forgotten one thing."

"Nay, I forgot nought," said the Sheriff; yet all the same his heart sank within him.

"But I say thou hast forgot something," quoth Robin. "We keep a merry inn here in the greenwood, but whoever becometh our guest must pay his reckoning."

Then the Sheriff laughed, but the laugh was hollow. "Well, jolly boys," quoth he, "we have had a merry time together today, and even if ye had not asked me, I would have given you a score of pounds for the sweet entertainment I have had."

"Nay," quoth Robin seriously, "it would ill beseem us to treat your worship so meanly. By my faith, Sir Sheriff, I would be ashamed to show my face if I did not reckon the King's deputy at three hundred pounds. Is it not so, my merry men all?"

Then "Ay!" cried all, in a loud voice.

"Three hundred devils!" roared the Sheriff. "Think ye that your beggarly feast was worth three pounds, let alone three hundred?"

"Nay," quoth Robin, gravely. "Speak not so roundly, your worship. I do love thee for the sweet feast thou hast given me this day in merry Nottingham Town; but there be those here who love thee not so much. If thou wilt look down the cloth thou wilt see Will Stutely, in whose eyes thou hast no great favor; then two other stout fellows are there here that thou knowest not, that were wounded in a brawl nigh Nottingham Town, some time ago—thou wottest when; one of them was sore hurt in one arm, yet he hath got the use of it again. Good Sheriff, be advised by me; pay thy score without more ado, or maybe it may fare ill with thee."

As he spoke the Sheriff's ruddy cheeks grew pale, and he said nothing more but looked upon the ground and gnawed his nether lip. Then slowly he drew forth his fat purse and threw it upon the cloth in front of him.

"Now take the purse, Little John," quoth Robin Hood, "and see that the reckoning be right. We would not doubt our Sheriff, but he might not like it if he should find he had not paid his full score."

Then Little John counted the money, and found that the bag held three hundred pounds in silver and gold. But to the Sheriff it seemed as if every clink of the bright money was a drop of blood from his veins; and when he saw it all counted out in a heap of silver and gold, filling a wooden platter, he turned away and silently mounted his horse.

"Never have we had so worshipful a guest before!" quoth Robin; "and, as the day waxeth late, I will send one of my young men to guide thee out of the forest depths."

"Nay, heaven forbid!" cried the Sheriff, hastily. "I can find mine own way, good man, without aid."

"Then I will put thee on the right track mine own self," quoth Robin; and, taking the Sheriff's horse by the bridle rein, he led him into the main forest path; then, before he let him go, he said, "Now, fare thee well, good Sheriff, and when next thou thinkest to despoil some poor prodigal, remember thy feast in Sherwood Forest. 'Ne'er buy a horse, good friend, without first looking into its mouth,' as our good gaffer Swanthold says. And so, once more, fare thee well." Then he clapped his hand to the horse's back, and off went nag and Sheriff through the forest glades.

Then bitterly the Sheriff rued the day that first he meddled with Robin Hood, for all men laughed at him and many ballads were sung by folk throughout the country, of how the Sheriff went to shear and came home shorn to the very quick. For thus men sometimes overreach themselves through greed and guile.

2

LITTLE JOHN
GOES TO THE FAIR
AT NOTTINGHAM TOWN

NOW WE WILL TELL OF THE MERRY ADVENTURES THAT BEFELL Little John at the shooting-match at Nottingham, and how he overcame Eric o' Lincoln in the famous bout at quarterstaff in that town; also how he entered the Sheriff's service, and of his merry encounter with the Sheriff's cook. So listen to what follows.

SPRING HAD GONE SINCE THE SHERIFF'S FEAST IN SHERWOOD, and summer also, and the mellow month of October had come. All the air was cool and fresh; the harvests were gathered home, the young birds were full fledged, the hops were plucked, and apples were ripe. But though time had so smoothed things over that men no longer talked of the horned beasts that the Sheriff wished to buy, he was still sore about the matter and could not bear to hear Robin Hood's name spoken in his presence.

With October had come the time for holding the great Fair which was celebrated every five years at Nottingham Town, to which folk came from far and near throughout the country. At such times archery was always the main sport of the day, for the Nottinghamshire yeomen were the best hand at the longbow in all Merry England; but this year the Sheriff hesitated a long time before he issued proclamation of the Fair, fearing lest Robin Hood and his band might come to it. At first he had a great part of a mind not to proclaim the Fair, but second thought told him that men would laugh at him and say among themselves that he was afraid of Robin Hood, so he put that thought by. At last he fixed in his mind that he would offer such a prize as they would not care to shoot for. At such times it had been the custom to offer a half score of marks or a tun of ale, so this year he proclaimed that a prize of two fat steers should be given to the best bowman.

When Robin Hood heard what had been proclaimed he was vexed, and said, "Now beshrew this Sheriff that he should offer such a prize that none but shepherd hinds will care to shoot for it! I would have loved nothing better than to have had another bout at merry Nottingham Town, but if I should win this prize naught would it pleasure or profit me."

Then up spoke Little John: "Nay, but hearken, good master," said he, "only today Will Stutely, young David of Doncaster, and I were at the sign of the Blue Boar, and there we heard all the news of this merry Fair, and also that the Sheriff hath offered this prize that we of Sherwood might not care to come to the Fair; so, good master, if thou wilt, I would fain go and strive to win even this poor thing among the stout yeomen who will shoot at Nottingham Town."

"Nay, Little John," quoth Robin, "thou art a sound stout fellow, yet thou lackest the cunning that good Stutely hath, and I would not have harm befall thee for all Nottinghamshire. Nevertheless if thou wilt go, take some disguise lest there be those there who may know thee."

"So be it, good master," quoth Little John; "yet all the disguise that I wish is a good suit of scarlet instead of this of Lincoln green. I will draw the cowl of my jacket about my head so that it will hide my brown hair and beard, and then, I trust, no one will know me."

68

"It is much against my will," said Robin Hood, "ne'ertheless, if thou dost wish it, get thee gone, but bear thyself seemingly, Little John, for thou art mine own right hand man and I could ill bear to have harm befall thee."

So Little John clad himself all in scarlet, and started off to the Fair at Nottingham Town.

RIGHT MERRY WERE THESE FAIR DAYS AT NOTTINGHAM, WHEN THE GREEN before the great town gate was dotted with booths standing in rows, with tents of many-colored canvas, hung about with streamers and garlands of flowers, and the folk came from all the countryside, both gentle and common. In some booths there was dancing to merry music, in others flowed ale and beer, and in others yet again sweet cakes and barley sugar were sold; and sport was going outside the booths also, where some minstrel sang ballads of the olden time, playing a second upon the harp, or where the wrestlers struggled with one another within the sawdust ring; but the people gathered most of all around a raised platform where stout fellows played at quarterstaff.

So Little John came to the Fair. All scarlet were his hose and jerkin, and scarlet was his cowled cap, with a scarlet feather stuck in the side of it. Over his shoulders was slung a stout bow of yew, and across his back hung a quiver of good round arrows. Many turned to look after such a stout, tall fellow, for his shoulders were broader by a palm's breadth than any that were there, and he stood a head taller than all the other men. The lasses, also, looked at him askance, thinking they had never seen a lustier youth.

First of all he went to the booth where stout ale was sold, and, standing aloft on a bench he called to all that were near to come and drink with him. "Hey, sweet lads!" cried he, "who will drink ale with a stout yeoman? Come, all! come, all! Let us be merry, for the day is sweet and the ale is tingling. Come hither, good yeoman, and thou, and thou; for not a farthing shall one of you pay. Nay, turn hither, thou lusty beggar, and thou jolly tinker, for all shall be merry with me."

Thus he shouted, and all crowded around, laughing, while the brown ale flowed; and they called Little John a brave fellow, each swearing that he loved him as his own brother; for when one has entertainment with nothing to pay, one loves the man that gives it to one.

The next place Little John went to was the dancing booth, where three men made sweet music with bagpipes. Here he laid aside his bow and his quiver, and joined in the sport, dancing so long that none could stand against him. A score of lasses came, one after another, and strove to dance him down, but could not do so; for Little John leaped so high, snapping his fingers the while, and shouted so loud, that every lass vowed that she had never seen so sweet a lad in all her life before.

Then, after he had danced a long time, he strolled to the platform where they were at cudgel-play, for he loved a bout at quarterstaff, as he loved meat and drink; and here befell an adventure that was sung in ballads throughout the mid-country for many a day.

One fellow there was that cracked crowns of every one who threw cap into the ring. This was Eric o' Lincoln, of great renown, whose name had been sung in ballads throughout the countryside. When Little John reached the stand he found none fighting, but only bold Eric walking up and down the platform, swinging his staff and shouting lustily: "Now, who will come and strike a stroke for the lass he loves the best, with a good Lincolnshire yeoman? How now, lads? step up! step up! or else the lasses' eyes are not bright hereabouts, or the blood of Nottingham youth is sluggish and cold. Lincoln against Nottingham, say I! for no one hath put foot upon the boards this day such as we of Lincoln call a cudgel-player."

At this, one would nudge another with his elbow, saying, "Go thou, Ned!" or "Go thou, Thomas!" but no lad cared to gain a cracked crown for nothing.

Presently Eric saw where little John stood among the others, a head and shoulders above them all, and he called to him loudly, "Halloa, thou long-legged fellow in scarlet! Broad are thy shoulders and thick thy head; is not thy lass fair enough for thee to take cudgel in hand for her sake? In truth, I believe that Nottingham men do turn to bone and sinew, for neither heart nor courage have they! Now, thou great lout, wilt thou not twirl staff for Nottingham?"

"Ay," quoth Little John, "had I but mine own good staff here, it would pleasure me hugely to crack thy knave's pate, thou saucy braggart! I wot it would be well for thee an thy cock's comb were cut!" Thus he spoke, slowly at first, for he was slow to move; but his wrath gathered headway like a great stone rolling down a hill, so that at the end he was full of anger.

Then Eric o' Lincoln laughed aloud. "Well spoken for one who fears to meet me fairly, man to man," said he. "Saucy art thou thine own self, and, if thou puttest foot upon these boards, I will make thy saucy tongue rattle within thy teeth!"

"Now," quoth Little John, "is there never a man here that will lend me a good stout staff till I try the mettle of yon fellow?" At this, half a score reached him their staves, and he took the stoutest and heaviest of them all. Then, looking up and down the cudgel, he said, "Now, I have in my hand but a splint of wood,—a barley-straw, an it were,—yet I trow it will have to serve me; so here goeth." Thereupon he cast the cudgel upon the stand, and, leaping lightly after it, snatched it up in his hand again.

Then each man stood in his place and measured the other with fell looks until he that directed the sport cried, "Play!" At this they stepped forth, each grasping his staff tightly in the middle. Then those that stood around saw the stoutest game of quarterstaff that e'er Nottingham Town beheld. At first Eric o' Lincoln thought that he would gain an easy advantage, so he came forth as if he would say, "Watch, good people, how that I carve you this cockerel right speedily"; but he presently found it to be no such speedy matter. Right deftly he struck, and with great skill of fence, but he had found his match in Little John. Once, twice, thrice he struck, and three times Little John turned the blows to the left hand and to the right. Then quickly and with a dainty backhanded blow he rapped Eric beneath his guard so shrewdly that it made his head ring again. Then Eric stepped back to gather his wits, while a great shout went up and all were glad that Nottingham had cracked Lincoln's crown; and thus ended the first bout of the game.

Then presently the director of the sport cried, "Play!" and they came together again; but now Eric played warily, for he found his man was of right good mettle, and also he had no sweet memory of the blow that he had got; so this bout neither Little John nor the Lincoln man caught a stroke within his guard; then, after a while, they parted again, and this made the second bout.

Then for the third time they came together, and at first Eric strove to be wary, as he had been before; but, growing mad at finding himself so foiled, he lost his wits, and began to rain blows so fiercely and so fast that they rattled like hail on penthouse roof; but, in spite of all, he did not reach within Little John's guard. Then at last Little John saw his chance and seized it right cleverly. Once more, with a quick blow, he rapped Eric beside the head, and ere he could regain himself, Little John slipped his right hand down to his left, and, with a swinging blow, smote the other so sorely upon the crown that down he fell as though he would never move again.

Then the people shouted so loud that folk came running from all about to see what was the ado; while Little John leaped down from the stand and gave the staff back to him that had lent it to him. And thus ended the famous bout between Little John and Eric o' Lincoln of great renown.

But now the time had come when those who were to shoot with the long bow were to take their places, so the people began flocking to the butts where the shooting was to be. Near the target, in a good place, sat the Sheriff, upon a raised dais, with many gentlefolk around him. When the archers had taken their places, the herald came forward and proclaimed the rules of the game, and how each should shoot three shots, and to him that should shoot the best the prize of two fat steers was to belong. A score of brave shots were gathered there, and among them some of the keenest hands at the long bow in Lincoln and Nottinghamshire; and among them Little John stood taller than all the rest. "Who is yon stranger clad all in scarlet?" said some; and others answered, "It is he that hath but now so soundly cracked the crown of Eric o' Lincoln." Thus the people talked among themselves, until at last it reached even the Sheriff's ears.

And now each man stepped forward and shot in turn; but though each shot well, Little John was the best of all, for three times he struck the clout, and once only the length of a barleycorn from the centre. "Hey for the tall archer!" shouted the crowd; and some among them shouted, "Hey for Reynold Greenleaf!" for this was the name that Little John had called himself that day.

Then the Sheriff stepped down from the raised seat and come to where the archers stood, while all doffed their caps that saw him coming. He looked keenly at Little John, but did not know him, though he said, after a while, "How now, good fellow, methinks there is that about thy face that I have seen erewhile."

"Mayhap it may be so," quoth Little John, "for often have I seen your worship"; and, as he spoke, he looked steadily into the Sheriff's eyes, so that the latter did not suspect who he was.

"A brave blade art thou, good friend," said the Sheriff, "and I hear that thou hast well upheld the skill of Nottinghamshire against that of Lincoln this day. What may be thy name, good fellow?"

"Men do call me Reynold Greenleaf, your worship," said Little John; and the old ballad that tells of this, adds, "So in truth, he was a green leaf, but of what manner of tree the Sheriff wotted not."

"Now, Reynold Greenleaf," quoth the Sheriff, "thou art the fairest hand at the long bow that mine eyes ever beheld, next to that false knave, Robin Hood, from whose wiles Heaven forfend me! Wilt thou join my service, good fellow? Thou shalt be paid right well, for three suits of clothes shalt thou have a year, with good food and as much ale as thou canst drink; and, beside this, I will pay thee forty marks each Michaelmastide."

"Then here stand I a free man, and right gladly will I enter thy household," said Little John; for he thought he might find some merry jest, should he enter the Sheriff's service.

"Fairly hast thou won the fat steers," said the Sheriff, "and thereunto I will add a butt of good March beer, for joy of having gotten such a man; for, I wot, thou shootest as fair a shaft as Robin Hood himself."

"Then," said Little John, "for joy of having gotten myself into thy service, I will give fat steers and brown ale to all these good folk, to make them merry withal." At this arose a great shout, many casting their caps aloft, for joy of the gift.

Then some built great fires and roasted the steers, and others broached the butt of ale, with which all made themselves merry; then, when they had eaten and drunk as much as they could, and when the day faded and the great moon arose, all red and round, over the spires and towers of Nottingham Town, they joined hands and danced around the fires, to the music of bagpipes and harps. But long before this merrymaking had begun, the Sheriff and his new servant, Reynold Greenleaf, were in the Castle of Nottingham.

3

HOW LITTLE JOHN LIVED
AT THE SHERIFF'S HOUSE

THUS LITTLE JOHN ENTERED INTO THE SHERIFF'S SERVICE, and found the life he led there easy enough, for the Sheriff made him his right-hand man, and held him in great favor. He sat nigh the Sheriff at meat, and he ran beside his horse when he went a-hunting; so that, what with hunting and hawking a little, and eating rich dishes and drinking good sack and sleeping until late hours in the morning, he grew as fat as a stall-fed ox. Thus things floated easily along with the tide, until one day when the Sheriff went a-hunting, there happened that which broke the smooth surface of things.

This morning the Sheriff and many of his men set forth to meet certain lords, to go a-hunting. He looked all about him for his good man, Reynold Greenleaf, but, not finding him, was vexed, for he wished to show Little John's skill to his noble friends. As for Little John, he lay abed, snoring lustily, till the sun was high in the heavens. At last he opened his eyes

74

and looked about him, but did not move to arise. Brightly shone the sun in at the window, and all the air was sweet with the scent of woodbine that hung in sprays about the wall without, for the cold winter was past and spring was come again, and Little John lay still, thinking how sweet was everything on this fair morn. Just then he heard, faint and far away, a distant bugle-note sounding thin and clear. The sound was small, but, like a little pebble dropped into a glassy fountain, it broke all the smooth surface of his thoughts, until his whole soul was filled with disturbance. His spirit seemed to awaken from its sluggishness, and his memory brought back to him all the merry greenwood life,—how the birds were singing blithely there this bright morning, and how his loved companions and friends were feasting and making merry, or perhaps talking of him with sober speech; for when he first entered the Sheriff's service he did so in jest; but the hearthstone was warm during the winter, and the fare was full, and so he had abided, putting off from day to day his going back to Sherwood, until six long months had passed. But now he thought of his good master, and of Will Stutely, whom he loved better than any one in all the world, and of young David of Doncaster, whom he had trained so well in all manly sports, till there came over his heart a great and bitter longing for them all, so that his eyes filled with tears. Then he said aloud: "Here I grow fat like a stall-fed ox and all my manliness departeth from me while I become a sluggard and dolt. But I will arouse me and go back to mine own dear friends once more, and never will I leave them again till life doth leave my lips." So saying, he leaped from bed, for he hated his sluggishness now.

When he came downstairs he saw the Steward standing near the pantry door,—a great, fat man, with a huge bundle of keys hanging to his girdle. Then Little John said, "Ho, Master Steward, a hungry man am I, for nought have I had for all this blessed morn. Therefore, give me to eat."

Then the Steward looked grimly at him and rattled the keys in his girdle, for he hated Little John because he had found favor with the Sheriff. "So, Master Reynold Greenleaf, thou art an hungered, art thou?" quoth he. "But, fair youth, if thou livest long enough, thou wilt find that he who getteth overmuch sleep for an idle head goeth with an empty stomach. For what sayeth the old saw, Master Greenleaf? is it not 'The late fowl findeth but ill faring'?"

"Now, thou great purse of fat!" cried Little John, "I ask thee not for fool's wisdom, but for bread and meat. Who art thou, that thou shouldst deny me to eat? By Saint Dunstan, thou hadst best tell me where my breakfast is, if thou wouldst save broken bones!"

"Thy breakfast, Master Fireblaze, is in the pantry," answered the Steward.

"Then fetch it hither!" cried Little John, who waxed angry by this time.

"Go thou and fetch it thine own self," quoth the Steward. "Am I thy slave, to fetch and carry for thee?"

"I say, go thou, bring it me!"

"I say, go thou, fetch it for thyself!"

"Ay, marry, that will I, right quickly!" quoth Little John, in a rage; and, so saying, he strode to the pantry and tried to open the door; but found it locked, whereat the Steward laughed and rattled his keys. Then the wrath of Little John boiled over, and, lifting his clenched fist, he smote the pantry door, bursting out three panels, and making so large an opening that he could easily stoop and walk through it.

When the Steward saw what was done, he waxed mad with rage; and, as Little John stooped to look within the pantry, he seized him from behind by the nape of the neck, pinching him sorely and smiting him over the head with his keys till the yeoman's ears rang again. At this Little John turned upon the Steward and smote him such a buffet that the fat man fell to the floor and lay there as though he would never move again. "There," quoth Little John, "think well of that stroke and never keep a good breakfast from a hungry man again."

So saying, he crept into the pantry and looked about him to see if he could find something to appease his hunger. He saw a great venison pasty and two roasted capons, beside which was a platter of plover's eggs; moreover, there was a flask of sack and one of canary,—a sweet sight to a hungry man. These he took down from the shelves and placed upon a sideboard, and prepared to make himself merry.

Now the Cook, in the kitchen across the courtyard, heard the loud talking between Little John and the Steward, and also the blow that Little John struck the other, so he came running across the court and up the stairway to where the Steward's pantry was, bearing in his hands the spit with the roast still upon it. Meanwhile the Steward had gathered his wits about him and risen to his feet, so that when the Cook came to the Steward's pantry he saw him glowering through the broken door at Little John, who was making ready for a good repast, as one dog glowers at another that has a bone. When the Steward saw the Cook, he came to him, and, putting one arm over his shoulder, "Alas, sweet friend!" quoth he,— for the Cook was a tall, stout man—"seest thou what that vile knave, Reynold Greenleaf, hath done? He hath broken in upon our master's goods, and hath smitten me a buffet upon the ear, so that I thought I was dead. Good Cook, I love thee well, and thou shalt have a good pottle of our master's best wine every day, for thou art an old and faithful servant. Also, good Cook, I have ten shillings that I mean to give as a gift to thee. But hatest thou not to see a vile upstart like this Reynold Greenleaf taking it upon him so bravely?"

"Ay, marry, that do I," quoth the Cook boldly, for he liked the Steward because of his talk of the wine and of the ten shillings. "Get thee gone straightway to thy room, and I will bring out this knave by his ears." So saying, he laid aside his spit and drew the sword that hung by his side; whereupon the Steward left as quickly as he could, for he hated the sight of naked steel.

Then the Cook walked straightway to the broken pantry door, through which he saw Little John tucking a napkin beneath his chin, and preparing to make himself merry.

"Why, how now, Reynold Greenleaf?" said the Cook; "thou art no better than a thief, I wot. Come thou straight forth, man, or I will carve thee as I would carve a sucking pig."

"Nay, good Cook, bear thou thyself more seemingly, or else I will come forth to thy dole. At most times I am as a yearling lamb, but when one cometh between me and my meat, I am a raging lion, as it were."

"Lion or no lion," quoth the valorous Cook, "come thou straight forth, else thou art a coward heart as well as a knavish thief."

"Ha!" cried Little John, "coward's name have I never had; so, look to thyself, good Cook, for I come forth straight, the roaring lion I did speak of but now."

Then he, too, drew his sword and came out of the pantry; then, putting themselves into position, they came slowly together, with grim and angry looks; but suddenly Little John lowered his point. "Hold, good Cook!" said he. "Now, I bethink me it were ill of us to fight with good victuals standing so nigh, and such a feast as would befit two stout fellows such as we are. Marry, good friend, I think we should enjoy this fair feast ere we fight. What sayest thou, jolly Cook?"

At this speech the Cook looked up and down, scratching his head in doubt, for he loved good feasting. At last he drew a long breath, and said to Little John, "Well, good friend, I like thy plan right well; so, pretty boy, say I, let us feast, with all my heart, for one of us may sup in Paradise before nightfall."

So each thrust his sword back into the scabbard, and entered the pantry; then, after they had seated themselves, Little John drew his dagger and thrust it into the pie. "A hungry man must be fed," quoth he, "so, sweet chuck, I help myself without leave." But the Cook did not lag far behind, for straightway his hands also were deeply thrust within the goodly pasty. After this, neither of them spoke further, but used their teeth to better purpose. But though neither spoke, they looked at one another, each thinking within himself that he had never seen a more lusty fellow than the one across the board.

At last, after a long time had passed, the Cook drew a full, deep breath, as though of much regret, and wiped his hands upon the napkin, for he could eat no more. Little John, also, had enough, for he pushed the pasty aside, as though he would say, "I want thee by me no more, good friend." Then he took the pottle of sack, and said he, "Now, good fellow, I swear by all that is bright, that thou art the stoutest companion at eating that ever I had. Lo! I drink thy health." So saying, he clapped the flask to his lips and cast his eyes aloft, while the good wine flooded his throat. Then he passed the pottle to the Cook, who also said, "Lo, I drink thy health, sweet fellow!" Nor was he behind Little John in drinking any more than in eating.

"Now," quoth Little John, "thy voice is right round and sweet, jolly lad; I doubt not thou canst sing a ballad most blithely; canst thou not?"

"Truly, I have trolled one now and then," quoth the Cook; "yet I would not sing alone."

"Nay, truly," said Little John, "that were but ill courtesy. Strike up thy ditty, and I will afterwards sing one to match it, if I can."

"So be it, pretty boy," quoth the Cook. "And hast thou e'er heard the song of the Deserted Shepherdess?" "Truly, I know not," answered Little John; "but sing thou away and let me hear." Then the Cook took another draught from the pottle, and, clearing his throat, sang right sweetly,—

THE SONG OF THE DESERTED SHEPHERDESS

"In Lenten time, when leaves wax green,
And pretty birds begin to mate,
When lark doth sing, and thrush, I ween,
And stockdove coveth soon and late,
Fair Phillis sat beside a stone,
And thus I heard her make her moan:
'O willow, willow, willow:
I'll take me of thy branches fair
And twine a wreath of deck my hair.

"'The thrush hath taken him a she,
The robin, too, and eke the dove;
My Robin hath deserted me,
And left me for another love.
So here, by brookside, all alone,
I sit me down and make my moan.
O willow, willow, willow, willow!
I'll take me of thy branches fair
And twine a wreath to deck my hair.'

"But ne'er came herring from the sea,
But good as he were in the tide;
Young Corydon came o'er the lea,
And sat him Phillis down beside .
So, presently, she changed her tone,
And 'gan to cease her from her moan,
'O willow, willow, willow, willow!
Thou mayst e'en keep thy garlands fair,
I want them to deck my hair.'"

"Now, by my faith," cried Little John, "that same is a right good song, and hath truth in it, also."

"Glad am I thou one also, for ne'er should a man be merry alone, or sing and list not."

"Then I will sing thee a song of a right good knight of Arthur's court, and how he cured his heart's wound without running upon the dart again, as did thy Phillis; for I wot she did but cure one smart by giving herself another. So, list thou while I sing—

THE GOOD KNIGHT AND HIS LOVE

"When Arthur, King, did rule this land,
A goodly king was he,
And had he of stout knights a band
Of merry company.

"Among them all, both great and small,
A good stout knight was there,
A lusty childe, and eke a tall,
That loved a lady fair.

"But nought would she to do with he,
But turned her face away;
So gat he gone to far countrye,
And left that lady gay,

> *"There all alone he made his moan,*
> *And eke did sob and sigh,*
> *And weep till it would move a stone,*
> *And he was like to die.*
>
> *"But still his heart did feel the smart,*
> *And eke the dire distress,*
> *And rather grew his pain more sharp*
> *As grew his body less.*
>
> *"Then gat he back where was good sack*
> *And merry companye,*
> *And soon did cease to cry 'Alack!'*
> *When blithe and gay was he.*
>
> *"From which I hold, and feel full bold*
> *To say, and eke believe,*
> *That gin the belly go not cold*
> *The heart will cease to grieve."*

"Now, by my faith," cried the Cook, as he rattled the pottle against the sideboard, "I like that same song hugely, and eke the motive of it, which lieth like a sweet kernel in a hazel-nut."

"Now thou art a man of shrewd opinions," quoth Little John, "and I love thee truly as thou wert my brother."

"And I love thee, too. But the day draweth on, and I have my cooking to do ere our master cometh home; so let us e'en go and settle this brave fight we have in hand."

"Ay, marry," quoth Little John, "and that right speedily. Never have I been more laggard in fighting than in eating and drinking. So come thou straight forth into the passage-way, where there is good room to swing a sword, and I will try to serve thee."

Then they both stepped forth into the broad passage that led to the Steward's pantry, where each man drew his sword again, and without more ado fell upon the other as though he would hew his fellow limb for limb.

Then their swords clashed upon one another with great din, and sparks flew from each blow in showers. So they fought up and down the hall for an hour and more, neither striking the other a blow, though they strove their best to do so; for both were skilful at the fence; so nothing came of all their labor. Ever and anon they rested, panting; then, after getting their wind, at it they would go again more fiercely than ever. At last Little John cried aloud, "Hold, good Cook!" whereupon each rested upon his sword, panting.

"Now will I make my vow," quoth Little John, "thou art the very best swordsman that ever mine eyes beheld. Truly, I had thought to carve thee ere now."

"And I had thought to do the same by thee," quoth the Cook; "but I have missed the mark somehow."

"Now I have been thinking within myself," quoth Little John, "what we are fighting for; but albeit I do not rightly know."

"Why, no more do I," said the Cook. "I bear no love for that pursy Steward, but I thought that we had engaged to fight with one another, and that it must be done."

"Now," quoth Little John, "it doth seem to me that instead of striving to cut one another's throats, it were better for us to be boon companions. What sayst thou, jolly Cook, wilt thou go with me to Sherwood Forest and join with Robin Hood's band? Thou shalt live a merry life within the woodlands, and sevenscore good companions shalt thou have, one of whom is mine own self. Thou shalt have two suits of Lincoln green each year, and forty marks in pay."

"Now, thou art a man after mine own heart!" cried the Cook right heartily; "and, as thou speakest of it, that is the very service for me. I will go with thee, and that right gladly. Give me thy palm, sweet fellow, and I will be thine own companion from henceforth. What may be thy name, lad?"

"Men do call me Little John, good fellow."

"How? And art thou indeed Little John, and Robin Hood's own right-hand man? Many a time and oft have I heard of thee, but never did I hope to set eyes upon thee. And thou art indeed the famous Little John!" And the Cook seemed lost in amazement, and looked upon his companion with open eyes.

"I am Little John, indeed, and I will bring to Robin Hood this day a right stout fellow to join his merry band. But ere we go, good friend, it seemeth to me to be a vast pity that, as we have had so much of good Sheriff's food, we should not also carry off some of his silver plate to Robin Hood, as a present from his worship."

"Ay, marry is it," said the Cook. And so they began hunting about, and took as much silver as they could lay hands upon, clapping it into a bag, and when they had filled the sack they set forth to Sherwood Forest.

Plunging into the woods, they came at last to the greenwood tree, where they found Robin Hood and threescore of his merry men lying upon the fresh green grass. When Robin and his men saw who it was that came, they leaped to their feet. "Now welcome!" cried Robin Hood, "Now welcome, Little John! for long hath it been since we have heard from thee, though we all knew that thou hadst joined the Sheriff's service. And how hast thou fared all these long days?"

"Right merrily have I lived at the Lord Sheriff's," answered Little John, "and I have come straight thence. See, good master! I have brought thee his cook, and even his silver plate." Thereupon he told Robin Hood and his merry men that were there all that had befallen him since he had left them to go to the Fair at Nottingham Town. Then all shouted with laughter, except Robin Hood; but he looked grave.

"Nay, Little John," said he, "thou art a brave blade and a trusty fellow. I am glad thou hast brought thyself back to us, and with such a good companion as the Cook, whom we all welcome to Sherwood. But I like not so well that thou hast stolen the Sheriff's plate like some paltry thief. The Sheriff hath been punished by us, and hath lost three hundred pounds, even as he sought to despoil another; but he hath done nought that we should steal his household plate from him."

Though Little John was vexed with this, he strove to pass it off with a jest. "Nay, good master," quoth he, "if thou thinkest the Sheriff gave us not the plate, I will fetch him, that he may tell us with his own lips he giveth it all to us." So saying, he leaped to his feet, and was gone before Robin Hood could call him back.

Little John ran for full five miles till he came to where the Sheriff of Nottingham and a gay company were hunting near the forest. When Little John came to the Sheriff he doffed his cap and bent his knee. "God save thee, good master," quoth he.

"Why, Reynold Greenleaf!" cried the Sheriff, "whence comest thou and where hast thou been?"

"I have been in the forest," answered Little John, speaking amazedly, "and there I saw a sight such as ne'er before man's eyes beheld! Yonder I saw a young hart all in green from top to toe, and about him was a herd of three-score deer, and they, too, were all of green from head to foot. Yet I dared not shoot, good master, for fear lest they should slay me."

"Why, how now, Reynold Greenleaf," cried the Sheriff; "art thou dreaming, or art thou mad, that thou dost bring me such a tale?"

"Nay, I am not dreaming nor am I mad," said Little John; "and if thou wilt come with me, I will show thee this fair sight, for I have seen it with mine own eyes. But thou must come alone, good master, lest the others frighten them and they get away."

So the party all rode forward, and Little John led them downward into the forest.

"Now, good master," quoth he at last, "we are nigh where I saw this herd."

Then the Sheriff descended from his horse and bade them wait for him until he should return; and Little John led him forward through a close copse until suddenly they came to a great open glade, at the end of which Robin Hood sat beneath the shade of the great oak tree, with his merry men all about him. "See, good Master Sheriff," quoth Little John, "yonder is the hart of which I spake to thee."

At this the Sheriff turned to Little John, and said bitterly, "Long ago, I thought I remembered thy face, but now I know thee. Woe betide thee, Little John, for thou hast betrayed me this day."

Then Little John laughed aloud. "Good Master Sheriff," said he, "thou dost indeed know me, and I am Little John. But let me tell thee, all this would not have happened had not thy beggarly Steward starved me, and had he given me food to eat when I asked it. But if he gave none to me, the green hart will give thee another feast, and when thou goest back, tell thy Steward the time will come when he and I shall have a reckoning."

In the mean time Robin Hood had come to them. "Now welcome, Master Sheriff," said he. "Hast thou come today to take another feast with me?"

"Nay, heaven forbid!" said the Sheriff, in tones of deep earnest. "I care for no feast and have no hunger today."

"Nevertheless," quoth Robin, "if thou hast no hunger, maybe thou hast thirst, and well I know thou wilt take a cup of sack with me. But I am grieved that thou wilt not feast with me, for thou couldst have victuals to thy liking, for there stands thy Cook."

Then he led the Sheriff, will-he-nill-he, to the seat he knew so well beneath the greenwood tree.

"Ho, lads!" cried Robin, "fill our good friend, the Sheriff, a right brimming cup of sack and fetch it hither, for he is faint and weary."

Then one of the band brought the Sheriff a cup of sack, bowing low as he handed it to him; but the Sheriff could not touch the wine, for he saw it served in one of his own silver flagons, on one of his own silver plates.

"How now," quoth Robin, "dost thou not like our new silver service? We have gotten a bag of it this day." So saying, he held up the sack of silver that Little John and the Cook had brought with them.

Then the Sheriff's heart was bitter within him; but, not daring to say anything, he only gazed upon the ground. Robin looked keenly at him for a time before he spoke again; then said he, "Now, Master Sheriff, the last time thou camest to Sherwood Forest thou didst come seeking to despoil a poor spendthrift, and thou wert despoiled thine own self; but now thou comest seeking to do no harm, nor do I know that thou hast despoiled any man. I take my tithes from fat priests and lordly squires, to help those that they despoil and to raise up those that they bow down; but I know not that thou hast tenants of thine own whom thou hast wronged in any way. Therefore, take thou thine own again, nor will I dispossess thee today of so much as one farthing. Come with me, and I will lead thee from the forest back to thine own party again."

Then, slinging the bag upon his shoulder, he turned away, the Sheriff following him, all too perplexed in mind to speak. So they went forward until they came to within a furlong of the spot where the Sheriff's companions were waiting for him. Then Robin Hood gave the sack of silver back to the Sheriff. "Take thou thine own again," he said, "and, hearken to me, good Sheriff, take thou a piece of advice with it. Try thy servants well ere thou dost engage them again so readily." Then, turning, he left the other standing bewildered, with the sack in his hands.

The company that waited for the Sheriff were all amazed to see him come out of the forest bearing a heavy sack upon his shoulders; but though they questioned him, he answered never a word, acting like one who walks in a dream. Without a word, he placed the bag across his nag's back, and then, mounting, rode away, all following him; but all the time there was a great turmoil of thoughts within his head, tumbling one over the other. And thus ends the merry tale of Little John and how he entered the Sheriff's service.

PART THIRD

Recounting three merry adventures that befell Robin Hood and certain others, by which he gained sore bones and three good merry men all in one day.

LITTLE JOHN AND THE TANNER OF BLYTH

IT OFTEN COMES ABOUT IN THIS WORLD THAT UNLUCKY happenings fall upon one in such measure that it seems, as the saying is, that every cat that one strokes flies into one's face. Thus it was with Robin Hood and Little John one bright day in the merry Maytime; so listen and you shall hear how Dame Luck so buffeted them that their bones were sore for many a day thereafter.

ONE FINE DAY, NOT LONG AFTER LITTLE JOHN HAD LEFT abiding with the Sheriff and had come back, with his worship's cook, to the merry greenwood, as has just been told, Robin Hood and a few chosen fellows of his band lay upon the soft sward beneath the greenwood tree where they dwelt. The day was warm and sultry, so that whilst most of the band were scattered through the forest upon this mission and upon that, these few stout fellows lay lazily beneath the shade of the tree, in the soft afternoon, passing jests among themselves and telling merry stories, with laughter and mirth.

All the air was laden with the bitter fragrance of the May, and all the bosky shades of the woodlands beyond rang with the sweet song of birds,—the throstle-cock, the cuckoo, and the wood-pigeon,—and with the song of birds mingled the cool sound of the gurgling brook that leaped out of the forest shades, and ran fretting amid its rough, gray stones across the sunlit open glade before the trysting-tree. And a fair sight was that half-score of tall, stout yeomen, all clad in Lincoln green, lying beneath the broad-spreading branches of the great oak tree, amid the quivering leaves of which the sunlight shivered and fell in dancing patches upon the grass.

The good old times have gone by when such men grow as grew then; when sturdy quarterstaff and long bow toughened a man's thews till they were like leather. Around Robin Hood that day there lay the very flower of English yeomanrie. Here the great Little John, with limbs as tough as the gnarled oak, yet grown somewhat soft from good living at the Sheriff's house in Nottingham Town; there Will Stutely, his face as brown as a berry from sun and wind, but, for all that, the comeliest yeoman in the midcountry, only excepting Allan a Dale, the minstrel, of whom you shall hear anon. Beside these was Will Scathelock, as lank as a greyhound, yet as fleet of foot as a buck of three years' growth; young David of Doncaster, with great stout limbs only less than those of Little John in size, the tender beard of early youth now just feathering his chin, and others of great renown both far and near.

Suddenly Robin Hood smote his knee.

"By Saint Dunstan," quoth he, "I had nigh forgot that quarter-day cometh on apace, and yet no cloth of Lincoln green in all our store. It must be looked to, and that in quick season. Come, busk thee, Little John! stir those lazy bones of thine, for thou must get thee straightway to our good gossip, the draper, Hugh Longshanks of Ancaster. Bid him send us straightway twentyscore yards of fair cloth of Lincoln green; and mayhap the journey may take some of the fat from off thy bones, that thou hast gotten from lazy living at our dear Sheriff's."

"Nay," muttered Little John (for he had heard so much upon this score that he was sore upon the point), "nay, truly, mayhap I have more flesh upon my joints than I once had, yet, flesh or no flesh, I doubt not that I could still hold my place and footing upon a narrow bridge against e'er a yeoman in Sherwood, or Nottinghamshire, for the matter of that, even though he had no more fat about his bones than thou hast, good master."

At this reply a great shout of laughter went up, and all looked at Robin Hood, for each man knew that Little John spake of a certain fight that happened between their master and himself, through which they first became acquainted.

"Nay," quoth Robin Hood, laughing louder than all, "Heaven forbid that I should doubt thee, for I care for no taste of thy staff myself, Little John. I must needs own that there are those of my band can handle a seven-foot staff more deftly than I; yet no man in all Nottinghamshire can draw gray-goose shaft with my fingers. Nevertheless, a journey to Ancaster may not be ill for thee; so go thou, as I bid, and thou hadst best go this very evening, for since thou hast abided at the Sheriff's many know thy face, and if thou goest in broad daylight, thou mayst get thyself into a coil with some of his worship's men-at-arms. Bide thou here till I bring thee money to pay our good Hugh. I warrant he hath no better customers in all Nottinghamshire than we," So saying, Robin left them and entered the forest.

Not far from the trysting tree was a great rock in which a chamber had been hewn, the entrance being barred by a massive oaken door two palms' breadth in thickness, studded about with spikes, and fastened with a great padlock. This was the treasure-house of the band, and thither Robin Hood went, and, unlocking the door, entered the chamber, from which he brought forth a bag of gold, which he gave to Little John, to pay Hugh Longshanks withal, for the cloth of Lincoln green.

Then up got Little John, and, taking the bag of gold, which he thrust into his bosom, he strapped a girdle about his loins, took a stout pikestaff full seven feet long in his hand, and set forth upon his journey.

So he strode whistling along the leafy forest path that led to Fosse Way, turning neither to the right hand nor the left, until at last he came to where the path branched, leading on the one hand onward to Fosse Way, and on the other, as well Little John knew, to the merry Blue Boar Inn. Here Little John suddenly ceased whistling, and stopped in the middle of the path. First he looked up and then he looked down, and then, tilting his cap over one eye, he slowly scratched the back part of his head. For thus it was: at the sight of these two roads, two voices began to alarum within him, that one crying, "There lies the road to the Blue Boar Inn, a can of brown October, and a merry night with sweet companions such as thou mayst find there;" the other, "There lies the way to Ancaster and the duty thou art sent upon." Now the first of these two voices was far the louder, for Little John had grown passing fond of good living through abiding at the Sheriff's house; so, presently, looking up into the blue sky, across which bright clouds were sailing like silver boats, and swallows skimming in circling flight, quoth he, "I fear me it will rain this evening, so I'll e'en stop at the Blue Boar till it passes by, for I know my good master would not have me wet to the skin." So, without more ado, off he strode down the path that lay the way of his likings. Now there was no sign of any foul weather, but when one wishes to do a thing, as Little John did, one finds no lack of reasons for the doing.

Four merry wags were at the Blue Boar Inn; a butcher, a beggar and two barefoot friars. Little John heard them singing from afar, as he walked through the hush of the mellow twilight that was now falling over hill and dale. Right glad were they to welcome such a merry blade as Little John. Fresh cans of ale were brought, and with jest and song and merry tales the hours slipped away on fleeting wings. None thought of time or tide till the night was so far gone that Little John put by the thought of setting forth upon his journey again that night, and so bided at the Blue Boar Inn until the morrow.

Now it was an ill piece of luck for Little John that he left his duty for his pleasure, and he paid a great score for it, as we are all apt to do in the same case, as you shall see.

Up he rose at the dawn of the next day, and, taking his stout pikestaff in his hand, he set forth upon his journey once more, as though he would make up for lost time.

In the good town of Blyth there lived a stout tanner, celebrated far and near for feats of strength and many tough bouts at wrestling and the quarterstaff. For five years he had held the midcountry champion belt for wrestling, till the great Adam o' Lincoln cast him in the ring and broke one of his ribs; but at quarterstaff he had never yet met his match in all the country about. Beside all this, he dearly loved the long bow, and a sly jaunt in the forest when the moon was full and the dun deer in season; so that the King's rangers kept a shrewd eye upon him and his doings, for Arthur a Bland's house was apt to have a plenty of meat in it that was more like venison than the law allowed.

Now Arthur had been to Nottingham Town the day before Little John set forth on his errand, there to sell a halfscore of tanned cowhides. At the dawn of the same day that Little John left the inn, he started from Nottingham, homeward for Blyth. His way led, all in the dewy morn, past the verge of Sherwood Forest, where the birds were welcoming the lovely day with a great and merry jubilee. Across the Tanner's shoulders was slung his stout quarterstaff, ever near enough to him to be gripped quickly, and on his head was a cap of doubled cowhide, so tough that it could hardly be cloven even by a broadsword.

"Now," quoth Arthur a Bland to himself, when he had come to that part of the road that cut through a corner of the forest, "no doubt at this time of year the dun deer are coming from the forest depths nigher to the open meadow lands. Mayhap I may chance to catch a sight of the dainty brown darlings thus early in the morn." For there was nothing he loved better than to look upon a tripping herd of deer, even when he could not tickle their ribs with a clothyard shaft. Accordingly, quitting the path, he went peeping this way and that through the underbrush, spying now here and now there, with all the wiles of a master of woodcraft, and of one who had more than once donned a doublet of Lincoln green.

Now as Little John stepped blithely along, thinking of nothing but of such things as the sweetness of the hawthorn buds that bedecked the hedgerows, or the crab-trees that stood here and there all covered with fair pink blossoms, or gazing upward at the lark, that, springing from the dewy grass, hung aloft on quivering wings in the yellow sunlight, pouring forth its song that fell like a falling star from the sky, his luck led him away from the highway, not far from the spot where Arthur a Bland was peeping this way and that through the leaves of the thickets. Hearing a rustling of the branches, Little John stopped, and presently caught sight of the brown cowhide cap of the Tanner moving amongst the bushes.

"I do much wonder," quoth Little John to himself, "what yon knave is after, that he should go thus peeping and peering about. I verily believe that yon scurvy varlet is no better than a thief, and cometh here after our own and the good King's dun deer." For by much roving in the forest, Little John had come to look upon all the deer in Sherwood as belonging to Robin Hood and his band as much as to good King Harry. "Nay," quoth he again, after a time, "this matter must e'en be looked into." So, quitting the high-road, he also entered the thickets, and began spying around after stout Arthur a Bland.

So for a long time they both of them went hunting about, Little John after the Tanner, and the Tanner after the deer. At last Little John trod upon a stick, which snapped under his foot, whereupon, hearing the noise, the Tanner turned quickly and caught sight of the yeoman. Seeing that the Tanner had spied him out, Little John put a bold face upon the matter.

"Halloa," quoth he, "what art thou doing here, thou naughty fellow? Who art thou that comest ranging Sherwood's paths? In very sooth thou hast an evil cast of countenance, and I do think, truly, that thou art no better than a thief, and comest after our good King's deer."

"Nay," quoth the Tanner boldly,—for, though taken by surprise, he was not a man to be frightened by big words,—"thou liest in thy teeth. I am no thief, but an honest craftsman. As for my countenance, it is what it is; and, for the matter of that, thine own is none too pretty, thou saucy fellow."

"Ha!" quoth Little John, in a great loud voice, "wouldst thou give me back-talk? Now I have a great part of a mind to crack thy pate for thee. I would have thee know, fellow, that I am, as it were, one of the King's foresters. Leastwise," muttered he to himself, "I and my friends do take good care of our good sovereign's deer."

"I care not who thou art," answered the bold Tanner, "and unless thou hast many more of thy kind by thee, thou canst never make Arthur a Bland cry 'A mercy.'"

"Is it so?" cried Little John, in a rage. "Now, by my faith, thou saucy rogue, thy tongue hath led thee into a pit thou wilt have a sorry time getting out of; for I will give thee such a drubbing as ne'er has thou had in all thy life before. Take thy staff in thy hand, fellow, for I will not smite an unarmed man."

"Marry come up with a murrain!" cried the Tanner, for he, too, had talked himself into a fume. "Big words ne'er killed so much as a mouse. Who art thou that talkest so freely of cracking the head of Arthur a Bland?

If I do not tan thy hide this day as ne'er I tanned a calf's hide in all my life before, split my staff into skewers for lamb's flesh and call me no more brave man! Now look to thyself, fellow!"

"Stay!" said Little John; "let us first measure our cudgels. I do reckon my staff longer than thine, and I would not take vantage of thee by even so much as an inch."

"Nay, I pass not for length," answered the Tanner. "My staff is long enough to knock down a calf; so look to thyself, fellow, I say again."

So, without more ado, each gripped his staff in the middle, and, with fell and angry looks, they came slowly together.

Now news had been brought to Robin Hood how that Little John, instead of doing his bidding, had passed by duty for pleasure, and so had stopped overnight with merry company at the Blue Boar Inn, instead of going straight to Ancaster. So, being vexed to his heart by this, he set forth at dawn of day to seek Little John at the Blue Boar, or at least to meet the yeoman on the way, and ease his heart of what he thought of the matter. As thus he strode along in anger, putting together the words he would use to chide Little John, he heard, of a sudden, loud and angry voices, as of men in a rage, passing fell words back and forth from one to the other. At this, Robin Hood stopped and listened. "Surely," quoth he to himself, "that is Little John's voice, and he is talking in anger also. Methinks the other is strange to my ears. Now Heaven forfend that my good trusty Little John should have fallen into the hands of the King's rangers. I must see to this matter, and that quickly."

Thus spoke Robin Hood to himself, all his anger passing away like a breath from the windowpane, at the thought that perhaps his trusty right-hand man was in some danger of his life. So cautiously he made his way through the thickets whence the voices came, and, pushing aside the leaves, peeped into the little open space where the two men, staff in hand, were coming slowly together.

"Ha!" quoth Robin to himself, "here is merry sport afoot. Now I would give three golden angels from my own pocket if yon stout fellow would give Little John a right sound drubbing! It would please me to see him well thumped for having failed in my bidding. I fear me, though, there is but poor chance of my seeing such a pleasant sight." So saying, he stretched himself at length upon the ground, that he might not only see the sport the better, but that he might enjoy the merry sight at his ease.

As you may have seen two dogs that think to fight, and walking slowly round and round each other, neither cur wishing to begin the combat, so those two stout yeomen moved slowly around, each watching for a chance to take the other unaware, and so get in the first blow. At last Little John struck like a flash, and, "rap," the Tanner met the blow and turned it aside, and then smote back at Little John, who also turned the blow; and so this mighty battle began. Then up and down and back and forth they trod, the blows falling so thick and fast that, at a distance, one would have thought that half a score of men were fighting. Thus they fought for nigh a half an hour, until the ground was all ploughed up with the digging of their heels, and their breathing grew labored like the ox in the furrow. But Little John suffered the most, for he had become unused to such stiff labor, and his joints were not as supple as they had been before he went to dwell with the Sheriff.

All this time Robin Hood lay beneath the bush, rejoicing at such a comely bout of quarterstaff. "By my faith!" quoth he to himself, "never had I thought to see Little John so evenly matched in all my life. Belike, though, he would have overcome yon stout fellow before this had he been in his former trim."

At last Little John saw his chance, and, throwing all the strength he felt going from him into one blow that might have felled an ox, he struck at the Tanner with might and main. And now did the Tanner's cowhide cap stand him in good stead, and but for it he might never have held staff in hand again. As it was, the blow he caught beside the head was so shrewd that it sent him staggering across the little glade, so that, if Little John had had the strength to follow up his vantage, it would have been ill for stout Arthur. But he regained himself quickly, and, at arm's length, struck back a blow at Little John, and this time the stroke reached its mark, and down went Little John at full length, his cudgel flying from his hand as he fell. Then, raising his staff, stout Arthur dealt him another blow upon the ribs.

"Hold!" roared Little John. "Wouldst thou strike a man when he is down?"

"Ay, marry would I," quoth the Tanner, giving him another thwack with his staff.

"Stop!" roared Little John. "Help! hold, I say! I yield me! I yield me, I say, good fellow!"

"Hast thou had enough?" asked the Tanner, grimly, holding his staff aloft.

"Ay, marry, and more than enough."

"And thou dost own that I am the better man of the two?"

"Yea, truly, and a murrain seize thee!" said Little John, the first aloud and the last to his beard.

"Then thou mayst go thy ways; and thank thy patron saint that I am a merciful man," said the Tanner.

"A plague o' such mercy as thine!" said Little John, sitting up and feeling his ribs where the Tanner had cudgelled him. "I make my vow, my ribs feel as though every one of them were broken in twain. I tell thee, good fellow, I did think there was never a man in all Nottinghamshire could do to me what thou hast done this day."

"And so thought I, also," cried Robin Hood, bursting out of the thicket and shouting with laughter till the tears ran down his cheeks. "O man, man!" said he, as well as he could for his mirth, "'a didst go over like a bottle knocked from a wall. I did see the whole merry bout, and never did I think to see thee yield thyself so, hand and foot, to any man in all merry England. I was seeking thee, to chide thee for leaving my bidding undone; but thou hast been paid all I owed thee, full measure, pressed down and overflowing, by this good fellow. Marry, 'a did reach out his arm full length whilst thou stood gaping at him, and, with a pretty rap, tumbled thee over as never have I seen one tumbled before." So spoke bold Robin, and all the time Little John sat upon the ground, looking as though he had sour curds in his mouth. "What may be thy name, good fellow?" said Robin, next, turning to the Tanner.

"Men do call me Arthur a Bland," spoke up the Tanner, boldly; "and now what may be thy name?"

"Ha, Arthur a Bland!" quoth Robin, "I have heard thy name before, good fellow. Thou didst break the crown of a friend of mine at the fair at Ely last October. The folk there call him Jock o' Nottingham; we call him Will Scathelock. This poor fellow whom thou hast so belabored is counted the best hand at the quarterstaff in all merry England. His name is Little John, and mine Robin Hood."

"How!" cried the Tanner, "art thou indeed the great Robin Hood, and is this the famous Little John? Marry, had I known who thou art, I would never have been so bold as to lift my hand against thee. Let me help thee to thy feet, good Master Little John, and let me brush the dust from off thy coat."

"Nay," quoth Little John, testily, at the same time rising carefully, as though his bones had been made of glass, "I can help myself, good fellow, without thy aid; and, let me tell thee, had it not been for that vile cowskin cap of thine, it would have been ill for thee this day."

At this Robin laughed again, and, turning to the Tanner, he said, "Wilt thou join my band, good Arthur? for I make my vow thou art one of the stoutest men that ever mine eyes beheld."

"Will I join thy band?" cried the Tanner, joyfully; "ay, marry, will I! Hey for a merry life!" cried he, leaping aloft and snapping his fingers, "and hey for the life I love! Away with tanbark and filthy vats and foul cowhides! I will follow thee to the ends of the earth, good master, and not a herd of dun deer in all the forest but shall know the sound of the twang of my bowstring."

"As for thee, Little John," said Robin, turning to him and laughing, "thou wilt start once more for Ancaster, and we will go part way with thee, for I will not have thee turn again to either the right hand or the left till thou hast fairly gotten away from Sherwood. There are other inns that thou knowest yet, hereabouts." Thereupon, leaving the thickets, they took once more to the highway, and departed upon their business.

2

ROBIN HOOD AND WILL SCARLET

THUS THEY TRAVELLED ALONG THE SUNNY ROAD, THREE STOUT FELLOWS such as you could hardly match anywhere else in all merry England. Many stopped to gaze after them as they strode along, so broad were their shoulders and so sturdy their gait.

Quoth Robin Hood to Little John, "Why didst thou not go straight to Ancaster, yesterday, as I told thee? Thou hadst not gotten thyself into such a coil hadst thou done as I ordered."

"I feared the rain that threatened," said Little John in a sullen tone, for he was vexed at being so chafed by Robin with what had happened to him.

"The rain!" cried Robin, stopping of a sudden in the middle of the road, and looking at Little John in wonder. "Why, thou great oaf! Not a drop of rain has fallen these three days, neither has any threatened, nor hath there been a sign of foul weather in earth or sky or water."

"Nevertheless," growled Little John, "the holy Saint Swithin holdeth the waters of the heavens in his pewter pot, and he could have poured them out, had he chosen, even from a clear sky; and wouldst thou have had me wet to the skin?"

At this Robin Hood burst into a roar of laughter. "O Little John!" said he, "what butter wits hast thou in that head of thine! Who could hold anger against such a one as thou art?"

So saying, they all stepped out once more, with the right foot foremost, as the saying is.

After they had travelled some distance, the day being warm and the road dusty, Robin Hood waxed thirsty; so, there being a fountain of water as cold as ice, just behind the hedgerow, they crossed the stile and came to where the water bubbled up from beneath a mossy stone. Here, kneeling and making cups of the palms of their hands, they drank their fill, and then, the spot being cool and shady, they stretched their limbs and rested them for a space.

In front of them, over beyond the hedge, the dusty road stretched away across the plain; behind them the meadow lands and bright green fields of tender young corn lay broadly in the sun, and overhead spread the shade of the cool, rustling leaves of the beechen tree. Pleasantly to their nostrils came the tender fragrance of the purple violets and wild thyme that grew within the dewy moisture of the edge of the little fountain, and pleasantly came the soft gurgle of the water; all else was sunny silence, broken only now and then by the crow of a distant cock, borne up to them on the wings of the soft and gentle breeze, or the drowsy drone of the humble-bee burrowing in the clover blossoms that grew in the sun, or the voice of the busy housewife in the nearest farmhouse. All was so pleasant and so full of the gentle joy of the bright May time, that for a long time neither of the three cared to speak, but each lay on his back, gazing up through the trembling leaves of the trees to the bright sky overhead. At last, Robin, whose thoughts were not quite so busy wool-gathering as those of the others, and who had been gazing around him now and then, broke the silence.

"Heyday!" quoth he, "yon is a gayly-feathered bird, I take my vow."

The others looked and saw a young man walking slowly down the highway. Gay was he, indeed, as Robin had said, and a fine figure he cut, for his doublet was of scarlet silk and his stockings also; a handsome sword hung by his side, the embossed leathern scabbard being picked out with fine threads of gold; his cap was of scarlet velvet, and a broad feather hung down behind and back of one ear. His hair was long and yellow and curled upon his shoulders, and in his hand he bore an early rose, which he smelt at daintily now and then.

"By my life!" quoth Robin Hood, laughing, "saw ye e'er such a pretty, mincing fellow?"

"Truly, his clothes have overmuch prettiness for my taste," quoth Arthur a Bland; "but, ne'ertheless, his shoulders are broad and his loins are narrow. And seest thou, good master, how that his arms hang from his body? They dangle not down like spindles, but hang stiff and bend at the elbow. I take my vow, there be no bread and milk limbs in those find clothes, but stiff joints and tough thews."

"Methinks thou art right, friend Arthur," said Little John. "I do verily think that yon is no such rose-leaf and whipped-cream gallant as he would have one take him to be."

"Pah!" quoth Robin Hood, "the sight of such a fellow doth put a nasty taste into my mouth! Look how he doth hold that fair flower betwixt his thumb and finger, as he would say, 'Good rose, I like thee not so ill but I can bear thy odor for a little while.' I take it ye are both wrong, and verily believe that were a furious mouse to run across his path, he would cry, 'La!' or 'Alack-a-day!' and fall straightway into a swoon. I wonder who he may be."

"Some great baron's son, I doubt not," answered Little John, "with good and true men's money lining his purse."

"Ay, marry, that is true, I make no doubt," quoth Robin. "What a pity that such men as he, that have no thought but to go abroad in gay clothes, should have good fellows, whose shoes they are not fit to tie, dancing at their bidding. By Saint Dunstan, Saint Alfred, Saint Withold, and all the good men in the Saxon calendar, it doth make me mad to see such gay lordlings from over the sea go stepping on the necks of good Saxons who owned this land before ever their great-grandsires chewed rind of brawn! By the bright bow of Heaven, I will have their ill-gotten gains from them, even though I hang for it as high as e'er a forest tree in Sherwood!"

"Why, how now, master," quoth Little John, "what heat is this? Thou dost set thy pot-a-boiling, and mayhap no bacon to cook! Methinks yon fellow's hair is over light for Norman locks. He may be a good man and true for aught thou knowest."

"Nay," said Robin, "my head against a leaden farthing, he is what I say. Whenever saw ye Saxon mince along like that, as though he feared to muddy the toes of his shoes? At least, I will go forth and stop him, and see whether his purse be free of foul money. If I am wrong, then he may go forward upon his journey without the loss of so much as a groat; but if I am right, I will pluck him as close as ever a goose was plucked for live feathers in midsummer. Thou sayst he is a sturdy fellow, Little John. Lie thou here and watch till I show thee how woodland life toughens a man, as easy living, such as thine hath been of late, drags him down. So, like ye both here, I say, till I show you how I drub this fellow." So saying, Robin Hood stepped forth from the shade of the beech tree, crossed the stile, and stood in the middle of the road, with his hands on his hips, in the stranger's path.

Meantime the stranger, who had been walking so slowly that all this talk was held before he came opposite the place where they were, neither quickened his pace nor seemed to see that such a man as Robin Hood was in the world. So Robin stood in the middle of the road, waiting while the other walked slowly forward, smelling his rose, and looking this way and that, and everywhere except at Robin.

"Hold!" cried Robin, when at last the other had come close to him. "Hold! stand where thou art!"

"Wherefore should I hold, good fellow?" said the stranger in soft and gentle voice; "and wherefore should I stand where I am? Ne'ertheless, as thou dost desire that I should stay, I will abide for a short time, that I may hear what thou mayst have to say to me."

"Then," quoth Robin, "as thou dost so fairly do as I tell thee, and dost give me such soft speech, I will also treat thee with all due courtesy. I would have thee know, fair friend, that I am, as it were, a votary at the shrine of Saint Wilfred, who, thou mayst know, took, willy-nilly, all their gold from the heathen, and melted it up into candlesticks. Wherefore, upon such as come hereabouts, I levy a certain toll, which I use for a better purpose, I hope, than to make candlesticks withal. Therefore, sweet chuck, I would have thee deliver to me thy purse, that I may look into it, and judge, to the best of any poor powers, whether thou hast more wealth about thee than our law allows. For, as our good Gaffer Swanthold sayeth, 'He who is fat from overliving must needs lose blood.' "

All this time the youth had been sniffing at the rose that he held betwixt his thumb and finger. "Nay," said he with a gentle smile, when Robin Hood had done, "I do love to hear thee talk, thou pretty fellow, and if, haply, thou art not yet done, finish, I beseech thee. I have yet some little time to stay."

"I have said all," quoth Robin; "and now, if thou wilt give me thy purse, I will let thee go thy way without let or hindrance so soon as I shall see what it may hold. I will take none from thee if thou has but little."

"Alas! it doth grieve me much," said the other, "that I cannot do as thou dost wish. I have nothing to give thee. Let me go my way, I prythee. I have done thee no harm."

"Nay, thou goest not," quoth Robin, "till thou hast shown me thy purse."

"Good friend," said the other, gently, "I have business elsewhere. I have given thee much time and have heard thee patiently. Prythee, let me now depart in peace."

"I have spoken to thee, friend," said Robin, sternly, "and I now tell thee again, that thou goest not one step forward till thou hast done as I bid thee." So saying, he raised his quarterstaff above his head in a threatening way.

"Alas!" said the stranger, sadly, "it doth grieve me that this thing must be. I fear much that I must slay thee, thou poor fellow!" So saying, he drew his sword.

"Put by thy weapon," quoth Robin; "I would take no vantage of thee. Thy sword cannot stand against an oaken staff such as mine. I could snap it like a barley straw. Yonder is a good oaken thicket by the roadside; take thee a cudgel thence and defend thyself fairly, if thou hast a taste for a sound drubbing."

First the stranger measured Robin with his eye, and then he measured the oaken staff. "Thou art right, good fellow," said he presently; "truly, my sword is no match for that cudgel of thine. Bide thee a while till I get me a staff." So saying, he threw aside the rose that he had been holding all this time, thrust his sword back into the scabbard, and, with a more hasty step than he had yet used, stepped to the roadside where grew the little clump of ground oaks Robin had spoken of. Choosing among them, he presently found a sapling to his liking. He did not cut it, but, rolling up his sleeves a little way, he laid hold of it, placed his heel against the ground, and, with one mighty pull, plucked the young tree up by the roots from out the very earth. Then he came back, trimming away the roots and tender stems with his sword as quietly as if he had done naught to speak of.

Little John and the Tanner had been watching all that passed, but when they saw the stranger drag the sapling up from the earth, and heard the rending and snapping of its roots, the Tanner pursed his lips together, drawing his breath between them in a long inward whistle.

"By the breath of my body!" said Little John, as soon as he could gather his wits from their wonder, "sawest thou that, Arthur? Marry, I think our poor master will stand but an ill chance with yon fellow. By Our Lady, he plucked up yon green tree as it were a barley straw."

Whatever Robin Hood thought, he stood his ground, and now he and the stranger in scarlet stood face to face.

Well did Robin Hood hold his own that day as a midcountry yeoman. This way and that they fought, and back and forth, Robin's skill against the stranger's strength. The dust of the highway rose up around them like a cloud, so that at times Little John and the Tanner could see nothing, but only hear the rattle of the staves against one another. Thrice Robin Hood struck the stranger; once upon the arm and twice upon the ribs, and yet had he warded all the other's blows, only one of which, had it met its mark, would have laid stout Robin lower in the dust than he had ever gone before. At last the stranger struck Robin's cudgel so fairly in the middle that he could hardly hold his staff in his hand; again he struck, and Robin bent beneath the blow; a third time he struck, and now not only fairly beat down

Robin's guard, but gave him such a rap, also, that down he tumbled into the dusty road.

"Hold!" cried Robin Hood, when he saw the stranger raising his staff once more. "I yield me!"

"Hold!" cried Little John, bursting from his cover, with the Tanner at his heels. "Hold! give over, I say!"

"Nay," answered the stranger quietly, "if there be two more of you, and each as stout as this good fellow, I am like to have my hands full. Nevertheless, come on, and I will strive my best to serve you all."

"Stop!" cried Robin Hood, "we will fight no more. I take my vow, this is an ill day for thee and me, Little John. I do verily believe that my wrist, and eke my arm, are palsied by the jar of the blow that this stranger struck me."

Then Little John turned to Robin Hood. "Why, how now, good master," said he, "Alas! thou art in an ill plight. Marry, thy jerkin is all befouled with the dust of the road. Let me help thee to arise."

"A plague on thy aid!" cried Robin, angrily. "I can get to my feet without thy help, good fellow."

"Nay, but let me at least dust thy coat for thee. I fear thy poor bones are mightily sore," quoth Little John, soberly, but with a sly twinkle in his eyes.

"Give over, I say!" quoth Robin in a fume. "My coat hath been dusted enough already, without aid of thine." Then, turning to the stranger, he said, "What may be thy name, good fellow?"

"My name is Gamwell," answered the other.

"Ha!" cried Robin, "is it even so? I have near kin of that name. Whence camest thou, fair friend?"

"From Maxfield Town I come," answered the stranger. "There was I born and bred, and thence I come to seek my mother's young brother, whom men call Robin Hood. So, if perchance thou mayst direct me"—

"Ha! Will Gamwell!" cried Robin, placing both hands upon the other's shoulders and holding him off at arm's length. "Surely, it can be none other! I might have known thee by that pretty maiden air of thine,—that dainty, finicking manner of gait. Dost thou not know me, lad? Look upon me well."

"Now, by the breath of my body!" cried the other, "I do believe from my heart that thou art mine own Uncle Robin. Nay, certain it is so!" and each flung his arms around the other, kissing him upon the cheek. Then once more Robin held his kinsman off at arm's length and scanned him keenly from top to toe. "Why, how now," quoth he, "what change is here? Verily, some eight or ten years ago I left thee a stripling lad, with great joints and ill-hung limbs, and lo! here thou art, as tight a fellow as e'er I set mine eyes upon. Dost thou not remember, lad, how I showed thee the proper way to nip the goose feather betwixt thy fingers and throw out thy bow arm steadily? Thou gavest great promise of being a keen archer. And dost thou not mind how I taught thee to fend and parry with the cudgel?"

"Yea," said young Gamwell, "and I did so look up to thee, and thought thee so above all other men that, I make my vow, had I known who thou wert, I would never have dared to lift hand against thee this day. I trust I did thee no great harm."

"No, no," quoth Robin, hastily, and looking sideways at Little John, "thou didst not harm me. But say no more of that, I prythee. Yet I will say, lad, that I hope I may never feel again such a blow as thou didst give me. By 'r Lady, my arm doth tingle yet from finger-nail to elbow. Truly, I thought that I was palsied for life. I tell thee, coz, that thou art the strongest man that ever I laid mine eyes upon. I take my vow, I felt my stomach quake when I beheld thee pluck up yon green tree as thou didst. But tell me, how camest thou to leave Sir Edward and thy mother?"

"Alas!" answered young Gamwell, "it is an ill story, uncle, that I have to tell thee. My father's steward, who came to us after old Giles Crookleg died, was ever a saucy varlet, and I know not why my father kept him, saving that he did oversee with great judgment. It used to gall me to hear him speak up so boldly to my father, who, thou knowest, was ever a patient man to those about him, and slow to anger and harsh words. Well, one day—and an ill day it was for that saucy fellow—he sought to berate my father, I standing by. I could stand it no longer, good uncle, so, stepping forth, I gave him a box o' the ear, and—wouldst thou believe it?—the fellow straightway died o't. I think they said I broke his neck, or something o' the like. So off they packed me to seek thee and escape the law. I was on my way when thou sawest me, and here I am."

"Well, by the faith of my heart," quoth Robin Hood, "for any one escaping the law, thou wast taking it the most easily that ever I beheld in all my life. Whenever did any one in all the world see one who had slain a man, and was escaping because of it, tripping along the highway like a dainty court damsel, sniffing at a rose the while?"

"Nay, uncle," answered Will Gamwell, "over haste never churned good butter, as the old saying hath it. Moreover, I do verily believe that this over-strength of my body hath taken the nimbleness out of my heels. Why, thou didst but just now rap me thrice, and I thee never a once, save by over-bearing thee by my strength."

"Nay," quoth Robin, "let us say no more on that score. I am right glad to see thee, Will, and thou wilt add great honor and credit to my band of merry fellows. But thou must change thy name, for warrants will be out presently against thee; so, because of thy gay clothes, thou shalt henceforth and for aye be called Will Scarlet."

"Will Scarlet," quoth Little John, stepping forward and reaching out his great palm, which the other took, "Will Scarlet, the name fitteth thee well. Right glad am I to welcome thee amongst us. I am called Little John; and this is a new member who has just joined us, a stout tanner named Arthur a Bland. Thou art like to achieve fame, Will, let me tell thee, for there will be many a merry ballad sung about the country, and many a merry story told in Sherwood of how Robin Hood taught Little John and Arthur a Bland the proper way to use the quarterstaff; likewise, as it were, how our good master bit off so large a piece of cake that he choked on it."

"Nay, good Little John," quoth Robin, gently, for he liked ill to have such a jest told of him, "Why should we speak of this little matter? Prythee, let us keep this day's doings amongst ourselves."

"With all my heart," quoth Little John. "But, good master, I thought that thou didst love a merry story, because thou hast so often made a jest about a certain increase of fatness on my joints, of flesh gathered by my abiding with the Sheriff of—"

"Nay, good Little John," said Robin, hastily, "I do bethink me I have said full enough on that score."

"It is well," quoth Little John, "for in truth I myself have tired of it somewhat. But now I bethink me, thou didst also seem minded to make a jest of the rain that threatened last night; so—"

"Nay, then," said Robin Hood, testily, "I was mistaken. I remember me now it did seem to threaten rain."

"Truly, I did think so myself," quoth Little John; "therefore, no doubt, thou dost think it was wise of me to abide all night at the Blue Boar Inn, instead of venturing forth in such stormy weather; dost thou not?"

"A plague of thee and thy doings!" cried Robin Hood. "If thou wilt have it so, thou wert right to abide wherever thou didst choose."

"Once more, it is well," quoth Little John. "As for myself, I have been blind this day. I did not see thee drubbed; I did not see thee tumbled heels over head in the dust; and if any man says that thou wert, I can with a clear conscience rattle his lying tongue betwixt his teeth."

"Come," cried Robin, biting his nether lip, while the others could not forbear laughing, "We will go no farther today, but will return to Sherwood, and thou shalt go to Ancaster another time, Little John."

So said Robin, for now that his bones were sore, he felt as though a long journey would be an ill thing for him. So, turning their backs, they retraced their steps whence they came.

3

THE MERRY ADVENTURE
WITH MIDGE THE MILLER

WHEN THE FOUR YEOMEN HAD TRAVELLED FOR A LONG TIME toward Sherwood again, high noontide being past, they began to wax hungry. Quoth Robin Hood, "I would that I had somewhat to eat. Methinks a good loaf of white bread, with a piece of snow-white cheese, washed down with a draught of humming ale, were a feast for a king."

"Since thou speakest of it," said Will Scarlet, "methinks it would not be amiss myself. There is that within me crieth out, 'Victuals, good friend, victuals!'"

"I know a house near by," said Arthur a Bland, "and, had I but the money, I would bring ye that ye speak of; to wit, a sweet loaf of bread, a fair cheese, and a skin of brown ale."

"For the matter of that, thou knowest I have money by me, good master," quoth Little John.

"Why, so thou hast, Little John," said Robin. "How much money will it take, good Arthur, to buy us meat and drink?"

"I think that six broad pennies will buy food enow for a dozen men," said the Tanner.

"Then give him six pennies, Little John," quoth Robin, "for methinks food for three men will about fit my need. Now get thee gone, Arthur, with the money, and bring the food here, for there is a sweet shade in that thicket yonder, beside the road, and there will we eat our meal."

So Little John gave Arthur the money, and the others stepped to the thicket, there to await the return of the Tanner.

After a time he came back, bearing with him a great brown loaf of bread and a fair, round cheese, and a goat-skin full of stout March beer, slung over his shoulders. Then Will Scarlet took his sword and divided the loaf and the cheese into four fair portions, and each man helped himself. Then Robin Hood took a deep pull at the beer. "Aha!" said he, drawing in his breath, "never have I tasted sweeter drink than this."

After this no man spake more, but each munched away at his bread and cheese lustily, with ever and anon a pull at the beer.

At last Will Scarlet looked at a small piece of bread he still held in his hand, and quoth he, "Methinks I will give this to the sparrows." So, throwing it from him, he brushed the crumbs from his jerkin.

"I, too," quoth Robin, "have had enough, I think." As for Little John and the Tanner, they had by this time eaten every crumb of their bread and cheese.

"Now, sweet friends," quoth Robin, gathering up the skin of beer, that was not yet nearly empty, "I do wish that ye may ever have such happiness as a good stout meal like this bringeth to my heart. Thus pledging you all, I drink to your health, that it may ever remain such as it is this day." So saying, he took a long, hearty pull at the stout beer. Next Will Scarlet took the skin, then Little John, and, last of all, the stout Tanner. A good full skin of beer, as fat as a town tradesman, began the round; a poor, flabby hide came forth, as weak and limp as an aged man.

"Now," quoth Robin, "I do feel myself another man, and would fain enjoy something pleasant before going farther upon our journey. I do bethink me, Will, that thou didst use to have a pretty voice, and one that tuned sweetly upon a song. Prythee, give us one ere we journey farther."

"Truly, I do not mind turning a tune," answered Will Scarlet; "but I would not sing alone."

"Nay, others will follow. Strike up, lad," quoth Robin.

"In that case, 'tis well," said Will Scarlet. "I do call to mind a song that a certain minstrel used to sing in my father's hall, upon occasion. I know no name for it, and so can give you none; but thus it is." Then, clearing his throat, he sang as follows:—

> *"In the merry blossom time,*
>   *When love-longings flood the breast,*
> *When the flower is on the lime,*
>   *When the small fowl builds her nest,*
> *Sweetly sings the nightingale*
>   *And the throstle-cock so bold;*
> *Cuckoo in the dewy dale,*
>   *And the turtle in the wild.*
> *But the robin I love dear,*
> *For he singeth through the year.*
>   *Robin! Robin!*
>   *Merry Robin!*
> *So I'd have my true love be:*
>   *Not to fly*
>   *At the nigh*
> *Sign of cold adversity.*
>
> *"When the Spring brings sweet delights,*
>   *When aloft the lark doth rise,*
> *Lovers woo o' mellow nights,*
>   *And youths peep in maidens' eyes,*
> *That time blooms the eglantine,*
>   *Daisies pied upon the hill,*
> *Cowslips fair and columbine,*
>   *Dusky violets by the rill.*

But the Ivy green doth grow
When the north wind bringeth snow.
Ivy! Ivy!
Stanch and true!
Thus I'd have her love to be;
Not to die
At the nigh
Breath of cold adversity."

"'Tis well sung," quoth Robin; "but, cousin, I tell thee plain, I would rather hear a stout fellow like thee sing some lusty ballad than a finicking song of flowers and birds, and what not. Yet, thou didst sing it fair, and 'tis none so bad a snatch of a song, for the matter of that. Now, Tanner, it is thy turn next."

"I know not," quoth Arthur, smiling, with his head on one side, like a budding lass that is asked to dance, "I know not that I can match our sweet friend's song; moreover, I do verily think that I have caught a cold and have a certain tickling and huskiness in the windpipe."

"Nay, sing up, friend," quoth Little John, who sat next to him, patting him upon the shoulder. "Thou hast a fair, round, mellow voice; let us have a touch of it."

"Nay, an ye will ha' a poor thing," said Arthur, "I will do my best. Have ye ever heard of the wooing of Sir Keith, the stout young Cornish knight, in good King Arthur's time?"

"Methinks I have heard somewhat of it," said Robin; "but ne'ertheless strike up thy ditty and let us hear it, for, as I do remember me, it is a gallant song; so out with it, good fellow."

Thereupon, clearing his throat, the Tanner, without more ado, began to sing the ballad of

THE WOOING OF SIR KEITH

"King Arthur sat in his royal hall,
And about on either hand
Was many a noble lordling tall,
The greatest in the land.

"Sat Lancelot with raven locks,
  Gawaine with golden hair,
Sir Tristram, Kay who kept the locks,
  And many another there.

"And through the stainèd windows bright,
  From o'er the red tiled eaves,
The sunlight blazed with colored light
  On golden helms and greaves.

"But suddenly a silence came
  About the Table Round,
For up the hall there walked a dame
  Bent nigh unto the ground.

"Her nose was hooked, her eyes were bleared,
  Her locks were lank and white;
Upon her chin there grew a beard;
  She was a grewsome sight.

"And so with crawling step she came
  And kneeled at Arthur's feet;
Quoth Kay, 'She is the foulest dame
  That e'er my sight did greet.'

" 'O mighty King! of thee I crave
  A boon an bended knee;'
'Twas thus she spoke. 'What wouldst thou have,'
  Quoth Arthur King, 'of me?'

"Quoth she, 'I have a foul disease
  Doth gnaw my very heart,
And but one thing can bring me ease
  Or cure my bitter smart.

" 'There is no rest, no ease for me
  North, east, or west, or south,
Till Christian knight will willingly
  Thrice kiss me on the mouth.

" 'Nor wedded may this childe have been
  That giveth ease to me;
Nor may he be constrained, I ween,
  But kiss me willingly.

" 'So is there here one Christian knight
  Of such a noble strain
That he will give a tortured wight
  Sweet ease of mortal pain?'

" 'A wedded man,' quoth Arthur, King,
  'A wedded man I be,
Else would I deem it noble thing
  To kiss thee willingly.

" 'Now, Lancelot, in all men's sight
  Thou art the head and chief
Of chivalry. Come, noble knight,
  And give her quick relief.'

"But Lancelot he turned aside
  And looked upon the ground,
For it did sting his haughty pride
  To hear them laugh around.

" 'Come thou, Sir Tristram,' quoth the King.
  Quoth he, 'It cannot be,
For ne'er can I my stomach bring
  To do it willingly.'

" 'Wilt thou, Sir Kay, thou scornful wight?'
    Quoth Kay, 'Nay, by my troth!
What noble dame would kiss a knight
    That kissed so foul a mouth?'

" 'Wilt thou, Gawaine?' 'I cannot, King.'
    'Sir Geraint?' 'Nay, not I;
My kisses no relief could bring,
    For sooner would I die.'

"Then up and spake the youngest man
    Of all about the board,
'Now such relief as Christian can
    I'll give to her, my lord.'

"It was Sir Keith, a youthful knight,
    Yet strong of limb and bold,
With beard upon his chin as light
    As finest threads of gold.

"Quoth Kay, 'He hath no mistress yet
    That he may call his own,
But here is one that's quick to get,
    As she herself has shown.'

"He kissed her once, he kissed her twice,
    He kissed her three times o'er,
A wondrous change came in a trice.
    And she was foul no more.

"Her cheeks grew red as any rose,
    Her brow as white as lawn,
Her bosom like the winter snows,
    Her eyes like those of fawn.

"Her breath grew sweet as summer breeze
That blows the meadows o'er;
Her voice grew soft as rustling trees,
And cracked and harsh no more.

"Her hair grew glittering like the gold,
Her hands as white as milk;
Her filthy rags, so foul and old,
Were changed to robes of silk.

"In great amaze the knights did stare.
Quoth Kay, 'I make my vow
If it will please thee, lady fair,
I'll gladly kiss thee now."

"But young Sir Keith kneeled on one knee
And kissed her robes so fair.
'O let me be thy slave,' said he,
'For none to thee compare.'

"She bent her down, she kissed his brow,
She kissed his lips and eyes.
Quoth she, 'Thou art my master now,
My lord, my love, arise!

" 'And all the wealth that is mine own,
My lands, I give to thee,
For never knight hath lady shown
Such noble courtesy.

" 'Bewitched was I, in bitter pain,
But thou hast set me free,
So now I am myself again,
I give myself to thee.' "

"Yea, truly," quoth Robin Hood, when the Tanner had made an end of singing, "it is as I remember it, a fair ditty, and a ballad with a pleasing tune of a song."

"It hath oftentimes seemed to me," said Will Scarlet, "that it hath a certain motive in it, e'en such as this: That a duty which seemeth to us sometimes ugly and harsh, when we do kiss it fairly upon the mouth, so to speak, is no such foul thing after all."

"Methinks thou art right," quoth Robin, "and, contrariwise, that when we kiss a pleasure that appeareth gay it turneth foul to us; is it not so, Little John? Truly such a thing hath brought thee sore thumps this day. Nay, man, never look down in the mouth. Clear thy pipes and sing us a ditty."

"Nay," said Little John, "I have none as fair as that merry Arthur has trolled. They are all poor things that I know. Moreover, my voice is not in tune today, and I would not spoil even a tolerable song by ill singing."

Upon this all pressed Little John to sing, so that when he had denied them a proper length of time, such as is seemly in one that is asked to sing, he presently yielded. Quoth he, "Well, an ye will ha' it so, I will give you what I can. Like to fair Will, I have no title to my ditty, but this it runs." Then clearing his voice he sang:—

> *"O Lady mine, the spring is here,*
> *With a hey nonny nonny;*
> *The sweet love season of the year,*
> *With a ninny ninny nonny;*
> *Now lad and lass*
> *Lie in the grass*
> *That groweth green*
> *With flowers between.*
> *The buck doth rest,*
> *The leaves do start,*
> *The cock doth crow,*
> *The breeze doth blow,*
> *And all things laugh in—"*

"Who may yon fellow be coming along the road?" said Robin, breaking into the song.

"I know not," quoth Little John, in a surly voice. "But this I do know, that it is an ill thing to do to check the flow of a good song."

"Nay, Little John," said Robin, "be not vexed, I prythee; but I have been watching him coming along, bent beneath that great bag over his shoulder, ever since thou didst begin thy song. Look, Little John, I pray, and see if thou knowest him."

Little John looked whither Robin Hood pointed. "Truly," quoth he, after a time, "I think yon fellow is a certain young miller I have seen now and then around the edge of Sherwood; a poor wight, methinks, to spoil a good song about."

"Now thou speakest of him," quoth Robin Hood, "methinks I myself have seen him now and then. Hath he not a mill over beyond Nottingham Town, nigh to the Salisbury road?"

"Thou art right; that is the man," said Little John.

"A good stout fellow," quoth Robin. "I saw him crack Ned o' Bradford's crown about a fortnight since, and never saw I hair lifted more neatly in all my life before."

By this time the young miller had come so near that they could see him clearly. His clothes were dusted with flour, and over his back he carried a great sack of meal, bending so as to bring the whole weight upon his shoulders, and across the sack was a thick quarterstaff. His limbs were stout and strong, and he strode along the dusty road right sturdily with the heavy sack across his shoulders. His cheeks were ruddy as a winter hip, his hair was flaxen in color, and on his chin was a downy growth of flaxen beard.

"A good honest fellow," quoth Robin Hood, "and such a one as is a credit to English yeomanrie. Now let us have a merry jest with him. We will forth as though we were common thieves and pretend to rob him of his honest gains. Then we will take him into the forest and give him a feast of such as his stomach never held in all his life before. We will flood his throat with good canary and send him home with crowns in his purse for every penny he hath. What say ye, lads?"

"Truly, it is a merry thought," said Will Scarlet.

"It is well planned," quoth Little John, "but all the saints preserve us from any more drubbings this day! Marry, my poor bones ache so that I—"

"Prythee peace, Little John," quoth Robin. "Thy foolish tongue will get us both well laughed at yet."

"My foolish tongue, forsooth," growled Little John to Arthur a Bland. "I would it could keep our master from getting us into another coil this day."

But now the Miller, plodding along the road, had come opposite to where the yeomen lay hidden, whereupon all four of them ran at him and surrounded him.

"Hold, friend!" cried Robin to the Miller; whereupon he turned slowly, with the weight of the bag upon his shoulder, and looked at each in turn all bewildered, for though a good stout man his wits did not skip like roasting chestnuts.

"Who bids me stay?" said the Miller in a voice deep and gruff, like the growl of a great dog.

"Marry that do I," quoth Robin; "and let me tell thee, friend, thou hadst best mind my bidding."

"And who art thou, good friend?" said the Miller, throwing the great sack of meal from his shoulder to the ground; "and who are those with thee?"

"We be four good Christian men," quoth Robin, "and would fain help thee by carrying part of thy heavy load for thee."

"I give you all thanks," said the Miller, "but my bag is none that heavy that I cannot carry it e'en by myself."

"Nay, thou dost mistake, " quoth Robin, "I meant that thou mightest perhaps have some heavy farthings or pence about thee, not to speak of silver and gold. Our good Gaffer Swanthold sayeth that gold is an over heavy burden for a two-legged ass to carry; so we would e'en lift some of this load from thee."

"Alas!" cried the Miller; "what would ye do to me? I have not about me so much as a clipped groat. Do me no harm, I pray you, but let me depart in peace. Moreover, let me tell you that ye are upon Robin Hood's ground, and should he find you seeking to rob an honest craftsman, he will clip your ears to your heads and scourge you even to the walls of Nottingham."

"In truth I fear Robin Hood no more than I do myself," quoth jolly Robin. "Thou must this day give up to me every penny thou hast about thee. Nay, if thou dost budge an inch I will rattle this staff about thine ears."

"Nay, smite me not!" cried the Miller, throwing up his elbow as though he feared the blow. "Thou mayst search me if thou wilt, but thou wilt find nothing upon me, pouch, pocket, or skin."

"Is it so?" quoth Robin Hood, looking keenly upon him. "Now I believe that what thou tellest is no true tale. If I am not much mistook thou hast somewhat in the bottom of that fat sack of meal. Good Arthur, empty the bag upon the ground; I warrant thou wilt find a shilling or two in the flour."

"Alas!" cried the Miller, falling upon his knees, "spoil not all my good meal! It can better you not, and will ruin me. Spare it, and I will give up the money in the bottom of the bag."

"Ha!" quoth Robin, nudging Will Scarlet, "Is it so? And have I found where thy money lies? Marry, I have a wondrous nose for the blessed image of good King Harry. I thought that I smelt gold and silver beneath the barley meal. Bring it straight forth, Miller."

Then slowly the Miller arose to his feet, and slowly and unwillingly he untied the mouth of the bag, and slowly thrust his hands into the meal and began fumbling about with his arms buried to the elbows in the barley flour. The others gathered round him, their heads together, looking and wondering what he would bring forth.

So they stood, all with their heads close together, gazing down into the sack. But while he pretended to be searching for the money, the Miller gathered two great handfuls of meal, "Ha," quoth he, "here they are, the beauties." Then, as the others leaned still more forward to see what he had, he suddenly cast the meal into their faces, filling their eyes and noses and mouths with the flour, blinding and half choking them. Arthur a Bland was worse off than any, for his mouth was open, agape with wonder of what was to come, so that a great cloud of flour flew down his throat, setting him a-coughing till he could scarcely stand.

Then, while all four stumbled about, roaring with the smart of the meal in their eyeballs, and while they rubbed their eyes till the tears made great channels on their faces through the meal, the Miller seized another handful of flour and another and another, throwing it in their faces, so that even had they had a glimmering of light before they were now as blind as ever a beggar in Nottinghamshire, while their hair and beards and clothes were as white as snow.

Then catching up his great crab staff, the Miller began laying about him as though he were clean gone mad. This way and that skipped the four, like peas on a drumhead, but they could neither see to defend themselves nor to run away. Thwack! thwack! went the Miller's cudgel across their backs, and at every blow great white clouds of flour rose in the air from their jackets and went drifting down the breeze.

"Stop!" roared Robin at last. "Give over, good friend, I am Robin Hood!"

"Thou liest, thou knave," cried the Miller, giving him a rap on the ribs that sent up a great cloud of flour like a puff of smoke. "Stout Robin never robbed an honest tradesman. Ha! thou wouldst have any money, wouldst thou?" And he gave him another blow. "Nay, thou art not getting thy share, thou long-legged knave. Share and share alike." And he smote Little John across the shoulders so that he sent him skipping half across the road. "Nay, fear not, it is thy turn now, black beard." And he gave the Tanner a crack that made him roar for all his coughing. "How now, red coat, let me brush the dust from thee!" cried he, smiting Will Scarlet. And so he gave them merry words and blows until they could scarcely stand, and whenever he saw one like to clear his eyes he threw more flour in his face.

At last Robin Hood found his horn, and clapping it to his lips blew three loud blasts upon it.

Now it chanced that Will Stutely and a party of Robin's men were in the glade not far from where this merry sport was going forward. Hearing the hubbub of voices, and blows that sounded like the noise of a flail in the barn in winter time, they stopped, listening, and wondering what was toward. Quoth Will Stutely, "Now if I mistake not there is some stout battle with cudgels going forward not far hence. I would fain see this pretty sight." So saying, he and the whole party turned their steps whence the noise came. When they had come near where all the tumult sounded they heard the three blasts of Robin's bugle horn.

"Quick!" cried young David of Doncaster. "Our master is in sore need!" So, without stopping a moment, they dashed forward with might and main and burst forth from the covert into the high-road.

But what a sight was that which they saw. The road was all white with meal, and five men stood there also white with meal from top to toe, for much of the barley flour had fallen back upon the Miller.

"What is thy need, master?" cried Will Stutely. "And what doth all this mean?"

"Why," quoth Robin in a mighty passion, "yon traitor fellow hath come as nigh slaying me as e'er a man in all the world. Hadst thou not come quickly, good Stutely, thy master had been dead."

Hereupon, whilst he and the three others rubbed the meal from their eyes, and Will Stutely and his men brushed their clothes clean, he told them all; how that he had meant to pass a jest upon the Miller, which same had turned so grievously upon them.

"Quick, men, seize the vile Miller!" cried Stutely, who was nigh choking with laughter as were the rest; whereupon several ran upon the stout fellow, and seizing him bound his arms behind his back with bowstrings.

"Ha!" cried Robin, when they brought the trembling Miller to him. "Thou wouldst murder me, wouldst thou? By my faith—" Here he stopped and stood glaring upon the Miller with a grim look. But Robin's anger could not hold, so first his eyes twinkled, and then in spite of all he broke into a laugh.

Now when they saw their master laugh, the yeomen who stood around could contain themselves no longer, and a mighty shout of laughter went up from all. Many could not stand, but rolled upon the ground from pure merriment.

"What is thy name, good fellow?" said Robin at last to the Miller, who stood gaping and as though he were in a maze.

"Alas, sir, I am Midge, the Miller's son," said he in a frightened voice.

"I make my vow," quoth merry Robin, smiting him upon the shoulder, "thou art the mightiest Midge that e'er mine eyes beheld. Now wilt thou leave thy dusty mill and come and join my band? By my faith, thou art too stout a man to spend thy days betwixt the hopper and the till."

"Then truly, if thou dost forgive me for the blows I struck, not knowing who thou wast, I will join with thee right merrily," said the Miller.

"Then have I gained this day," quoth Robin, "the three stoutest yeomen in all Nottinghamshire. We will get us away to the greenwood tree, and there hold a merry feast in honor of our new friends, and mayhap a cup or two of good sack and canary may mellow the soreness of my poor joints and bones, though I warrant it will be many a day before I am again the man I was." So saying, he turned and led the way, the rest following, and so they entered the forest once more and were lost to sight.

So that night all was ablaze with crackling fires in the woodlands, for though Robin and those others spoken of, only excepting Midge, the Miller's son, had many a sore bump and bruise here and there on their bodies, they were still not so sore in the joints that they could not enjoy a jolly feast given all in welcome to the new members of the band. Thus with songs and jesting and laughter that echoed through the deeper and more silent nooks of the forest, the night passed quickly along, as such merry times are wont to do, until at last each man sought his couch and silence fell on all things and all things seemed to sleep.

Thus came about three merry adventures in one day, the one stepping upon the heels of another.

But Little John's tongue was ever one that was not easy of guidance, so that, inch by inch, the whole story of his fight with the Tanner and Robin's fight with Will Scarlet leaked out. And so I have told it that you may laugh at the merry tale along with me.

Now happenings so come upon us in this world that the serious things of this world become so mixed up with the merry things that our life is all of a jumble of black and white, as it were, like the boards of checkered black and white upon which country folk play draughts at the inn beside the blazing fire of a winter's night.

So things fell out with Robin Hood, for this day of merry sport, through which we have just trudged and buffeted with him and certain other mad wags, was speedily followed by one in which, though merriment was a-doing, more weighty matters were undertaken. So listen to what follows.

PART FOURTH

In which it is told how Allan a Dale was brought to Robin Hood, who promised to help him in trouble. Also how Robin sought the curtal Friar of Fountain Abbey with that aim in view. Likewise it is recounted how Robin Hood brought two true lovers together that would else have been made unhappy all their lives.

1

ROBIN HOOD AND
ALLAN A DALE

It has just been told how three unlucky adventures fell upon Robin Hood and Little John all in one day, bringing them sore ribs and aching bones. So next we will tell how they made up for those ill happenings by a good action that came about not without some small pain to Robin.

Two days had passed by, and somewhat of the soreness had passed away from Robin Hood's joints, yet still, when he moved of a sudden and without thinking, pain here and there would, as it were, jog him, crying, "Thou hast had a drubbing, good fellow."

The day was bright and jocund, and the morning dew still lay upon the grass. Under the greenwood tree sat Robin Hood; on one side was Will Scarlet, lying at full length upon his back, gazing up into the clear sky, with hands clasped behind his head; upon the other side sat Little John, fashioning a cudgel out of a stout crab-tree limb; elsewhere upon the grass sat or lay many others of the band.

Will Scathelock, who was as full of tales and legends as an egg is of meat, was telling of the adventures that befell brave Sir Carodoc of the Shrunken Arm, of King Arthur's time, and of his love to his one true maid, and of what they dared and suffered for each other's sake. That noble story you yourself may read some time, for it has been written and sung in more than one ancient tale and ballad, both in courtly and in homely phrase. To this all listened without a word, and when it was done many drew deep breaths, being carried away by the tale of knightly daring and noble sacrifice.

"It doth make a man better," quoth Robin Hood, "to hear of those noble men that lived so long ago. When one doth list to such tales, his soul doth say, 'Put by thy poor little likings and seek to do likewise.' Truly, one may not do as nobly one's self, but in the striving one is better. I mind me our good Gaffer Swanthold was wont to say, 'He who jumps for the moon and gets it not leaps higher than he who stoops for a penny in the mud.' "

"Truly," quoth Will Stutely, "it is a fine thought, but nevertheless, good master, the one gets a penny and the other gets nought, and, without the penny, one is like to go with an empty stomach. These same stories are well to listen to but ill to follow, say I."

"By the faith of my heart," quoth merry Robin, "thou dost ever trip up a lofty thought that gazes in the sky, and dost bring its nose in the dust. Nevertheless, thou hast a shrewd wit in thy head, good Stutely; and now that thou bringest me to things of the world, I do bethink me that we have had no one to dine with us for this long time. Our money groweth low in the purse, for no one hath come to pay a reckoning for many a day. Now busk thee, good Stutely, and choose thee six men, and get thee gone to Fosse Way or thereabouts, and see that thou bringest some one to eat with us this evening. Meantime we will prepare a grand feast to do whosoever may come the great honor. And stay, good Stutely. I would have thee take Will Scarlet with thee, for it is meet that he should become acquaint with the ways of the forest."

"Now do I thank thee, good master," quoth Stutely, springing to his feet, "that thou hast chosen me for this adventure. Truly, my limbs do grow slack through abiding idly here. As for two of my six, I will choose Midge the Miller, and Arthur a Bland, for, as well thou knowest, good master, they are stout fists at the quarterstaff. Is it not so, Little John?"

At this all laughed but Little John, and Robin, who twisted up his face. "I can speak for Midge," said he, "and likewise for my cousin Scarlet. This very blessed morn I looked at my ribs and found them as many colors as a beggar's cloak."

So, having chosen four more stout fellows, Will Stuteley and his band set forth to Fosse Way, to find whether they might not come across some rich guest to feast that day in Sherwood with Robin and his band.

For all the livelong day they abided near this highway. Each man had brought with him a good store of cold meat and a bottle of stout March beer to stay his stomach till the home-coming. So when high noontide had come they sat them down upon the soft grass, beneath a green and wide-spreading hawthorn bush, and held a hearty and jovial feast. After this, one kept watch while the others napped, for it was a still and sultry day.

Thus they passed the time pleasantly enow, but no guest such as they desired showed his face in all the time that they lay hidden there. Many passed along the dusty road in the glare of the sun: now it was a bevy of chattering damsels merrily tripping along; now it was a plodding tinker; now a merry shepherd lad; now a sturdy farmer; all gazing ahead along the road, unconscious of the seven stout fellows that lay hidden so near them. Such were the travellers along the way; but fat abbot, rich esquire, or money-laden usurer came there none.

At last the sun began to sink low in the heavens; the light grew red and the shadows long. The air grew full of silence, the birds twittered sleepily, and from afar came, faint and clear, the musical song of the milkmaid calling the kine home to the milking.

Then Stutely arose from where he was lying. "A plague of such ill luck!" quoth he. "Here have we abided all day, and no bird worth the shooting, so to speak, hath come within wood with empty reach of our bolt. Had I gone forth on an innocent errand, I had met a dozen stout priests or a score of pursy money-lenders. But it is ever thus: the dun deer are never so scarce as when one has a gray goose feather nipped betwixt the fingers. Come, lads, let us pack up and home again, say I." Accordingly, the others arose, and, coming forth from out the thicket, they all turned their toes back again to Sherwood.

After they had gone some distance, Will Stutely, who headed the party, suddenly stopped. "Hist!" quoth he, for his ears were as sharp as those of a five-year-old fox. "Hark, lads! Methinks I hear a sound." At this all stopped and listened with bated breath, albeit for a time they could hear nothing, their ears being duller than Stutely's. At length they heard a faint and melancholy sound, like some one in lamentation.

"Ha!" quoth Will Scarlet, "this must be looked into. There is some one in distress nigh to us here."

"I know not," quoth Will Stutely, shaking his head doubtfully, "our master is ever rash about thrusting his finger into a boiling pot; but, for my part, I see no use in getting ourselves into mischievous coils. Yon is a man's voice, if I mistake not, and a man should be always ready to get himself out from his own pothers." Thus spoke Will Stutely, yet, in truth, only half meant what he said. Nevertheless, since he had escaped so narrowly from out the Sheriff's clutches he had grown somewhat over-cautious.

Then out spake Will Scarlet boldly. "Now out upon thee, to talk in that manner, Stutely! Stay, if thou dost list. I go to see what may be the trouble of this poor creature."

"Nay," quoth Stutely, "thou dost leap so quickly thou'lt tumble into the ditch. Who said I would not go? Come along, say I." Thus saying, he led the way, the others following, till, after they had gone a short distance, they came to a little opening in the woodland, whence a brook, after gurgling out from under the tangle of overhanging bushes, spread out into a broad and glassy pebbled pool. By the side of this pool, and beneath the branches of a willow, lay a youth upon his face, weeping aloud, the sound of which had first caught the quick ears of Stutely. His golden locks were tangled, his clothes were all awry, and everything about him betokened sorrow and woe. Over his head, from the branches of the osier, hung a beautiful harp of polished wood inlaid with gold and silver in fantastic devices. Beside him lay a stout ashen blow and half a score of fair, smooth arrows.

"Halloa!" shouted Will Stutely, when they had come out from the forest into the little open spot. "Who art thou, fellow, that liest there killing all the green grass with salt water?"

Hearing the voice, the stranger sprang to his feet, and, snatching up his bow and fitting a shaft, held himself in readiness for whatever ill might befall him.

"Truly," said one of the yeomen, when they had seen the young stranger's face, "I do know that lad right well. He is a certain minstrel that I have seen hereabouts more than once. It was only a week ago I saw him skipping across the hill like a yearling doe. A fine sight he was then, with a flower at his ear and a cock's plume stuck in his cap; but now, methinks, our cockerel is shorn of his gay feathers."

"Pah!" cried Will Stutely, coming up to the stranger, "wipe thine eyes, man! I do hate to see a tall, stout fellow so snivelling like a girl of fourteen over a dead tomtit. Put down thy bow, man! we mean thee no harm."

But Will Scarlet, seeing how the stranger, who had a young and boyish look, was stung by the words that Stutely had spoken, came to him and put his hand upon the youth's shoulder. "Nay, thou art in trouble, poor boy!" said he, kindly. "Mind not what these fellows have said. They are rough, but they mean thee well. Mayhap they do not understand a lad like thee. Thou shalt come with us, and perchance we may find a certain one that can aid thee in thy perplexities, whatsoever they may be."

"Yea, truly, come along," said Will Stutely, gruffly. "I meant thee no harm, and may mean thee some good. Take down thy singing tool from off this fair tree, and away with us."

The youth did as he was bidden, and, with bowed head and sorrowful step, accompanied the others, walking beside Will Scarlet.

So they wended their way through the forest. The bright light faded from the sky and a glimmering gray fell over all things. From the deeper recesses of the forest the strange whispering sounds of night-time came to the ear; all else was silent, saving only for the rattling of their footsteps amid the crisp, dry leaves of the last winter. At last a ruddy glow shone before them here and there through the trees; a little farther and they came to the open glade, now bathed in the pale moonlight. In the centre of the open crackled a great fire, throwing a red glow on all around. At the fire were roasting juicy steaks of venison, pheasants, capons, and fresh fish from the river. All the air was filled with the sweet smell of good things cooking.

The little band made its way across the glade, many yeomen turning with curious looks and gazing after them, but none speaking or questioning them. So, with Will Scarlet upon one side and Will Stutely upon the other, the stranger came to where Robin Hood sat on a seat of moss under the greenwood tree, with Little John standing beside him.

"Good even, fair friend," said Robin Hood, rising as the other drew near. "And hast thou come to feast with me this day?"

"Alas! I know not," said the lad, looking around him with dazed eyes, for he was bewildered with all that he saw. "Truly, I know not whether I be in a dream," said he to himself in low voice.

"Nay, marry," quoth jolly Robin, laughing; "thou art awake, as thou wilt presently find, for a fine feast is a-cooking for thee. Thou art our honored guest this day."

Still the young stranger looked about him, as though in a dream. Presently he turned to Robin. "Methinks," said he, "I know now where I am and what hath befallen me. Art not thou the great Robin Hood?"

"Thou hast hit the bull's eye," quoth Robin, clapping him upon the shoulder. "Men hereabouts do call me by that name. Sin' thou knowest me, thou knowest also that he who feasteth with me must pay his reckoning. I trust thou hast a full purse with thee, fair stranger."

"Alas!" said the stranger, "I have no purse nor no money either, saving only the half of a sixpence, the other half of which mine own dear love doth carry in her bosom, hung about her neck by a strand of silken thread."

At this speech a great shout of laughter went up from those around, whereat the poor boy looked as he would die of shame; but Robin Hood turned sharply to Will Stutely. "Why, how now," quoth he, "is this the guest that thou hast brought us to fill our purse? Methinks thou has brought but a lean cock to the market."

"Nay, good master," answered Will Stutely, grinning, "he is no guest of mine; it was Will Scarlet that brought him thither. Nevertheless as thou mayst remember a certain talk this morning of duty and what not being better than a penny plucked from the dust, methinks here is a fine chance for practising charity."

Then up spoke Will Scarlet, and told how they had found the lad in sorrow, and how he had brought him to Robin, thinking that he might perchance aid him in his trouble. Then Robin Hood turned to the youth, and, placing his hand upon the other's shoulder, held him off at arm's length, scanning his face closely.

"A young face," quoth he in a low voice, half to himself, "a kind face, a good face. 'Tis like a maiden's for purity, and withal, the fairest that e'er mine eyes did see; but, if I may judge fairly by thy looks, grief cometh to young as well as to old." At these words, spoken so kindly, the poor lad's eyes brimmed up with tears. "Nay, nay," said Robin, hastily, "cheer up, lad; I warrant thy case is not so bad that it cannot be mended. What may be thy name?"

"Allan a Dale is my name, good master."

"Allan a Dale," repeated Robin, musing. "Allan a Dale. It doth seem to me that the name is not altogether strange to mine ears. Yea, surely thou art the minstrel of whom we have been hearing lately, whose voice so charmeth all men. Dost thou not come from the Dale of Rotherstream, over beyond Stavely?"

"Yea, truly," answered Allan, "I do come thence."

"How old art thou, Allan?" said Robin.

"I am but twenty years of age."

"Methinks thou art over young to be perplexed with trouble," quoth Robin, kindly; then, turning to the others, he cried, "Come, lads, busk ye and get our feast ready; only thou, Will Scarlet, and thou, Little John, stay here with me."

Then, when the others had gone, each man about his business, Robin turned once more to the youth. "Now, lad," said he, "tell us thy troubles, and speak freely. A flow of words doth ever ease the heart of sorrows; it is like opening the waste weir when the mill-dam is over full. Come, sit thou here beside me, and speak at thine ease."

Then straightway the youth told the three yeomen all that was in his heart; at first in broken words and phrases, then freely and with greater ease when he saw that all listened closely to what he said. So he told them how he had come from York to the sweet vale of Rother, travelling the country through as a minstrel, stopping now at castle, now at hall, and now at farmhouse; how he had spent one sweet evening in a certain broad, low farmhouse, where he sang before a stout franklin and a maiden as pure and lovely as the first snowdrop of spring; how he had played and sung to her, and how sweet Ellen o' the Dale had listened to him and had loved him. Then, in a low, sweet voice, scarcely louder than a whisper, he told how he had watched for her and met her now and then when she went abroad, but was all too afraid in her sweet presence to speak to her, until at last, beside the banks of Rother, he had spoken of his love, and she had whispered that which had made his heartstrings quiver for joy. Then they broke a sixpence between them, and vowed to be true to one another forever.

Next he told how her father had discovered what was a-doing, and had taken her away from him so that he never saw her again, and his heart was sometimes like to break; how this morn, only one short month and a half from the time that he had seen her last, he had heard and knew it to be so, that she was to marry old Sir Stephen of Trent, two days hence, for Ellen's father thought it would be a grand thing to have his daughter marry so high, albeit she wished it not; nor was it wonder that a knight should wish to marry his own sweet love, who was the most beautiful maiden in all the world.

To all this the yeomen listened in silence, the clatter of many voices, jesting and laughing, sounding around them, and the red light of the fire shining on their faces and in their eyes. So simple were the poor boy's words, and so deep his sorrow, that even Little John felt a certain knotty lump rise in his throat.

"I wonder not," said Robin, after a moment's silence, "that thy true love loved thee, for thou hast surely a silver cross beneath thy tongue, even like good Saint Francis, that could charm the birds of the air by his speech."

"By the breath of my body," burst forth Little John, seeking to cover his feelings with angry words, "I have a great part of a mind to go straightway and cudgel the nasty life out of the body of that same vile Sir Stephen. Marry, come up, say I—what a plague—does an old weazen think that tender lasses are to be bought like pullets o' a market day? Out upon him!—I—but no matter, only let him look to himself."

Then up spoke Will Scarlet. "Methinks it seemeth but ill done of the lass that she should so quickly change at others' bidding, more especially when it cometh to the marrying of a man as old as this same Sir Stephen. I like it not in her, Allan."

"Nay," said Allan, hotly, "thou dost wrong her. She is as soft and gentle as a stockdove. I know her better than any one in all the world. She may do her father's bidding, but if she marries Sir Stephen, her heart will break and she will die. My own sweet dear, I—" He stopped and shook his head, for he could say nothing further.

Whilst the others were speaking, Robin Hood had been sunk in thought. "Methinks I have a plan might fit thy case, Allan," said he. "But tell me first, thinkest thou, lad, that thy true love hath spirit enough to marry thee were ye together in church, the banns published, and the priest found, even were her father to say her nay?"

"Ay, marry would she," cried Allan, eagerly.

"Then, if her father be the man that I take him to be, I will undertake that he shall give you both his blessing as wedded man and wife, in the place of old Sir Stephen, and upon his wedding morn. But stay, now I bethink me, there is one thing reckoned not upon—the priest. Truly, those of the cloth do not love me overmuch, and when it comes to doing as I desire in such a matter, they are as like as not to prove stiff-necked. As to the lesser clergy, they fear to do me a favor because of abbot or bishop."

"Nay," quoth Will Scarlet, laughing, "so far as that goeth, I know of a certain friar that, couldst thou but get on the soft side of him, would do thy business even though Pope Joan herself stood forth to ban him. He is known as the Curtal Friar of Fountain Abbey, and dwelleth in Fountain Dale."

"But," quoth Robin, "Fountain Abbey is a good hundred miles from here. An we would help this lad, we have no time to go thither and back before his true love will be married. Naught is to be gained there, coz."

"Yea," quoth Will Scarlet, laughing again, "but this Fountain Abbey is not so far away as the one of which thou speakest, uncle. The Fountain Abbey of which I speak is no such rich and proud place as the other, but a simple little cell; yet, withal, as cosy a spot as ever stout anchorite dwelt within. I know the place well, and can guide thee thither, for, though it is a goodly distance, yet methinks a stout pair of legs could carry a man there and back in one day."

"Then give me thy hand, Allan," cried Robin, "and let me tell thee, I swear by the bright hair of Saint Ælfrida that this time two days hence Ellen a Dale shall be thy wife. I will seek this same Friar of Fountain Abbey tomorrow day, and I warrant I will get upon the soft side of him, even if I have to drub one soft."

At this Will Scarlet laughed again. "Be not too sure of that, good uncle," quoth he; "nevertheless, from what I know of him, I think this curtal friar will gladly join two such fair lovers, more especially if there be good eating and drinking afoot thereafter."

But now one of the band came to say that the feast was spread upon the grass; so, Robin leading the way, the others followed to where the goodly feast was spread. Merry was the meal. Jest and story passed freely, and all laughed till the forest rang again. Allan laughed with the rest, for his cheeks were flushed with the hope that Robin Hood had given him.

At last the feast was done, and Robin Hood turned to Allan, who sat beside him. "Now, Allan," quoth he, "so much has been said of thy singing that we would fain have a taste of thy skill ourselves. Canst thou not give us something?"

"Surely," answered Allan, readily; for he was no third-rate songster that must be asked again and again, but said "yes" or "no" at the first bidding; so, taking up his harp, he ran his fingers lightly over the sweetly-sounding strings, and all was hushed about the cloth. Then, backing his voice with sweet music on his harp, he sang

MAY ELLEN'S WEDDING
(Giving an account of how she was beloved by a
fairy prince, who took her to his own home.)

1.
"May Ellen sat beneath a thorn,
And in a shower around

The blossoms fell at every breeze
 Like snow upon the ground,
And in a lime-tree near was heard
 The sweet song of a strange, wild bird.

2.

"O sweet, sweet, sweet, O piercing sweet,
 O lingering sweet the strain!
May Ellen's heart within her breast
 Stood still with blissful pain:
And so, with listening, upturned face,
She sat as dead in that fair place.

3.

" 'Come down from out the blossoms, bird!
 Come down from out the tree,
And on my heart I'll let thee lie,
 And love thee tenderly!'
Thus cried May Ellen, soft and low,
From where the hawthorn shed its snow.

4.

"Down dropped the bird on quivering wing,
 From out the blossoming tree,
And nestled in her snowy breast.
 'My love! my love!' cried she;
Then straightway home, 'mid sun and flower,
She bare him to her own sweet bower.

5.

"The day hath passed to mellow night,
 The moon floats o'er the lea,
And in its solemn, pallid light
 A youth stands silently:
A youth of beauty strange and rare,
Within May Ellen's bower there.

6.

"He stood where o'er the pavement cold
The glimmering moonbeams lay.
May Ellen gazed with wide, scared eyes,
Nor could she turn away,
For, as in mystic dreams we see
A spirit, stood he silently.

7.

"All in a low and breathless voice,
'Whence comest thou?' said she;
'Art thou the creature of a dream,
Or a vision that I see?'
Then soft spake he, as night winds shiver
Through straining reeds beside the river.

8.

" 'I came, a bird on feathered wing,
From distant Faery land
Where murmuring waters softly sing
Upon the golden strand,
Where sweet trees are forever green;
And there my mother is the queen.'

9.

"No more May Ellen leaves her bower
To grace the blossoms fair;
But in the hushed and midnight hour
They hear her talking there,
Or, when the moon is shining white,
They hear her singing through the night.

10.

" 'Oh don thy silks and jewels fine,'
   May Ellen's mother said,
'For hither comes the Lord of Lyne
   And thou this lord must wed.'
May Ellen said, 'It may not be.
He ne'er shall find his wife in me.'

11.

"Up spoke her brother, dark and grim:
   'Now by the bright blue sky:
E'er yet a day hath gone for him
   Thy wicked bird shall die!
For he hath wrought thee bitter harm,
By some strange art or cunning charm.'

12.

"Then, with a sad and mournful song,
   Away the bird did fly,
And o'er the castle eaves, and through
   The gray and windy sky.
'Come forth!' then cried the brother grim,
'Why dost thou gaze so after him?'

13.

"It is May Ellen's wedding day,
   The sky is blue and fair,
And many a lord and lady gay
   In church are gathered there.
The bridegroom was Sir Hugh the Bold,
All clad in silk and cloth of gold.

14.

"In came the Bride in samite white,
   With a white wreath on her head;

Her eyes were fixed with a glassy look,
  Her face was as the dead,
And when she stood among the throng,
  She sang a wild and wondrous song.

15.

"Then came a strange and rushing sound
  Like the coming wind doth bring,
And in the open windows shot
  Nine swans on whistling wing,
And high above the heads they flew,
In gleaming flight the darkness through.

16.

"Around May Ellen's head they flew
  In wide and windy flight,
And three times round the circle drew.
  The guests shrank in affright,
And the Priest beside the altar there,
Did cross himself with muttered prayer.

17.

"But the third time they flew around,
  Fair Ellen straight was gone,
And in her place, upon the ground,
  There stood a snow-white swan.
Then, with a wild and lovely song,
It joined the swift and wingèd throng.

18.

"There's ancient men at weddings been,
  For sixty years and more,
But such a wondrous wedding day,
  They never saw before.
But none could check and none could stay,
The swans that bore the Bride away."

Not a sound broke the stillness when Allan a Dale had done, but all sat gazing at the handsome singer, for so sweet was his voice and so sweet the music that each man sat with bated breath, lest one drop more should come and he should lose it.

"By my faith and my troth," quoth Robin at last, drawing a deep breath, "lad, thou art—Thou must not leave our company, Allan! Wilt thou not stay with us here in the sweet green forest? Truly, I do feel my heart go out toward thee with great love."

Then Allan took Robin's hand and kissed it. "I will stay with thee always, dear master," said he, "for never have I known such kindness as thou hast shown me this day."

Then Will Scarlet stretched forth his hand and shook Allan's in token of fellowship, as did Little John likewise. And thus the famous Allan a Dale became one of Robin Hood's band.

2

ROBIN SEEKETH THE CURTAL FRIAR OF THE FOUNTAIN

THE STOUT YEOMEN OF SHERWOOD FOREST WERE EVER EARLY risers of a morn, more especially when the summer time had come, for then in the freshness of the dawn the dew was always the brightest, and the song of the small birds the sweetest.

Quoth Robin, "Now will I go to seek this same Friar of Fountain Abbey of whom we spake yesternight, and I will take with me four of my good men, and these four shall be Little John, Will Scarlet, David of Doncaster, and Arthur a Bland. Bide the rest of you here, and Will Stutely shall be your chief whilst I am gone."

Then straightway Robin Hood donned a fine steel coat of chain mail, over which he put on a light jacket of Lincoln green. Upon his head he clapped a steel cap, and this he covered by one of soft white leather, in which stood a nodding cock's plume. By his side he hung a good broadsword of tempered steel, the bluish blade marked all over with strange figures of dragons, winged women, and what not. A gallant sight was Robin so arrayed, I wot, the glint of steel showing here and there as the sunlight caught brightly the links of polished mail that showed beneath his green coat.

So, having arrayed himself, he and the four yeomen set forth upon their way. Will Scarlet taking the lead, for he knew better than the others whither to go. Thus, mile after mile, they strode along, now across a brawling stream, now along a sunlit road, now adown some sweet forest path, over which the trees met in green and rustling canopy, and at the end of which a herd of startled deer dashed away, with rattle of leaves and crackle of branches. Onward they walked with song and jest and laughter till high noon-tide was passed, when at last they came to the banks of a wide, glassy, and lily-padded stream. Here a broad beaten path stretched along beside the banks, on which path labored the horses that tugged at the slow moving barges, laden with barley-meal or what not, from the countryside to the many-towered town. But now, in the hot silence of the midday, no horse was seen nor any man beside themselves. Behind them and before them stretched the river, its placid bosom ruffled here and there by the purple dusk of a small breeze. Sweet green osiers bordered the banks, and far away the red-tiled eaves of some tall tower glimmered in the sun, the weather-vane a spark against the blue sky. And now they travelled more easily, for the road was level and hard. Around them and over the surface of the water skimmed and dipped the swallows, gray dragon-flies darted hither and thither glistening in the sun, and now and then a solitary heron rose splashing and with startled cry from its hiding place among the reeds and sedges that grew in the shallow margin of the stream.

"Now, good uncle," quoth Will Scarlet at last, when they had walked for a long time beside this sweet bright river, "just beyond yon bend ahead of us is a shallow ford which in no place is deeper than thy mid-thigh, and upon the other side of the stream is a certain little hermitage hidden amidst the bosky tangle of the thickets wherein dwelleth the Friar of Fountain Dale. Thither will I lead thee, for I know the way; albeit it is not overhard to find."

"Nay," quoth jolly Robin, stopping suddenly, "had I thought that I should have had to wade water, even were it so crystal a stream as this, I had donned other clothes than I have upon me. But no matter now, for after all a wetting will not wash the skin away, and what must be must. But bide ye here, lads, for I would enjoy this merry adventure alone. Nevertheless, listen well, and if ye hear me sound upon my bugle-horn, come quickly."

" 'Tis ever thus," said Little John, half muttering; "thou dost alway seek these ventures alone, whilst we, whose lives are but of small worth beside thine, and who would be but too glad to enter upon them, must sit, as it were, twiddling our thumbs in idleness."

"Nay, Little John," quoth jolly Robin, "this venture, I wot, is without danger to me. I know thou art overready to peril thyself; nevertheless, bide thou here this time as I bid thee." So saying he turned and left them, striding onward alone.

Robin had walked no farther than where the bend of the road hid his good men from his view, when he stopped suddenly, for he thought that he heard voices. He stood still and listened, and presently heard words passed back and forth betwixt what seemed to be two men, and yet the two voices were wondrously alike. The sound came from over behind the bank, that here was steep and high, dropping from the edge of the road a half a score of feet to the sedgy verge of the river.

" 'Tis strange," muttered Robin to himself after a space, when the voices had ceased their talking; "surely there be two people that spoke the one to the other, and yet methinks their voices are mightily alike. I make my vow that never have I heard the like in all my life before. Truly, if this twain are to be judged by their voices no two peas were ever more alike. I will look into this matter." So saying, he came softly to the river bank, and laying him down upon the grass peered over the edge and down below.

All was cool and shady beneath the bank. A stout osier grew, not straight upward, but leaning across the water, shadowing the spot with its soft foliage. All around grew a mass of feathery ferns such as hide and nestle in cool places, and up to Robin's nostrils came the tender odor of the wild thyme, that loves the moist verges of running streams. Here, with his broad back against the rugged trunk of the willow tree, and half hidden by the soft ferns around him, sat a stout, brawny fellow, but no other man was there. His head was as round as a ball, and covered with a mat of close-clipped curly black hair that grew low down on his forehead. But his crown was shorn as smooth as the palm of one's hand, which, together with his loose robe, cowl, and string of beads, showed that which his looks never would have done, that he was a Friar. His cheeks were as red and shining as a winter crab, albeit they were nearly covered over with a close curly black beard, as were his chin and upper lip likewise. His neck was thick like that of a north country bull, and his round head closely set upon shoulders e'en a match for those of Little John himself. Beneath his bushy black brows danced a pair of little gray eyes that could not stand still for very drollery of humor. No man could look into his face and not feel his heart-strings tickled by the merriment of their look. By his side lay a steel cap, which he had laid off for the sake of the coolness to his crown. His legs were stretched wide apart, and betwixt his knees he held a great pasty compounded of juicy meats of divers kinds made savory with tender young onions, both meat and onions being mingled with a good rich gravy. In his right fist he held a great piece of brown crust at which he munched sturdily, and every now and then he thrust his left hand into the pie and drew it forth full of meat; anon he would take a mighty pull at a great bottle of Malmsey that lay beside him.

"By my faith," quoth Robin to himself, "I do verily believe that this is the merriest feast, the merriest wight, the merriest place, and the merriest sight in all merry England. Methought there was another here, but it must have been this holy man talking to himself."

So Robin lay watching the Friar, and the Friar, all unknowing that he was so overlooked, ate his meal placidly. At last he was done, and, having first wiped his greasy hands upon the ferns and wild thyme (and sweeter napkin ne'er had king in all the world), he took up his flask and began talking to himself as though he were another man, and answering himself as though he were somebody else.

"Dear lad, thou art the sweetest fellow in all the world, I do love thee as a lover loveth his lass. La, thou dost make me shamed to speak so to me in this solitary place, no one being by, and yet if thou wilt have me say so, I do love thee as thou lovest me. Nay then, wilt thou not take a drink of good Malmsey? After thee, lad, after thee. Nay, I beseech thee, sweeten the draught with thy lips (here he passed the flask from his right hand to his left). An thou wilt force it on me so I must needs do thy bidding, yet with the more pleasure do I so as I drink thy very great health (here he took a long, deep draught). And now, sweet lad, 'tis thy turn next (here he passed the bottle from his left hand back again to his right). I take it, sweet chuck, and here's wishing thee as much good as thou wishest me." Saying this he took another draught, and truly he drank enough for two.

All this time merry Robin lay upon the bank and listened, while his stomach so quaked with laughter that he was forced to press his palm across his mouth to keep it from bursting forth; for, truly, he would not have spoiled such a goodly jest for the half of Nottinghamshire.

Having gotten his breath from his last draught, the Friar began talking again in this wise: "Now, sweet lad, canst thou not sing me a song? La, I know not, I am but in an ill voice this day; prythee ask me not; dost thou not hear how I croak like a frog? Nay, nay, thy voice is as sweet as any bullfinch; come, sing, I prythee, I would rather hear thee sing than eat a fair feast. Alas, I would fain not sing before one that can pipe so well and hath heard so many goodly songs and ballads, ne'ertheless, an thou wilt have it so, I will do my best. But now methinks that thou and I might sing some fair song together; dost thou not know a certain dainty little catch called 'The Loving Youth and the Scornful Maid'? Why, truly, methinks I have heard it ere now. Then dost thou not think that thou couldst take the lass's part if I take the lad's? I know not but I will try; begin thou with the lad and I will follow with the lass."

Then, singing first with a voice deep and gruff, and anon in one high and squeaking, he blithely trolled the merry catch of

THE LOVING YOUTH AND THE SCOURNFUL MAID

HE.

"Ah, it's wilt thou come with me, my love?
    And it's wilt thou, love, be mine?
For I will give unto thee, my love,
    Gay knots and ribbons so fine.
I'll woo thee, love, on my bended knee,
And I'll pipe sweet songs to none but thee.

Then it's hark! hark! hark!
To the wingèd lark.
And it's hark to the cooing dove!
And the bright daffodil
Groweth down by the rill,
So come thou and be my love.

SHE.

"Now get thee away, young man so fine;
Now get thee away, I say;
For my true love shall never be thine,
And so thou hadst better not stay.
Thou art not a fine enough lad for me,
So I'll wait till a better young man I see.
For it's hark! hark! hark!
To the wingèd lark,
And it's hark to the cooing dove!
And the bright daffodil
Groweth down by the rill,
Yet never I'll be thy love.

HE.

"Then straight will I seek for another fair she,
For many a maid can be found,
And as thou wilt never have aught of me,
By thee will I never be bound.
For never is a blossom in the field so rare,
But others are found that are just as fair.
So it's hark! hark! hark!
To the joyous lark,
And it's hark to the cooing dove!
And the bright daffodil

Groweth down by the rill,
And I'll seek me another dear love.

SHE.

"Young man, turn not so very quick away
Another fair lass to find.
Methinks I have spoken in haste today,
Nor have I made up my mind,
And if thou only wilt stay with me,
I'll love no other, sweet lad, but thee."

Here Robin could contain himself no longer but burst forth into a might roar of laughter; then, the holy Friar keeping on with the song, he joined in the chorus, and together they sang, or, as one might say, bellowed:—

"So it's hark! hark! hark!
To the joyous lark,
And it's hark to the cooing dove!
For the bright daffodil
Groweth down by the rill,
And I'll be thine own true love."

So they sang together, for the stout Friar did not seem to have heard Robin's laughter, neither did he seem to know that the yeoman had joined in with the song, but, with eyes half closed, looking straight before him and wagging his round head from side to side in time to the music, he kept on bravely to the end, he and Robin finishing up with a mighty roar that might have been heard a mile. But no sooner had the last word been sung than the holy man seized his steel cap, clapped it on his head, and springing to his feet cried in a great voice, "What spy have we here? Come forth, thou limb of evil, and I will carve thee into as fine pudding-meat as e'er a wife in Yorkshire cooked of a Sunday." Hereupon he drew from beneath his robes a great broadsword full as stout as was Robin's.

"Nay, put up thy pinking iron, friend," quoth Robin, standing up with the tears of laughter still on his cheeks. "Folk who have sung so sweetly together should not fight thereafter." Hereupon he leaped down the bank to where the other stood. "I tell thee, friend," said he, "my throat is as parched with that song as e'er a barley stubble in October. Hast thou haply any Malmsey left in that stout pottle?"

"Truly," said the Friar in a glum voice, "thou dost ask thyself freely where thou art not bidden. Yet I trust I am too good a Christian to refuse any man drink that is athirst. Such as there is o't thou art welcome to a drink of the same." And he held the pottle out to Robin.

Robin took it without more ado, and putting it to his lips tilted his head back, while that which was within said "glug! glug! glug!" for more than three winks, I wot. The stout Friar watched Robin anxiously the while, and when he was done took the pottle quickly. He shook it, held it betwixt his eyes and the light, looked reproachfully at the yeoman, and straightway placed it at his own lips. When it came away again there was naught within it.

"Dost thou know the country hereabout, thou good and holy man?" asked Robin, laughing.

"Yea, somewhat," answered the other, dryly.

"And dost thou know of a certain spot called Fountain Abbey?"

"Yea, somewhat."

"Then perchance thou knowest also of a certain one who goeth by the name of the Curtal Friar of Fountain Abbey."

"Yea, somewhat."

"Well then, good fellow, holy father, or whatever thou art," quoth Robin, "I would know whether this same Friar is to be found upon this side of the river or the other."

"Truly, the river hath no side but the other," said the Friar.

"How dost thou prove that?" asked Robin.

"Why, thus;" said the Friar, noting the points upon his fingers. "The other side of the river is the other, thou grantest?"

"Yea, truly."

"Yet the other side is but one side, thou dost mark?"

"No man could gainsay that," said Robin.

"Then if the other side is one side, this side is the other side. But the other side is the other side, therefore both sides of the river are the other side. Q. E. D."

" 'Tis well and pleasantly argued," quoth Robin; "yet I am still in the dark as to whether this same Curtal Friar is upon the side of the river on which we stand or upon the side of the river on which we do not stand."

"That," quoth the Friar, "is a practical question upon which the cunning rules appertaining to logic touch not. I do advise thee to find that out by the aid of thine own five senses; sight, feeling, and what not."

"I do wish much," quoth Robin, looking thoughtfully at the stout priest, "to cross yon ford and strive to find this same good Friar."

"Truly," said the other, piously, "it is a goodly wish on the part of one so young. Far be it from me to check thee in so holy a quest. Friend, the river is free to all."

"Yea, good father," said Robin; "but thou seest that my clothes are of the finest and I fain would not get them wet. Methinks thy shoulders are stout and broad; couldst thou not find it in thy heart to carry me across?"

"Now, by the white hand of the holy Lady of the Fountain!" burst forth the Friar in a mighty rage; "dost thou, thou poor puny stripling, thou kiss-my-lady-la poppenjay; thou—thou— What shall I call thee? Dost thou ask me, the holy Tuck, to carry thee? Now I swear—" Here he paused suddenly, then slowly the anger passed from his face, and his little eyes twinkled once more. "But why should I not?" quoth he, piously: "Did not the holy Saint Christopher ever carry the stranger across the river? and should I, poor sinner that I am, be ashamed to do likewise? Come with me, stranger, and I will do thy bidding in an humble frame of mind." So saying he clambered up the bank, closely followed by Robin, and led the way to the shallow pebbly ford, chuckling to himself the while as though he were enjoying some goodly jest within himself.

Having come to the ford, he girded up his robes about his loins, tucked his good broadsword beneath his arm, and stooped his back to take Robin upon it. Suddenly he straightened up. "Methinks," quoth he, "thou'lt get thy weapon wet. Let me tuck it beneath mine arm along with mine own."

"Nay, good father," said Robin. "I would not burden thee with aught of mine but myself."

"Dost thou think," said the Friar, mildly, "that the good Saint Chrisopher would ha' sought his own ease so? Nay, give me thy tool as I bid thee, for I would carry it as a penance to my pride."

Upon this, without more ado, Robin Hood unbuckled his sword from his side and handed it to the other, who thrust it with his own beneath his arm. Then once more the Friar bent his back, and, Robin having mounted upon it, he stepped sturdily into the water, and so strode onward, splashing in the shoal, and braking all the smooth surface into ever-widening rings. At last he reached the other side and Robin leaped lightly from his back.

"Many thanks, good father," quoth he. "Thou art indeed a good and holy man. Prythee give me my sword and let me away, for I am in haste."

At this the stout Friar looked upon Robin for a long time, his head on one side, and with a most waggish twist to his face; then he slowly winked his right eye. "Nay, good youth," said he, gently, "I doubt not that thou art in haste with thine affairs, yet thou dost think nothing of mine. Thine are of a carnal nature; mine are of a spiritual nature, a holy work, so to speak; moreover, mine affairs do lie upon the other side of this steam. I see by thy quest of this same holy recluse that thou art a good young man and most reverent to the cloth. I did get wet coming hither, and am sadly afraid that should I wade the water again I might get certain cricks and pains i' the joints that would mar my devotions for many a day to come. I know that since I have so humbly done thy bidding thou wilt carry me back again. Thou seest how Saint Godrick, that holy hermit whose natal day this is, hath placed in my hands two swords and in thine never a one. Therefore be persuaded, good youth, and carry me back again."

Robin Hood looked up and he looked down, biting his nether lip. Quoth he, "Thou cunning Friar, thou hast me fair and fast enow. Let me tell thee that not one of thy cloth hath so hoodwinked me in all my life before. I might have known from thy looks that thou wert no such holy man as thou didst pretend to be."

"Nay," interrupted the Friar, "I bid thee speak not so scurrilously neither, lest thou mayst perchance feel the prick of an inch or so of blue steel."

"Tut, tut," said Robin, "speak not so, Friar; the loser hath ever the right to use his tongue as he doth list. Give me my sword; I do promise to carry thee back straightway. Nay, I will not lift the weapon against thee."

"Marry, come up," quoth the Friar, "I fear thee not, fellow. Here is thy skewer; and get thyself presently ready, for I would hasten back."

So Robin took his sword again and buckled it at his side; then he bend his stout back and took the Friar upon it.

Now I wot Robin Hood had a heavier load to carry in the Friar than the Friar had in him. Moreover he did not know the ford, so he went stumbling among the stones, now stepping into a deep hole, and now nearly tripping over a bowlder, while the sweat ran down his face in beads from the hardness of his journey and the heaviness of his load. Meantime, the Friar kept digging his heels into Robin's sides and bidding him hasten, calling him many ill names the while. To all this Robin answered never a word, but, having softly felt around till he found the buckle of the belt that held the Friar's sword, he worked slyly at the fastenings, seeking to loosen them. Thus it came about that, by the time he had reached the other bank with his load, the Friar's sword-belt was loose albeit he knew it not; so when Robin stood on dry land and the Friar leaped from his back, the yeoman gripped hold of the sword so that blade, sheath, and strap came away from the holy man, leaving him without a weapon.

"Now then," quoth merry Robin, panting as he spake and wiping the sweat from his brow, "I have thee, fellow. This time that same Saint of whom thou didst speak but now hath delivered two swords into my hand and hath stripped thine away from thee. Now if thou dost not carry me back, and that speedily, I swear I will prick thy skin till it is as full of holes as a slashed doublet."

The good Friar said not a word for a while, but he looked at Robin with a grim look. "Now," said he at last, "I did think that thy wits were of the heavy sort and knew not that thou wert so cunning. Truly, thou hast me upon the hip. Give me my sword, and I promise not to draw it against thee save in self-defense; also I promise to do thy bidding and take thee upon my back and carry thee."

So jolly Robin gave him his sword again, which the Friar buckled to his side, and this time looked to it that it was more secure in its fastenings; then tucking up his robes once more, he took Robin Hood upon his back and without a word stepped into the water, and so waded on in silence while Robin sat laughing upon his back. At last he reached the middle of the ford where the water was deepest. Here he stopped for a moment, and then, with a sudden lift of his hand and heave of his shoulders, fairly shot Robin over his head as though he were a sack of grain.

Down went Robin into the water with a mighty splash. "There," quoth the holy man, calmly turning back again to the shore, "let that cool thy hot spirit, if it may."

Meantime, after much splashing, Robin had gotten to his feet and stood gazing about him all bewildered, the water running from him in pretty little rills. At last he shot the water out of his ears and spat some out of his mouth, and, gathering his scattered wits together, saw the stout Friar standing on the bank and laughing. Then, I wot, was Robin Hood a mad man. "Stay, thou villain!" roared he, "I am after thee straight, and if I do not carve thy brawn for thee this day, may I never lift finger again!" So saying, he dashed, splashing, to the bank.

"Thou needst not hasten thyself unduly," quoth the stout Friar. "Fear not; I will abide here, and if thou dost not cry 'Alack-a-day' ere long time is gone, may I never more peep through the brake at a fallow deer."

And now Robin, having reached the bank, began, without more ado, to roll up his sleeves about his wrists. The Friar, also, tucked his robes more about him, showing a great, stout arm on which the muscles stood out like humps of an aged tree. Then Robin saw what he had not wotted of before, that the Friar had also a coat of chain mail beneath his gown.

"Look, to thyself," cried Robin, drawing his good sword.

"Ay, marry," quoth the Friar, who held his already in his hand. So, without more ado, they came together, and thereupon began a fierce and mighty battle. Right and left, and up and down, and back and forth they fought. The swords flashed in the sun and then met with a clash that sounded far and near. I wot this was no playful bout at quarterstaff. but a grim and serious fight of real earnest. Thus they strove for an hour or more, pausing every now and then to rest, at which times each looked at the other with wonder, and thought that never had he seen so stout a fellow; then once again they would go at it more fiercely than ever. Yet in all this time neither had harmed the other nor caused his blood to flow. At last merry Robin cried, "Hold thy hand, good friend!" whereupon both lowered their swords.

"Now I crave a boon ere we begin again," quoth Robin, wiping the sweat from his brow; for they had striven so long that he began to think that it would be an ill-done thing either to be smitten himself or to smite so stout and brave a fellow.

"What wouldst thou have of me?" asked the Friar.

"Only this," quoth Robin; "that thou wilt let me blow thrice upon my bugle horn."

The Friar bent his brows and looked shrewdly at Robin Hood. "Now I do verily think that thou hast some cunning trick in this," quoth he. "Ne'ertheless, I fear thee not, and will let thee have thy wish, providing thou wilt also let me blow thrice upon this little whistle."

"With all my heart," quoth Robin; "so, here goes for one." So saying, he raised his silver horn to his lips, and blew thrice upon it, clear and high.

Meantime, the Friar stood watching keenly for what might come to pass, holding in his fingers the while a pretty silver whistle, such as knights use for calling their hawks back to their wrists, which whistle always hung at his girdle along with his rosary.

Scarcely had the echo of the last note of Robin's bugle come winding back from across the river, when four tall men in Lincoln green came running around the bend of the road, each with a bow in his hand and an arrow ready nocked upon the string.

"Ha! is it thus, thou traitor knave!" cried the Friar. "Then, marry, look to thyself!" so saying, he straightway clapped the hawk's whistle to his lips and blew a blast that was both loud and shrill. And now there came a crackling of the bushes that lined the other side of the road, and presently forth from the covert burst four great, shaggy hounds.

"At 'em, Sweet Lips! at 'em, Bell Throat! at 'em, Beauty! at 'em, Fangs!" cried the Friar, pointing at Robin.

And now it was well for that yeoman that a tree stood nigh him beside the road, else had he had an ill chance of it. Ere one could say "Gaffer Downthedale" the hounds were upon him, and he had only time to drop his sword and leap lightly into the tree, around which the hounds gathered, looking up at him as though he were a cat on the eaves. But the Friar quickly called off his dogs. "At 'em!" cried he, pointing down the road to where the yeomen were standing stock still with wonder of what they saw. As the hawk darts down upon its quarry, so sped the four dogs at the yeomen; but when the four men saw the hounds so coming, all with one accord, saving only Will Scarlet, drew each man his goose feather to his ear and let fly his shaft.

And now the old ballad telleth of a wondrous thing that happened, for thus it says, that each dog so shot at leaped lightly aside, and as the arrow passed him whistling, caught it in his mouth and bit it in twain. Now it would have been an ill day for these four good fellows had not Will Scarlet stepped before the others and met the hounds as they came rushing. "Why, how now, Fangs!" cried he, sternly. "Down, Beauty! down, sirrah! What means this?"

At the sound of his voice each dog shrank back quickly, and then straightway came to him and licked his hands and fawned upon him, as is the wont of dogs that meet one they know. Then the four yeomen came forward, the hounds leaping around Will Scarlet joyously. "Why, how now!" cried the stout Friar, "what means this? Art thou wizard to turn those wolves into lambs? Ha!" cried he, when they had come still nearer, "can I trust mine eyes? What means it that I see young Master William Gamwell in such company?"

"Nay, Tuck," said the young man, as the four came forward to where Robin was now clambering down from the tree in which he had been roosting, he having seen that all danger was over for the time; "nay, Tuck my name is no longer Will Gamwell, but Will Scarlet; and this is my good uncle, Robin Hood, with whom I am abiding just now."

"Truly, good master," said the Friar, looking somewhat abashed and reaching out his great palm to Robin, "I ha' oft heard thy name both sung and spoken of, but I never thought to meet thee in battle. I crave thy forgiveness, and do wonder not that I found so stout a man against me."

"Truly, most holy father," said Little John, "I am more thankful than e'er I was in all my life before that our good friend Scarlet knew thee and thy dogs. I tell thee seriously that I felt my heart crumble away from me when I saw my shaft so miss its aim, and those great beasts of thine coming straight at me."

"Thou mayst indeed be thankful, friend," said the Friar, gravely. "But, Master Will, how cometh it that thou dost now abide in Sherwood?"

"Why, Tuck, dost thou not know of my ill happening with my father's steward?" answered Scarlet.

"Yea, truly, yet I knew not that thou wert in hiding because of it. Marry, the times are all awry when a gentleman must lie hidden for so small a thing."

"But we are losing time," quoth Robin, "and I have yet to find that same curtal Friar."

"Why, uncle, thou hast not far to go," said Will Scarlet, pointing to the Friar, "for there he stands beside thee."

"How?" quoth Robin, "art thou the man that I have been at such pains to seek all day, and have got such a ducking for?"

"Why, truly," said the Friar, demurely, "some do call me the curtal Friar of the Fountain Dale; others again call me in jest the Abbot of Fountain Abbey; others still again call me simple Friar Tuck."

"I like the last name best," quoth Robin, "for it doth slip more glibly off the tongue. But why didst thou not tell me thou wert he I sought, instead of sending me searching for black moonbeams?"

"Why, truly, thou didst not ask me, good master," quoth stout Tuck; "but what didst thou desire of me?"

"Nay," quoth Robin, "the day growth late, and we cannot stand longer talking here. Come back with us to Sherwood, and I will unfold all to thee as we travel along."

So, without tarrying, longer, they all departed, with the stout dogs at their heels, and wended their way back to Sherwood again; but it was long past nightfall ere they reached the greenwood tree.

Now listen, for next I will tell how Robin Hood compassed the happiness of two young lovers, aided by the merry Friar Tuck of Fountain Dale.

ROBIN HOOD COMPASSETH THE MARRIAGE OF TWO TRUE LOVERS

AND NOW HAD COME THE MORNING WHEN FAIR ELLEN WAS TO be married, and on which merry Robin had sworn that Allan a Dale should, as it were, eat out of the platter that had been filled for Sir Stephen of Trent. Up rose Robin Hood, blithe and gay, up rose his merry men one and all, and up rose last of all stout Friar Tuck, winking the smart of sleep from out his eyes. Then, whilst the air seemed to brim over with the song of many birds, all blended together and all joying in the misty morn, each man laved face and hands in the leaping brook, and so the day began.

"Now," quoth Robin, when they had broken their fast, and each man had eaten his fill, "it is time for us to set forth upon the undertaking that we have in hand for today. I will choose me one score of my good men to go with me, for I may need aid; and thou, Will Scarlet, wilt abide here and be the chief whiles I am gone." Then searching through all the band, each man of whom crowded forward eager to be chosen, Robin called such as he wished by name, until he had a score of stout fellows, the very flower of his yeomanrie. Beside Little John and Will Stutely were nigh all those famous lads of whom I have already told you. Then, while those so chosen ran leaping, full of joy, to arm themselves with bow and shaft and broadsword, Robin Hood stepped aside into the covert, and there donned a gay coat such as might have been worn by some strolling minstrel, and slung a harp across his shoulder, the better to carry out that part.

And now I warrant Robin Hood was a sight to make all men stare. His hose were of green, but his jerkin was of mixed red and yellow, all hung about with streamers and knots and tags and ribbons of red and yellow also. Upon his head he wore a tall hat of red leather, and thrust therein was a nodding peacock's plume.

All the band stared and many laughed, for never had they seen their master in such a fantastic guise before. Little John walked all around him, seriously observing him narrowly, with his neck craned and his head on one side. As you may have seen the barnyard cock walk slowly round some unwonted thing, such as a sleeping cat or what not, pausing anon and anon, moving again with doubtful step, wondering the while and clucking to himself; so walked Little John around Robin with such words as, "La! Look ye there now! is it sooth? 'tis pretty, I wot!" At last he stopped in front of Robin. "By my soul," said he, "this same is a dainty and pretty dress that thou hast upon thee, good master. Never hath sweeter bodily clothing been seen sin' good Saint Wolfhad, the martyr, saw one sitting upon a rock painting his tail purple and green."

"Truly," quoth Robin, holding up his arms and looking down at himself, "I do think it be somewhat of a gay, gaudy, grasshopper dress; but it is a pretty thing for all that, and doth not ill befit the turn of my looks albeit I wear it but for the nonce. But stay, Little John, here are two bags that I would have thee carry in thy pouch for the sake of safe-keeping. I can ill care for them myself beneath this motley."

"Why, master," quoth Little John, taking the bags and weighing them in his hand, "here is the chink of gold."

"Well, what an there be," said Robin; "it is mine own coin, and the band is none the worse for what is there. Come, busk ye lads;" and he turned quickly away, "get ye ready straightway." Then gathering the score together in a close rank, in the midst of which were Allan a Dale and Friar Tuck, he led them forth upon their way from the forest shades.

So they walked on for a long time till they had come out of Sherwood and to the vale of Rother stream. Here were different sights from what one saw in the forest; hedge-rows, broad fields of barley corn, pasture lands rolling upward till they met the sky and all dotted over with flocks of white sheep, hayfields whence came the odor of new-mown hay that lay in smooth swathes over which skimmed the swifts in rapid flight; such they saw, and different was it, I wot, from the tangled depths of the sweet woodlands, but full as fair. Thus Robin led his band, walking blithely with chest thrown out and head thrown back, snuffing the odors of the gentle breeze that came drifting from over the hayfields.

"Truly," quoth he, "the dear world is as fair here as in the woodland shades. Who calls it a vale of tears? Methinks it is but the darkness in our minds that bringeth gloom to the world. For what sayeth that merry song thou singest, Little John? is it not thus?—

"For when my love's eyes do shine, do shine
And when her lips smile so rare,
The day it is jocund and fine, so fine,
Though let it be wet or be fair,
And when the stout ale is all flowing so fast,
Our sorrows and troubles are things of the past."

"Nay," said Friar Tuck piously, "ye do think of profane things and of naught else; yet, truly, there be better safe-guards against care and woe than ale drinking and bright eyes, to wit, fasting and meditation. Look upon me, have I the likeness of a sorrowful man?"

At this a great shout of laughter went up from all around, for the night before the stout Friar had emptied twice as many canakins of ale as any one of all the merry men.

"Truly," quoth Robin, when he could speak for laughter, "I should say that thy sorrows were about equal to thy goodliness."

So they stepped along, talking, singing, jesting, and laughing, until they had come to a certain little church that belonged to the great estates owned by the rich Priory of Emmet. Here it was that fair Ellen was to be married on that morn, and here was the spot toward which the yeomen had pointed their toes. On the other side of the road from where the church stood with waving fields of barley around, ran a stone wall along the roadside. Over the wall from the highway was a fringe of young trees and bushes, and here and there the wall itself was covered by a mass of blossoming woodbine that filled all the warm air far and near with its sweet summer odor. Then straightway the yeomen leaped over the wall, alighting on the tall soft grass upon the other side, frightening a flock of sheep that lay there in the shade so that they scampered away in all directions. Here was a sweet cool shadow both from the wall and from the fair young trees and bushes, and here sat the yeomen down, and glad enough they were to rest after their long tramp of the morning.

"Now," quoth Robin, "I would have one of you watch and tell me when he sees any one coming to the church, and the one I choose shall be young David of Doncaster. So get thee upon the wall, David, and hide beneath the woodbine so as to keep watch."

Accordingly young David did as he was bidden, the others stretching themselves at length upon the grass, some talking together and others sleeping. Then all was quiet save only for the low voices of those that talked together, and for Allan's restless footsteps pacing up and down, for his soul was so full of disturbance that he could not stand still, and saving, also, for the mellow snoring of Friar Tuck, who enjoyed his sleep with a noise as of one sawing soft wood very slowly. Robin lay upon his back and gazed aloft into the leaves of the trees, his thought leagues away, and so a long time passed.

Then up spoke Robin: "Now tell us, young David of Doncaster, what dost thou see?"

Then David answered, "I see the white clouds floating and I feel the wind a-blowing and three black crows are flying over the wold; but naught else do I see, good master."

So silence fell again and another time passed, broken only as I have said, till Robin, growing impatient, spake again. "Now tell me, young David, what dost thou see by this?"

And David answered, "I see the windmills swinging and three tall poplar trees swaying against the sky, and a flock of field-fares are flying over the hill; but naught else do I see, good master."

So another time passed, till at last Robin asked young David once more what he saw; and David said, "I hear the cuckoo singing, and I see how the wind makes waves in the barley field; and now over the hill to the church cometh an old friar, and in his hands he carries a great bunch of keys; and lo! now he cometh to the church door."

Then up rose Robin Hood and shook Friar Tuck by the shoulder. "Come, rouse thee, holy man!" cried he; whereupon, with much grunting, the stout Tuck got to his feet. "Marry, bestir thyself," quoth Robin, "for yonder, in the church door, is one of thy cloth. Go thou and talk to him, and so get thyself into the church, that thou mayst be there when thou art wanted; meantime, Little John, Will Stutely, and I will follow thee anon."

So Friar Tuck clambered over the wall, crossed the road, and came to the church, where the old Friar was still laboring with the great key, the lock being somewhat rusty and he somewhat old and feeble.

"Halloa, brother," quoth Tuck, "let me aid thee." So saying, he took the key from the other's hand, and quickly opened the door with a turn of it.

"Who art thou, good brother?" asked the old Friar, in a high, wheezing voice. "Whence comest thou, and whither art thou going?" And he winked and blinked at stout Friar Tuck like an owl at the sun.

"Thus do I answer thy questions, brother," said the other. "My name is Tuck, and I go no farther than this spot, if thou wilt haply but let me stay while this same wedding is going forward. I come from Fountain Dale, and, in truth, am a certain poor hermit, as one may say, for I live in a cell beside the fountain blessed by that holy Saint Ethelrada, which same suffered the sharpest martyrdom that ever befell a woman, to wit, she had her tongue cut out, so that she could speak no more words than a dead jackdaw, as it were. But what befell? Marry, listen. Straight came this blessed woman to that same fountain,—so it was, and yet I am fain to confess that ne'er ha I got much good from the waters thereof; for cold water doth ever stir my inward parts with certain gripings and what not."

"But," piped the old brother, in his high, wheezing voice, "I do much wish to know what befell this holy woman upon coming to that same blessed fountain."

"Marry, a' drank o' the waters, and straightway regained that which an evil-minded fellow might say, and many might think, was no such heavenly gift, and that was her powers of speech. But, if I understand aught, there is to be a gay wedding here today; so, if thou mindest not, I would fain rest me in the cool shade within, for I would like to see this fine sight."

"Truly, thou art welcome, brother," said the old man, leading the way within. Meantime, Robin Hood, in his guise of harper, together with Little John and Will Stutely, had come to the church. Robin sat him down on a bench beside the door, but Little John, carrying the two bags of gold, went within, as did Will Stutely.

So Robin sat by the door, looking up the road and down the road to see who might come, till, after a time, he saw six horsemen come riding sedately and slowly, as became them, for they were churchmen in high orders. Then, when they had come nearer, Robin saw who they were, and knew them. The first was the Bishop of Hereford, and a fine figure he cut, I wot. His vestments were of the richest silk, and around his neck was a fair chain of beaten gold. The cap that hid his tonsure was of black velvet, and around the edges of it were rows of jewels that flashed in the sunlight, each stone being set in gold. His hose were of flame-colored silk, and his shoes of black velvet, the long, pointed toes being turned up and fastened to his knees, and on either instep was embroidered a cross in gold thread. Beside the Bishop rode the Prior of Emmet upon a mincing palfrey. Rich were his clothes also, but not so gay as the stout Bishop's. Behind these were two of the higher brethren of Emmet, and behind these again two retainers belonging to the Bishop; for the Lord Bishop of Hereford strove to be as like the great barons as was in the power of one in holy orders.

When Robin saw this train drawing near, with flash of jewels and silk and jingle of silver bells on the trappings of the nags, he looked sourly upon them. Quoth he to himself, "Yon Bishop is overgaudy for a holy man. I do wonder whether his patron, who, methinks, was Saint Thomas, was given to wearing golden chains about his neck, silk clothing upon his body, and pointed shoes upon his feet; the money for all of which, God wot, hath been wrung from the sweat of poor tenants. Bishop, Bishop, thy pride may have a fall ere thou wottest of it."

So the holy men came to the church; the Bishop and the Prior jesting and laughing between themselves about certain fair dames, their words more befitting the lips of laymen, methinks, than holy clerks. Then they dismounted, and the Bishop, looking around, presently caught sight of Robin standing in the doorway. "Halloa, good fellow," quoth he, in a jovial voice, "who art thou that struttest in such gay feathers?"

"A harper am I from the North country," quoth Robin; "and I can touch the strings, I wot, as never another man in all merry England can do. Truly, good Lord Bishop, many a knight and burgher, clerk and layman, have danced to my music, willy nilly, and most times greatly against their will; such is the magic of my harping. Now this day, my Lord Bishop, if I may play at this wedding, I do promise that I will cause the fair bride to love the man she marries with a love that shall last as long as that twain shall live together."

"Ha! is it so?" cried the Bishop. "Meanest thou this is sooth?" and he looked keenly at Robin, who gazed boldly back again into his eyes. "Now, if thou wilt cause this maiden (who hath verily bewitched my poor cousin Stephen) thus to love the man she is to marry, as thou sayst thou canst, I will give thee whatsoever thou wilt ask me in due measure. Let me have a taste of thy skill, fellow."

"Nay," quoth Robin, "my music cometh not without I choose, even at a lord bishop's bidding. In sooth I will not play until the bride and bridegroom come."

"Now, thou art a saucy varlet to speak so to my crest," quoth the Bishop, frowning on Robin. "Yet, I must needs bear with thee. Look, Prior, hither cometh our cousin, Sir Stephen, and his lady-love."

And now, around the bend of the high-road, came others, riding upon horses. The first of all was a tall, thin man, of knightly bearing, dressed all in black silk, with a black velvet cap upon his head, turned up with scarlet. Robin looked, and had no doubt that this was Sir Stephen, both because of his knightly carriage and of his gray hairs. Beside him rode a stout Saxon franklin, Ellen's father, Edward of Deirwold; behind those two came a litter borne by two horses, and therein was a maiden whom Robin knew must be Ellen. Behind this litter rode six men-at-arms, the sunlight flashing on their steel caps as they came jingling up the dusty road.

So these also came to the church, and there Sir Stephen leaped from his horse, and, coming to the litter, handed fair Ellen out therefrom. Then Robin Hood looked at her, and could wonder no longer how it came about that so proud a knight as Sir Stephen of Trent wished to marry a common franklin's daughter; nor did he wonder that no ado was made about the matter, for she was the fairest maiden that ever he had beheld. Now, however, she was all pale and drooping, like a fair white lily snapped at the stem; and so, with bent head and sorrowful look, she went within the church, Sir Stephen leading her by the hand.

"Why dost thou not play, fellow?" quoth the Bishop, looking sternly at Robin.

"Marry," said Robin, calmly, "I will play in greater wise than your lordship thinks; but not till the right time hath come."

Said the Bishop to himself, while he looked grimly at Robin, "When this wedding is gone by I will have this fellow well whipped for his saucy tongue and bold speech."

And now fair Ellen and Sir Stephen stood before the altar, and the Bishop himself came in his robes and opened his book, whereat fair Ellen looked up and about her in bitter despair, like the fawn that finds the hounds on her haunch. Then, in all his fluttering tags and ribbons of red and yellow, Robin Hood strode forward. Three steps he took from the pillar, whereby he leaned, and stood between the bride and bridegroom.

"Let me look upon this lass," he said in a loud voice. "Why, how now! what have we here? Here be lilies in the cheeks, and not roses such as befit a bonny bride. This is no fit wedding. Thou, Sir Knight, so old, and she so young, and thou thinkest to make her thy wife? I tell thee it may not be, for thou art not her own true love."

At this all stood amazed, and knew not where to look nor what to think or say, for they were all bewildered with the happening; so, whilst every one looked at Robin as though they had been changed to stone, he clapped his bugle-horn to his lips and blew three blasts so loud and clear, they echoed from floor to rafter as though they were sounded by the trump of doom. Then straightway Little John and Will Stutely came leaping and stood upon either side of Robin Hood, and quickly drew their broadswords, the while a mighty voice rolled over the heads of all: "Here be I, good master, when thou wantest me;" for it was Friar Tuck that so called from the organ loft.

And now all was hubbub and noise. Stout Edward strode forward raging, and would have seized his daughter to drag her away, but Little John stepped between and thrust him back. "Stand back, old man," said he; "thou art a hobbled horse this day."

"Down with the villains!" cried Sir Stephen, and felt for his sword, but it hung not beside him on his wedding day.

Then the men-at-arms drew their swords, and it seemed like that blood would wet the stones; but suddenly came a bustle at the door and loud voices, steel flashed in the light, and the crash of blows sounded. The men-at-arms fell back, and up the aisle came leaping eighteen stout yeomen all clad in Lincoln green, with Allan a Dale at their head. In his hand he bore Robin Hood's good stout trusty bow of yew, and this he gave to him, kneeling the while upon one knee.

Then up spake Edward of Deirwold in a deep voice of anger: "Is it thou, Allan a Dale, that hath bred all this coil in a church?"

"Nay," quoth merry Robin, "that have I done, and I care not who knoweth it, for my name is Robin Hood."

At this name a sudden silence fell. The Prior of Emmet and those that belonged to him gathered together like a flock of frightened sheep when the scent of the wolf is nigh, while the Bishop of Hereford, laying aside his book, crossed himself devoutly. "Now Heaven keep us this day," said he, "from that evil man!"

"Nay," quoth Robin, "I mean you no harm; but here is fair Ellen's betrothed husband, and she shall marry him or pain will be bred to some of you."

Then up spake stout Edward in a loud and angry voice: "Now I say nay! I am her father, and she shall marry Sir Stephen and none other."

Now all this time, whilst everything was in turmoil about him, Sir Stephen had been standing in proud and scornful silence. "Nay, fellow," said he, coldly, "thou mayst take thy daughter back again; I would not marry her after this day's doings could I gain all merry England thereby. I tell thee plainly, I loved thy daughter, old as I am, and would have taken her up like a jewel from the sty, yet, truly, I knew not that she did love this fellow, and was beloved by him. Maiden, if thou dost rather choose a beggarly minstrel than a high-born knight, take thy choice. I do feel it shame that I should thus stand talking amid this herd, and so I will leave you." Thus saying he turned, and, gathering his men about him, walked proudly down the aisle. Then all the yeomen were silenced by the scorn of his words, only Friar Tuck leaned over the edge of the choir loft, and called out to him ere he had gone, "Good den, Sir Knight. Thou wottest old bones must alway make room for young blood." But Sir Stephen neither answered nor looked up, but passed out from the church as though he had heard naught, his men following him.

Then the Bishop of Hereford spoke hastily: "I, too, have no business here, and so will depart"; and he made as though he would go. But Robin Hood laid hold of his clothes and held him. "Stay, my Lord Bishop," said he, "I have yet somewhat to say to thee." The Bishop's face fell, but he stayed as Robin bade him, for he saw he could not go.

Then Robin Hood turned to stout Edward of Deirwold, and said he: "Give thy blessing on thy daughter's marriage to his yeoman, and all will be well. Little John, give me the bags of gold. Look, farmer. Here are two hundred bright golden angels; give thy blessing, as I say, and I will count them out to thee as thy daughter's dower. Give not thy blessing, and she shall be married all the same, but not so much as a cracked farthing shall cross thy palm. Choose."

Then Edward looked upon the ground with bent brows, turning the matter over and over in his mind; but he was a shrewd man and one, withal, that made the best use of a cracked pipkin; so at last he looked up and said, but in no joyous tone, "If the wench will go her own gait, let her go. I had thought to make a lady of her; yet if she chooses to be what she is like to be, I have naught to do with her henceforth. Ne'ertheless I will give her my blessing when she is duly wedded."

"It may not be," spake up one of those of Emmet. "The banns have not been duly published, neither is there any priest here to marry them."

"How sayst thou?" roared Tuck from the choir loft. "No priest? Marry, here stands as holy a man as thou art, any day of the week, a clerk in orders, I would have thee know. As for the question of banns, stumble not over that straw, brother, for I will publish them." So saying, he called the banns; and, says the old ballad, lest three times should not be enough, he published them nine times o'er. Then straightway he came down from the loft, and forthwith performed the marriage service; and so Allan and Ellen were duly wedded.

And now Robin counted out two hundred golden angels to Edward of Deirwold, and he, upon his part, gave his blessing, yet not, I wot, as though he meant it with overmuch good will. Then the stout yeomen crowded around and grasped Allan's palm, and he, holding Ellen's hand within his own, looked about him all dizzy with his happiness.

Then at last jolly Robin turned to the Bishop of Hereford, who had been looking on at all that passed with a grim look. "My Lord Bishop," quoth he, "thou mayst bring to thy mind that thou didst promise me that did I play in such wise as to cause this fair lass to love her husband, thou wouldst give me whatsoever I asked in reason. I have played my play, and she loveth her husband, which she would not have done but for me; so now fulfil thy promise. Thou hast upon thee that which, methinks, thou wouldst be the better without, therefore, I prythee, give me that golden chain that hangeth about thy neck as a wedding present for this fair bride."

Then the Bishop's cheeks grew red with rage and his eyes flashed. He looked at Robin with a fell look, but saw that in the yeoman's face which bade him pause. Then slowly he took the chain from about his neck and handed it to Robin, who flung it over Ellen's head so that it hung glittering about her shoulders. Then said merry Robin, "I thank thee, on the bride's part, for thy handsome gift, and truly thou thyself art more seemly without it. Now, shouldst thou ever come nigh to Sherwood I much hope that I shall give thee there such a feast as thou hast ne'er had in all thy life before."

"May Heaven forfend!" cried the Bishop, earnestly; for he knew right well what manner of feast it was that Robin Hood gave his guests in Sherwood forest.

But now Robin Hood gathered his men together, and, with Allan and his young bride in their midst, they all turned their footsteps toward the woodlands. On the way thither Friar Tuck came close to Robin and plucked him by the sleeve. "Thou dost lead a merry life, good master," quoth he, "but dost thou not think that it would be for the welfare of all your souls to have a good stout chaplain, such as I, to oversee holy matters? Truly, I do love this life mightily." At this merry Robin Hood laughed amain, and bade him stay and become one of their band if he wished.

That night there was such a feast held in the greenwood as Nottinghamshire never saw before. To that feast you and I were not bidden, and pity it is that we were not; so, lest we should both feel the matter the more keenly, I will say no more about it.

Thus ends the merry story of Allan a Dale, and how Robin Hood and Friar Tuck benefited him. And now we shall hear anon of other troubles than those that beset gentle lovers, and how Robin Hood helped a good stout knight that was in sore need of aid. So listen to what follows.

PART FIFTH

*In which it is told how that Robin Hood met a sorrowful knight,
and brought him to Sherwood. Also, how the Bishop of Hereford was
more generous than he desired to be. Likewise it is told how Sir
Richard of the Lea paid his debts in due season, both to the Prior of
Emmet and to Robin Hood.*

1

ROBIN HOOD AIDETH A SORROWFUL KNIGHT

SO PASSED THE GENTLE SPRINGTIME AWAY IN BUDDING BEAUTY; its silver showers and sunshine, its green meadows and its flowers. So, likewise, passed the summer with its yellow sunlight, its quivering heat and deep, bosky foliage, its long twilights and its mellow nights, through which the frogs croaked and fairy folk were said to be out on the hillsides. All this had passed and the time of fall had come, bringing with it its own pleasures and joyousness; for now, when the harvest was gathered home, merry bands of gleaners roamed the country about, singing along the roads in the daytime, and sleeping beneath the hedgerows and the hayricks at night. Now the hips burned red in the tangled thickets and the haws waxed black in the hedgerows, the stubble lay all crisp and naked to the sky, and the green leaves were fast turning russet and brown. Also, at this merry season, good things of the year are gathered in in great store. Brown ale lies ripening in the cellar, hams and bacon hang in the smoke-shed, and crabs are stowed away in the straw for roasting in the winter time, when the north wind piles the snow in drifts around the gables and the fire crackles warm upon the hearth.

So passed the seasons then, so they pass now, and so they will pass in time to come, whilst we come and go like leaves of the tree that fall and are soon forgotten.

QUOTH ROBIN HOOD, SNUFFING THE AIR, "HERE IS A FAIR day, Little John, and one that we can ill waste in idleness. Choose such men as thou dost need, and go thou east while I will wend to the west, and see that each of us bringeth back some goodly guest to dine this day beneath the greenwood tree."

"Marry," cried Little John, clapping his palms together for joy, "thy bidding fitteth my liking like haft to blade. I'll bring thee back a guest this day, or come not back mine own self."

Then they each chose such of the band as they wished, and so went forth by different paths from the forest.

Now, you and I cannot go two ways at the same time whilst we join in these merry doings; so we will e'en let Little John follow his own path while we tuck up our skirts and trudge after Robin Hood. And here is good company, too; Robin Hood, Will Scarlet, Allan a Dale, Will Scathelock, Midge, the Miller's son, and others. A score or more of stout fellows had abided in the forest, with Friar Tuck, to make ready for the home-coming, but all the rest were gone either with Robin Hood or Little John.

They travelled onward, Robin following his fancy and the others following Robin. Now they wended their way through an open dale with cottage and farm lying therein, and now again they entered woodlands once more. Passing by fair Mansfield Town, with its towers and battlements and spires all smiling in the sun, they came at last out of the forest lands. Onward they journeyed, through highway and byway, through villages where good wives and merry lasses peeped through the casements at the fine show of young men, until at last they came over beyond Alverton in Derbyshire. By this time high noontide had come, yet they had met no guest such as was worth their while to take back to Sherwood; so, coming at last to a certain spot where a shrine stood at the crossing of two roads,

Robin called upon them to stop, for here on either side was shelter of high hedgerows, behind which was good hiding, whence they could watch the roads at their ease, whilst they ate their midday meal. Quoth merry Robin, "Here, methinks, is good lodging, where peaceful folk, such as we be, can eat in quietness; therefore we will rest here, and see what may, perchance, fall into our luck-pot." So they crossed a stile and came behind a hedgerow where the mellow sunlight was bright and warm, and where the grass was soft, and there sat them down. Then each man drew from the pouch that hung beside him that which he had brought to eat, for a merry walk such as this had been sharpens the appetite till it is as keen as a March wind. So no more words were spoken, but each man saved his teeth for better use,— munching at brown crust and cold meat right lustily.

In front of them, one of the high-roads crawled up the steep hill and then dipped suddenly over its crest, sharp-cut with hedgerow and shaggy grass against the sky. Over the top of the windy hill peeped the eaves of a few houses of the village that fell back into the valley behind; there, also, showed the top of a windmill, the sails slowly rising and dipping from behind the hill against the clear blue sky, as the light wind moved them with creaking and labored swing.

So the yeomen lay behind the hedge and finished their midday meal; but still the time slipped along, and no one came. At last, a man came slowly riding over the hill, and down the stony road toward the spot where Robin and his band lay hidden. He was a good stout knight, but sorrowful of face and downcast of mien. His clothes were plain and rich, but no chain of gold, such as folk of his stand in life wore at most times, hung around his neck, and no jewel was about him; yet no one could mistake him for aught but one of proud and noble blood. His head was bowed upon his breast and his hands drooped limp on either side; and so he came slowly riding, as though sunk in sad thoughts, whilst even his good horse, the reins loose upon his neck, walked with hanging head, as though he shared his master's grief.

Quoth Robin Hood, "Yon is verily a sorry-looking gallant, and doth seem to have donned ill-content with his jerkin this morning; nevertheless, I will out and talk with him, for there may be some pickings here for a hungry daw. Methinks his dress is rich, though he himself is so downcast. Bide ye here till I look into this matter." So saying, he arose and left them, crossed the road to the shrine, and there stood, waiting for the sorrowful Knight to come near him. So, presently, when the Knight came riding slowly along, jolly Robin stepped forward and laid his hand upon the bridle rein. "Hold, Sir Knight," quoth he. "I prythee tarry for a short time, for I have a few words to say to thee."

"What art thou, friend, who dost stop a traveller in this manner upon his most gracious Majesty's highway?" said the Knight.

"Marry," quoth Robin, "that is a question hard to answer. One man calleth me kind, another calleth me cruel; this one calleth me good, honest fellow, and that one vile thief. Truly, the world hath as many eyes to look upon a man withal as there are spots on a toad; so, with what pair of eyes thou regardest me lieth entirely with thine own self. My name is Robin Hood."

"Truly, good Robin," said the Knight, a smile twitching at the corners of his mouth, "thou hast a quaint conceit. As for the pair of eyes with which I regard thee, I would say that they are as favorable as may be, for I hear much good of thee and little ill. What is thy will of me?"

"Now, I make my vow, Sir Knight," quoth Robin, "thou hast surely learned thy wisdom of good Gaffer Swanthold, for he sayeth, 'Fair words are as easy spoke as foul, and bring good will in the stead of blows.' Now I will show thee the truth of this saying; for, if thou wilt go with me this day to Sherwood Forest, I will give thee as merry a feast as ever thou hadst in all thy life."

"Thou art indeed kind," said the Knight, "but methinks thou wilt find me but an ill-seeming and sorrowful guest. Thou hadst best let me pass on my way in peace."

"Nay," quoth Robin, "thou mightst go thine own way but for one thing, and that I will tell thee. We keep an inn, as it were, in the very depths of Sherwood, but so far from high-roads and beaten paths that guests do not often come nigh us; so I and my friends set off merrily and seek them when we grow dull of ourselves. Thus the matter stands, Sir Knight; yet I will furthermore tell thee that we count upon our guests paying a reckoning."

"I take thy meaning, friend," said the Knight, gravely, "but I am not thy man, for I have no money by me."

"Is it sooth?" said Robin, looking at the Knight keenly. "I can scarce choose but believe thee; yet, Sir Knight, there be those of thy order whose word is not to be trusted as much as they would have others believe. Thou wilt think no ill if I look for myself in this matter." Then, still holding the horse by the bridle rein, he put his fingers to his lips and blew a shrill whistle, whereupon fourscore yeomen came leaping over the stile, and ran to where the Knight and Robin stood. "These," said Robin, looking upon them proudly, "are some of my merry men. They share and share alike with me all joys and troubles, gains and losses. Sir Knight, I prythee tell me what money thou hast about thee."

For a time the Knight said not a word, but a slow red arose into his cheeks; at last he looked Robin in the face and said: "I know not why I should be ashamed, for it should be no shame to me; but, friend, I tell thee the truth, when I say that in my purse are ten shillings, and that that is every groat that Sir Richard of the Lea hath in all the wide world."

When Sir Richard ended a silence fell, until at last Robin said: "And dost thou pledge me thy knightly word that this is all thou hast with thee?"

"Yea," answered Sir Richard, "I do pledge thee my most solemn word, as a true knight, that it is all the money I have in the world. Nay, here is my purse, ye may find for yourselves the truth of what I say." And he held his purse out to Robin.

"Put up thy purse, Sir Richard," quoth Robin. "Far be it from me to doubt the word of so gentle a knight. The proud I strive to bring low, but those that walk in sorrow I would aid if I could. Come, Sir Richard, cheer up thy heart and go with us into the greenwood. Even I may perchance aid thee, for thou surely knowest how the good Athelstane was saved by the little blind mole that digged a trench over which he that sought the king's life stumbled."

"Truly, friend," said Sir Richard, "methinks thou meanest kindness in thine own way; nevertheless my troubles are such that it is not likely that thou canst cure them. But I will go with thee this day into Sherwood." Hereupon he turned his horse's head, and they all wended their way to the woodlands, Robin walking on one side of the Knight and Will Scarlet on the other, whilst the rest of the band trudged behind.

After they had travelled thus for a time Robin Hood spake. "Sir Knight," said he, "I would not trouble thee with idle questions; but dost thou find it in thy heart to tell me thy sorrows?"

"Truly, Robin," quoth the Knight, "I see no reason why I should not do so. Thus it is: My castle and my lands are in pawn for a debt that I owe. Three days hence the money must be paid or else all mine estate is lost forever, for then it falls into the hands of the Priory of Emmet, and what they swallow they never give forth again."

Quoth Robin, "I understand not why those of thy kind live in such a manner that all their wealth passeth from them like snow beneath the springtide sun."

"Thou wrongest me, Robin," said the Knight, "for listen: I have a son but twenty winters old, nevertheless he has won his spurs as knight. Last year, on a certain evil day, the jousts were held at Chester, and thither my son went, as did I and my lady wife. I wot it was a proud time for us, for he unhorsed each knight that he tilted against. At last he ran a course with a certain great knight, Sir Walter of Lancaster, yet, though my son was so youthful, he kept his seat, albeit both spears were shivered to the haft; but it happened that a splinter of my boy's lance ran through the visor of Sir Walter's helmet, and pierced through his eye into his brain, so that he died ere his esquire could unlace his helm. Now, Robin, Sir Walter had great friends at court, therefore his kinsmen stirred up things against my son so that, to save him from prison, I had to pay a ransom of six hundred pounds in gold. All might have gone well even yet, only that, by ins and outs and crookedness of laws, I was shorn like a sheep that is clipped to the quick. So it came that I had to pawn my lands to the Priory of Emmet for more money, and a hard bargain they drove with me in my hour of need. Yet I would have thee understand I grieve so for my lands only because of my dear lady wife."

"But where is thy son now?" asked Robin, who had listened closely to all the Knight had said.

"In Palestine," said Sir Richard, "battling like a brave Christian soldier for the cross and the holy sepulchre. Truly, England was an ill place for him because of Sir Walter's death, and the hate of the Lancastrian's kinsmen."

"Truly," said Robin, much moved, "thine is a hard lot. But tell me, what is owing to Emmet for thine estates?"

"Only four hundred pounds," said Sir Richard.

At this Robin smote his thigh in anger. "O the bloodsuckers!" cried he. "A noble estate to be forfeit for four hundred pounds! But what will befall thee if thou dost lose thy lands, Sir Richard?"

"It is not mine own lot that doth trouble me in that case," said the Knight, "but my dear lady's; for should I lose my land she will have to betake herself to some kinsman and there abide in charity, which, methinks, would break her proud heart. As for me, I will over the salt sea, and so to Palestine to join my son in fight for the holy sepulchre."

Then up spake Will Scarlet. "But hast thou no friend that will help thee in thy dire need?"

"Never a man," said Sir Richard. "Whilst I was rich enow at home, and had friends, they blew great boasts of how they loved me. But when the oak falls in the forest the swine run from beneath it lest they should be smitten down also. So my friends have left me; for not only am I poor but I have great enemies."

Then Robin said, "Thou sayst thou hast no friends, Sir Richard. I make no boast, but many have found Robin Hood a friend in their troubles. Cheer up, Sir Knight, I may help thee yet."

The Knight shook his head with a faint smile, but for all that Robin's words made him more blithe of heart, for in truth hope, be it never so faint, bringeth a gleam into darkness, like a little rushlight that costeth but a groat.

The day was well-nigh gone when they came near to the greenwood tree. Even at a distance they saw by the number of men that Little John had come back with some guest, but when they came near enough, who should they find but the Lord Bishop of Hereford. The good Bishop was in a fine stew, I wot. Up and down he walked beneath the tree like a fox caught in a hencoop. Behind him were three black friars standing close together in a frightened group, like three black sheep in a tempest. Hitched to the branches of the trees close at hand were six horses, one of them a barb with gay trappings upon which the Bishop was wont to ride, and the others laden with packs of divers shapes and kinds, one of which made Robin's eyes glisten, for it was a box not over large, but heavily bound with bands and ribs of iron.

When the Bishop saw Robin and those with him come into the open he made as though he would have run toward the yeoman, but the fellow that guarded the Bishop and the three friars thrust his quarterstaff in front, so that his lordship was fain to stand back, though with frowning brow and angry speech.

"Stay, my Lord Bishop," cried jolly Robin, in a loud voice, when he saw what had passed; "I will come to thee with all speed, for I would rather see thee than any man in merry England." So saying, he quickened his steps, and soon came to where the Bishop stood fuming.

"How now," quoth the Bishop in a loud and angry voice, when Robin had so come to him, "is this the way that thou and thy band treat one so high in the church as I am? I and these brethren were passing peacefully along the high-road with our packhorses, and a half score of men to guard them, when up comes a great strapping fellow full seven feet high, with fourscore or more men back of him, and calls upon me to stop—me, the Lord Bishop of Hereford, mark thou! Whereupon my armed guards—beshrew them for cowards!—straight ran away. But look ye; not only did this fellow stop me, but he threatened me, saying that Robin Hood would strip me as bare as a winter hedge. Then, beside all this, he called me such vile names as 'fat priest,' 'man-eating bishop,' 'money-gorging usurer,' and what not, as though I were no more than a strolling beggar or tinker. Moreover, when I came here I found a great fat man, a mock priest, that slapped me upon the shoulder as though I, God wot, were a pothouse fellow."

"Marry, come up with a wanion!" cried Friar Tuck, bustling forward and thrusting himself in front of the Bishop; "Marry come up, I say!" and he snapped his fingers under the Bishop's nose, whereat the other started back as though the snap were a clap of thunder. "Mock priest! thou callest me, forsooth! Look ye now, Bishop, I wot I am as holy a man as thou art, and might have been a bishop mine own self, had I not been born under a hedge. I am as learned, too, as thou art, albeit I could never master that vile

Latin, my tongue being only shaped for good stout English; yet I tell thee, I can say my 'Paters' and 'Aves' with no more a slip o' the tongue than thou, thou fat man!"

At this the Bishop glared upon the stout Friar like an angry cat, whilst even Sir Richard laughed; only Robin kept a grave face. "Stand back, Tuck," said he, "thou shouldst not beard his lordship's reverence in this; Alas! my lord, that thou hast been so ill-treated by my band! I tell thee truly that we greatly reverence thy cloth. Little John, stand forth straightway."

At these words Little John came forward, twisting his face into a whimsical look, as though he would say, "Ha' mercy upon me, good master." Then Robin turned to the Bishop of Hereford and said: "Was this the man who spake so boldly to your lordship?"

"Ay, truly it was the same," said the Bishop; "a naughty fellow, I wot."

"And didst thou, Little John," said Robin, in a sad voice, "call his lordship a fat priest?"

"Ay," said Little John, sorrowfully.

"And a man-eating bishop?"

"Ay," said Little John, more sorrowfully than before.

"And a money-gorging usurer?"

"Ay," said Little John, in so sorrowful a voice that it might have drawn tears from the Dragon of Wentley.

"Alas, that these things should be!" said jolly Robin, turning to the Bishop, "for I have ever found Little John a truthful man."

At this a roar of laughter went up, whereat the blood rushed into the Bishop's face till it was cherry red from crown to chin; but he said nothing, and only swallowed his words, though they well-nigh choked him.

"Nay, my Lord Bishop," said Robin, "we are rough fellows, but I trust not such ill men as thou thinkest, after all. There is not a man here that would harm a hair of thy reverence's head. I know thou art galled by our jesting, but we are all equal here in the greenwood, for there are no bishops nor barons nor earls among us, but only men, so thou must share our life with us whilst thou dost abide here. Come, busk ye, my merry men, and get the feast ready. Meantime we will show our guests our woodland sports."

So, whilst some went to kindle the fires for roasting meats, others ran leaping to get their cudgels and long bows. Then Robin brought forward Sir Richard o' the Lea. "My Lord Bishop," said he, "here is another guest that we have with us this day. I wish that thou mightst know him better, for I and all my men will strive to honor you both at this merrymaking."

"Sir Richard," said the Bishop, in a reproachful tone, "methinks thou and I are companions and fellow sufferers in this den of—" He was about to say "thieves," but he stopped suddenly and looked askance at Robin Hood.

"Speak out, Bishop," quoth Robin, laughing. "We of Sherwood check not an easy flow of words. 'Den of thieves' thou wast about to say."

Quoth the Bishop, "Mayhap that was what I meant to say, Sir Richard; but this I will say, that I saw thee just now laugh at the scurrilous jests of these fellows. It would have been more becoming of thee, methinks, to have checked them with frowns instead of spurring them on by laughter."

"I meant no harm to thee," said Sir Richard; "but a merry jest is a merry jest, and I may truly say I would have laughed at it had it been against mine own self."

But now Robin Hood called upon certain ones of his band who spread soft moss upon the ground and laid deer skins thereon. Then Robin bade his guests be seated, and so they all three sat down, some of the chief men, such as Little John, Will Scarlet, Allan a Dale, and others, stretching themselves upon the ground near by. Then a garland was set up at the far end of the glade, and thereat the bowmen shot, and such shooting was done that day as it would have made one's heart leap to see. And all the while Robin talked so quaintly to the Bishop and the Knight that, the one forgetting his vexation and the other his troubles, they both laughed aloud again and again.

Then men shot three rounds of arrows each, and although the garland was but three palms' breadth wide, and was full sevenscore yards distant, only two arrows went without the ring. "By Our Lady, good friend," said the Bishop to Robin, "never did I see such shooting in all my life as these men of thine do. But I have heard so oft of thy skill, canst thou not show us a touch of it?"

"Why," quoth Robin, "the light groweth somewhat dim, and things begins to glimmer, ne'ertheless I will try what I can do." So saying he arose from where he sat, then, drawing his dagger, he cut a hazel wand a little greater in girth than a man's thumb, and peeling the bark therefrom, he walked with measured steps fourscore yards distance. There he thrust the staff into the ground and came back to where the others sat, and Allan a Dale handed him his good stout yew bow, which Robin forthwith strung. Then emptying his quiver upon the ground, he searched among the arrows carefully till he had chosen one to his liking. Having so done, he nocked the arrow and stood in position, and all around was so hushed that you might have heard the falling of a leaf. Then he drew the string quickly to his ear, and straightened his bow arm, and ere you could draw a breath loosed the string with a twang. So swift flew the arrow that the eye could not follow it, but a great shout went up from the yeomen when it had sped, and Will Scathelock ran leaping and brought the wand, and lo, the arrow was sticking in the wood which it had cleft. Then all the yeomen shouted again till those about the fires came running, for they were proud of their master's skill, which none could hope to match.

But meantime Robin had set him down again between his guests; then, without giving them time for word of praise, he called upon those of his band who were the most deft at quarterstaff. So they sat and watched the game till the shades of evening fell, and there was no light in which to give stroke or parry.

Then Allan a Dale came forth and tuned his harp, and all was hushed around, and he sang in his wonderous voice songs of love, of war, of glory, and of sadness, and all listened without a movement or a sound. So Allan sang till the great round silver moon gleamed with its clear white light amid the upper tangle of the mazy branches of the trees.

At last two fellows came to say that the feast was ready spread, so Robin, leading his guests with either hand, brought them to where great smoking dishes, that sent savory smells far and near, stood along the white linen cloth spread on the grass. All around was a glare of torches that lit everything up with a red light. Then, straightway sitting down, all fell to with noise and hubbub, the rattling of platters blending with the sound of loud talking and laughter. A long time the feast lasted, but at last all was over, and the bright wine and humming ale passed briskly. Then Robin Hood called aloud for silence, and all was hushed till he spoke.

"I have a story to tell you all, so listen to what I have to say," quoth he; whereupon, without more ado, he told them all about Sir Richard, and how his lands were in pawn. But, as he went on, the Bishop's face, that had erst been smiling and ruddy with merriment, waxed serious, and he put aside the horn of wine he held in his hand, for he knew the story of Sir Richard, and his heart sank within him with grim forebodings. Then, when Robin Hood had done, he turned to the Bishop of Hereford. "Now, my Lord Bishop," said he, "dost thou not think this is ill done of any one, much more of a churchman, who should live in humbleness and charity?"

To this the Bishop answered not a word, but looked upon the ground with moody eyes.

Quoth Robin, "Now, thou art the richest bishop in all England; canst thou not help this needy brother?" But still the Bishop answered not a word.

Then Robin turned to Little John, and quoth he, "Go thou and Will Stutely and bring forth those five pack-horses yonder." Whereupon the two yeomen did as they were bidden, those about the cloth making room on the green, where the light was brightest, for the five horses which Little John and Will Stutely presently led forward.

"Who hath the score of the goods?" asked Robin Hood, looking at the Black Friars.

Then up spake the smallest of all, in a trembling voice,—an old man he was, with a gentle, wrinkled face. "That have I; but, I pray thee, harm me not."

"Nay," quoth Robin, "I have never harmed harmless man yet; but give it to me, good father." So the old man did as he was bidden, and handed Robin the tablet on which was marked down the account of the various packages upon the horses. This Robin handed to Will Scarlet, bidding him to read the same. So Will Scarlet, lifting his voice that all might hear, began:—

"Three bales of silk to Quentin, the mercer at Ancaster."

"That we touch not," quoth Robin, "for this Quentin is an honest fellow, who hath risen by his own thrift." So the bales of silk were laid aside without being opened.

"One bale of silk velvet for the Abbey of Beaumont."

"What do these priests want of silk velvet?" quoth Robin. "Nevertheless, though they need it not, I will not take all from them. Measure it off into three lots, one to be sold for charity, one for us, and one for the abbey." So this, too, was done as Robin Hood bade.

"Twoscore of great wax candles for the Chapel of Saint Thomas."

"That belongeth fairly to the chapel," quoth Robin, "so lay it to one side. Far be it from us to take from the blessed Saint Thomas that which belongeth to him." So this, also, was done according to Robin's bidding, and the candles were laid to one side, along with honest Quentin's unopened bales of silk. So the list was gone through with, and the goods adjudged according to what Robin thought most fit. Some things were laid aside untouched, and many were opened and divided into three equal parts, for charity, for themselves, and for the owners. And now all the ground in the torchlight was covered over with silks and velvets and cloths of gold and cases of rich wines, and so they came to the last line upon the tablet,—

"A box belonging to the Lord Bishop of Hereford."

At these words the Bishop shook as with a chill, and the box was set upon the ground.

"My Lord Bishop, hast thou the key of this box?" asked Robin.

The Bishop shook his head.

"Go, Will Scarlet," said Robin, "thou art the strongest man here—bring a sword straightway, and cut this box open, if thou canst." Then up rose Will Scarlet and left them, coming back in a short time, bearing a great two-handed sword. Thrice he smote that strong, iron-bound box, and at the third blow it burst open and a great heap of gold came rolling forth, gleaming red in the light of the torches. At this sight a murmur went all around among the band, like the sound of the wind in distant trees; but no man came forward nor touched the money.

Quoth Robin, "Thou, Will Scarlet, thou, Allan a Dale, and thou, Little John, count it over."

A long time it took to count all the money, and when it had been duly scored up, Will Scarlet called out that there were fifteen hundred golden pounds in all. But in among the gold they found a paper, and this Will Scarlet read in a loud voice, and all heard that this money was the rental and fines and forfeits from certain estates belonging to the Bishopric of Hereford.

"My Lord Bishop," said Robin Hood, "I will not strip thee, as Little John said, like a winter hedge, for thou shalt take back one third of thy money. One third of it thou canst well spare to us for thy entertainment and that of thy train, for thou art very rich; one third of it thou canst better spare for charity, for Bishop, I hear that thou art a hard master to those beneath thee and a close hoarder of gains that thou couldst better and with more credit to thyself give to charity than spend upon thy own likings."

At this the Bishop looked up, but he could say never a word; yet he was thankful to keep some of his wealth.

Then Robin turned to Sir Richard of the Lea, and quoth he, "Now, Sir Richard, the church seemed like to despoil thee, therefore some of the overplus of church gains may well be used in aiding thee. Thou shalt take that five hundred pounds laid aside for people more in need than the Bishop is, and shalt pay thy debts to Emmet therewith."

Sir Richard looked at Robin until something arose in his eyes that made all the lights and the faces blur together. At last he said, "I thank thee, friend, from my heart, for what thou doest for me; yet think not ill if I cannot take thy gift freely. But this I will do: I will take the money and pay my debts, and in a year and a day hence will return it safe either to thee or to the Lord Bishop of Hereford. For this I pledge my most solemn knightly word. I feel free to borrow, for I know no man that should be more bound to aid me than one so high in that church that hath driven such a hard bargain with me."

"Truly, Sir Knight," quoth Robin, "I do not understand those fine scruples that weigh with those of thy kind; but, nevertheless, it shall all be as thou dost wish. But thou hadst best bring the money to me at the end of the year, for mayhap I may make better use of it than the Bishop." Thereupon, turning to those near him, he gave his orders, and five hundred pounds were counted out and tied up in a leathern bag for Sir Richard. The rest of the treasure was divided, and part taken to the treasure-house of the band, and part put by with the other things for the Bishop.

Then Sir Richard arose. "I cannot stay later, good friends," said he, "for my lady will wax anxious if I come not home; so I crave leave to depart."

Then Robin Hood and all his merry men arose, and Robin said, "We cannot let thee go hence unattended, Sir Richard."

Then up spake Little John: "Good master, let me choose a score of stout fellows from the band, and let us arm ourselves in a seemly manner, and so serve as retainers to Sir Richard till he can get others in our stead."

"Thou hast spoken well, Little John, and it shall be done," said Robin.

Then up spake Will Scarlet: "Let us give him a golden chain to hang about his neck, such as befits one of his blood, and also golden spurs to wear at his heels."

Then Robin Hood said, "Thou hast spoken well, Will Scarlet, and it shall be done."

Then up spake Will Stutely: "Let us give him yon bale of rich velvet and yon roll of cloth of gold to take home to his noble lady wife as a present from Robin Hood and his merry men all."

At this all clapped their hands for joy, and Robin said: "Thou hast well spoken, Will Stutely, and it shall be done."

Then Sir Richard o' the Lea looked all around and strove to speak, but could scarcely do so for the feelings that choked him; at last he said in a husky, trembling voice, "Ye shall all see, good friends, that Sir Richard o' the Lea will ever remember your kindness this day. And if ye be at any time in dire need or trouble, come to me and my lady, and the walls of Castle Lea shall be battered down ere harm shall befall you. I—" He could say nothing further, but turned hastily away.

But now Little John and nineteen stout fellows, whom he had chosen for his band, came forth all ready for the journey. Each man wore upon his breast a coat of linked mail, and on his head a cap of steel, and at his side a good stout sword. A gallant show they made as they stood all in a row. Then Robin came and threw a chain of gold about Sir Richard's neck, and Will Scarlet knelt and buckled the golden spurs upon his heel; and now Little

John led forward Sir Richard's horse, and the Knight mounted. He looked down at Robin for a little time, then of a sudden stooped and kissed his cheek. All the forest glades rang with the shout that went up as the Knight and the yeomen marched off through the woodland with glare of torches and gleam of steel, and so were gone.

Then up spake the Bishop of Hereford in a mournful voice: "I, too, must be jogging, good fellow, for the night waxes late."

But Robin laid his hand upon the Bishop's arm and stayed him. "Be not so hasty, Lord Bishop," said he. "Three days hence Sir Richard must pay his debts to Emmet; until that time thou must be content to abide with me lest thou breed trouble for the Knight. I promise thee that thou shalt have great sport, for I know that thou art fond of hunting the dun deer. Lay by thy mantle of melancholy, and strive to lead a joyous yeoman life for three stout days. I promise thee thou shalt be sorry to go when the time has come."

So the Bishop and his train abided with Robin for three days, and much sport his lordship had in that time, so that, as Robin had said, when the time had come for him to go he was sorry to leave the greenwood. At the end of three days Robin set him free, and sent him forth from the forest with a guard of yeomen to keep freebooters from taking what was left of the packs and bundles.

But, as the Bishop rode away, he vowed within himself that he would sometime make Robin rue the day that he stopped him in Sherwood.

But now we shall follow Sir Richard; so listen, and you shall hear what befell him, and how he paid his debts at Emmet Priory, and likewise in due season to Robin Hood.

2

HOW SIR RICHARD OF THE LEA PAID HIS DEBTS TO EMMET

THE LONG HIGHWAY STRETCHED STRAIGHT ON, GRAY AND dusty in the sun. On either side were dykes full of water bordered by osiers, and far away in the distance stood the towers of Emmet Priory with tall poplar trees around.

Along the causeway rode a knight with a score of stout men-at-arms behind him. The Knight was clad in a plain long robe of gray serge, gathered in at the waist with a broad leathern belt, from which hung a long dagger and a stout sword. But though he was so plainly dressed himself, the horse he rode was a noble barb, and its trappings were rich with silk and silver bells.

So thus the band journeyed along the causeway between the dykes, till at last they reached the great gate of Emmet Priory. There the Knight called to one of his men and bade him knock at the porter's lodge with the haft of his sword.

The porter was drowsing on his bench within the lodge, but at the knock he roused himself and, opening the wicket, came hobbling forth and greeted the Knight, whilst a tame starling that hung in a wicker cage within piped out, "*In cælo quies! In cælo quies!*" such being the words that the poor old lame porter had taught him to speak.

"Where is thy prior?" asked the Knight of the old porter.

"He is at meat, good knight, and he looketh for thy coming," quoth the porter, "for, if I mistake not, thou art Sir Richard o' the Lea."

"I am Sir Richard of the Lea; then I will go seek him forthwith," said the Knight.

"But shall I not send thy horse to stable?" said the porter. "By Our Lady, it is the noblest nag, and the best harnessed, that e'er I saw in all my life before." And he stroked the horse's flank with his palm.

"Nay," quoth Sir Richard, "the stables of this place are not for me, so make way, I prythee." So saying he pushed forward, and, the gates being opened, he entered the stony courtyard of the Priory, his men behind him. In they came with rattle of steel and clashing of swords, and ring of horses' feet on cobble-stones, whereat a flock of pigeons that strutted in the sun flew with flapping wings to the high eaves of the round towers.

WHILST THE KNIGHT WAS RIDING ALONG THE CAUSEWAY TO Emmet, a merry feast was toward in the refectory there. The afternoon sun streamed in through the great arched windows, and lay in broad squares of light upon the stone floor and across the board covered with a snowy linen cloth, whereon was spread a princely feast. At the head of the table sat Prior Vincent of Emmet all clad in soft robes of fine cloth and silk; on his head was a black velvet cap picked out with gold, and around his neck hung a heavy chain of gold, with a great locket pendant therefrom. Beside him, on the arm of his great chair, roosted his favorite falcon, for the Prior was fond of the gentle craft of hawking. On his right hand sat the Sheriff of Nottingham in rich robes of purple all trimmed about with fur, and on his left a famous doctor of law in dark and sober garb. Below these sat the high cellarer of Emmet, and others chief among the brethren.

Jest and laughter passed around, and all was as merry as merry could be. The weazened face of the man of law was twisted into a wrinkled smile, for in his pouch were fourscore golden angels that the Prior had paid him in fee for the case betwixt him and Sir Richard of the Lea. The learned doctor had been paid beforehand, for he had not overmuch trust in the holy Vincent of Emmet.

Quoth the Sheriff of Nottingham, "But art thou sure, Sir Prior, that thou hast the lands so safe?"

"Ay, marry," said Prior Vincent, smacking his lips after a deep draught of wine; "I have kept a close watch upon him, albeit he was unawares of the same, and I know right well that he hath no money to pay me withal."

"Ay, true," said the man of law in a dry, husky voice, "his land is surely forfeit if he cometh not to pay; but, Sir Prior, thou must get a release beneath his sign manual, or else thou canst not help to hold the land without trouble from him."

"Yea," said the Prior, "so thou hast told me ere now, but I know that this knight is so poor that he will gladly sign away his lands for two hundred pounds of hard money."

Then up spake the high cellarer: "Methinks it is a shame to so drive a misfortunate knight to the ditch. I think it sorrow that the noblest estate in Derbyshire should so pass away from him for a paltry five hundred pounds. Truly, I—"

"How now," broke in the Prior, in a quivering voice, his eyes glistening and his cheeks red with anger, "dost thou prate to my very beard, sirrah? By Saint Hubert, thou hadst best save thy breath to cool thy pottage, else it may scald thy mouth."

"Nay," said the man of law, smoothly, "I dare swear this same knight will never come to settlement this day, but will prove recreant. Nevertheless, we will seek some means to gain his lands from him, so never fear."

But even as the doctor spoke there came a sudden clatter of horses' hoofs and a jingle of iron mail in the courtyard below. Then up spake the Prior, and called upon one of the brethren that sat below the salt, and bade him look out of the window and see who was below, albeit he knew right well it could be none but Sir Richard.

So the brother arose and went and looked, and he said, "I see below a score of stout men-at-arms and a knight just dismounting from his horse. He is dressed in long robes of gray which, methinks, are of poor seeming; but the horse he rideth upon hath the richest coursing that ever I saw. The Knight dismounts and they come this way, and are even now below in the great hall."

"Lo, see ye there now," quoth Prior Vincent. "Here ye have a knight with so lean a purse as scarce to buy him a crust of bread to munch, yet he keeps a band of retainers, and puts rich trappings upon his horse's hide, whilst his own back goeth bare. Is it not well that such men should be brought low?"

"But art thou sure," said the little doctor, tremulously, "that this knight will do us no harm? Such as he are fierce when crossed, and he hath a band of naughty men at his heels. Mayhap thou hadst better give an extension of his debt." Thus he spake, for he was afraid Sir Richard might do him a harm.

"Thou needst not fear," said the Prior, looking down at the little man beside him. "This knight is gentle, and would as soon think of harming an old woman as thee."

As the Prior finished, a door at the lower end of the refectory swung open, and in came Sir Richard, with folded hands and head bowed upon his breast. Thus humbly he walked slowly up the hall, whilst his men-at-arms stood about the door. When he had come to where the Prior sat, he knelt upon one knee. "Save and keep thee, Sir Prior," said he; "I am come to keep my day."

Then the first word that the Prior said to him was, "Hast thou brought my money?"

"Alas! I have not so much as one penny upon my body," said the Knight; whereat the Prior's eyes sparkled.

"Now, thou art a shrewd debtor, I wot," said he. Then, "Sir Sheriff, I drink to thee."

But still the Knight kneeled upon the hard stones, so the Prior turned to him again. "What wouldst thou have?" quoth he, sharply.

At these words, a slow red mounted into the Knight's cheeks; but still he knelt. "I would crave thy mercy," said he. "As thou hopest for Heaven's mercy, show mercy to me. Strip me not of my lands, and so reduce a true knight to poverty."

"Thy day is broken and thy lands forfeit," said the man of law, plucking up his spirits at the Knight's humble speech.

Quoth Sir Richard, "Thou man of law, wilt thou not befriend me in mine hour of need?"

"Nay," said the other, "I hold with this holy Prior, who hath paid me my fees in hard gold, so that I am bounden to him."

"Wilt thou not be my friend, Sir Sheriff?" said Sir Richard.

"Nay, 'fore Heaven," quoth the Sheriff of Nottingham, "this is no business of mine, yet I will do what I may," and he nudged the Prior beneath the cloth with his knee. "Wilt thou not ease him of some of his debts, Sir Prior?"

At this the Prior smiled grimly. "Pay me three hundred pounds, Sir Richard," said he, "and I will give thee quittance of thy debt."

"Thou knowest, Sir Prior, that it is as easy for me to pay four hundred pounds as three hundred," said Sir Richard. "But wilt thou not give me another twelvemonth to pay my debt?"

"Not another day," said the Prior, sternly.

"And is this all thou wilt do for me?" asked the Knight.

"Now, out upon thee, false Knight!" cried the Prior, bursting forth in anger. "Either pay thy debt as I have said or release thy land, and get thee gone from out my hall."

Then Sir Richard arose to his feet. "Thou false, lying priest!" said he, in so stern a voice that the man of law shrunk affrighted, "I am no false knight, as thou knowest full well, but have ever held my place in the press and the tourney. Hast thou so little courtesy that thou wouldst see a true knight kneel for all this time, or see him come into thy hall and never offer him meat or drink?"

Then quoth the man of law, in a trembling voice, "This is surely an ill way to talk of matters appertaining to business; let us be mild in speech. What wilt thou pay this knight, Sir Prior, to give thee release of his land?"

"I would have given him two hundred pounds," quoth the Prior, "but since he hath spoken so vilely to my teeth, not one groat over one hundred pounds will he get."

"Hadst thou offered me a thousand pounds, false Prior," said the Knight, "thou wouldst not have got an inch of my land." Then turning to where his men-at-arms stood near the door, he called, "Come hither," and beckoned with his finger; whereupon the tallest of them all came forward and handed him a long leathern bag. Sir Richard took the bag and shot from it upon the table a glittering stream of golden money. "Bear in mind, Sir Prior," said he, "that thou hast promised me quittance for three hundred pounds. Not one farthing above that shalt thou get." So saying, he counted out three hundred pounds and pushed it toward the Prior.

But now the Prior's hands dropped at his sides and the Prior's head hung upon his shoulder, for not only had he lost all hopes of the land, but he had forgiven the Knight one hundred pounds of his debt and had needlessly paid the man of law fourscore angels. To him he turned, and quoth he, "Give me back my money that thou hast."

"Nay," cried the other, shrilly, "it is but my fee that thou didst pay me, and thou gettest it not back again." And he hugged his gown about him.

"Now, Sir Prior," quoth Sir Richard, "I have held my day and paid all the dues demanded of me; so, as there is no more betwixt us, I leave this vile place straightway." So saying, he turned upon his heel and strode away.

All this time the Sheriff had been staring with wide-open eyes and mouth agape at the tall man-at-arms, who stood as though carved out of stone. At last he gasped out, "Reynold Greenleaf!"

At this, the tall man-at-arms, who was no other than Little John, turned, grinning, to the Sheriff. "I give thee good den, fair gossip," quoth he. "I would say, sweet Sheriff, that I have heard all thy pretty talk this day, and it shall be duly told unto Robin Hood. So, farewell for the nonce, till we meet again in Sherwood Forest." Then he, also, turned and followed Sir Richard down the hall, leaving the Sheriff, all pale and amazed, shrunk together upon his chair.

A merry feast it was to which Sir Richard came, but a sorry lot he left behind him, and little hunger had they for the princely food spread before them. Only the learned doctor was happy, for he had his fee.

But now a twelvemonth and a day has passed since Prior Vincent of Emmet sat at feast, as has just been told, and once more the mellow fall of another year has come. But the year had brought great change, I wot, to the lands of Sir Richard of the Lea; for, where before shaggy wild grasses grew upon the meadow lands, now all stretch away in golden stubble, betokening that a rich and plentiful crop had been gathered therefrom. A year had made a great change in the castle, also, for, where were empty moats and the crumbling of neglect, all was now orderly and well kept.

Bright shone the sun on battlement and tower, and in the blue air overhead a flock of clattering jackdaws flew around the gilded weathervane and spire. Then, in the brightness of the morning, the drawbridge fell across the moat with a rattle and clank of chains, the gate of the castle swung slowly open, and a goodly array of steel-clad men-at-arms, with a knight all clothed in chain-mail, as white as frost on briar and thorn of a winter morning, came flashing out from the castle courtyard. In his hand the Knight held a great spear, from the point of which fluttered a blood-red pennant as broad as the palm of one's hand. So this troop came forth from the castle, and in the midst of them walked three pack-horses laden with parcels of divers shapes and kinds.

Thus rode forth good Sir Richard of the Lea to pay his debt to Robin Hood this bright and merry morn. Along the highway they wended their way, with measured tramp of feet and rattle and jingle of sword and harness. Onward they marched till they came nigh to Denby, where, from the top of a hill, they saw, over beyond the town, many gay flags and streamers floating in the bright air. Then Sir Richard turned to the man-at-arms nearest to him. "What is toward yonder at Denby today?" quoth he.

"Please your worship," answered the man-at-arms, "a merry fair is held there today, and a great wrestling-match, towhich many folk have come, for a prize hath been offered of a pipe of red wine, a fair golden ring, and a pair of gloves, all of which go to the best wrestler."

"Now, by my faith," quoth Sir Richard, who loved good manly sports right well, "this will be a goodly thing to see. Methinks we have time to stay a little while on our journey, and see this merry sport." So he turned his horse's head aside toward Denby and the fair, and thither he and his men made their way.

There they found a great hubbub of merriment. Flags and streamers were floating, tumblers were tumbling on the green, bag-pipes were playing, and lads and lasses were dancing to the music. But the crowd were gathered most of all around a ring where the wrestling was going forward, and thither Sir Richard and his men turned their steps.

Now when the judges of the wrestling saw Sir Richard coming and knew who he was, the chief of them came down from the bench where he and the others sat, and went to the Knight and took him by the hand, beseeching him to come and sit with them and judge the sport. So Sir Richard got down from his horse, and went with the others to the bench raised beside the ring.

Now there had been great doings that morning, for a certain yeoman named Egbert, who came from Stoke over in Staffordshire, had thrown with ease all those that came against him; but a man of Denby, well known through all the countryside as William with the Scar, had been biding his time with the Stoke man; so, when Egbert had thrown every one else, stout William leaped into the ring. Then a tough bout followed, and at last he threw Egbert heavily, whereat there was a great shouting and shaking of hands, for all the Denby men were proud of their wrestler.

When Sir Richard came, he found stout William puffed up by the shouts of his friends, walking up and down the ring, daring any one to come and try a throw with him. "Come one, come all!" quoth he. "Here stand I, William of the Scar, against any man. If there is none in Derbyshire to come against me, come all who will, from Nottingham, Stafford, or York, and if I do not make them one and all root the ground with their noses like swine in the forests, call me no more brave William the wrestler."

At this all laughed; but above all the laughter a loud voice was heard to cry out, "Sin' thou talkest so big, here cometh one from Nottinghamshire to try a fall with thee, fellow"; and straightway a tall youth with a tough quarterstaff in his hand came pushing his way through the crowd, and at last leaped lightly over the rope into the ring. He was not as heavy as stout William, but he was taller and broader in the shoulders, and all his joints were well knit. Sir Richard looked upon him keenly, then, turning to one of the judges, he said, "Knowest thou who this youth is? Methinks I have seen him before."

"Nay," said the judge, "he is a stranger to me."

Meantime, without a word, the young man, laying aside his quarterstaff, began to take off his jerkin and body clothing until he presently stood with naked arms and body; and a comely sight he was when so bared to the view, for his muscles were cut round and smooth and sharp like swift-running water.

And now each man spat upon his hands, and, clapping them upon his knees, squatted down, watching the other keenly, so as to take the vantage of him in the grip. Then like a flash they leaped together, and a great shout went up, for William had gotten the better hold of the two. For a short time they strained and struggled and writhed, and then stout William gave his most cunning trip and throw, but the stranger met it with greater skill than his, and so the trip came to nought. Then, of a sudden, with a twist and a wrench, the stranger loosed himself, and he of the scar found himself locked in a pair of arms that fairly made his ribs crack. So, with heavy, hot breathing, they stood for a while straining, their bodies all glistening with sweat, and great drops of sweat trickling down their faces. But the stranger's hug was so close that at last stout William's muscles softened under his grip, and he gave a sob. Then the youth put forth all his strength, and gave a sudden trip with his heel, and a cast over his right hip, and down stout William went, with a sickening thud, and lay as though he would never move hand nor foot again.

But now no shout went up for the stranger, but an angry murmur was heard among the crowd, so easily had he won the match. Then one of the judges, who was a kinsman to William of the Scar, rose with trembling lip and baleful look. Quoth he, "If thou hast slain that man it will go ill with thee, let me tell thee, fellow."

But the stranger answered boldly, "He took his chance with me as I took mine with him. No law can touch me to harm me, even if I slew him, so that it was fairly done in the wrestling ring."

"That we shall see," said the judge, scowling upon the youth, whilst once more an angry murmur ran around the crowd; for, as I have said, the men of Denby were proud of stout William of the Scar.

Then up spoke Sir Richard, gently. "Nay," said he, "the youth is right; if the other dieth, he dieth in the wrestling ring, where he took his chance, and was cast fairly enow."

But in the mean time three men had come forward and lifted stout William from the ground, and found that he was not dead, though badly shaken by his heavy fall. Then the chief judge rose and said, "Young man, the prize is duly thine. Here is the red gold ring, and here the gloves, and yonder stands the pipe of wine to do with whatsoever thou dost list."

At this the youth, who had donned his clothes and taken up his staff again, bowed, without a word, then, taking the gloves and the ring, and thrusting the one into his girdle and slipping the other upon his thumb, he turned and, leaping lightly over the ropes again, made his way through the crowd, and was gone.

"Now, I wonder who yon youth may be," said the judge, turning to Sir Richard; "he seemeth like a stout Saxon from his red cheeks and fair hair. This William of ours is a stout man, too, and never have I seen him cast in the ring before, albeit he hath not yet striven with such great wrestlers as Thomas of Cornwall, Diccon of York, and young David of Doncaster. Hath he not a firm foot in the ring, thinkest thou, Sir Richard?"

"Ay, truly; and yet this youth threw him fairly, and with wondrous ease. I much wonder who he can be." Thus said Sir Richard in a thoughtful voice.

For a time the Knight stood talking to those about him, but at last he arose and made ready to depart, so he called his men about him, and tightening the girths of his saddle, he mounted his horse once more.

Meanwhile the young stranger made his way through the crowd, but, as he passed, he heard all around him such words muttered as, "Look at the cockeril!" "Behold how he plumeth himself!" "I dare swear he cast good William unfairly!" "Yea, truly, saw ye not bird-lime upon his hands?"

"It would be well to cut his cock's comb!" To all this the stranger paid no heed, but strode proudly about as though he heard it not. So he walked slowly across the green to where the booth stood wherein was dancing, and standing at the door he looked in on the sport. As he stood thus a stone struck his arm of a sudden with a sharp jar, and, turning, he saw that an angry crowd of men had followed him from the wrestling ring. Then, when they saw him turn so, a great hooting and yelling arose from all, so that the folk came running out from the dancing booth to see what was to do. At last a tall, broad-shouldered, burly blacksmith strode forward from the crowd swinging a mighty blackthorn club in his hand.

"Wouldst thou come here to our fair town of Denby, thou Jack in the Box, to overcome a good honest lad with vile, juggling tricks?" growled he in a deep voice like the bellow of an angry bull. "Take that, then!" And of a sudden he struck a blow at the youth that might have felled an ox. But the other turned the blow deftly aside, and gave back another so terrible that the Denby man went down with a groan, as though he had been smitten by lightning. When they saw their leader fall the crowd gave another angry shout; but the stranger placed his back against the tent near which he stood, swinging his terrible staff, and so fell had been the blow that he struck the stout smith, that none dared to come within the measure of his cudgel, so the press crowded back, like a pack of dogs from a bear at bay. But now some coward hand from behind threw a sharp jagged stone that smote the stranger on the crown, so that he staggered back, and the red blood gushed from the cut and ran down his face and over his jerkin. Then, seeing him dazed with this vile blow, the crowd rushed upon him, so that they overbore him and he fell beneath their feet.

Now it might have gone ill with the youth, even to the losing of his young life, had not Sir Richard come to this fair; for of a sudden shouts were heard, and steel flashed in the air, and blows were given with the flat of swords, whilst through the midst of the crowd Sir Richard of the Lea came spurring on his white horse. Then the crowd, seeing the steel-clad knight and the armed men, melted away like snow on the warm hearth, leaving the young man all bloody and dusty upon the ground.

Finding himself free, the youth arose, and, wiping the blood from his face, looked up. Quoth he, "Sir Richard of the Lea, mayhap thou hast saved my life this day."

"Who art thou that knowest Sir Richard of the Lea so well?" quoth the Knight. "Methinks I have seen thy face before, young man."

"Yea, thou hast," said the youth, "for men call me David of Doncaster."

"Ha!" said Sir Richard; "I wonder that I knew thee not, David; but thy beard hath grown longer, and thou thyself art more set in manhood since this day twelvemonth. Come hither into the tent, David, and wash the blood from thy face. And thou, Ralph, bring him straightway a clean jerkin. Now I am sorry for thee, yet I am right glad that I have had a chance to pay a part of my debt of kindness to thy good master, Robin Hood, for it might have gone ill with thee had I not come, young man."

So saying, the Knight led David into the tent, and there the youth washed the blood from his face and put on the clean jerkin.

In the mean time a whisper had gone around from those that stood nearest that this was none other than the great David of Doncaster, the best wrestler in all the midcountry, who only last spring had cast stout Adam o' Lincoln in the ring at Selby, in Yorkshire, and now held the midcountry champion belt. Thus it happened that when young David came forth from the tent along with Sir Richard, the blood all washed from his face, and his soiled jerkin changed for a clean one, no sounds of anger were heard, but all pressed forward to see the young man, feeling proud that one of the great wrestlers of England should have entered the ring at Denby fair. For thus fickle is a mass of men.

Then Sir Richard called aloud, "Friends, this is David of Doncaster; so think it no shame that your Denby man was cast by such a wrestler. He beareth you no ill-will for what hath passed, but let it be a warning to you how ye treat strangers henceforth. Had ye slain him it would have been an ill day for you, for Robin Hood would have harried your town as the kestrel harries the dove-cote. I have bought the pipe of wine from him, and now I give it freely to you to drink as ye list. But never hereafterwards fall upon a man for being a stout yeoman."

At this all shouted amain; but in truth they thought more of the wine than of the Knight's words. Then Sir Richard, with David beside him and his men-at-arms around, turned about and left the fair.

But in after days, when the men that saw that wrestling bout were bent with age, they would shake their heads when they heard of any stalwart game, and say, "Ay, ay; but thou shouldst have seen the great David of Doncaster cast stout William with the Scar at Denby fair."

Robin Hood stood in the merry greenwood with Little John and most of his stout yeomen around him, awaiting Sir Richard's coming. At last a glint of steel was seen through the brown forest leaves, and forth from the covert into the open rode Sir Richard at the head of his men. He came straight forward to Robin Hood, and leaping from off his horse clasped the yeoman in his arms.

"Why, how now," said Robin, after a time, holding Sir Richard off and looking at him from top to toe; "methinks thou art a gayer bird than when I saw thee last."

"Yes, thanks to thee, Robin," said the Knight, laying his hand upon the yeoman's shoulder. "But for thee I would have been wandering in misery in a far country by this time. But I have kept my word, Robin, and have brought back the money that thou didst lend me, and which I have doubled four times over again, and so become rich once more. Along with this money I have brought a little gift to thee and thy brave men from my dear lady and myself." Then, turning to his men, he called aloud, "Bring forth the packhorses."

But Robin stopped them. "Nay, Sir Richard," said he, "think it not bold of me to cross thy bidding, but we of Sherwood do no business till after we have eaten and drank"; whereupon, taking Sir Richard by the hand, he led him to the seat beneath the greenwood tree, whilst others of the chief men of the band came and seated themselves around. Then, quoth Robin, "How cometh it that I saw young David of Doncaster with thee and thy men, Sir Knight?"

Then straightway the Knight told all about his stay at Denby and of the happening at the fair, and how it was like to go hard with young David; so he told his tale, and quoth he, "It was this, good Robin, that kept me so late on the way, otherwise I would have been here an hour agone."

Then, when he had done speaking, Robin stretched out his hand and grasped the Knight's palm. Quoth he in a trembling voice, "I owe thee a debt I can never hope to repay, Sir Richard, for let me tell thee, I would rather lose my right hand than have such ill befall young David of Doncaster as seemed like to come upon him at Denby."

So they talked until after a while one came forward to say that the feast was spread; whereupon all arose and went thereto. When at last it was done, the Knight called upon his men to bring the packhorses forward, which they did according to his bidding. Then one of the men brought the Knight a strong box, which he opened and took from it a bag and counted out five hundred pounds, the sum of the money he had gotten from Robin.

"Sir Richard," quoth Robin, "thou wilt pleasure us all if thou wilt keep that money as a gift from us of Sherwood. Is it not so, my lads?"

Then all shouted "Ay" with a mighty voice.

"I thank you all deeply," said the Knight, earnestly, "but think it not ill of me if I cannot take it. Gladly have I borrowed it from you, but it may not be that I can take it as a gift."

Then Robin Hood said no more, but gave the money to Little John to put away in the treasury, for he had shrewdness enough to know that nought breeds ill-will and heart-bitterness like gifts forced upon one that cannot choose but take them.

Then Sir Richard had the packs laid upon the ground and opened, whereupon a great shout went up that made the forest ring again, for lo, there were tenscore bows of finest Spanish yew, all burnished till they shone again, and each bow inlaid with fanciful figures in silver, yet not inlaid so as to mar their strength. Beside these were tenscore quivers of leather embroidered with golden thread, and in each quiver were a score of shafts with burnished heads that shone like silver; each shaft also was feathered with peacock's plumes and innocked with silver.

Sir Richard gave to each yeoman a bow and a quiver of arrows, but to Robin he gave a stout bow inlaid with the cunningest workmanship in gold, whilst each arrow in his quiver was innocked with gold.

Then all shouted again for joy of the fair gift, and all swore among themselves that they would die if need be for Sir Richard and his lady.

At last the time came when Sir Richard must go, whereupon Robin Hood called his band around him, and each man of the yeomen took a torch in his hand to light the way through the woodlands. So they came to the edge of Sherwood, and there the Knight kissed Robin upon the cheeks and left him and was gone.

Thus Robin Hood helped a noble knight out of his dire misfortunes, that else would have smothered the happiness from his life.

Now listen, and you shall next hear of certain merry adventures that befell Robin Hood and Little John, and how one turned beggar and the other barefoot friar; likewise what each gained thereby.

PART SIXTH

In which it is told how that Robin Hood and Little John turned, the one a beggar and the other a strolling Friar, and went forth to seek adventures. Likewise it is told how Little John prayed to some purpose, and how Robin Hood drubbed four beggars and outwitted a corn engrosser.

1

LITTLE JOHN TURNS
BAREFOOT FRIAR

COLD WINTER HAD PASSED AND SPRING HAD COME. NO LEAFY thickness had yet clad the woodlands, but the budding leaves hung like a tender mist about the trees. In the open country the meadow lands lay a sheeny green, the cornfields a dark velvety color, for they were thick and soft with the growing blades. The plough-boy shouted in the sun, and in the purple new-turned furrows flocks of birds hunted for fat worms. All the broad moist earth smiled in the warm light, and each little green hill clapped its hands for joy.

On a deer's hide, stretched on the ground in the open in front of the greenwood tree, sat Robin Hood basking in the sun like an old dog fox. Leaning back with his hands clasped about his knees, he lazily watched Little John rolling a stout bow-string from long strands of hempen thread, wetting the palms of his hands ever and anon, and rolling the cord upon his thigh. Near by sat Allan a Dale fitting a new string to his harp.

Quoth Robin at last, "Methinks I would rather roam this forest in the gentle springtime than be king of all merry England. What palace in the broad world is as fair as this sweet woodland just now, and what king in all the world hath such appetite for plover's eggs and lampreys as I for juicy venison and sparkling ale? Gaffer Swanthold speaks truly when he saith, 'Better a crust with content than honey with a sour heart.'"

"Yea," quoth Little John, as he rubbed his new-made bow-string with yellow beeswax, "the life we lead is the life for me. Thou speakest of the springtime, but methinks even the winter hath its own joys. Thou and I, good master, have had more than one merry day, this winter past, at the Blue Boar. Dost thou not remember that night thou and Will Stutely and Friar Tuck and I passed at that same hostelry with the two beggars and the strolling friar?"

"Yea," quoth merry Robin, laughing; "that was the night that Will Stutely must needs snatch a kiss from the stout hostess, and got a canakin of ale emptied over his head for his pains."

"Truly, it was the same," said Little John, laughing also. "Methinks that was a goodly song that the strolling friar sang. Friar Tuck, thou hast a quick ear for a tune, dost thou not remember it?"

"I did have the catch of it one time," said Tuck. "Let me see"; and he touched his forefinger to his forehead in thought, humming to himself, and stopping ever and anon to fit what he had got to what he searched for in his mind. At last he found it all, and clearing his throat, sang merrily:—

> *"In the blossoming hedge the robin cock sings,*
> *For the sun it is merry and bright,*
> *And he joyfully hops and he flutters his wings,*
> *For his heart is all full of delight.*
> *For the May bloometh fair,*
> *And there's little of care,*
> *And plenty to eat in the Maytime rare.*
> *When the flowers all die,*

Then off he will fly,
To keep himself warm
In some jolly old barn
Where the snow and the wind neither chill him nor harm.

"And such is the life of the strolling friar,
With a plenty to eat and to drink;
For the goodwife will keep him a seat by the fire,
And the pretty girls smile at his wink.
Then he lustily trolls,
As he onward strolls,
As rollicking song for the saving of souls.
When the wind doth blow,
With the coming of snow,
There's a place by the fire
For the fatherly friar,
And a crab in the bowl for his heart's desire."

Thus Friar Tuck sang in a rich and mellow voice, rolling his head from side to side in time with the music, and when he had done, all clapped their hands and shouted with laughter, for the song fitted him well.

"In very sooth," quoth Little John, "it is a goodly song, and, were I not a yeoman of Sherwood Forest, I had rather be a strolling friar than aught else in the world."

"Yea, it is a goodly song," said Robin Hood; "but methought those two burly beggars told the merrier tales and led the merrier life. Dost thou not remember what that great black-bearded fellow told of his begging at the fair in York?"

"Yea," said Little John, "but what told the friar of the Harvest-home in Kentshire? I hold that he led a merrier life than the other two."

"Truly, for the honor of the cloth," quoth Friar Tuck, "I hold with my good gossip, Little John."

"Now," quoth Robin, "I hold to mine own mind. But what sayst thou, Little John, to a merry adventure this fair day? Take thou a friar's gown from our chest of strange garments, and don the same, and I will stop the first beggar I meet and change clothes with him. Then let us wander the country about, this sweet day, and see what befalls each of us."

"That fitteth my mind," quoth Little John, "so let us forth, say I."

Thereupon Little John and Friar Tuck went to the storehouse of the band, and there chose for the yeoman the robe of a gray friar. Then they came forth again, and a mighty roar of laughter went up, for not only had the band never seen Little John in such guise before, but the robe was too short for him by a good palm's breadth. But Little John's hands were folded in his loose sleeves, and Little John's eyes were cast upon the ground, and at his girdle hung a great, long string of beads.

"Tut, tut!" quoth Friar Tuck, nudging him with his elbow, "look not down in that way; raise thine eyes boldly, or else all will know thee to be a cheat, and ne'er a lass will give thee a smile, and ne'er a goodwife a crust, in all the countryside." At this all laughed again, swearing that never was there so strapping a friar in all merry England as Little John made.

And now Little John took up his stout staff, at the end of which hung a chubby little leathern pottle, such as palmers carry at the tips of their staves; but in it was something, I wot, more like good Malmsey than cold spring water, such as godly pilgrims carry. Then up rose Robin and took his stout staff in his hand, likewise, and slipped ten golden angels into his pouch; for no beggar's garb was among the stores of the band, so he was fain to run his chance of meeting a beggar and buying his clothes of him.

So, all being made ready, the two yeomen set forth on their way, striding lustily along all in the misty morning. Thus they walked down the forest path until they came to the highway, and then along the highway till it split in twain, leading on one hand to Blyth and on the other to Gainsborough. Here the yeomen stopped.

Quoth Jolly Robin, "Take thou the road to Gainsborough, and I will take that to Blyth. So, fare thee well, holy father, and mayst thou not ha' cause to count thy beads in earnest ere we meet again."

"Good den, good beggar that is to be," quoth Little John, "and mayst thou have no cause to beg for mercy ere I see thee next."

So each stepped sturdily upon his way until a green hill rose between them, and the one was hid from the sight of the other.

Little John walked along, whistling, for no one was nigh upon all the road. In the budding hedges the little birds twittered merrily, and on either hand the green hills swept up to the sky, the great white clouds of spring-time sailing slowly over their crowns in lazy flight. Up hill and down dale walked Little John, the fresh wind blowing in his face and his robes fluttering behind him, and so at last he came to a cross-road that led to Tuxford. Here he met three pretty lasses, each bearing a basket of eggs to market. Quoth he, "Whither away, fair maids?" And he stood in their path, with his legs apart, holding his staff in front of them, to stop them.

Then they huddled together and nudged one another, and one presently spake up and said, "We are going to the Tuxford market, holy Friar, to sell our eggs."

"Now out upon it!" quoth Little John, looking upon them with his head on one side. "Surely, it is a pity that such fair lasses should be forced to carry eggs to market. Let me tell you, an I had the shaping of things in this world, ye should all three have been clothed in the finest silks, and ride upon milk-white horses, with pages at your side, and feed upon nothing but whipped cream and strawberries; for such a life would surely befit your looks."

At this speech all three of the pretty maids looked down, blushing and simpering. One said, "La!" another, "Marry, a' maketh sport of us!" and the third, "Listen, now, to the holy man!" but at the same time they looked at Little John from out the corners of their eyes.

"Nay," quoth Little John, roundly, "holy man or no holy man, I know a fair lass when I see her, and if e'er a man hereabouts sayeth ye are not the fairest three in all Nottinghamshire, I'll knock his vile teeth down his lying throat with this stout staff. Hear ye that, now!"

Then all the lasses cried, "La!" again.

"Now, look you," said Little John, "I cannot see such dainty damsels as ye are carrying baskets along a highroad. Let me take them mine own self, and one of you, if ye will, may carry my staff for me."

"Nay," said one of the lasses, "but thou canst not carry three baskets all at one time."

"Yea, but I can," said Little John, "and that I will show you presently. I thank the good Saint Wilfred that he hath given me a pretty wit. Look ye, now. Here I take this great basket, so; here I tie my rosary around the handle, thus; and here I slip the rosary over my head and sling the basket upon my back, in this wise." And Little John did according to his words, the basket hanging down behind him like a pedler's pack; then, giving his staff to one of the maids, and taking a basket upon either arm, he turned his face toward Tuxford Town, and stepped forth merrily, a laughing maid on either side, and one walking ahead, carrying the staff. In this wise they journeyed along, and every one they met stopped and looked after them, laughing, for never had anybody seen such a merry sight as this tall, strapping Gray Friar, with robes all too short for him, laden with eggs, and tramping the road with three pretty lasses. For this Little John cared not a whit, but when such folks gave jesting words to him he answered back as merrily, speech for speech.

So they stepped along toward Tuxford, chatting and laughing, until they came nigh to the town. Here Little John stopped and set down the baskets, for he did not care to go into the town lest he should, perchance, meet some of the Sheriff's men. "Alas! sweet chucks," quoth he, "here I must leave you. I had not thought to come this way, but I am glad that I did so. Now, ere we part, we must drink sweet friendship." So saying, he unslung the leathern pottle from the end of his staff, and, drawing the stopper therefrom, he handed it to the lass who had carried his staff, first wiping the mouth of the pottle upon his sleeve. Then each lass took a fair drink of what was within, and when it had passed all around, Little John finished what was left, so that not another drop could be squeezed from it. Then, kissing each lass sweetly, he wished them all good den, and left them. But the maids stood looking after him as he walked away whistling. "What a pity," quoth one, "that such a stout, lusty lad should be in holy orders."

"Marry," quoth Little John to himself, as he strode along, "yon was no such ill happening; Saint Dunstan send me more of the like."

After he had trudged along for a time he began to wax thirsty again in the warmth of the day. He shook his leathern pottle beside his ear, but not a sound came therefrom. Then he placed it to his lips and tilted it high aloft, but not a drop was there. "Little John! Little John!" said he sadly to himself, shaking his head the while, "woman will be thy ruin yet, if thou dost not take better care of thyself."

But at last he reached the crest of a certain hill, and saw below a sweet little thatched inn lying snugly in the dale beneath him, toward which the road dipped sharply. At the sight of this a voice within him cried aloud, "I give thee joy, good friend, for yonder is thy heart's delight, to wit, a sweet rest and a cup of brown beer." So he quickened his pace down the hill, and so came to the little inn, from which hung a sign with a stag's head painted upon it. In front of the door a clucking hen was scratching in the dust with a brood of chickens about her heels, the sparrows were chattering of house-hold affairs under the eaves, and all was so sweet and peaceful that Little John's heart laughed within him. Beside the door stood two stout cobs with broad soft paddled saddles, well fitted for easy travelling, and speaking of rich guests in the parlor. In front of the door three merry fellows, a tinker, a pedler, and a beggar, were seated on a bench in the sun quaffing stout ale.

"I give you good den, sweet friends," quoth Little John, striding up to where they sat.

"Give thee good den, holy father," quoth the merry Beggar with a grin. "But look thee, thy gown is too short. Thou hadst best cut a piece off the top and tack it to the bottom, so that it may be long enough. But come, sit beside us here and take a taste of ale, if thy vows forbid thee not."

"Nay," quoth Little John, also grinning, "the blessed Saint Dunstan hath given me a free dispensation for all indulgence in that line." And he thrust his hand into his pouch for money to pay his score.

"Truly," quoth the Tinker, "without thy looks belie thee, holy friar, the good Saint Dunstan was wise, for without such dispensation his votary is like to ha' many a penance to make. Nay, take thy hand from out thy pouch, brother, for thou shalt not pay this shot. Ho, landlord, a pot of ale!"

So the ale was brought and given to Little John. Then, blowing the froth a little away to make room for his lips, he tilted the bottom of the pot higher and higher, till it pointed to the sky, and he had to shut his eyes to keep the dazzle of the sunshine out of them. Then he took the pot away, for there was nothing in it, and heaved a full deep sigh, looking at the others with moist eyes and shaking his head solemnly.

"Ho, landlord!" cried the Pedler, "bring this good fellow another pot of ale, for truly it is a credit to us all to have one amongst us who can empty a canakin so lustily."

So they talked among themselves merrily, until after a while quoth Little John, "Who rideth those two nags yonder?"

"Two holy men like thee, brother," quoth the Beggar. "They are now having a goodly feast within, for I smelt the steam of a boiled pullet just now. The landlady sayeth they come from Fountain Abbey, in Yorkshire, and go to Lincoln on matters of business."

"They are a merry couple," said the Tinker, "for one is as lean as an old wife's spindle, and the other as fat as a suet pudding."

"Talking of fatness," said the Pedler, "thou thyself lookest none too ill-fed, holy friar."

"Nay, truly," said Little John, "thou seest in me what the holy Saint Dunstan can do for them that serve him upon a handful of parched pease and a trickle of cold water."

At this a great shout of laughter went up. "Truly, it is a wondrous thing," quoth the Beggar; "I would have made my vow, to see the masterly manner in which thou didst tuck away yon pot of ale, that thou hadst not tasted clear water for a brace of months. Has not this same holy Saint Dunstan taught thee a goodly song or two?"

"Why, as for that," quoth Little John, grinning, "mayhap he hath lent me aid to learn a ditty or so."

"Then, prythee, let us hear how he hath taught thee," quoth the Tinker.

At this Little John cleared his throat, and, after a word or two about a certain hoarseness that troubled him, sang thus:—

> "Ah, pretty, pretty maid, whither dost thou go?
> I prythee, prythee, wait for thy lover also,
>   And we'll gather the rose
>   As it sweetly blows,
> For the merry, merry winds are blo-o-o-wing."

Now it seemed as though Little John's songs were never to get sung, for he had got no farther than this when the door of the inn opened and out came the two brothers of Fountain Abbey, the landlord following them, and, as the saying is, washing his hands with humble soap. But when the brothers of Fountain Abbey saw who it was that sang, and how he was clad in the robes of a gray friar, they stopped suddenly, the fat little Brother drawing his heavy eyebrows together in a mighty frown, and the thin Brother twisting up his face as though he had sour beer in his mouth. Then, as Little John gathered his breath for a new verse, "How, now," roared forth the fat Brother, his voice coming from him like loud thunder from a little cloud; "thou naughty fellow, is this a fit place for one in thy garb to tipple and sing profane songs?"

"Nay," quoth Little John, "sin' I cannot tipple and sing, like your worship's reverence, in such a goodly place as Fountain Abbey, I must e'en tipple and sing where I can."

"Now, out upon thee," cried the tall lean Brother in a harsh voice; "now, out upon thee, that thou shouldst so disgrace thy cloth by this talk and bearing."

"Marry, come up!" quoth Little John. "Disgrace, sayest thou? Methinks it is more disgrace for one of our garb to wring hard-earned farthings out of the gripe of poor lean peasants. Is it not so, brother?"

At this the Tinker and the Pedler and the Beggar nudged one another, and all grinned, and the friars scowled blackly at Little John; but they could think of nothing further to say, so they turned to their horses. Then Little John arose of a sudden from the bench where he sat, and ran to where the brothers of Fountain Abbey were mounting. Quoth he, "Let me hold your horses' bridles for you. Truly, your words have smitten my sinful heart, so that I will abide no longer in this den of evil, but will go forward with you. No vile temptation, I wot, will fall upon me in such holy company."

"Nay, fellow," said the lean Brother harshly, for he saw that Little John made sport of them, "we want none of thy company, so get thee gone."

"Alas," quoth Little John, "I am truly sorry that ye like me not nor my company, but as for leaving you it may not be, for my heart is so moved, that, willy-nilly, I must go with you for the sake of your holy company."

Now at this talk all the good fellows on the bench grinned till their teeth glistened, and even the landlord could not forbear to smile. As for the friars, they looked at one another with a puzzled look, and knew not what to do in the matter. They were so proud that it made them feel sick with shame to think of riding along the high-road with a strolling friar, in robes all too short for him, running beside them, but yet they could not make Little John stay against his will, for they knew he could crack the bones of both of them in a twinkling were he so minded. Then up spake the fat Brother more mildly than he had done before. "Nay, good brother," said he, "we will ride fast, and thou wilt tire to death at the pace."

"Truly, I am grateful to thee for the thought of me," quoth Little John; "but have no fear, brother; my limbs are stout, and I could run like a hare from here to Gainsborough."

At these words a sound of laughing came from the bench, whereat the lean Brother's wrath boiled over, like water into the fire, with great fuss and noise. "Now, out upon thee, thou naughty fellow!" he cried. "Art thou not ashamed to bring disgrace so upon our cloth? Bide thee here, thou sot, with these porkers. Thou art no fit company for us."

"La ye there now!" quoth Little John. "Thou hearest, landlord; thou art not fit company for these holy men; go back to thine ale-house. Nay, if these most holy brothers of mine do but give me the word, I'll beat thy head with this stout staff till it is as soft as whipped eggs."

At these words a great shout of laughter went up from those on the bench, and the landlord's face grew red as a cherry from smothering his laugh in his stomach; but he kept his merriment down, for he wished not to bring the ill-will of the brothers of Fountain Abbey upon him by unseemly mirth. So the two brethren, as they could do naught else, having mounted their nags, turned their noses toward Lincoln, and rode away.

"I cannot stay longer, sweet friends," quoth Little John, as he pushed in betwixt the two cobs, "therefore I wish you good den. Off we go, we three." So saying, he swung his stout staff over his shoulder and trudged off, measuring his pace with that of the two nags.

The two brothers glowered at Little John when he so pushed himself betwixt them, then they drew as far away from him as they could, so that the yeoman walked in the middle of the road, whilst they rode on the foot-path on either side of the way. As they so went away, the Tinker, the Pedler, and the Beggar ran skipping out into the middle of the highway, each with a pot in his hand, and looked after them laughing.

Whilst they were in sight of those at the inn the two brothers walked their horses soberly, not caring to make ill matters worse by seeming to run away from Little John, for they could not but think how it would sound in folks' ears when they heard how the brethren of Fountain Abbey scampered away from a strolling friar, like the Ugly One, when the blessed Saint Dunstan loosed his nose from the red-hot tongs where he had held it fast; but when they had crossed the crest of the hill and the inn was lost to sight, quoth the fat Brother to the thin Brother, "Brother Ambrose, had we not better mend our pace?"

"Why truly, gossip," spoke up Little John, "methinks it would be well to boil our pot a little faster, for the day is passing on. So if it will not jolt thy fat too much, onward, say I."

At this the two friars said nothing, but they glared again on Little John with baleful looks; then, without another word, they clucked to their horses, and both broke into a canter. So they galloped for a mile and more, and Little John ran betwixt them as lightly as a stag, and never turned a hair with the running. At last the fat Brother drew his horse's rein with a groan, for he could stand the shaking no longer. "Alas," said Little John, with not so much as a catch in his breath, "I did sadly fear that the roughness of this pace would shake thy poor old fat paunch."

To this the fat Friar said never a word, but he stared straight before him, and he gnawed his nether lip. And now they travelled forward more quietly, Little John in the middle of the road whistling merrily to himself, and the two friars in the footpath on either side saying never a word.

Then presently they met three merry minstrels, all clad in red, who stared amain to see a Gray Friar with such short robes walking in the middle of the road, and two brothers, with heads bowed with shame, riding upon richly-caparisoned cobs on the foot-paths. When they had come near to the minstrels, Little John waved his staff like an usher clearing the way. "Make way!" he cried, in a loud voice, "Make way! make way! for here we go; we three!" Then how the minstrels stared, and how they laughed! But the fat

Friar shook as with an ague, and the lean Friar bowed his head over his horse's neck.

Then next they met a stout burgher and his wife and their two fair daughters, all dressed in their Sunday best, riding from their cousin's house in the country back to Tuxford again. These Little John saluted gravely. Quoth he, "Good den, good folk. Here we go, we three." At this the women stared, for women do not take a joke so quickly as men; but the merry old burgher laughed till his fat side shook and his cheeks grew red and water stood in his eyes.

Then the third they met were two noble knights in rich array, with hawk on wrist, and likewise two fair ladies clad in silks and velvets, all a-riding on noble steeds. These all made room, staring, as Little John and the two friars came along the road. To them Little John bowed humbly. "Give you greeting, lords and ladies," said he. "But here we go, we three."

Then all laughed, and one of the fair ladies cried out, "What three meanest thou, merry friend?"

Little John looked over his shoulder, for they had now passed each other, and he called back, "Big Jack, lean Jack, and fat Jack-pudding."

At this the fat Friar gave a groan and seemed as if he were like to fall from his saddle for shame; the other brother said nothing, but he looked before him with a grim and stony look.

Just ahead of them the road took a sudden turn around a high hedge, and some twoscore paces beyond the bend another road crossed the one they were riding upon. When they had come to the cross-road and were well away from those they had left, then lean Friar drew rein suddenly. "Look ye, fellow," quoth he, in a voice quivering with rage, "we have had enough of thy vile company, and care no longer to be made sport of. Go thy way, and let us go ours in peace."

"La there, now!" quoth Little John. "Methought we were such a merry company, and here thou dost blaze up like fat in the pan. But truly, I ha' had enow of you today, though I can ill spare your company. I know ye will miss me, but gin ye want me again, whisper to Goodman Wind, and he will bring news thereof to me. But ye see I am a poor man and ye are rich. I pray you give me a penny or two to buy me bread and cheese at the next inn."

"We have no money, fellow," said the lean Friar, harshly. "Come, Brother Thomas, let us forward."

But Little John caught the horses by the bridle-reins, one in either hand. "Ha' ye in truth no money about you whatsoever?" said he. "Now, I pray you, brothers, for charity's sake, give me somewhat to buy a crust of bread, e'en though it be only a penny."

"I tell thee, fellow, we have no money," thundered the fat little Friar with the great voice.

"Ha' ye, in holy truth, no money?" asked Little John.

"Not a farthing," said the lean Friar, sourly.

"Not a groat," said the fat Friar, loudly.

"Nay," quoth Little John, "this must not be. Far be it from me to see such holy men as ye are depart from me with no money. Get both of you down straightway from off your horses, and we will kneel here in the middle of the cross-roads and pray the blessed Saint Dunstan to send us some money to carry us on our journey."

"What sayest thou, thou limb of evil!" cried the lean Friar, fairly gnashing his teeth with rage. "Dost thou bid me, the high cellarer of Fountain Abbey, to get down from my horse and kneel in the dirty road to pray to some beggarly Saxon saint?"

"Now," quoth Little John, "I ha' a great part of a mind to crack thy head for thee for speaking thus of the good Saint Dunstan! But get down straightway, for my patience will not last much longer, and I may forget that ye are both in holy orders." So saying, he twirled his stout staff till it whistled again.

At this speech both friars grew as pale as dough. Down slipped the fat Brother from off his horse on one side, and down slipped the lean Brother on the other.

"Now, brothers, down on your knees and pray," said Little John; thereupon, putting his heavy hands upon the shoulder of each, he forced them to their knees, he kneeling also. Then Little John began to beseech Saint Dunstan for money, which he did in a great loud voice. After he had so besought the Saint for a time, he bade the friars feel in their pouches and see if the Saint had sent them anything; so each put his hand slowly in the pouch that hung beside him, but brought nothing thence.

"Ha!" quoth Little John, "have your prayers so little virtue? Then let us at it again."

Then straightway he began calling on Saint Dunstan again, somewhat in this wise: "O gracious Saint Dunstan! send some money straightway to these poor folk, lest the fat one waste away and grow as lean as the lean one, and the lean one waste away to nothing at all, ere they get to Lincoln Town; but send them only ten shillings apiece, lest they grow puffed up with pride. Any more than that that thou sendest, send to me."

"Now," quoth he, rising, "let us see what each man hath." Then he thrust his hand into his pouch, and drew thence four golden angels. "What have ye, brothers?" said he.

Then once again each friar slowly thrust his hand into his pouch, and once again brought it out with nothing in it.

"Have ye nothing?" quoth Little John. "Nay, I warrant there is somewhat that hath crept into the seams of your pouches, and so ye ha' missed it. Let me look."

So he went first to the lean Friar, and, thrusting his hand into the pouch, he drew forth a leathern bag, and counted therefrom one hundred and ten pounds of golden money. "I thought," quoth Little John, "that thou hadst missed, in some odd corner of thy pouch, the money that the blessed Saint had sent thee. And now let me see whether thou hast not some, also, brother." Thereupon he thrust his hand into the pouch of the fat Friar, and drew thence a bag like the other and counted out from it threescore and ten pounds. "Look, ye now," quoth he, "I knew the good Saint had sent thee some pittance that thou, also, hadst missed."

Then, giving them one pound between them, he slipped the rest of the money into his own pouch, saying, "Ye pledged me your holy word that ye had no money. Being holy men, I trust that ye would not belie your word so pledged, therefore I know the good Saint Dunstan hath sent this in answer to my prayers. But as I only prayed for ten shillings to be sent to each of you, all over and above that belongeth by rights to me, and so I take it. I give you good den, brothers, and may ye have a pleasant journey henceforth." So saying, he turned and left them, striding away. The friars looked at one another with a woeful look, and slowly and sadly they mounted their horses again and rode away with never a word.

But Little John turned his footsteps back again to Sherwood Forest, and merrily he whistled as he strode along.

And now we will see what befell Robin Hood in his venture as beggar.

ROBIN HOOD TURNS BEGGAR

AFTER JOLLY ROBIN HAD LEFT LITTLE JOHN AT THE FORKING of the roads, he walked merrily onward in the mellow sunshine that shone about him.

Ever and anon he would skip and leap or sing a snatch of song, for pure joyousness of the day; for, because of the sweetness of the springtide, his heart was as lusty within him as that of a colt newly turned out to grass. Sometimes he would walk a long distance, gazing aloft at the great white swelling clouds that moved slowly across the deep blue sky; anon he would stop and drink in the fullness of life of all things, for the hedgerows were budding tenderly and the grass of the meadows was waxing long and green; again he would stand still and listen to the pretty song of the little birds in the thickets or hearken to the clear crow of the cock daring the sky to rain, whereat he would laugh, for it took but little to tickle Robin's heart into merriment. So he trudged manfully along, ever willing to stop for this reason or for that, and ever ready to chat with such merry lasses as he met now and then. So the morning slipped along, but yet he met no beggar with whom he could change clothes. Quoth he, "If I do not change my luck in haste, I am like to have an empty day of it, for it is well nigh half gone already, and, although I have had a merry walk through the countryside, I know nought of a beggar's life."

Then, after a while, he began to grow hungry, whereupon his mind turned from thoughts of springtime and flowers and birds and dwelt upon boiled capons, Malmsey, white bread, and the like, with great tenderness. Quoth he to himself, "I would I had Willie Wynkin's wishing coat; I know right well what I should wish for, and this it should be." Here he marked upon the fingers of his left hand with the forefinger of his right hand those things which he wished for. "Firstly, I would have a sweet brown pie of tender larks; mark ye, not dry cooked, but with a good sop of gravy to moisten it withal. Next, I would have a pretty pullet, fairly boiled, with tender pigeons' eggs, cunningly sliced, garnishing the platter around. With these I would have a long, slim loaf of wheaten bread that hath been baked upon the hearth; it should be warm from the fire, with glossy brown crust, the color of the hair of mine own maid, Marian, and this same crust should be as crisp and brittle as the thin white ice that lies across the furrows in the early winter's morning. These will do for the more solid things; but with these I must have three pottles, fat and round, one full of Malmsey, one of Canary, and one brimming full of mine own dear lusty sack." Thus spoke Robin to himself, his mouth growing moist at the corners with the thoughts of the good things he had raised in his own mind.

So, talking to himself, he came to where the dusty road turned sharply around the hedge, all tender with the green of the coming leaf, and there he saw before him a stout fellow sitting upon a stile, swinging his legs in idleness. All about this lusty rogue dangled divers pouches and bags of different sizes and kinds, a dozen or more, with great, wide, gaping mouths, like a brood of hungry daws. His coat was gathered in at his waist, and was patched with as many colors as there are stripes upon a Maypole in the springtide. On his head he wore a great tall leathern cap, and across his knees rested a stout quarterstaff of blackthorn, full as long and heavy as Robin's. As jolly a beggar was he as ever trod the lanes and byways of Nottinghamshire, for his eyes were as gray as slate, and snapped and twinkled and danced with merriment, and his black hair curled close all over his head in little rings of kinkyness.

"Halloa, good fellow," quoth Robin, when he had come nigh to the other, "what art thou doing here this merry day, when the flowers are peeping and the buds are swelling?"

Then the other winked one eye, and straightway trolled forth in a merry voice:—

> "I sit upon the stile,
> And I sing a little while
> As I wait for my own true dear, O,
> For the sun is shining bright,
> And the leaves are dancing light,
> And the little fowl sings she is near, O.

"And so it is with me, bully boy, saving that my doxy cometh not."

"Now that is a right sweet song," quoth Robin, "and, were I in the right mind to listen to thee, I could bear well to hear more; but I have two things of seriousness to ask of thee; so listen, I prythee."

At this the jolly Beggar cocked his head on one side, like a rogue of a magpie. Quoth he, "I am an ill jug to pour heavy things into, good friend, and, if I mistake not, thou hast few serious words to spare at any time."

"Nay," quoth jolly Robin, "what I would say first is the most serious of all thoughts to me, to wit, 'where shall I get somewhat to eat and drink?' "

"Sayst thou so?" quoth the Beggar. "Marry, I make no such serious thoughts upon the matter. I eat when I can get it, and munch my crust when I can get no crumb; likewise, when there is no ale to be had I wash the dust from out my throat with a trickle of cold water. I was sitting here, as thou camest upon me, bethinking myself whether I should break my fast or no. I do love to let my hunger grow mightily keen ere I eat, for then a dry crust is as good to me as a venison pasty with suet and raisins is to stout

King Harry. I have a sharp hunger upon me now, but methinks in a short while it will ripen to a right mellow appetite."

"Now, in good sooth," quoth merry Robin, laughing, "thou hast a quaint tongue betwixt thy teeth. But hast thou truly nought but a dry crust about thee? Methinks thy bags and pouches are fat and lusty for such thin fare."

"Why, mayhap there is some other cold fare therein," said the Beggar, slyly.

"And hast thou nought to drink but cold water?" said Robin.

"Never so much as a drop," quoth the Beggar. "Over beyond yon clump of trees is as sweet a little inn as ever thou hast lifted eyelid upon; but I go not thither, for they have a nasty way with me. Once, when the good Prior of Emmet was dining there, the landlady set a dear little tart of stewed crabs and barley-sugar upon the window-sill to cool, and, seeing it there, and fearing it might be lost, I took it with me till that I could find the owner thereof. Ever since then they have acted very ill toward me; yet truth bids me say that they have the best ale there that ever rolled over my tongue."

At this Robin laughed aloud. "Marry," quoth he, "they did ill toward thee for thy kindness. But tell me truly, what hast thou in thy pouches?"

"Why," quoth the Beggar, peeping into the mouths of his bags, "I find here a goodly piece of pigeon pie, wrapped in a cabbage leaf to hold the gravy. Here I behold a dainty streaked piece of brawn, and here a fair lump of white bread. Here I find four oaten cakes and a cold knuckle of ham. Ha! in sooth 'tis strange; but here I behold six eggs that must have come by accident from some poultry yard hereabouts. They are raw, but roasted upon the coals, and spread with a piece of butter that I see"—

"Peace, good friend!" cried Robin, holding up his hand. "Thou makest my poor stomach quake with joy for what thou tellest me so sweetly. If thou wilt give me to eat, I will straightway hie me to that little inn thou didst tell of but now, and will bring a skin of ale for thy drinking and mine."

"Friend, thou hast said enough," said the Beggar, getting down from the stile; "I will feast thee with the best that I have and bless Saint Cedric for thy company. But, sweet chuck, I prythee bring three quarts of ale at least, one for thy drinking and two for mine, for my thirst is such that methinks I can drink ale as the sands of the River Dee drink salt water."

So Robin straightway left the Beggar, who, upon his part, went to a budding lime bush back of the hedge, and there spread his feast upon the grass and roasted his eggs upon a little fagot fire, with a deftness gained by long labor in that line. After a while back came Robin bearing a goodly skin of ale upon his shoulder, which he laid upon the grass. Then, looking upon the feast spread upon the ground,—and a fair sight it was to look upon,—he slowly rubbed his hand over his stomach, for to his hungry eyes it seemed the fairest sight that he had beheld in all his life.

"Friend," said the Beggar, "let me feel the weight of that skin."

"Yea, truly," quoth Robin, "help thyself, sweet chuck, and meantime let me see whether thy pigeon pie is fresh or no."

So the one seized upon the ale and the other upon the pigeon pie, and nothing was heard for a while but the munching of food and the gurgle of ale as it left the skin.

At last, after a long time had passed thus, Robin pushed the food from him and heaved a great sigh of deep content, for he felt as though he had been made all over anew.

"And now, good friend," quoth he, leaning upon one elbow, "I would have at thee about that other matter of seriousness of which I spoke not long since."

"How!" said the Beggar, reproachfully; "thou wouldst surely not talk of things appertaining to serious affairs upon such ale as this!"

"Nay," quoth Robin, laughing. "I would not check thy thirst, sweet friend; drink whilst I talk to thee. Thus it is: I would have thee know that I have taken a liking to thy craft and would fain have a taste of a beggar's life mine own self."

Said the Beggar: "I marvel not that thou hast taken a liking to my manner of life, good fellow, but 'to like' and 'to do' are two matters of different sorts. I tell thee, friend, one must serve a long apprenticeship ere one can learn to be even so much as a clapper-dudgeon, much less a crank or any Abraham-man. I tell thee, lad, thou art too old to enter upon that which it may take thee years to catch the hang of."

"Mayhap that may be so," quoth Robin, "for I bring to mind that Gaffer Swanthold sayeth Jack Shoemaker maketh ill bread; Tom Baker maketh ill shoon. Nevertheless, I have a mind to taste a beggar's life, and need but the clothing to be as good as any."

"I tell thee, fellow," said the Beggar, "if thou wert clad as sweetly as good Saint Wynten, the patron of our craft, thou wouldst never make a beggar. Marry, the first jolly traveller that thou wouldst meet would beat thee to a pudding for thrusting thy nose into a craft that belongeth not to thee."

"Nevertheless," quoth Robin, "I would have a try at it; and methinks I shall change clothes with thee, for thy garb seemeth to be pretty, not to say gay. So not only will I change clothes, but I will give thee two golden angels to boot. I have brought my stout staff with me, thinking that I might have to rap some one of the brethren of thy cloth over the head by way of argument in this matter, but I love thee so much for the feast thou hast given me that I would not lift even my little finger against thee, so thou needst not have a crumb of fear."

To this the Beggar listened with his knuckles resting against his hips, and when Robin had ended he cocked his head on one side and thrust his tongue into his cheek.

"Marry come up," quoth he at last. "Lift thy finger against me, forsooth! Art thou out of thy wits, man? My name is Riccon Hazel, and I come from Holywell, in Flintshire, over by the River Dee. I tell thee, knave, I have cracked the head of many a better man than thou art, and even now I would scald thy crown for thee but for the ale thou hast given me. Now thou shalt not have so much as one tag-rag of my coat, even could it save thee from hanging."

"Now, fellow," said Robin, "it would ill suit me to spoil thy pretty head for thee, but I tell thee plainly, that but for this feast I would do that to thee would stop thy travelling the country for many a day to come. Keep thy lips shut, lad, or thy luck will tumble out of thy mouth with thy speech!"

"Now out, and alas for thee, man, for thou hast bred thyself ill this day!" cried the Beggar, rising and taking up his staff. "Take up thy club and defend thyself, fellow, for I will not only beat thee but I will take from thee thy money and leave thee not so much as a clipped groat to buy thyself a lump of goose-grease to rub thy cracked crown withal. So defend thyself, I say."

Then up leaped merry Robin and snatched up his staff also. "Take my money, if thou canst," quoth he. "I promise freely to give thee every farthing if thou dost touch me." And he twirled his staff in his fingers till it whistled again.

Then the Beggar swung his staff also, and struck a mighty blow at Robin, which the yeoman turned. Three blows the Beggar struck, yet never one touched so much as a hair of Robin's head. Then stout Robin saw his chance, and, ere you could count three, Riccon's staff was over the hedge, and Riccon himself lay upon the green grass with no more motion than you could find in an empty pudding-bag.

"How now!" quoth merry Robin, laughing. "Wilt thou have my hide or my money, sweet chuck?" But to this the other answered never a word. Then Robin, seeing his plight, and that he was stunned with the blow, ran, still laughing, and brought the skin of ale and poured some of it on the Beggar's head and some down his throat, so that presently he opened his eyes and looked around as though wondering why he lay upon his back.

Then Robin, seeing that he had somewhat gathered the wits that had just been rapped out of his head, said: "Now, good fellow, wilt thou change clothes with me, or shall I have to tap thee again? Here are two golden angels if thou wilt give me freely all thy rags and bags and thy cap and things. If thou givest them not freely I much fear me I shall have to—" and he looked up and down his staff.

Then Riccon sat up and rubbed the bump on his crown. "Now, out upon it!" quoth he. "I did think to drub thee sweetly, fellow. I know not how it is, but I seem, as it were, to have bought more beer than I can drink. If I must give up my clothes, I must, but first promise me, by thy word as a true yeoman, that thou wilt take nought from me but my clothes."

"I promise on the word of a true yeoman," quoth Robin, thinking that the fellow had a few pennies that he would save.

Thereupon the Beggar drew a little knife that hung at his side, and, ripping up the lining of his coat, drew thence ten bright golden pounds, which he laid upon the ground beside him with a cunning wink at Robin. "Now thou mayst have my clothes and welcome," said he, "and thou mightest have had them in exchange for thine without the cost of a single farthing, far less two golden angels."

"Marry," quoth Robin, laughing, "thou art a sly fellow, and I tell thee truly, had I known thou hadst so much money by thee maybe thou mightst not have carried it away, for I warrant thou didst not come honestly by it."

Then each stripped off his clothes and put on those of the other, and as lusty a beggar was Robin Hood as e'er you could find of a summer's day. But stout Riccon of Holywell skipped and leaped and danced for joy of the fair suit of Lincoln green that he had so gotten. Quoth he, "I am a gay feathered bird now. Truly, my dear Moll Peascod would never know me in this dress. Thou mayst keep the cold pieces of the feast, friend, for I mean to live well and lustily while my money lasts and my clothes are gay."

So he turned and left Robin and, crossing the stile, was gone, but Robin heard him singing from beyond the hedge as he strode away:—

> *"For Polly is smiling and Molly is glad*
> *When the beggar comes in at the door,*
> *And Jack and Dick call him a fine lusty lad,*
> *And the hostess runs up a great score.*
> *Then hey, Willy Waddykin,*
> *Stay, Billy Waddykin,*
> *And let the brown ale flow free, flow free,*
> *The beggar's the man for me."*

Robin listened till the song ended in the distance, then he also crossed the stile into the road, but turned his toes away from where the Beggar had gone. The road led up a gentle hill and up the hill Robin walked, a half score or more of bags dangling about his legs. Onward he strolled for a long time, but other adventure he found not. The road was bare of all else but himself, as he went kicking up little clouds of dust at each footstep; for it was noontide, the most peaceful time of all the day, next to twilight. All the earth was silent in the restfulness of eating-time; the plough-horses stood in the furrow munching, with great bags over their noses holding sweet food, the ploughman sat under the hedge and the plough-boy also, and they, too, were munching, each one holding a great piece of bread in one fist and a great piece of cheese in the other.

So Robin, with all the empty road to himself, strode along whistling merrily, his bags and pouches bobbing and dangling at his thighs. At last he came to where a little grass-grown path left the road and, passing through a stile and down a hill, led into a little dell and on across a rill in the valley and up the hill on the other side, till it reached a windmill that stood on the cap of the rise where the wind bent the trees in swaying motion. Robin looked at the spot and liked it, and, for no reason but that his fancy led him, he took the little path and walked down the grassy sunny slope of the open meadow, and so came to the little dingle and, ere he knew it, upon four lusty fellows that sat with legs outstretched around a goodly feast spread upon the ground.

Four merry beggars were they, and each had slung about his neck a little board that rested upon his breast. One board had written upon it, "I am blind," another, "I am deaf," another, "I am dumb," and the fourth, "Pity the lame one." But although all these troubles written upon the boards seemed so grievous, the four stout fellows sat around feasting as merrily as though Cain's wife had never opened the pottle that held misfortunes, and let them forth like a cloud of flies to pester us.

The deaf man was the first to hear Robin, for he said, "Hark, brothers, I hear some one coming." And the blind man was the first to see him, for he said, "He is an honest man, brothers, and one of like craft to ourselves." Then the dumb man called to him in a great voice and said, "Welcome, brother; come and sit whilst there is still some of the feast left and a little Malmsey in the pottle." At this the lame man, who had taken off his wooden leg and unstrapped his own leg, and was sitting with it stretched out upon the grass so as to rest it, made room for Robin among them. "We are glad to see thee, brother," said he, holding out the flask of Malmsey.

"Marry," quoth Robin, laughing, and weighing the flask in his hands ere he drank, "methinks it is no more than seemly of you all to be glad to see me, seeing that I bring sight to the blind, speech to the dumb, hearing to the deaf, and such a lusty leg to a lame man. I drink to your happiness, brothers, as I may not drink to your health, seeing ye are already hale, wind and limb."

At this all grinned, and the Blind beggar, who was the chief man among them, and was the broadest shouldered and most lusty rascal of all, smote Robin upon the shoulder swearing he was a right merry wag.

"Whence comest thou, lad?" asked the Dumb man.

"Why," quoth Robin, "I came this morning from sleeping overnight in Sherwood."

"Is it even so?" said the Deaf man. "I would not for all the money we four are carrying to Lincoln Town sleep one night in Sherwood. If Robin Hood caught one of our trade in his woodlands he would, methinks, clip his ears."

"Methinks he would, too," quoth Robin, laughing "But what money is this that ye speak of?"

Then up spake the Lame man: "Our king, Peter of York," said he, "hath sent us to Lincoln with those moneys that—"

"Stay, brother Hodge," quoth the Blind man, breaking into the talk; "I would not doubt our brother here, but bear in mind we know him not. What art thou, brother? Upright-man, Jurkman, Clapper-dudgeon, Dommerer, or Abram-man?"

At these words Robin looked from one man to the other with mouth agape. "Truly," quoth he, "I trust I am an upright man, at least, I strive to be; but I know not what thou meanest by such jargon, brother. It were much more seemly, methinks, if yon Dumb man, who hath a sweet voice, would give us a song."

At these words a silence fell on all, and after a while the Blind man spoke again. Quoth he, "Thou dost surely jest when thou sayest that thou dost not understand such words. Answer me this: Hast thou ever fibbed a chouse quarrons in the Rome pad for the loure in his bung?"

"Now out upon it," quoth Robin Hood, testily; "an ye make sport of me by pattering such gibberish, it will be ill for you all, I tell you. I have the best part of a mind to crack the heads of all four of you, and would do so, too, but for the sweet Malmsey ye have given me. Brother, pass the pottle lest it grow cold."

But all the four beggars leaped to their feet when Robin had done speaking, and the Blind man snatched up a heavy knotted cudgel that lay beside him on the grass, as did the others likewise. Then Robin, seeing that things were like to go ill with him, albeit he knew not what all the coil was about, leaped to his feet also, and, catching up his trusty staff, clapped his back against the tree and stood upon his guard against them. "How, now!" cried he, twirling his staff betwixt his fingers, "would you four stout fellows set upon one man? Stand back, ye rascals, or I will score your pates till they have as many marks upon them as a pot-house door! Are ye mad? I have done you no harm."

"Thou liest!" quoth the one who pretended to be blind, and who, being the lustiest villain, was the leader of the others; "thou liest! for thou hast come amongst us as a vile spy. But thine ears have heard too much for thy body's good, and thou goest not forth from this place unless thou goest feet foremost, for this day thou shalt die! Come, brothers, all together! Down with him!" Then, whirling up his cudgel, he rushed upon Robin as an angry bull rushes upon a red rag. But Robin was ready for any happening. "Crick! Crack!" he struck two blows as quick as wink, and down went the Blind man, rolling over and over upon the grass.

At this the others bore back and stood at a little distance scowling upon Robin. "Come on, ye scum!" cried he, merrily. "Here be cakes and ale for all. Now, who will be next served?"

To this speech the beggars answered never a word, but they looked at Robin as great Blunderbore looked upon stout Jack, the slayer of giants, as though they would fain eat him, body and bones; nevertheless, they did not care to come nigher to him and his terrible staff. Then, seeing them so hesitate, Robin of a sudden leaped upon them, striking even as he leaped. Down went the Dumb man, and away flew his cudgel from his hand as he fell. At this the others ducked to avoid another blow, then, taking to their heels, scampered, the one one way and the other the other, as though they had the west wind's boots upon their feet. Robin looked after them, laughing, and thought that never had he seen so fleet a runner as the Lame man; but neither of the beggars stopped nor turned around, for each felt in his mind the wind of Robin's cudgel about his ears.

Then Robin turned to the two stout knaves lying upon the ground. Quoth he, "These fellows spake somewhat about certain moneys they were taking to Lincoln; methinks I may find it upon this stout blind fellow, who hath as keen sight as e'er a trained woodsman in Nottingham or Yorkshire. It were a pity to let sound money stay in the pockets of such thieving knaves." So saying he stooped over the burly rascal and searched among his rags and tatters, till presently his fingers felt a leathern pouch slung around his body beneath his patched and tattered coat. This he stripped away, and, weighing it in his hands, bethought himself that it was mightily heavy. "It were a sweet thing," said he to himself, "if this were filled with gold instead of copper pence." Then, sitting down upon the grass, he opened the pocket and looked into it. There he found four round rolls wrapped up in dressed sheepskin; one of these rolls he opened; then his mouth gaped and his eyes stared, I wot, as though they would never close again, for what did he see but fifty pounds of bright golden money! He opened the other pockets and found in each one the same, fifty bright new-stamped golden pounds. Quoth Robin, "I have oft heard that the Beggars' Guild was over rich, but never did I think that they sent such sums as this to their treasury. I shall take it with me; for it will be better used for charity and the good of my merry band than in the enriching of such knaves as these." So saying he rolled up the money in the sheepskin again, and putting it back in the purse, he thrust the pouch into his own bosom. Then taking up the flask of Malmsey he held it toward the two fellows lying on the grass, and quoth he, "Sweet friends, I drink your health and thank you dearly for what ye have so kindly given me this day, and so I wish you good den." Then, taking up his staff, he left the spot and went merrily upon his way.

But when the two stout beggars that had been rapped upon the head roused themselves and sat up, and when the others had gotten over their fright and come back, they were as sad and woebegone as four frogs in dry weather, for two of them had cracked crowns, their Malmsey was all gone, and they had not so much as a farthing to cross their palms withal. As for the treasury of the Beggars' Guild at the Inn of the Beggar's Bush, near Lincoln Town, it was two hundred pounds poorer than it would have been had bold Robin not met the blind man, the deaf man, the dumb man, and the lame man nigh to the highroad that led to Blyth.

But after Robin left the little dell he strode along merrily, singing as he went; and so blithe was he and such a stout beggar, and, withal, so fresh and clean, that every merry lass he met had a sweet word for him and felt no fear, whilst the very dogs, that most times hate the sight of a beggar, snuffed at his legs in friendly wise and wagged their tails pleasantly; for dogs know an honest man by his smell, and an honest man Robin was—in his own way.

Thus he went along till at last he had come to the wayside cross nigh Ollerton, and, being somewhat tired, he sat him down to rest upon the grassy bank in front of it. "It groweth nigh time," quoth he to himself, "that I were getting back again to Sherwood; yet it would please me well to have one more merry adventure ere I go back again to my jolly band."

So he looked up the road and down the road to see who might come, until at last he saw some one drawing near, riding upon a horse. When the traveller came nigh enough for him to see him well, Robin laughed, for a strange enough figure he cut. He was a thin, weazened man, and, to look upon him, you could not tell whether he was thirty years old or sixty, so dried up was he even to skin and bone. As for the nag, it was as thin as the rider, and both looked as though they had been baked in Mother Huddle's Oven, where folk are dried up so that they live forever. The poor nag's neck bent down instead of up, as most horses' do, and his mane was as ragged as though the mice had made nests in it; his backbone stood up sharp and jagged, like a new-turned furrow when the plough first passes, and his ribs showed beneath his skin like the hoops on a barrel of five-year-old ale. Thus the horse came hobbling along, and at every step the rider popped up and down in his saddle, so that his head bobbed and wagged upon his lean neck all in time to the motion of the nag. At this sight merry Robin laughed till the tears stood on his cheeks, for, as though to make the sight still more droll, the rider wore great clogs upon his feet instead of shoon, the soles whereof were made of wood half a palm's breadth in thickness, and studded all over with great nails.

But although Robin laughed, he knew the wayfarer to be a certain rich corn engrosser of Worksop, who more than once had bought all the grain in the countryside and held it till it reached even famine prices, thus making much money from the needs of poor people, and for this he was hated far and near by every one that knew aught of him.

Quoth Robin to himself, when he saw who it was that came, "Oho, my thieving magpie! It is thou, is it? Now I would that I could pluck thee bare, even to the naked skin! But thou art so sly that I misdoubt finding aught of thy ill-gotten gains upon thee so nigh to Sherwood. Nevertheless, I will see what can be done; for, as Gaffer Swanthold says, 'If Ned never tries, Ned never does.' "

So, after a while, the Corn Engrosser came riding up to where Robin sat; whereupon merry Robin stepped straightway forth, in all his rags and tatters, his bags and pouches dangling about him, and laid his hand upon the horse's bridle-rein, calling upon the other to stop.

"Who art thou, fellow, that doth dare to stop me thus upon the King's highway?" said the lean man, in a dry, sour voice.

"Pity a poor beggar," quoth Robin. "Give me but a farthing to buy me a piece of bread."

"Now, out upon thee!" snarled the other. "Such sturdy rogues as thou art are better safe in the prisons or dancing upon nothing, with a hempen collar about the neck, than strolling the highways so freely."

"Tut," quoth Robin, "how thou talkest! Thou and I are brothers, man. Do we not both take from the poor people that which they can ill spare? Do we not make our livings by doing nought of any good? Do we not both live without touching palm to honest work? Have we either of us ever rubbed thumbs over honestly-gained farthings? Go to! We are brothers, I say; only thou art rich and I am poor; wherefore, I prythee once more, give me a penny."

"Dost thou prate so to me, sirrah?" cried the Corn Engrosser, in a rage. "Now I will have thee soundly whipped if ever I catch thee in any town where the law can lay hold of thee! As for giving thee a penny, I swear to thee that I have not so much as a single groat in my purse. Were Robin Hood himself to take me, he might search me from crown to heel without finding the smallest piece of money upon me. I trust I am too sly to travel so nigh to Sherwood with money in my pouch, and that thief at large in the woods."

Then merry Robin looked up and down, as if to see that there was no one nigh, and then, coming close to the Corn Engrosser, he stood on tiptoe and spake in his ear: "Thinkest thou in sooth that I am a beggar, as I seem to be? Look upon me. There is not a grain of dirt upon my hands or my face or my body; didst thou ever see a beggar so? I tell thee I am as honest a man as thou art. Look, friend." Here he took the purse of money from his breast, and showed to the dazzled eyes of the Corn Engrosser the bright golden pieces. "Friend, these rags serve but to hide an honest rich man from the eyes of Robin Hood."

"Put up thy money, lad," cried the other, quickly. "Art thou a fool, to trust to beggar's rags to shield thee from Robin Hood? If he caught thee he would strip thee to the skin, for he hates a lusty beggar as he doth a fat priest or those of my kind."

"Is it indeed so?" quoth Robin. "Had I known this, mayhap I had not come hereabouts in this garb. But I must go forward now, as much depends upon my journeying. Where goest thou, friend?"

"I go to Grantham," said the Corn Engrosser; "but I shall lodge tonight at Newark; if I can get so far upon my way."

"Why, I myself am on the way to Newark," quoth merry Robin; "so that, as two honest men are better than one in roads beset by such a fellow as this Robin Hood, I will jog along with thee, if thou hast no dislike to my company."

"Why, as thou art an honest fellow and a rich fellow," said the Corn Engrosser, "I mind not thy company; but, in sooth, I have no great fondness for beggars."

"Then forward," quoth Robin, "for the day wanes and it will be dark ere we reach Newark." So off they went, the lean horse hobbling along as before, and Robin running beside, albeit he was so quaking with laughter within him that he could hardly stand; yet he dared not laugh aloud, lest the Corn Engrosser should suspect something. So they travelled along till they reached a hill just on the outskirts of Sherwood. Here the lean man checked his lean horse into a walk, for the road was steep, and he wished to save his nag's strength, having far to go ere he reached Newark. Then he turned in his saddle and spake to Robin again, for the first time since they had left the cross. "Here is thy greatest danger, friend," said he, "for here we are nighest to that vile thief, Robin Hood, and the place where he dwells. Beyond this we come again to the open honest country, and so are more safe in our journeying."

"Alas!" quoth Robin, "I would that I had as little money by me as thou hast, for this day I fear that Robin Hood will get every groat of my wealth."

Then the other looked at Robin and winked cunningly. Quoth he, "I tell thee, friend, that I have nigh as much by me as thou hast, but it is hidden so that never a knave in Sherwood could find it."

"Thou dost surely jest," quoth Robin. "How could one hide so much as two hundred pounds upon his person?"

"Now, as thou art so honest a fellow, and, withal, so much younger than I am, I will tell thee that which I have told to no man in all the world before, and thus thou mayst learn never again to do such a foolish thing as to trust to beggar's garb to guard thee against Robin Hood. Seest thou these clogs upon my feet?"

"Yea," quoth Robin, laughing; "truly, they are large enough for any man to see, even were his sight as foggy as that of Peter Patter, who never could see when it was time to go to work."

"Peace, friend," said the Corn Engrosser, "for this is no matter for jesting. The soles of these clogs are not what they seem to be, for each one is a sweet little box; and by twisting the second nail from the toe, the upper of the shoe and part of the sole lifts up like a lid, and in the spaces within are fourscore and ten bright golden pounds in each shoe, all wrapped in hair, to keep them from clinking and so telling tales of themselves."

When the Corn Engrosser had told this, Robin broke into a roar of laughter, and, laying his hands upon the bridle-rein, stopped the sad-looking nag. "Stay, good friend," quoth he, between bursts of merriment; "thou art the slyest old fox that e'er I saw in all my life!—In the soles of his shoon, quotha!—If ever I trust a poor seeming man again, shave my head and paint it blue! A corn factor, a horse jockey, an estate agent, and a jackdaw for cunningness, say I!" And he laughed again till he shook in his shoes with mirth.

All this time the Corn Engrosser had been staring at Robin, his mouth agape with wonder. "Art thou mad," quoth he, "to talk in this way, so loud and in such a place? Let us forward, and save thy mirth till we are safe and sound at Newark."

"Nay," quoth Robin, the tears of merriment wet on his cheeks, "on second thoughts I go no farther than here, for I have good friends hereabouts. Thou mayst go forward if thou dost list, thou sweet pretty fellow, but thou must go forward barefoot, for I am afraid that thy shoon must be left behind. Off with them, friend, for I tell thee I have taken a great fancy to them."

At these words the corn factor grew pale as a linen napkin. "Who art thou that talkest so?" said he.

Then merry Robin laughed again, and quoth he, "Men hereabouts call me Robin Hood; so, sweet friend, thou hadst best do my bidding and give me thy shoes, wherefore hasten, I prythee, or else thou wilt not get to fair Newark Town till after dark."

At the sound of the name of Robin Hood the corn factor quaked with fear, so that he had to seize his horse by the mane to save himself from falling off its back. Then straightway, and without more words, he stripped off his clogs and let them fall upon the road. Robin, still holding the bridle-rein, stooped and picked them up; then he said, "Sweet friend, I am used to ask those that I have dealings with to come and feast at Sherwood with me. I will not ask thee, because of our pleasant journey together; for I tell thee there be those in Sherwood that would not be so gentle with thee as I have been. The name of Corn Engrosser leaves a nasty taste upon the tongue of all honest men. Take a fool's advice of me and come no more so nigh to Sherwood, or mayhap some day thou mayst of a sudden find a clothyard shaft betwixt thy ribs. So, with this, I give thee good den." Hereupon he clapped his hand to the horse's flank and off went nag and rider. But the man's face was all bedewed with the sweat of fright, and never again, I wot, was he found so close to Sherwood Forest as he had been this day.

Robin stood and looked after him, and, when he was fairly gone, turned, laughing, and entered the forest carrying the shoes in his hand.

That night in sweet Sherwood the red fires glowed brightly in wavering light on tree and bush, and all around sat or lay the stout fellows of the band to hear Robin Hood and Little John tell their adventures. First Little John began and told about his meeting with the three lasses, amid great shouts of laughter, for he was quaint of speech, and told his doings merrily. Then Robin told of his meeting the stout beggar, and what befell behind the hedge under the lime tree.

Then Little John told of meeting the good fellows at the inn, and Robin told of his adventure with the four beggars, and showed the money he had taken from them. Last of all, Little John told how he had prayed to Saint Dunstan with the Gray Friars, and showed the gold that the Saint had sent him. This Robin matched with his story of meeting the Corn Engrosser at the cross near Ollerton, and held up the shoes that he had taken from the lean man. All listened closely, and again and again the woods rang with shouts of laughter.

When all was told, Friar Tuck spoke up, "Good master," said he, "thou hast had a pretty time, but still I hold to my saying, that the life of the barefoot friar is the merrier of the two."

"Nay," quoth Will Stutely, "I hold with our master, that he hath had the pleasanter doings of the two, for he hath had two stout bouts at quarterstaff this day."

So some of the band held with Robin Hood and some with Little John. As for me, I think—But I leave it with you to say for yourselves which you hold with.

After you have settled the matter in your minds, we will see how merry Robin went to famous London Town, and how he shot with the long bow before Queen Eleanor; likewise we will hear of the adventures that befell him thereafter; so listen to what follows.

PART SEVENTH

In which it is told how Queen Eleanor sent for Robin Hood to come to the Court at famous London Town, and how Robin Hood came at her bidding. Likewise, it is told how King Henry chased Robin through the land, yet caught him not.

1

ROBIN AND THREE OF HIS MERRY MEN SHOOT BEFORE QUEEN ELEANOR IN FINSBURY FIELDS

THE HIGH-ROAD STRETCHED WHITE AND DUSTY IN THE HOT summer afternoon sun, and the trees stood motionless along the roadside. All across the meadow lands the hot air danced and quivered, and in the limpid waters of the lowland brook, spanned by a little stone bridge, the fish hung motionless above the yellow gravel, and the dragon-fly sat quite still, perched upon the sharp tip of a spike of the rushes, with its wings glistening in the sun.

Along the road a youth came riding upon a fair milk-white barb, and the folk that he passed stopped and turned and looked after him, for never had so lovely a lad or one so gayly clad been seen in Nottingham before. He could not have been more than sixteen years of age, and was as fair as any maiden. His long yellow hair flowed behind him as he rode along, all clad in silk and velvet, with jewels flashing and dagger jingling against the pommel of the saddle. Thus came the Queen's Page, young Richard Partington, from famous London Town down into Nottinghamshire, upon her majesty's bidding, to seek Robin Hood in Sherwood Forest.

The road was hot and dusty and his journey had been long, for that day he had come all the way from Leicester Town, a good twenty miles and more; wherefore young Partington was right glad when he saw before him a sweet little inn, all shady and cool beneath the trees, in front of the door of which a sign hung pendant, bearing the picture of a Blue Boar. Here he drew rein and called loudly for a pottle of Rhenish wine to be brought him, for stout country ale was too coarse a drink for this young gentleman. Five lusty fellows sat upon the bench beneath the pleasant shade of the wide-spreading oak in front of the inn door, drinking ale and beer, and all stared amain at this fair and gallant lad. Two of the stoutest of them were clothed in Lincoln green, and a great heavy oaken staff leaned against the gnarled oak tree trunk beside each fellow.

The landlord came and brought a pottle of wine and a long narrow glass upon a salver, which he held up to the Page as he sat upon his horse. Young Partington poured forth the bright yellow wine, and holding the glass aloft, cried, "Here is to the health and long happiness of my royal mistress the noble Queen Eleanor; and may my journey and her desirings soon have end, and I find a certain stout yeoman men call Robin Hood."

At these words all stared, but presently the two stout yeomen in Lincoln green began whispering together. Then one of the two, whom Partington thought to be the tallest and stoutest fellow he had ever beheld, spoke up and said, "What seekest thou of Robin Hood, Sir Page? and what does our good Queen Eleanor wish of him? I ask this of thee, not foolishly, but with reason, for I know somewhat of this stout yeoman."

"An thou knowest aught of him, good fellow," said young Partington, "thou wilt do great service to him and great pleasure to our royal Queen by aiding me to find him."

Then up spake the other yeoman, who was a handsome fellow with sun-burnt face and nut-brown, curling hair, "Thou hast an honest look, Sir Page, and our Queen is kind and true to all stout yeomen. Methinks I and my friend here might safely guide thee to Robin Hood, for we know where he may be found. Yet I tell thee plainly, we would not for all merry England have aught of harm befall him."

"Set thy mind at ease; I bring nought of ill with me," quoth Richard Partington. "I bring a kind message to him from our Queen; therefore an ye know where he is to be found, I pray you to guide me thither."

Then the two yeomen looked at one another again, and the tall man said, "Surely it were safe to do this thing, Will;" whereat the other nodded. Thereupon both arose, and the tall yeoman said, "We think thou art true, Sir Page, and meanest no harm, therefore we will guide thee to Robin Hood as thou dost wish."

The Partington paid his score, and the yeomen coming forward, they straightway departed upon their way.

UNDER THE GREENWOOD TREE, IN THE COOL SHADE THAT spread all around upon the sward, with flickering lights here and there, Robin Hood and many of his band lay upon the soft green grass, whilst Allan a Dale sang and played upon his sweetly-sounding harp. All listened in silence, for young Allan's singing was one of the greatest joys in all the world to them; but as they so listened there came of a sudden a sound of horse's feet, and presently Little John and Will Stutely came forth from the forest path into the open glade, young Richard Partington riding between them upon his milk-white horse. The three came toward where Robin Hood sat, all the band staring with might and main, for never had they seen so gay a sight as this young Page, nor one so richly clad in silks and velvets and gold and jewels. Then Robin Hood arose and stepped forth to meet him, and Partington leaped from his horse, and doffing his cap of crimson velvet, met Robin as he came.

"Now, welcome!" cried Robin. "Now, welcome, fair youth; and tell me, I prythee, what bringeth one of so fair a presence and clad in such noble garb to our poor forest of Sherwood?"

Then young Partington said: "If I err not, thou art the famous Robin Hood, and these thy stout band of outlawed yeomen. To thee I bring greeting from our noble Queen Eleanor. Oft hath she heard thee spoken of and thy merry doings hereabouts, and fain would she behold thy face; therefore she bids me tell thee that if thou wilt presently come to London Town, she will do all in her power to guard thee against harm, and will send thee back safe to Sherwood Forest again. Four days hence, in Finsbury Fields, our good King Henry, of great renown, holdeth a grand shooting match, and all the most famous archers of merry England will be thereat. Our Queen would fain see thee strive with these, knowing that if thou wilt come thou wilt, with little doubt, carry off the prize. Therefore she hath sent me with this greeting, and furthermore sends thee, as a sign of great good will, this golden ring from off her own fair thumb, which I give herewith into thy hands."

Then Robin Hood bowed his head, and taking the ring kissed it right loyally, and then slipped it upon his little finger. Quoth he, "Sooner would I lose my life than this ring; and ere it departs from me, my hand shall be cold in death or stricken off at the wrist. Fair Sir Page, I will do our Queen's bidding, and will presently hie with thee to London; but, ere we go, I will feast thee here in the woodlands with the very best we have."

"It may not be," said the Page; "we have no time to tarry, therefore get thyself ready straightway; and if there be any of thy band that thou wouldst take with thee, our Queen bids me say that she will make them right welcome likewise."

"Truly, thou art right," quoth Robin, "and we have but short time to stay; therefore I will get me ready presently. I will choose three of my men, only, to go with me, and these three shall be Little John, mine own true right-hand man, Will Scarlet, my cousin, and Allan a Dale, my minstrel. Go, lads, and get ye ready straightway, and we will presently off with all speed that we may. Thou, Will Stutely, shalt be the chief of the band while I am gone."

Then Little John and Will Scarlet and Allan a Dale ran leaping, full of joy, to make themselves ready, whilst Robin also prepared himself for the journey. After a while they all four came forth, and a right fair sight they made, for Robin was clad in blue from head to foot, and Little John and Will Scarlet in good Lincoln green, and as for Allan a Dale, he was dressed in scarlet from the crown of his head to the toes of his pointed shoes. Each man wore beneath his cap a little head-covering of burnished steel set with rivets of gold, and underneath his jerkin a coat of linked mail, as fine as carded wool, yet so tough that no arrow could pierce it. Then, seeing all were ready, young Partington mounted his horse again, and the yeomen having shaken hands all around, the five departed upon their way.

That night they took up their inn in Melton Mowbray, in Leicestershire; and the next night they lodged at Kettering, in Northamptonshire; and the next at Bedford Town; and the next at St. Albans, in Hertfordshire. This place they left not long after the middle of the night, and traveling fast through the tender dawning of the summer day, when the dews lay shining on the meadows and faint mists hung in the dales, when the birds sang their sweetest and the cobwebs beneath the hedges glimmered like fairy cloth of silver, they came at last to the towers and walls of famous London Town, whilst the morn was still young and all golden toward the east.

Queen Eleanor sat in her royal bower, through the open casements of which poured the sweet yellow sunshine in great floods of golden light. All about her stood her ladies in waiting chatting in low voices, whilst she herself sat dreamily where the mild air came softly drifting into the room laden with the fresh perfumes of the sweet red roses that bloomed in the great garden beneath the wall. To her came one who said that her page, Richard Partington, and four stout yeomen waited her pleasure in the court below. Then Queen Eleanor arose joyously and bade them be straightway shown into her presence.

Thus Robin Hood and Little John and Will Scarlet and Allan a Dale came before the Queen into her own royal bower. Then Robin kneeled before the Queen with his hands folded upon his breast, saying, in simple phrase, "Here am I, Robin Hood. Thou didst bid me come, and lo, I do thy bidding. I give myself to thee as thy true servant, and will do thy commanding, even if it be to the shedding of the last drop of my life's blood."

But good Queen Eleanor smiled pleasantly upon him, bidding him to arise; then she made them all be seated to rest themselves after their long journey. Rich food was brought them and noble wines, and she had her own pages to wait upon the wants of the yeomen. At last, after they had eaten all they could, she began questioning them of their merry adventures. Then they told her all of the lusty doings herein spoken of, and among others that concerning the Bishop of Hereford and Sir Richard of the Lea, and how the Bishop had abided three days in Sherwood Forest. At this the Queen and the ladies about her laughed again and again, for they pictured to themselves the stout Bishop abiding in the forest and ranging the woods in lusty sport with Robin and his band. Then, when they had told all that they could bring to mind, the Queen asked Allan to sing to her, for his fame as a minstrel had reached even to the court at London Town. So straight way Allan took his harp in his hand, and, without more asking, touched the strings lightly till they all rang sweetly, then he sang thus:—

"Gentle river, gentle river,
Bright thy crystal waters flow,
Sliding where the aspens shiver,
Gliding where the lilies blow,

"Singing over pebbled shallows,
Kissing blossoms bending low,
Breaking 'neath the dipping swallows,
Purpling where the breezes blow.

"Floating on thy breast forever
Down thy current I could glide;
Grief and pain should reach me never
On thy bright and gentle tide.

"So my aching heart seeks thine, love,
There to find its rest and peace,
For, though loving, bliss is mine, love,
And my many troubles cease."

Thus Allan sang, and as he sang all eyes dwelt upon him and not a sound broke the stillness, and even after he had done the silence hung for a short space. So the time passed till the hour drew nigh for the holding of the great archery match in Finsbury Fields.

A GAY SIGHT WERE FAMOUS FINSBURY FIELDS ON THAT BRIGHT and sunny morning of lusty summer-time. Along the end of the meadow stood the booths for the different bands of archers, for the King's yeomen were divided into companies of fourscore men, and each company had a captain over it; so on the bright greensward stood ten booths of striped canvas, a booth for each band of the royal archers, and at the peak of each fluttered a flag in the mellow air, and the flag was the color that belonged to the captain of each band. From the centre booth hung the yellow flag of Tepus, the famous bow-bearer of the King; next to it, on one hand, was the blue flag of Gilbert of the White Hand, and on the other the blood-red pennant of stout young Clifton of Buckinghamshire. The seven other archer captains were also men of great renown; among them were Egbert of Kent and William of Southampton; but those first named were most famous of all. The noise of many voices in talk and laughter came from within the booths, and in and out ran the attendants like ants about an ant-hill. Some bore ale and beer, and some bundles of bowstrings or sheaves of arrows. On each side of the archery range were rows upon rows of seats reaching high aloft, and in the centre of the north side was a raised dais for the King and Queen, shaded by canvas of gay colors, and hung about with streaming silken pennants of red and blue and green and white. As yet the King and Queen had not come, but all the other benches were full of people, rising head above head high aloft till it made the eye dizzy to look upon them. Eightscore yards distant from the mark from which the archers were to shoot stood ten fair targets, each target marked by a flag of the color belonging to the band that was to shoot thereat. So all was ready and all waited for the coming of the King and Queen.

At last a great blast of bugles sounded, and into the meadow came riding six trumpeters with silver trumpets, from which hung velvet banners heavy with rich workings of silver and gold thread. Behind these came stout King Henry upon a dapple-gray stallion, with his Queen beside him upon a milk-white palfrey. On either side of them walked the yeomen of the guard, the bright sunlight flashing from the polished blades of the steel halberds they carried. Behind these came the Court in a great crowd, so that presently all the lawn was alive with bright colors, with silk and velvet, with waving plumes and gleaming gold, with flashing jewels and sword hilts; a gallant sight on that bright summer day.

Then all the people arose and shouted, so that their voices sounded like the storm upon the Cornish coast, when the dark waves run upon the shore and leap and break, surging amid the rocks; so, amid the roaring and the surging of the people, and the waving of scarfs and kerchiefs, the King and Queen came to their place, and, getting down from their horses, mounted the broad stairs that led to the raised platform, and there took their seats on two thrones bedecked with purple silks and cloths of silver and of gold.

When all was quiet a bugle sounded, and straightway the archers came marching in order from their tents. Fortyscore they were in all, as stalwart a band of yeomen as could be found in all the wide world. So they came in orderly fashion and stood in front of the dais where King Henry and his Queen sat. King Henry looked up and down their ranks right proudly, for his heart warmed within him at the sight of such a gallant band of yeomen. Then he bade his herald, Sir Hugh de Mowbray, stand forth and proclaim the rules governing the game. So Sir Hugh stepped to the edge of the platform and spoke in a loud clear voice, so that they could hear him even to the ends of the range, and thus he said:—

That each man should shoot seven arrows at the target that belonged to his band, and, of the fourscore yeomen of each band, the three that shot the best should be chosen. These three should shoot three arrows apiece, and the one that shot the best should again be chosen. Then each of these should again shoot three arrows apiece, and the one that shot the best should have the first prize, the one that shot the next best should have the second, and the one that shot the next best should have the third prize. Each of the others should have fourscore silver pennies for his shooting. The first prize was to be twoscore and ten golden pounds, a silver bugle horn inlaid with gold, and a quiver with ten white arrows tipped with gold and feathered with white swan's wing therein. The second prize was to be fivescore of the fattest bucks that run on Dallen Lea, to be shot when the yeoman that won them chose. The third prize was to be two tuns of good Rhenish wine.

So Sir Hugh spoke, and when he had done all the archers waved their bows aloft and shouted. Then each band turned and marched in order back to its place.

And now the shooting began, the captains first taking stand and speeding their shafts and then making room for the men who shot, each in turn after them. Two hundred and eightyscore shafts were shot in all, and so deftly were they sped that when the shooting was done each target looked like the back of a hedgehog when the farm dog snuffs at it. A long time was taken in this shooting, and when it was over the judges came forward, looked carefully at the targets, and proclaimed in a loud voice which three had shot the best from the separate bands. Then a great hubbub of voices arose, each man among the crowd that looked on calling for his favorite archer. Then ten fresh targets were brought forward, and every sound was hushed as the archers took their places once more.

This time the shooting was more speedily done, for only nine shafts were shot by each band. Not an arrow missed the targets, but in that of Gilbert of the White Hand five arrows were in the small white spot that marked the centre; of these five three were sped by Gilbert. Then the judges came forward again, and looking at the targets, called aloud the names of the archer chosen as the best bowman of each band. Of these Gilbert of the White Hand led, for six of the ten arrows he had shot had lodged in the centre; but stout Tepus and young Clifton trod close upon his heels; yet the others stood a fair chance for the second or third place. And now, amid the roaring of the crowd, those ten stout fellows that were left went back to their tents to rest for a while and change their bowstrings, for nought must fail at this next round, and no hand must tremble or eye grow dim because of weariness.

Then whilst the deep buzz and hum of talking sounded all around like the noise of the wind in the leafy forest, Queen Eleanor turned to the King, and quoth she, "Thinkest thou that these yeomen so chosen are the very best archers in all merry England?" "Yea, truly," said the King, smiling, for he was well pleased with the sport that he had seen; "and I tell thee, that not only are they the best archers in all merry England, but in all the wide world beside."

"But what wouldst thou say," quoth Queen Eleanor, "if I were to find three archers to match the best three yeomen of all thy guard?"

"I would say thou hast done what I could not do," said the King, laughing, "for I tell thee there lives not in all the world three archers to match Tepus and Gilbert and Clifton of Buckinghamshire."

"Now," said the Queen, "I know of three yeomen, and in truth I have seen them not long since, that I would not fear to match against any three that thou canst choose from among all thy forty score archers; and, moreover, I will match them here this very day. But I will only match them with thy archers providing that thou wilt grant a free pardon to all that may come in my behalf."

At this the King laughed loud and long. "Truly," said he, "thou art taking up with strange matters for a queen. If thou wilt bring those three fellows that thou speakest of I will promise faithfully to give them free pardon for forty days, to come or to go where so ever they please, nor will I harm a hair of their heads in all that time. Moreover, if these that thou bringest shoot better than my yeomen, man for man, they shall have the prizes for themselves according to their shooting. But as thou hast so taken up of a sudden with sports of this kind, hast thou a mind for a wager?"

"Why, in sooth," said Queen Eieanor, laughing, "I know nought of such matters, but if thou hast a mind to do somewhat in that way, I will strive to pleasure thee. What wilt thou wager upon thy men?"

Then the merry King laughed again, for he dearly loved a goodly jest; so he said, amidst his laughter, "I will wager thee ten tuns of Rhenish wine, ten tuns of the stoutest ale, and tenscore bows of tempered Spanish yew, with quivers and arrows to match."

All that stood around smiled at this, for it seemed a merry wager for a king to give to a queen; but Queen Eleanor bowed her head quietly. "I will take thy wager," said she, "for I know right well where to place those things that thou hast spoken of. Now, who will be on my side in this matter?" And she looked around upon them that stood about; but no one spake or cared to wager upon the Queen's side against such archers as Tepus and Gilbert and Clifton. Then the Queen spoke again: "Now, who will back me in this wager? Wilt thou, my Lord Bishop of Hereford?"

"Nay," quoth the Bishop, hastily, "it ill befits one of my cloth to deal in such matters. Moreover, there are no such archers as his majesty's in all the world; therefore I would but lost my money."

"Methinks the thought of thy gold weigheth more heavily with thee than the wrong to thy cloth," said the Queen, smiling; and at this a ripple of laughter went around, for every one knew how fond the Bishop was of his money. Then the Queen turned to a knight who stood near, whose name was Sir Robert Lee. "Wilt thou back me in this matter?" said she. "Thou art surely rich enough to risk so much for the sake of a lady."

"To pleasure my Queen I will do it," said Sir Robert Lee, "but for the sake of no other in all the world would I wager a groat, for no man can stand against Tepus and Gilbert and Clifton."

Then turning to the King, Queen Eleanor said, "I want no such aid as Sir Robert giveth me; but against thy wine and beer and stout bows of yew I wager this girdle all set with jewels from around my waist; and surely that is worth more than thine."

"Now, I take thy wager," quoth the King. "Send for thy archers straightway. But here come forth the others; let them shoot, and then I will match those that win against all the world."

"So be it," said the Queen. Thereupon, beckoning to young Richard Partington, she whispered something in his ear, and straightway the Page bowed and left the place, crossing the meadow to the other side of the range, where he was presently lost in the crowd. At this all that stood around whispered to one another, wondering what it all meant, and what three men the Queen was about to set against those famous archers of the King's guard.

And now the ten archers of the King's guard took their stand again, and all the great crowd was hushed to the stillness of death. Slowly and carefully each man shot his shafts, and so deep was the silence that you could hear every arrow rap against the target as it struck it. Then, when the last shaft had sped, a great roar went up; and the shooting, I wot, was well worthy of the sound. Once again Gilbert had lodged three arrows in the white; Tepus came second with two in the white and one in the black ring next to it; but stout Clifton had gone down and Hubert of Suffolk had taken the third place, for, while both those two good yeomen had lodged two in the white,

Clifton had lost one shot upon the fourth ring, and Hubert came in with one in the third.

All the archers around Gilbert's booth shouted for joy till their throats were hoarse, tossing their caps aloft, and shaking hands with one another.

In the midst of all this noise and hubbub five men came walking across the lawn toward the King's pavilion. The first was Richard Partington, and was known to most folk across the lawn there, but the others were strange to everybody. Beside young Partington walked a yeoman clad in blue, and behind came three others, two in Lincoln green and one in scarlet. This last yeoman carried three stout bows of yew tree, two fancifully inlaid with silver and one with gold. Whilst these five men came walking across the meadow, a messenger came running from the King's booth, and summoned Gilbert and Tepus and Hubert to go with him. And now the shouting quickly ceased, for all saw that something unwonted was toward, so the folk stood up in their places and leaned forward to see what was the ado.

When Partington and the others came before the spot where the King and Queen sat, the four yeomen bent their knees and doffed their caps unto her. King Henry leaned far forward and stared at them closely, but the Bishop of Hereford, when he saw their faces, started as though stung by a wasp. He opened his mouth as though about to speak, but, looking up, he saw the Queen gazing at him with a smile upon her lips, so he said nothing, but bit his nether lip, whilst his face was as red as a cherry.

Then the Queen leaned forward and spake in a clear voice, "Locksley," she said, "I have laid a wager with the King that thou and two of thy men can outshoot any three that he can send against you. Wilt thou do thy best for my sake?"

"Yea," quoth Robin Hood, to whom she spake, "I will do my best for thy sake, and, if I fail, I make my vow never to finger bowstring more."

Now, although Little John had been somewhat abashed in the Queen's bower, he felt himself the sturdy fellow he was when the soles of his feet pressed green grass again; so he said boldly, "Now, blessings on thy sweet face, say I. And there lived a man that would not do his best for thee—I will say nought, only I would like to have the cracking of his knave's pate!"

"Peace, Little John!" said Robin Hood, hastily, in a low voice; but good Queen Eleanor laughed aloud, and a ripple of merriment sounded all over the booth.

The Bishop of Hereford did not laugh, neither did the King, but he turned to the Queen, and quoth he, "Who are these men that thou hast brought before us?"

Then up spoke the Bishop, hastily, for he could hold his peace no longer: "Your majesty," quoth he, "yon fellow in blue is a certain outlawed thief of the midcountry, named Robin Hood; yon tall, strapping villain goeth by the name of Little John; the other fellow in green is a certain backsliding gentleman, known as Will Scarlet; the man in red is a rogue of a northern minstrel, named Allan a Dale."

At this speech the King's brows drew together blackly, and he turned to the Queen. "Is this true?" said he, sternly.

"Yea," said the Queen, smiling, "the Bishop hath told the truth; and truly he should know them well, for he and two of his friars spent three days in merry sport with Robin Hood in Sherwood Forest. I did little think that the good Bishop would so betray his friends. But bear in mind that thou hast pledged thy promise for the safety of these good yeomen for forty days."

"I will keep my promise," said the King, in a deep voice that showed the anger in his heart; "but when these forty days are gone let this outlaw look to himself, for mayhap things will not go so smoothly with him as he would like." Then he turned to his archers, who stood near the Sherwood yeomen, listening and wondering at all that passed. Quoth he, "Gilbert, and thou, Tepus, and thou, Hubert, I have pledged myself that ye shall shoot against these three fellows. If ye outshoot the knaves I will fill your caps with silver pennies; if ye fail ye shall lose your prizes that ye have won so fairly, and they go to them that shoot against you, man to man. Do your best, lads, and if ye win this bout ye shall be glad of it to the last days of your life. Go, now, and get you gone to the butts."

Then the three archers of the King turned and went back to their booths, and Robin and his men went to their places at the mark from which they were to shoot. Then they strung their bows and made themselves ready, looking over their quivers of arrows, and picking out the roundest and the best feathered.

But when the King's archers went to their tents, they told their friends all that had passed, and how that these four men were the famous Robin Hood and three of his band, to wit, Little John, Will Scarlet, and Allan a Dale. The news of this buzzed around among the archers in the booths, for there was not a man there that had not heard of these great midcountry yeomen. From the archers the news was taken up by the crowd that looked on at the shooting, so that at last everybody stood up, craning their necks to catch sight of the famous outlaws.

Six fresh targets were now set up, one for each man that was to shoot; whereupon Gilbert and Tepus and Hubert came straightway forth from the booths. Then Robin Hood and Gilbert of the White Hand tossed a farthing aloft to see who should lead in the shooting, and the lot fell to Gilbert's side; thereupon he called upon Hubert of Suffolk to lead.

Hubert took his place, planted his foot firmly, and fitted a fair, smooth arrow; then, breathing upon his finger-tips, he drew the string slowly and carefully. The arrow sped true, and lodged in the white; again he shot, and again he hit the clout; a third shaft he sped, but this time failed of the centre, and but struck the black, yet not more than a finger's breadth from the white. At this a shout went up, for it was the best shooting that Hubert had yet done that day.

Merry Robin laughed, and quoth he, "Thou wilt have an ill time bettering that round, Will, for it is thy turn next. Brace thy thews, lad, and bring not shame upon Sherwood."

Then Will Scarlet took his place; but, because of over-caution, he spoiled his target with the very first arrow that he sped, for he hit the next ring to the black, the second from the centre. At this Robin bit his lips. "Lad, lad," quoth he, "hold not the string so long! Have I not often told thee what Gaffer Swanthold sayeth, that 'over-caution spilleth the milk?'" To this Will Scarlet took heed, so the next arrow he shot lodged fairly in the centre ring; again he shot, and again he smote the centre; but, for all that, stout Hubert had outshot him, and showed the better target. Then all those that looked on clapped their hands for joy because that Hubert had over-come the stranger.

Quoth the King, grimly, to the Queen, "If thy archers shoot no better than that, thou art like to lose thy wager, lady." But Queen Eleanor smiled, for she looked for better things from Robin Hood and Little John.

And now Tepus took his place to shoot. He, also, took over-heed to what he was about, and so he fell into Will Scarlet's error. The first arrow he struck into the centre ring, but the second missed its mark, and smote the black; the last arrow was tipped with luck, for it smote the very centre of the clout, upon the black spot that marked it. Quoth Robin Hood, "That is the sweetest shot that hath been sped this day; but, nevertheless, friend Tepus, thy cake is burned, methinks. Little John, it is thy turn next."

So Little John took his place as bidden, and shot his three arrows quickly. He never lowered his bow arm in all the shooting, but fitted each shaft with his long bow raised; yet all three of his arrows smote the centre within easy distance of the black. At this no sound of shouting was heard, for, although it was the best shooting that had been done that day, the folk of London Town did not like to see the stout Tepus overcome by a fellow from the countryside, even were he as famous as Little John.

And now stout Gilbert of the White Hand took his place and shot with the greatest care; and again, for the third time in one day, he struck all three shafts into the clout.

"Well done, Gilbert!" quoth Robin Hood, smiting him upon the shoulder. "I make my vow, thou art one of the best archers that ever mine eyes beheld. Thou shouldst be a free and merry ranger like us, lad, for thou art better fitted for the greenwood than for the cobble-stones and gray walls of London Town." So saying, he took his place, and drew a fair, round arrow from his quiver, which he turned over and over ere he fitted it to his bowstring.

Then the King muttered in his beard, "Now, blessed Saint Hubert, if thou wilt but jog that rogue's elbow so as to make him smite even the second ring, I will give eightscore waxen candles three fingers' breadth in thickness to thy chapel nigh Matching." But it may be Saint Hubert's ears were stuffed with tow, for he seemed not to hear the King's prayer this day.

Having gotten three shafts to his liking, merry Robin looked carefully to his bowstring ere he shot. "Yea," quoth he to Gilbert, who stood nigh him to watch his shooting, "thou shouldst pay us a visit at merry Sherwood." Here he drew the bowstring to his ear. "In London"—here he loosed his shaft—"thou canst find nought to shoot at but rooks and daws; there one can tickle the ribs of the noblest stags in England." So he shot even whilst he talked, yet the shaft lodged not more than half an inch from the very centre.

"By my soul!" cried Gilbert. "Art thou the devil in blue, to shoot in that wise?"

"Nay," quoth Robin, laughing, "not quite so ill as that, I trust." And he took up another shaft and fitted it to the string. Again he shot, and again he smote his arrow close beside the centre; a third time he loosed his bowstring, and dropped his arrow just betwixt the other two and into the very centre, so that the feathers of all three were ruffled together, seeming from a distance to be one thick shaft.

And now a low murmur ran all among that great crowd, for never before had London seen such shooting as this; and never again would it see it after Robin Hood's day had gone. All saw that the King's archers were fairly beaten, and stout Gilbert clapped his palm to Robin's, owning that he could never hope to draw such a bowstring as Robin Hood or Little John. But the King, full of wrath, would not have it so, though he knew in his mind that his men could not stand against those fellows. "Nay!" cried he, clenching his hands upon the arms of his seat, "Gilbert is not yet beaten! Did he not strike the clout thrice? Although I have lost my wager, he hath not yet lost the first prize. They shall shoot again, and still again, till either he or that knave Robin Hood cometh off the best. Go thou, Sir Hugh, and bid them shoot another round, and another, until one or the other is overcome." Then Sir Hugh, seeing how wroth the King was, said never a word, but went straightway to do his bidding; so he came to where Robin Hood and the other stood, and told them what the King had said.

"With all my heart," quoth merry Robin, "I will shoot from this time till tomorrow day if it can pleasure my most gracious lord and king. Take thy place, Gilbert lad, and shoot."

So Gilbert took his place once more, but this time he failed, for, a sudden little wind arising, his shaft missed the centre ring, but by not more than the breadth of a barley straw.

"Thy eggs are cracked, Gilbert," quoth Robin, laughing; and straightway he loosed a shaft, and once more smote the white circle of the centre.

Then the King arose from his place, and not a word said he, but he looked around with a baleful look, and it would have been an ill day for any one that he saw with a joyous or a merry look upon his face. Then he and his Queen and all the court left the place, but the King's heart was brimming full of wrath within him.

After the King had gone, all the yeomen of the archer guard came crowding around Robin, and Little John, and Will, and Allan, to snatch a look at these famous fellows from the midcountry; and with them came many that had been onlookers at the sport, for the same purpose. Thus it happened presently that the yeomen, to whom Gilbert stood talking, were all surrounded by a crowd of people that formed a ring about them. "Marry," quoth Little John to Will Scarlet, "one would think that these poor fellows had never seen a stout yeoman ranger in all their lives before, or that we were some curious spectacle, like the Cumberland Giant, or the Welsh Dwarf, that we saw last month at the fair at Norwich."

After a while the three judges that had the giving away of the prizes came forward, and the chief of them all spake to Robin and said: "According to agreement, the first prize belongeth rightly to thee; so here I give thee the silver bugle, here the quiver of ten golden arrows, and here a purse of twoscore and ten golden pounds." And as he spake he handed those things to Robin, and then turned to Little John. "To thee," he said, "belongeth the second prize, to wit, fivescore of the finest harts that run on Dallen Lea. Thou mayest shoot them whensoever thou dost list." Last of all he turned to stout Hubert. "Thou," said he, "hast held thine own against the yeoman with whom thou didst shoot, and so thou hast kept the prize duly thine, to wit, two tuns of good Rhenish wine. These shall be delivered to thee whensoever thou dost list." Then he called upon the other seven of the King's archers who had last shot, and gave them each fourscore silver pennies.

Then up spake Robin, and quoth he, "This silver bulge I keep in honor of this shooting match; but thou, Gilbert, art the best archer of all the King's guard, and to thee I freely give this purse of gold. Take it, man, and would it were ten times as much, for thou art a right yeoman, good and true. Furthermore, to each of the ten that last shot I give one of these golden shafts apiece. Keep them always by you, so that ye may tell your grandchildren, an ye are ever blessed with them, that ye are the very stoutest yeomen in all the wide world."

At this all shouted aloud, for it pleased them to hear Robin speak so of them.

Then up spake Little John. "Good friend Tepus," said he, "I want not those harts of Dallen Lea that yon stout judge spoke of but now, for in truth we have enow and more than enow in our own country. Twoscore and ten I give to thee for thine own shooting, and five I give to each band for their pleasure."

At this another great shout went up, and many tossed their caps aloft, and swore among themselves that no better fellows ever walked the sod than Robin Hood and his stout yeomen.

Whilst they so shouted with loud voices, a tall burly yeoman of the King's guard came forward and plucked Robin by the sleeve. "Good master," quoth he, "I have somewhat to tell thee in thine ear; a silly thing, God wot, for one stout yeoman to tell another; but a young peacock of a page, one Richard Partington, was seeking thee without avail in the crowd, and, not being able to find thee, told me that he bore a message to thee from a certain lady that thou wottest of. This message he bade me tell thee privily, word for word, and thus it was. Let me see—I trust I have forgot it not— yea, thus it was: 'The lion growls. Beware thy head.'"

"Is it so?" quoth Robin, starting; for he knew right well that it was the Queen sent the message, and that she spake of the King's wrath. "Now, I thank thee, good fellow, for thou hast done me greater service than thou knowest of this day." Then he called his three yeomen together, and told them privately that they had best be jogging, as it was like to be ill for them so nigh merry London Town. So, without tarrying longer, they made their way through the crowd until they had come out from the press. Then, without stopping, they left London Town, and started away northward.

Thus ended the famous shooting match before Queen Eleanor. And now we will hear how ill King Harry kept his promise to his Queen that no harm should befall Robin Hood for forty days, in which time he might come and go as he wished.

2

THE CHASE OF
ROBIN HOOD

SO ROBIN HOOD AND THE OTHERS LEFT THE ARCHERY RANGE at Finsbury Fields, and, tarrying not, set forth straightway upon their homeward journey. It was well for them that they did so, for they had not gone more than three or four miles upon their way when six of the yeomen of the King's guard came bustling amongst the crowd that still lingered, seeking for Robin and his men, to seize upon them and make them prisoners. Truly, it was an ill-done thing in the King to break his promise, but it all came about through the Bishop of Hereford's doing, for thus it happened:—

After the King left the archery ground, he went straightway to his cabinet, and with him went the Bishop of Hereford and Sir Robert Lee; but the King said never a word to these two, but sat gnawing his nether lip, for his heart was galled within him by what had happened. At last the Bishop of Hereford spoke, in a low, sorrowful voice: "It is a sad thing, your majesty," quoth he, "that this knavish outlaw should be let to escape in this wise; for, let him but get back to Sherwood Forest safe and sound, and he may snap his fingers at King and King's men."

At these words the King raised his eyes and looked grimly upon the Bishop. "Sayst thou so?" quoth he. "Now, I will show thee, in good time, how much thou dost err, for, when the forty days are past and gone, I will seize upon this thieving outlaw, if I have to tear down all of Sherwood to find him. Thinkest thou that the laws of the King of England are to be so evaded by one poor knave without friends or money?"

Then the Bishop spoke again, in his soft, smooth voice: "Forgive my boldness, your majesty, and believe that I have naught but the good of England and your majesty's desirings at heart; but what would it boot though my gracious lord did root up every tree of Sherwood? Are there not other places for Robin Hood's hiding? Cannock Chase is not far from Sherwood, and the great Forest of Arden is not far from Cannock Chase. Beside these are many other woodlands in Nottingham and Derby, Lincoln and York, amid any of which your majesty might as well think to seize upon Robin Hood as to lay finger upon a rat among the dust and broken things of a garret. Nay, my gracious lord, if he doth once plant foot in the woodland, he is lost to the law forever."

At these words the King tapped his finger-tips upon the table beside him with vexation. "What wouldst thou have me do, Bishop?" quoth he. "Didst thou not hear me pledge my word to the Queen? Thy talk is as barren as the wind from the bellows upon dead coals."

"Far be it from me," said the cunning Bishop, "to point the way to one so clear-sighted as your majesty; but, were I the King of England, I should look upon the matter in this wise: I have promised my Queen, let us say, that for forty days the cunningest rogue in all England shall have freedom to come and go; but, lo! I find this outlaw in my grasp; shall I, then, foolishly cling to a promise so hastily given? Suppose that I had promised to do her majesty's bidding, whereupon she bade me to slay myself; should I, then, shut mine eyes and run blindly upon my sword? Thus would I argue within myself. Moreover, I would say unto myself, a woman knoweth nought of the great things appertaining to state government; and, likewise, I know a woman is ever prone to take up a fancy, even as she would pluck a daisy from the roadside, and then throw it away when the savor is gone; therefore, though she hath taken a fancy to this outlaw, it will soon wane away and be forgotten. As for me, I have the greatest villain in all England in my grasp; shall I, then, open my hand and let him slip betwixt my fingers? Thus, your majesty, would I say to myself, were I the King of England." So the Bishop talked, and the King lent his ear to his evil counsel, until, after a while, he turned to Sir Robert Lee, and bade him send six of the yeomen of the guard to take Robin Hood and his three men prisoners.

Now Sir Robert Lee was a gentle and noble knight, and he felt grieved to the heart to see the King so break his promise; nevertheless, he said nothing, for he saw how bitterly the King was set against Robin Hood; but he did not send the yeomen of the guard at once, but went first to the Queen, and told her all that had passed, and bade her send word to Robin of his danger. This he did not for the well-being of Robin Hood, but because he would save his lord's honor if he could. Thus it came about that when, after a while, the yeomen of the guard went to the archery field, they found not Robin and the others, and so got no cakes at that fair.

The afternoon was already well-nigh gone when Robin Hood, Little John, Will, and Allan set forth upon their homeward way, trudging along merrily through the yellow slanting light, which speedily changed to rosy red as the sun sank low in the heavens. The shadows grew long, and finally merged into the grayness of the mellow twilight. The dusty highway lay all white betwixt the dark hedgerows, and along it walked the four fellows like four shadows, the pat of their feet sounding loud, and their voices, as they talked, ringing clear upon the silence of the air. The great round moon was floating breathlessly up in the eastern sky when they saw before them the twinkling lights of Barnet Town, some ten or twelve miles from London. Down they walked through the stony streets and past the cosy houses with overhanging gables, before the doors of which sat the burghers and craftsmen in the mellow moonlight, with their families about them, and so came at last, on the other side of the hamlet, to a little inn, all shaded with roses and woodbines. Before this inn Robin Hood stopped, for the spot pleased him well. Quoth he, "Here will we take up our inn and rest for the night, for we are well away from London Town and our King's wrath. Moreover, if I mistake not, we will find sweet faring within. What say ye, lads?"

"In sooth, good master," quoth Little John, "thy bidding and my doing ever fit together like cakes and ale. Let us in, I say also."

Then up spake Will Scarlet: "I am ever ready to do what thou sayest, uncle, yet I could wish that we were farther upon our way ere we rest for the night. Nevertheless, if thou thinkest best, let us in for the night, say I also."

So in they went and called for the best that the place afforded. Then a right good feast was set before them, with two stout bottles of old sack to wash it down withal. These things were served by as plump and buxom a lass as you could find in all the land, so that Little John, who always had an eye for a fair lass, even when meat and drink were by, stuck his arms akimbo and fixed his eyes upon her, winking sweetly whenever he saw her looking toward him. Then you should have seen how the lass twittered with laughter, and how she looked at Little John out of the corners of her eyes, a dimple coming in either cheek; for the fellow had always a taking way with the women-folk.

"Come, come, Little John," quoth Robin, "leave the lass in peace, and fall to thy victuals, or thou wilt belike go with an empty stomach. Eat first and woo afterwards is as good a saying as one can open ears to."

"Nay," quoth Little John, boldly, "it is an ill saying for me, for who would turn to victuals and drink and let so fair a lass go, without paying heed to the sweet looks that the blessed saints have bestowed upon her? Come hither, thou dainty little duck, and pour forth some wine for me, that I may drink to thy good health, and pray the good Saint Withold that he send thee what is meet, to wit, a lord or an earl for a husband. By my soul, I would rather drink water that thou hadst poured into my cup than rich Muscat after any other she in all England!"

At this speech the other yeomen roared with laughter, and the lass looked down, blushing, and thought that Little John was as nice a lad as she had seen in all her life.

So the feast passed merrily, and never had that inn seen such lusty feeders as these four stout fellows; but at last they were done their eating, though it seemed as though they never would have ended, and sat loitering over the sack. As they so sat, the landlord came in of a sudden, and said that there was one at the door, a certain young esquire, Richard Partington, of the Queen's household, who wished to see the lad in blue, and speak with him, without loss of time. So Robin arose quickly, and, bidding the landlord not to follow him, left the others gazing at one another, and wondering what was about to happen.

When Robin came out of the inn, he found young Richard Partington sitting upon his horse in the white moonlight, awaiting his coming.

"What news bearest thou, Sir Page?" said Robin. "I trust that it is not of an ill nature."

"Why," said young Partington, "for the matter of that it is ill enow. The King hath been bitterly stirred up against thee by that vile Bishop of Hereford. He sent to arrest thee at the archery butts at Finsbury Fields, but not finding thee there, he hath gathered together his armed men, fiftyscore and more, and is sending them in haste along this very road to Sherwood, either to take thee on the way or to prevent thy getting back to the woodlands again. He hath given the Bishop of Hereford command over all these men, and thou knowest what thou hast to expect of the Bishop of Hereford—short shrift and a long rope. Two bands of horsemen are already upon the road, not far behind me, so thou hadst best get thee gone from this place straightway for, if thou tarriest longer, thou art like to sleep this night in a cold dungeon. This word the Queen hath bidden me bring to thee."

"Now, Richard Partington," quoth Robin, "this is the second time that thou hast saved my life, and if the proper time ever cometh I will show thee that Robin Hood never forgets these things. As for that Bishop of Hereford, if I ever catch him nigh to Sherwood again, things will be like to go ill with him. Thou mayest tell the Good Queen that I will leave this place without delay, and will let the landlord think that we are going to Saint Albans; but when we are upon the high-road again, I will go one way through the country and will send my men the other, so that if one falleth into the King's hands the others may haply escape. We will go by devious ways, and so, I hope, will reach Sherwood in safety. And now, Sir Page, I wish thee farewell."

"Farewell, thou bold yeoman," said young Partington, "and mayst thou reach thy hiding in safety." So each shook the other's hand, and the lad, turning his horse's head, rode back towards London, whilst Robin entered the inn once more.

There he found his yeomen sitting in silence, waiting his coming; like-wise the landlord was there, for he was curious to know what Master Partington had to do with the fellow in blue. "Up, my merry men!" quoth Robin, "this is no place for us, for those are after us with whom we will stand but an ill chance an we fall into their hands. So we will go forward once more, nor will we stop this night till we reach Saint Albans." Hereupon, taking out his purse, he paid the landlord his score, and so they left the inn.

When they had come to the high-road without the town, Robin stopped and told them all that had passed between young Partington and himself, and how that the King's men were after them with hot heels. Then he told them that here they should part company; they three going to the eastward and he to the westward, and so, skirting the main high-roads, would come by devious paths to Sherwood. "So, be ye wily," said Robin Hood, "and keep well away from the northward roads till ye have gotten well to the eastward. And thou, Will Scarlet, take the lead of the others, for thou hast a cunning turn to thy wits." Then Robin kissed the three upon the cheeks, and they kissed him, and so they parted company.

Not long after this, a score or more of the King's men came clattering up to the door of the inn at Barnet Town. Here they leaped from their horses and quickly surrounded the place, the leader of the band and four others entering the room where the yeomen had been. But they found that their birds had flown again, and that the King had been baulked a second time.

"Methought that they were naughty fellows," said the host, when he heard who the men-at-arms sought. "But I heard that blue-clad knave say that they would go straight forward to Saint Albans; so, an ye hurry forward, ye may, perchance, catch them on the high-road betwixt here and there." For this news the leader of the band thanked mine host right heartily, and, calling his men together, mounted and set forth again, gal-loping forward to Saint Albans upon a wild-goose chase.

After Little John and Will Scarlet and Allan a Dale had left the highway near Barnet, they travelled toward the eastward, without stopping, as long as their legs could carry them, until they came to Chelmsford, in Essex. Thence they turned northward, and came through Cambridge and

Lincolnshire, to the good town of Gainsborough. Then, striking to the westward and the south, they came at last to the northern borders of Sherwood Forest, without in all that time having met so much as a single band of the King's men. Eight days they journeyed thus ere they reached the woodlands in safety; but when they got to the greenwood glade, they found that Robin had not yet returned.

For Robin was not as lucky in getting back as his men had been, as you shall presently hear.

After having left the great northern road, he turned his face to the westward, and so came past Aylesbury, to fair Woodstock, in Oxfordshire. Thence he turned his footsteps northward, travelling for a great distance by way of Warwick Town, till he came to Dudley, in Staffordshire. Seven days it took him to journey thus far, and then he thought he had gotten far enough to the north, so, turning toward the eastward, shunning the main roads, and choosing byways and grassy lanes, he went, by way of Litchfield and Ashby de la Zouch, toward Sherwood, until he came to a place called Stanton. And now Robin's heart began to laugh aloud, for he thought that his danger had gone by, and that his nostrils would soon snuff the spicy air of the woodlands once again. But there is many a slip betwixt the cup and the lip, and this Robin was to find. For thus it was:—

When the King's men found themselves foiled at Saint Albans, and that Robin and his men were not to be found high nor low, they knew not what to do. Presently another band of horsemen came, and another, until all the moonlit streets were full of armed men. Betwixt midnight and dawn another band came to the town, and with them came the Bishop of Hereford. When he heard that Robin Hood had once more slipped out of the trap, he stayed not a minute, but, gathering his bands together, he pushed forward to the northward with speed, leaving orders for all the troops that came to Saint Albans to follow after him without tarrying. On the evening of the fourth day he reached Nottingham Town, and there straightway divided his men into bands of six or seven, and sent them all through the countryside, blocking every highway and byway to the eastward and the southward and the westward of Sherwood. The Sheriff of Nottingham called forth all his men likewise, and joined with the Bishop, for he saw that this was the best chance that had ever befallen of paying back his score in full to Robin Hood. Will Scarlet and Little John and Allan a Dale had just missed the King's men to the eastward, for the very next day after they had passed the line and entered Sherwood the roads through which they had travelled were blocked, so that, had they tarried in their journeying, they would surely have fallen into the Bishop's hands.

But of all this Robin knew not a whit; so he whistled merrily as he trudged along the road beyond Stanton, with his heart as free from care as the yolk of an egg is from cobwebs. At last he came to where a little stream spread across the road in a shallow sheet, tinkling and sparkling as it fretted over its bed of golden gravel. Here Robin stopped, being athirst, and, kneeling down, he made a cup of the palms of his hands, and began to drink. On either side of the road, for a long distance, stood tangled thickets of bushes and young trees, and it pleased Robin's heart to hear the little birds singing therein, for it made him think of Sherwood, and it seemed as though it had been a lifetime since he had breathed the air of the woodlands. But of a sudden, as he thus stooped, drinking, something hissed past his ear, and struck with a splash into the gravel and water beside him. Quick as a wink Robin sprang to his feet, and, at one bound, crossed the stream and the roadside, and plunged headlong into the thicket, without looking around, for he knew right well that that which had hissed so venomously beside his ear was a gray goose shaft, and that to tarry so much as a moment meant death. Even as he leaped into the thicket six more arrows rattled among the branches after him, one of which pierced his doublet, and would have struck deeply into his side but for the tough coat of steel that he wore. Then up the road came riding some of the King's men at headlong speed. They leaped from their horses and plunged straightway into the thicket after Robin. But Robin knew the ground better than they did, so crawling here, stooping there, and, anon, running across some little open, he soon left them far behind, coming out, at last, upon another road about eight hundred paces distant from the one he had left. Here he stood for a moment, listening to the distant shouts of the seven men as they beat up and down in the thickets like hounds that had lost the scent of the quarry. Then, buckling his belt more tightly around his waist, he ran fleetly down the road toward the eastward and Sherwood.

But Robin had not gone more than three furlongs in that direction when he came suddenly to the brow of a hill, and saw beneath him another band of the King's men seated in the shade along the roadside in the valley beneath. Then he paused not a moment, but, seeing that they had not caught sight of him, he turned and ran back whence he had come, knowing that it was better to run the chance of escaping those fellows that were yet in the thickets than to rush into the arms of those in the valley. So back he ran with all speed, and had gotten safely past the thickets, when the seven men came forth into the open road. They raised a great shout when they saw him, such as the hunter gives when the deer breaks cover, but Robin was then a quarter of a mile and more away from them, coursing over the ground like a greyhound. He never slackened his pace, but ran along, mile after mile, till he had come nigh to Mackworth, over beyond the Derwent River, nigh to Derby Town. Here, seeing that he was out of present danger, he slackened in his running, and at last sat him down beneath a hedge where the grass was the longest and the shade the coolest, there to rest and catch his wind.

"By my soul, Robin," quoth he to himself, "that was the narrowest miss that e'er thou hadst in all thy life. I do say most solemnly that the feather of that wicked shaft tickled mine ear as it whizzed past. This same running hath given me a most craving appetite for victuals and drink. Now I pray Saint Dunstan that he send me speedily some meat and beer."

It seemed as though Saint Dunstan was like to answer his prayer, for along the road came plodding a certain cobbler, one Quince, of Derby, who had been to take a pair of shoes to a farmer nigh Kirk Langly, and was now coming back home again, with a fair boiled capon in his pouch and a stout pottle of beer by his side, which same the farmer had given him for joy of such a stout pair of shoon. Good Quince was an honest fellow, but his wits were somewhat of the heavy sort, like unbaked dough, so that the only thing that was in his mind was, "Three shillings sixpence ha'penny for thy shoon, good Quince,—three shillings sixpence ha'penny for thy shoon," and this travelled round and round inside of his head, without another thought getting into his noddle, as a pea rolls round and round inside an empty quart pot.

"Halloa, good friend," quoth Robin, from beneath the hedge, when the other had gotten nigh enough, "whither away so merrily this bright day?"

Hearing himself so called upon, the Cobbler stopped, and, seeing a well-clad stranger in blue, he spoke to him in seemly wise. "Give ye good den, fair sir, and I would say that I come from Kirk Langly, where I ha' sold my shoon and got three shillings sixpence ha'penny for them in as sweet money as ever thou sawest, and honestly earned too, I would ha' thee know. But, an I may be so bold, thou pretty fellow, what dost thou there beneath the hedge?"

"Marry," quoth merry Robin, "I sit beneath the hedge here to drop salt on the tails of golden birds; but in sooth thou art the first chick of any worth I ha' seen this blessed day."

At these words the Cobbler's eyes opened big and wide, and his mouth grew round with wonder, like a knot-hole in a board fence. "Alack-a-day," quoth he, "look ye, now! I ha' never seen those same golden birds. And dost thou in sooth find them in these hedges, good fellow? Prythee, tell me, are there many of them? I would fain find them mine ownself."

"Ay, truly," quoth Robin, "they are as thick here as fresh herring in Cannock Chase."

"Look ye, now!" said the Cobbler, all drowned in wonder. "And dost thou in sooth catch them by dropping salt on their pretty tails?"

"Yea," quoth Robin, "but this salt is of an odd kind, let me tell thee, for it can only be gotten by boiling down a quart of moonbeams in a wooden platter, and then one hath but a pinch. But tell me, now, thou witty man, what hast thou gotten there in that pouch by thy side and in that pottle?"

At these words the Cobbler looked down at those things of which merry Robin spoke, for the thoughts of the golden bird had driven them from his mind, and it took him some time to scrape the memory of them back again. "Why," said he at last, "in the one is good March beer, and in the other is a fat capon. Truly, Quince the Cobbler will ha' a fine feast this day as I mistake not."

"But tell me, good Quince," said Robin, "hast thou a mind to sell those things to me? for the hearing of them sounds sweet in mine ears. I will give thee these gay clothes of blue that I have upon my body and ten shillings to boot for thy clothes and thy leather apron and thy beer and thy capon. What sayst thou, bully boy?"

"Nay, thou dost jest with me," said the Cobber, "for my clothes are coarse and patched, and thine are of fine stuff and very pretty."

"Never a jest do I speak," quoth Robin. "Come, strip thy jacket off and I will show thee, for I tell thee I like thy clothes well. Moreover, I will be kind to thee, for I will feast straightway upon the good things thou hast with thee, and thou shalt be bidden to the eating." At these words he began slipping off his doublet, and the Cobbler, seeing him so in earnest, began peeling off his clothes also, for Robin Hood's garb tickled his eye. So each put on the other fellow's clothes, and Robin gave the honest Cobbler ten bright new shillings. Quoth merry Robin, "I ha' been a many things in my life before, but never have I been an honest cobbler. Come, friend, let us fall to and eat, for something within me cackles aloud for that good fat capon." So both sat down and began to feast right lustily, so that when they were done the bones of the capon were picked as bare as charity.

Then Robin stretched his legs out with a sweet feeling of comfort within him. Quoth he, "By the turn of thy voice, good Quince, I know that thou hast a fair song or two running loose in thy head like colts in a meadow. I prythee, turn one of them out for me."

"A song or two I ha'," quoth the Cobbler; "poor things; poor things; but such as they are thou art welcome to one of them." So, moistening his throat with a swallow of beer, he began to sing thus:—

"Of all the joys, the best I love,
    Sing hey my frisking Nan, O,
And that which most my soul doth move,
    It is the clinking can, O.

"All other bliss I'd throw away,
    Sing hey my frisking Nan, O,
But this—"

The stout Cobbler got no further in his song, for of a sudden six horsemen burst upon them where they sat, and seized roughly upon the honest craftsman, hauling him to his feet, and nearly plucking the clothes from him as they did so. "Ha!" roared the leader of the band in a great big voice of joy, "have we then caught thee at last, thou blue-clad knave? Now, blessed be the name of Saint Hubert, for the good Bishop of Hereford hath promised that much to the band that shall bring thee to him. Oho! thou cunning rascal! thou wouldst look so innocent, forsooth! We know thee, thou old fox. But off thou goest with us to have thy brush clipped forthwith." At these words the poor Cobbler gazed all around him with his great blue eyes as round as those of a dead fish, while his mouth gaped as though he had swallowed all his words and so lost his speech.

Robin also gaped and stared in a wondering way, just as the Cobbler would have done in his place. "Alack-a-daisy, me," quoth he. "I know not whether I be sitting here or in no-man's land! What meaneth all this stir i' th' pot, dear good gentlemen? Surely this is a sweet, honest fellow."

" 'Honest fellow,' sayst thou, clown?" quoth one of the men. "Why, I tell thee that this is that same rogue that men call Robin Hood."

At this speech the Cobbler stared and gaped more than ever, for there was such a threshing of thoughts going on within his poor head that his wits were all befogged with the dust and chaff thereof. Moreover, as he looked at Robin Hood, and saw the yeoman look so like what he knew himself to be, he began to doubt and to think that mayhap he was the great outlaw in real sooth. Said he in a slow, wondering voice, "Am I in very truth that fellow?— Now I had thought—but nay, Quince, thou art mistook—yet—am I?— Nay, I must indeed be Robin Hood! Yet, truly, I had never thought to pass from an honest craftsman to such a great yeoman."

"Alas!" quoth Robin Hood, "look ye there, now! See how your ill-treatment hath curdled the wits of this poor lad and turned them all sour! I, myself, am Quince, the Cobbler of Derby Town."

"Is it so?" said Quince. "Then, indeed, I am somebody else, and can be none other than Robin Hood. Take me, fellows; but let me tell you that ye ha' laid hand upon the stoutest yeoman that ever trod the woodlands."

"Thou wilt play madman, wilt thou?" said the leader of the band.
"Here, Giles, fetch a cord and bind this knave's hands behind him. I warrant we will bring his wits back to him again when we get him safe before
our good Bishop at Tutbury Town." Thereupon they tied the Cobbler's
hands behind him, and led him off with a rope, as the farmer leads off the
calf he hath brought from the fair. Robin stood looking after them, and
when they were gone he laughed till the tears rolled down his cheeks; for he
knew that no harm would befall the honest fellow, and he pictured to himself the Bishop's face when good Quince was brought before him as Robin
Hood. Then, turning his steps once more to the eastward, he stepped out
right foot foremost toward Nottinghamshire and Sherwood Forest.

But Robin Hood had gone through more than he wotted off. His
journey from London had been hard and long, and in a se'ennight he had
travelled sevenscore and more of miles. He thought now to travel on
without stopping until he had come to Sherwood, but ere he had gone a half
a score of miles he felt his strength giving way beneath him like a river bank
which the waters have undermined. He sat him down and rested, but he
knew within himself that he could go no farther that day, for his feet felt
like lumps of lead, so heavy were they with weariness. Once more he arose
and went forward, but after travelling a couple of miles he was fain to give
the matter up, so, coming to an inn just then, he entered, and calling the
landlord bade him show him to a room, although the sun was only then just
sinking in the western sky. There were but three bedrooms in the place, and
to the meanest of these the landlord showed Robin Hood, but little Robin
cared for the looks of the place, for he could have slept that night upon a
bed of broken stones. So, stripping off his clothes without more ado, he
rolled into the bed and was asleep almost ere his head touched the pillow.

Not long after Robin had so gone to his rest a great cloud peeped
blackly over the hills to the westward. Higher and higher it arose until it
piled up into the night like a mountain of darkness. All around beneath it
came ever and anon a dull red flash, and presently a short grim mutter of
the coming thunder was heard. Then up rode four stout burghers of
Nottingham Town, for this was the only inn within five miles' distance, and
they did not care to be caught in such a thunder-storm as this that was

coming upon them. Leaving their nags to the stableman, they entered the best room of the inn, where fresh green rushes lay all spread upon the floor, and there called for the goodliest fare that the place afforded. After having eaten heartily they bade the landlord show them to their rooms, for they were aweary, having ridden all the way from Dronfield that day. So off they went, grumbling at having to sleep two in a bed, but their troubles on this score, as well as all others, were soon lost in the quietness of sleep.

And now came the first gust of wind, rushing past the place, clapping and banging the doors and shutters, smelling of the coming rain, and all wrapped in a cloud of dust and leaves. As though the wind had brought a guest along with it, the door opened of a sudden and in came a friar of Emmet Priory, and one in high degree, as was shown by the softness and sleekness of his robes and the richness of his rosary. He called to the landlord, and bade him first have his mule well fed and bedded in the stable, and then to bring him the very best there was in the house. So presently a savory stew of tripe and onions, with sweet little fat dumplings, was set before him, likewise a good stout pottle of Malmsey, and straightway the holy friar fell to with great courage and heartiness, so that in a short time nought was left but a little pool of gravy in the centre of the platter, not large enow to keep the life in a starving mouse.

In the mean time the storm broke. Another gust of wind went rushing by, and with it fell a few heavy drops of rain, which presently came rattling down in showers, beating against the casements like a hundred little hands. Bright flashes of lightning lit up every raindrop, and with them came cracks of thunder that went away rumbling and bumping as though Saint Swithin were busy rolling great casks of water across rough ground overhead. The women-folks screamed, and the merry wags in the tap room put their arms around their waists to soothe them into quietness.

At last the holy friar bade the landlord show him to his room; but when he heard that he was to bed with a cobbler, he was as ill contented a fellow as you could find in all England, nevertheless, there was nothing for it, and he must sleep there or nowhere; so, taking up his candle, he went off, grumbling like the now distant thunder.

When he came to the room where he was to sleep he held the light over Robin and looked at him from top to toe; then he felt better pleased, for, instead of a rough, dirty-bearded fellow, he beheld as fresh and clean a lad as one could find in a week of Sundays; so, slipping off his clothes, he also huddled into the bed, where Robin, grunting and grumbling in his sleep, made room for him. Robin was more sound asleep, I wot, than he had been for many a day, else he would never have rested so quietly with one of the friar's sort so close beside him. As for the friar, had he known whom Robin Hood was, you may well believe he would almost as soon have slept with an adder as with the man he had for a bedfellow.

So the night passed comfortably enough, but at the first dawn of day Robin opened his eyes and turned his head upon the pillow. Then how he gaped and how he stared, for there beside him lay one all shaven and shorn, so that he knew it must be a fellow in holy orders. He pinched himself sharply, but, finding he was awake, sat up in bed, whilst the other slumbered as peacefully as though he were safe and sound at home in Emmet Priory. "Now," quoth Robin to himself, "I wonder how this thing hath dropped into my bed during the night." So saying he arose softly, so as not to waken the other, and looking about the room he espied the Friar's clothes lying upon a bench near the wall. First he looked at the clothes, with his head on one side, and then he looked at the Friar and slowly winked one eye. Quoth he, "Good brother, What-e'er-thy-name-may-be, as thou hast borrowed my bed so freely I'll e'en borrow thy clothes in return." So saying, he straightway donned the holy man's garb, but kindly left the cobbler's clothes in the place of it. Then he went forth into the freshness of the morning, and the stableman that was up and about the stables opened his eyes as though he saw a green mouse before him, for such men as the friar of Emmet were not wont to be early risers; but the man bottled his thoughts, and only asked Robin whether he wanted his mule brought from the stable.

"Yea, my son," quoth Robin,—albeit he knew nought of the mule,— "and bring it forth quickly, I prythee, for I am late and must be jogging." So presently the stableman brought forth the mule, and Robin mounted it and went on his way rejoicing.

As for the holy friar, when he arose he was in as pretty a stew as any man in all the world, for his rich, soft robes were gone, likewise his purse with ten golden pounds in it, and nought was left but patched clothes and a leathern apron. He raged and swore like any layman, but as his swearing mended nothing and the landlord could not aid him, and as, moreover, he was forced to be at Emmet Priory that very morning upon matters of business, he was fain either to don the cobbler's clothes or travel the road in nakedness. So he put on the clothes, and, still raging and swearing vengeance against all the cobblers in Derbyshire, he set forth upon his way afoot; but his ills had not yet done with him, for he had not gone far ere he fell into the hands of the King's men, who marched him off, willy nilly, to Tutbury Town and the Bishop of Hereford. In vain he swore he was a holy man, and showed his shaven crown; off he must go, for nothing would do but that he was none other than Robin Hood.

Meanwhile merry Robin rode along contentedly, passing safely by two bands of the King's men, until his heart began to dance within him because of the nearness of Sherwood; so he travelled ever on to the eastward, till, of a sudden, he met a noble knight in a shady lane. Then Robin checked his mule quickly, and leaped from off its back. "Now, well met, Sir Richard of the Lea," cried he, "for rather than any other man in England would I see thy good face this day!" Then he told Sir Richard all the happenings that had befallen him, and that now at last he felt himself safe, being so nigh to Sherwood again. But when Robin had done, Sir Richard shook his head sadly. "Thou art in greater danger now, Robin, than thou hast yet been," said he, "for before thee lie bands of the Sheriff's men blocking every road and letting none pass through the lines without examining them closely. I myself know this, having passed them but now. Before thee lie the Sheriff's men and behind thee the King's men, and thou canst not hope to pass either way, for by this time they will know of thy disguise, and will be in waiting to seize upon thee. My castle and everything within it are thine, but nought could be gained there, for I could not hope to hold it against such a force as is now in Nottingham of the King's and the Sheriff's men." Having so spoken, Sir Richard bent his head in thought, and Robin felt his heart sink within him like that of the fox that hears the hounds at his heels, and finds his den blocked with earth so that there is no hiding for him. But presently Sir Richard spoke again, saying, "One thing thou canst do, Robin, and one only. Go back to London and throw thyself upon the mercy of our good Queen Eleanor. Come with me straightway to my castle. Doff these clothes and put on such as my retainers wear. Then I will hie me to London Town with a troop of men behind me, and thou shalt mingle with them, and thus will I bring thee to where thou mayest see and speak with the Queen. Thy only hope is to get to Sherwood, for there none can reach thee, and thou wilt never get to Sherwood but in this way."

So Robin went with Sir Richard of the Lea, and did as he said, for he saw the wisdom of that which the knight advised, and that this was his only chance of safety.

QUEEN ELEANOR WALKED IN HER ROYAL GARDEN, AMID THE roses that bloomed sweetly, and with her walked six of her ladies-in-waiting, chattering blithely together. Of a sudden a man leaped up to the top of the wall from the other side, and then, hanging for a moment, dropped lightly upon the grass within. All the ladies-in-waiting shrieked at the suddenness of his coming, but the man ran to the Queen and kneeled at her feet, and she saw it was Robin Hood.

"Why, how now, Robin!" cried she, "dost thou dare to come into the very jaws of the raging lion? Alas, poor fellow! thou art lost indeed if the King finds thee here. Dost thou not know that he is seeking thee through all the land?"

"Yea," quoth Robin, "I do know right well that the King seeks me, and therefore I have come; for, surely, no ill can befall me when he hath pledged his royal word to your majesty for my safety. Moreover, I know your majesty's kindness and gentleness of heart, and so I lay my life freely in your gracious hands."

"I take thy meaning, Robin Hood," said the Queen, "and that thou dost convey reproach to me, as well thou mayest, for I know that I have not done by thee as I ought to have done. I know right well that thou must have been hard pressed by peril to leap so boldly into one danger to escape another. Once more I promise thee mine aid, and will do all I can to send thee back in safety to Sherwood Forest. Bide thou here till I return." So saying, she left Robin in the garden of roses, and was gone a long time.

When she came back Sir Robert Lee was with her, and the Queen's cheeks were hot and the Queen's eyes were bright, as though she had been talking with high words. Then Sir Robert came straight forward to where Robin Hood stood, and he spoke to the yeoman in a cold, stern voice. Quoth he, "Our gracious Sovereign the King hath mitigated his wrath toward thee, fellow, and hath once more promised that thou shalt depart in peace and safety. Not only hath he promised this, but in three days he will send one of his pages to go with thee and see that none arrest thy journey back again. Thou mayst thank thy patron saint that thou hast such a good friend in our noble Queen, for, but for her persuasion and arguments, thou hadst been a dead man, I can tell thee. Let this peril that thou hast passed through teach thee two lessons. First, be more honest. Second, be not so bold in thy comings and goings. A man that walketh in the darkness as thou dost may escape for a time, but in the end he will surely fall into the pit. Thou hast put thy head in the angry lion's mouth, and yet thou hast escaped by a miracle. Try it not again." So saying, he turned and left Robin and was gone.

For three days Robin abided in London in the Queen's household, and at the end of that time the King's head page, Edward Cunningham, came, and taking Robin with him, departed northward upon his way to Sherwood. Now and then they passed bands of the King's men coming back again to London, but none of those bands stopped them, and so, at last, they reached the sweet, leafy woodlands.

Thus end the merry adventures which befell Robin Hood when he went to the famous shooting-match at London Town. And now we will hear of how the Bishop of Hereford and the Sheriff of Nottingham sought once more to take him in a different way. Likewise we will hear how merry King Richard of the Lion's Heart visited Robin Hood in the depths of Sherwood Forest.

PART EIGHTH

In which it is told how Robin Hood met Guy of Gisbourne in Sherwood Forest, and of the famous fight betwixt them. Also, how Little John fell into the Sheriff's hands through saving the life of three men. Likewise, it is told how good King Richard of the Lion's Heart came to Nottinghamshire and visited Robin Hood in Sherwood Forest.

1

ROBIN HOOD AND GUY OF GISBOURNE

A LONG TIME PASSED AFTER THE GREAT SHOOTING-MATCH, and during that time Robin followed one part of the advice of Sir Robert Lee, to wit, that of being less bold in his comings and his goings; for though mayhap he may not have been more honest (as most folks regard honesty), he took good care not to travel so far from Sherwood that he could not reach it again both easily and quickly.

Great changes had fallen in this time; for King Henry had died and King Richard had come to the crown that fitted him so well through many hard trials, and through adventures as stirring as any that ever befell Robin Hood. But though great changes came, they did not reach to Sherwood's shades, for there Robin Hood and his men dwelt as merrily as they had ever done, with hunting and feasting and singing and blithe woodland sports; for it was little the outside striving of the world troubled them.

The dawning of a summer's day was fresh and bright, and the birds sang sweetly in a great tumult of sound. So loud was their singing that it awakened Robin Hood where he lay sleeping, so that he stirred, and turned, and arose. Up rose Little John also, and all the merry men; then, after they had broken their fast, they set forth hither and thither upon the doings of the day.

Robin Hood and Little John walked down a forest path where all around the leaves danced and twinkled as the breeze trembled through them and the sunlight came flickering down. Quoth Robin Hood, "I make my vow, Little John, my blood tickles my veins as it flows through them this gay morn. What sayst thou to our seeking adventures, each one upon his own account?"

"With all my heart," said Little John. "We have had more than one pleasant doing in that way, good master. Here are two paths; take thou the one to the right hand, and I will take the one to the left, and then let us each walk straight ahead till he tumble into some merry doing or other."

"I like thy plan," quoth Robin, "therefore we will part here. But look thee, Little John, keep thyself out of mischief, for I would not have ill befall thee for all the world."

"Marry come up," quoth Little John, "how thou talkest! Methinks thou art wont to get thyself into tighter coils than I am like to do." .

At this Robin Hood laughed. "Why, in sooth, Little John," said he, "thou hast a blundering hard-headed way that seemeth to bring thee right side uppermost in all thy troubles; but let us see who cometh out best this day." So saying, he clapped his palm to Little John's and each departed upon his way, the trees quickly shutting the one from the other's sight.

Robin Hood strolled onward till he came to where a broad woodland road stretched before him. Overhead the branches of the trees laced together in flickering foliage, all golden where it grew thin to the sunlight; beneath his feet the ground was soft and moist from the sheltering shade. Here in this pleasant spot the sharpest adventure that ever befell Robin Hood came upon him; for, as he walked down the woodland path thinking of nought but the songs of the birds, he came of a sudden to where a man was seated upon the mossy roots beneath the shade of a broad-spreading oak tree. Robin Hood saw that the stranger had not caught sight of him, so he stopped and stood quite still, looking at the other a long time before he came forward. And the stranger, I wot, was well worth looking at, for never had Robin seen a figure like that sitting beneath the tree. From his head to his feet he was clad in a horse's hide, dressed with hair upon it. Upon his head was a cowl that hid his face from sight, and which was made of the horse's skin, the ears whereof stuck up like those of a rabbit. His body was clad in a jacket made of the hide, and his legs were covered with the hairy skin likewise. By his side was a heavy broadsword and a sharp, double-edged dagger. A quiver of smooth round arrows hung across his shoulders, and his stout bow of yew leaned against the tree beside him.

"Halloa, friend," cried Robin, coming forward at last, "who art thou that sittest there? And what is that that thou hast upon thy body? I make my vow I ha' never seen such a sight in all my life before. Had I done an evil thing, or did my conscience trouble me, I would be afraid of thee, thinking that thou wast some one from down below bringing a message bidding me come straightway to King Nicholas."

To this speech the other answered not a word, but he pushed the cowl back from his head and showed a knit brow, a hooked nose, and a pair of fierce, restless, black eyes, which altogether made Robin think of a hawk as he looked on his face. But beside this there was something about the lines on the stranger's face, and his thin cruel mouth, and the hard glare of his eyes, that made one's flesh creep to look upon.

"Who art thou, rascal?" said he at last, in a loud, harsh voice.

"Tut, tut," quoth merry Robin, "speak not so sourly, brother. Has thou fed upon vinegar and nettles this morning that thy speech is so stinging?"

"An thou likest not my words," said the other, fiercely, "thou hadst best be jogging, for I tell thee plainly, my deeds match them."

"Nay, but I do like thy words, thou sweet, pretty thing," quoth Robin, squatting down upon the grass in front of the other; "moreover, I tell thee thy speech is witty and gameson as any I ever heard in all my life."

The other said not a word, but he glared upon Robin with a wicked and baleful look, such as a fierce dog bestows upon a man ere it springs at his throat. Robin returned the gaze with one of wide-eyed innocence, not a shadow of a smile twinkling in his eyes or twitching at the corners of his mouth. So they sat staring at one another for a long time, until the stranger broke the silence suddenly. "What is thy name, fellow?" said he.

"Now," quoth Robin, "I am right glad to hear thee speak, for I began to fear the sight of me had stricken thee dumb. As for my name, it may be this or it may be that; but methinks it is more meet for thee to tell me, thine, seeing that thou art the greater stranger in these parts. Prythee, tell me, sweet chuck, why wearest thou that dainty garb upon thy pretty body?"

At these words the other broke into a short, harsh roar of laughter. "By the bones of the Dæmon Odin," said he, "thou art the boldest spoken man that ever I have seen in all my life. I know not why I do not smite thee down where thou sittest, for only two days ago I skewered a man over back of Nottingham Town for saying not half so much to me as thou hast done. I wear this garb, thou fool, to keep my body warm; likewise it is near as good as a coat of steel against a common sword-thrust. As for my name, I care not who knoweth it. It is Guy of Gisbourne, and thou mayst have heard it before. I come from the woodlands over in Herefordshire, upon the lands of the Bishop of that ilk. I am an outlaw, and get my living by hook and by crook in a manner it boots not now to tell of. Not long since the Bishop sent for me, and said that if I would do a certain thing that the Sheriff of Nottingham would ask of me, he would get me a free pardon, and give me tenscore pounds to boot. So straightway I came to Nottingham Town and found my sweet Sheriff; and what thinkest thou he wanted of me? Why, forsooth, to come here to Sherwood to hunt up one Robin Hood, also an outlaw, and to take him alive or dead. It seemeth that they have no one here to face that bold fellow, and so sent all the way to Herefordshire, and to me, for thou knowest the old saying, 'Set a thief to catch a thief.' As for the slaying of this fellow, it galleth me not a whit, for I would shed the blood of my own brother for the half of two hundred pounds."

To all this Robin listened, and as he listened his gorge rose. Well he knew of this Guy of Gisbourne, and of all the bloody and murderous deeds that he had done in Herefordshire, for his doings were famous throughout all the land. Yet, although he loathed the very presence of the man, he held his peace, for he had an end to serve. "Truly," quoth he, "I have heard of thy gentle doings. Methinks there is no one in all the wide world that Robin Hood would rather meet than thee."

At this Guy of Gisbourne gave another harsh laugh. "Why," quoth he, "it is a merry thing to think of one stout outlaw like Robin Hood meeting another stout outlaw like Guy of Gisbourne. Only in this case it will be an ill happening for Robin Hood, for the day he meets Guy of Gisbourne he shall die."

"But thou gentle, merry spirit," quoth Robin, "dost thou not think that mayhap this same Robin Hood may be the better man of the two? I know him right well, and many think that he is one of the stoutest men hereabouts."

"He may be the stoutest of men hereabouts," quoth Guy of Gisbourne, "yet, I tell thee, fellow, this sty of yours is not the wide world. I lay my life upon it I am the better man of the two. He an outlaw, forsooth! why I hear that he hath never let blood in all his life, saving when he first came to the forest. Some call him a great archer; marry, I would not be afraid to stand against him all the days of the year with a bow in my hand."

"Why, truly, some folk do call him a great archer," said Robin Hood; "but we of Nottinghamshire are famous hands with the long bow. Even I, though but a simple hand at the craft, would not fear to try a bout with thee."

At these words Guy of Gisbourne looked upon Robin with wondering eyes, and then gave another roar of laughter till the woods rang. "Now," quoth he, "thou art a bold fellow to talk to me in this way. I like thy spirit in so speaking up to me, for few men have dared to do so. Put up a garland, lad, and I will try a bout with thee."

"Tut, tut," quoth Robin, "only babes shoot at garlands hereabouts. I will put up a good Nottingham mark for thee." So saying he arose, and going to a hazel thicket not far off, he cut a wand about twice the thickness of a man's thumb. From this he peeled the bark, and, sharpening the point, stuck it up in the ground in front of a great oak tree. Thence he measured off fourscore paces, which brought him beside the tree where the other sat. "There," quoth he, "is the kind of mark that Nottingham yeomen shoot at. Now let me see thee split that wand if thou art an archer."

Then Guy of Gisbourne arose. "Now out upon it!" cried he. "The Devil himself could not hit such a mark as that."

"Mayhap he could and mayhap he could not," quoth merry Robin, "but that we shall never know till thou hast shot thereat."

At these words Guy of Gisbourne looked upon Robin with knit brows, but, as the yeoman still looked innocent of any ill meaning, he bottled his words and strung his bow in silence. Twice he shot, but neither time did he hit the wand, missing it the first time by a span and the second time by a good palm's breadth. Robin laughed and laughed. "I see now," quoth he, "that the Devil himself could not hit that mark. Good fellow, if thou art no better with the broadsword than thou art with the bow and arrow, thou wilt never overcome Robin Hood."

At these words Guy of Gisbourne glared savagely upon Robin. Quoth he, "Thou hast a merry tongue, thou villain; but take care that thou makest not too free with it, or I may cut it out from thy throat for thee."

Robin Hood strung his bow and took his place with never a word, albeit his heartstrings quivered with anger and loathing. Twice he shot, the first time hitting within an inch of the wand, the second time splitting it fairly in the middle. Then, without giving the other a chance for speech, he flung his bow upon the ground. "There, thou bloody villain!" cried he, fiercely, "let that show thee how little thou knowest of manly sports. And now look thy last upon the daylight, for the good earth hath been befouled long enough by thee, thou vile beast! This day, Our Lady willing, thou diest—I am Robin Hood." So saying, he flashed forth his bright sword in the sunlight.

For a time Guy of Gisbourne stared upon Robin as though bereft of wits; but his wonder quickly passed to a wild rage. "Art thou indeed Robin Hood?" cried he. "Now I am glad to meet thee, thou poor wretch! Shrive thyself, for thou wilt have no time for shriving when I am done with thee." So saying, he also drew his sword.

And now came the fiercest fight that ever Sherwood saw; for each man knew that either he or the other must die, and that no mercy was to be had in this battle. Up and down they fought, till all the sweet green grass was crushed and ground beneath the trampling of their heels. More than once the point of Robin Hood's sword felt the softness of flesh, and presently the ground began to be sprinkled with bright red drops, albeit not one of them came from Robin's veins. At last Guy of Gisbourne made a fierce and deadly thrust at Robin Hood, from which he leaped back lightly, but in so leaping he caught his heel in a root, and fell heavily upon his back. "Now, Holy Mary aid me!" muttered he, as the other leaped at him, with a grin of rage upon his face. Fiercely Guy of Gisbourne stabbed at the other with his great sword; but Robin caught the blade in his naked hand, and, though it cut his palm, he turned the point away so that it plunged deep into the ground close beside him; then, ere a blow could be struck again, he leaped to his feet, with his good sword in his hand. And now despair fell upon Guy of Gisbourne's heart in a black cloud, and he looked around him wildly, like a wounded hawk. Seeing that his strength was going from him, Robin leaped forward, and, quick as a flash, struck a back-handed blow beneath the sword arm. Down fell the sword from Guy of Gisbourne's grasp, and back he staggered at the stroke, and, ere he could regain himself, Robin's sword passed through and through his body. Round he spun upon his heel, and, flinging his hands aloft with a shrill, wild cry, fell prone upon his face upon the green sod.

Then Robin Hood wiped his sword and thrust it back in to the scabbard, and, coming to where Guy of Gisbourne lay, he stood over him with folded arms, talking to himself the while. "This is the first man I have slain since I shot the King's forester in the hot days of my youth, I ofttimes think bitterly, even yet, of that first life I took, but of this I am as glad as though I had slain a wild boar that lay waste a fair country. Since the Sheriff of Nottingham hath sent such a one as this against me, I will put on the fellow's garb and go forth to see whether I may not find his worship, and perchance pay him back some of the debt I owe him upon this score."

So saying, Robin Hood stripped the hairy garments from off the dead man, and put them on himself, all bloody as they were. Then, strapping the other's sword and dagger around his body and carrying his own in his hand, together with the two bows of yew, he drew the cowl of horse's hide over his face, so that none could tell who he was, and set forth from the forest, turning his steps toward the eastward and Nottingham Town. As he strode along the country roads, men, women, and children hid away from him, for the terror of Guy of Gisbourne's name and of his doings had spread far and near.

And now let us see what befell Little John while these things were happening.

Little John walked on his way through the forest paths until he had come to the outskirts of the woodlands, where, here and there, fields of barley, corn, or green meadow lands lay smiling in the sun. So he came to the high-road and to where a little thatched cottage stood back of a cluster of twisted crab-trees, with flowers in front of it. Here he stopped of a sudden, for he thought that he heard the sound of some one in sorrow. He listened, and found that it came from the cottage; so, turning his footsteps thither, he pushed open the wicket and entered the place. There he saw a gray-haired dame sitting beside a cold hearthstone, rocking herself to and fro and weeping bitterly.

Now Little John had a tender heart for the sorrows of other folk, so, coming to the old woman and patting her kindly upon the shoulder, he spoke comforting words to her, bidding her cheer up and tell him her troubles, for that mayhap he might do something to ease them. At all this the good dame shook her head; but all the same his kind words did soothe her somewhat, so after a while she told him all that bore upon her mind. That that morning she had three as fair, tall sons beside her as one could find in all Nottinghamshire, but that they were now taken from her, and were like to be hanged straightway; that, want having come upon them, her eldest boy had gone out, the night before, into the forest, and had slain a hind in the moonlight; that the King's rangers had followed the blood upon the grass until they had come to her cottage, and had there found the deer's meat in the cupboard; that, as neither of the younger sons would betray their brother, the foresters had taken all three away, in spite of the oldest saying that he alone had slain the deer; that, as they went, she had heard the rangers talking among themselves, saying that the Sheriff had sworn that he would put a check upon the great slaughter of deer that had been going on of late by hanging the very first rogue caught thereat upon the nearest tree, and that they would take the three youths to the King's Head

Inn, near Nottingham Town, where the Sheriff was abiding that day, there to await the return of a certain fellow he had sent into Sherwood to seek for Robin Hood.

To all this Little John listened, shaking his head sadly now and then. "Alas," quoth he, when the good dame had finished her speech, "this is indeed an ill case. But who is this that goeth into Sherwood after Robin Hood, and why doth he go to seek him? But no matter for that now; only that I would that Robin Hood were here to advise us. Nevertheless, no time may be lost in sending for him at this hour, if we would save the lives of thy three sons. Tell me, hast thou any clothes hereabouts that I may put on in place of these of Lincoln green? Marry, if our stout Sheriff catcheth me without disguise, I am like to be run up more quickly than thy sons, let me tell thee, dame."

Then the old woman told him that she had in the house some of the clothes of her good husband, who had died only two years before. These she brought to Little John, who, doffing his garb of Lincoln green, put them on in its stead. Then, making a wig and false beard of uncarded wool, he covered his own brown hair and beard, and, putting on a great, tall hat that had belonged to the old peasant, he took his staff in one hand and his bow in the other, and set forth with all speed to where the Sheriff had taken up his inn.

A mile or more from Nottingham Town, and not far from the southern borders of Sherwood Forest, stood the cosy inn bearing the sign of the King's Head. Here was a great bustle and stir on this bright morning for the Sheriff and a score of his men had come to stop there and await Guy of Gisbourne's return from the forest. Great hiss and fuss of cooking was going on in the kitchen, and great rapping and tapping of wine kegs and beer barrels was going on in the cellar. The Sheriff sat within, feasting merrily of the best the place afforded, and the Sheriff's men sat upon the bench before the door, quaffing ale, or lay beneath the shade of the broad-spreading oak trees, talking and jesting and laughing. All around stood the horses of the band, with a great noise of stamping feet and a great switching of tails. To this inn came the King's rangers, driving the widow's three sons before them. The hands of the three youths were tied tightly behind their backs, and a cord from neck to neck fastened them all together. So they were marched to the room where the Sheriff sat at meat, and stood trembling before him as he scowled sternly upon them.

"So," quoth he, in a great, loud, angry voice, "ye have been poaching upon the King's deer, have you? Now I will make short work of you this day, for I will hang up all three of you as a farmer would hang up three crows to scare others of the kind from the field. Our fair county of Nottingham hath been too long a breeding-place for such naughty knaves as ye are. I have put up with these things for many years, but now I will stamp them out once for all, and with you I will begin."

Then one of the poor fellows opened his mouth to speak, but the Sheriff roared at him in a loud voice to be silent, and bade the rangers to take them away till he had done his eating and could attend to the matters concerning them. So the three poor youths were marched outside, where they stood with bowed heads and despairing hearts, till after a while the Sheriff came forth. Then he called his men about him, and quoth he, "These three villains shall be hanged straightway, but not here, lest they breed ill-luck to this goodly inn. We will take them over yonder to that belt of woodlands, for I would fain hang them upon the very trees of Sherwood itself, to show those vile outlaws therein what they may expect of me if I ever have the good luck to lay hands upon them." So saying he mounted his horse, as did his men-at-arms likewise, and altogether they set forth for the belt of woodlands he had spoken of, the poor youths walking in their midst guarded by the rangers. So they came at last to the spot, and here nooses were fastened around the necks of the three, and the ends of the cords flung over the branch of a great oak tree that stood there. Then the three youths fell upon their knees and loudly besought mercy of the Sheriff; but the Sheriff of Nottingham laughed scornfully. "Now," quoth he, "I would that I had a priest here to shrive you; but, as none is nigh, you must e'en travel your road with all your sins packed upon your backs, and trust to Saint Peter to let you in through the gates of Paradise like three pedlers into the town."

In the mean time, whilst all this had been going forward, an old man had drawn near and stood leaning on his staff, looking on. His hair and beard were all curly and white, and across his back was a bow of yew that

looked much too strong for him to draw. As the Sheriff looked around ere
he ordered his men to string the three youths up to the oak tree, his eyes fell
upon this strange old man. Then his worship beckoned to him, saying,
"Come hither, father, I have a few words to say to thee." So Little John, for
it was none other than he, came forward, and the Sheriff looked upon him
thinking that there was something strangely familiar in the face before him.
"How, now," said he, "me thinks I have seen thee before. What may thy
name be, father?"

"Please your worship," said Little John, in a cracked voice like that of
an old man, "my name is Giles Hobble, at your worship's service."

"Giles Hobble; Giles Hobble," muttered the Sheriff to himself, turning
over the names that he had in his mind to try to find one to fit to this. "I
remember not thy name," said he at last, "but it matters not. Hast thou a
mind to earn sixpence this bright morn?"

"Ay, marry," quoth Little John, "for money is not so plenty with me that
I should cast sixpence away an I could earn it by an honest turn. What is it
your worship would have me do?"

"Why, this," said the Sheriff. "Here are three men that need hanging as
badly as any e'er I saw. If thou wilt string them up I will pay thee twopence
apiece for them. I like not that my men-at-arms should turn hangmen. Wilt
thou try thy hand?"

"In sooth," said Little John, still in the old man's voice, "I ha' never done
such a thing before; but an a sixpence is to be earned so easily I might as
well ha' it as anybody. But, your worship, are these naughty fellows shrived?"

"Nay," said the Sheriff, laughing, "never a whit; but thou mayst turn thy
hand to that also if thou art so minded. But hasten, I prythee, for I would
get back to mine inn betimes."

So Little John came to where the three youths stood trembling, and,
putting his face to the first fellow's cheek as though he were listening to him,
he whispered softly into his ear, "Stand still, brother, when thou feelest thy
bonds cut, but when thou seest me throw my woollen wig and beard from
my head and face, cast the noose from thy neck and run for the woodlands."
Then he slyly cut the cord that bound the youth's hands; who, upon his
part, stood still as though he were yet bound. Then he went to the second

fellow, and spoke to him in the same way, and also cut his bonds. This he did to the third likewise, but all so slyly that the Sheriff, who sat upon his horse laughing, wotted not what was being done, nor his men either.

Then Little John turned to the Sheriff. "Please your worship," said he, "will you give me leave to string my bow? for I would fain help these fellows along the way, when they are swinging, with an arrow beneath the ribs."

"With all my heart," said the Sheriff, "only, as I said before, make thou haste in thy doings."

Little John put the tip of his bow to his instep, and strung the weapon so deftly that all wondered to see an old man so strong. Next he drew a good smooth arrow from his quiver and fitted it to the string; then, looking all around to see that the way was clear behind him, he suddenly cast away the wool from his head and face, shouting in a mighty voice, "Run!" Quick as a flash the three youths flung the nooses from their necks and sped across the open to the woodlands as the arrow speeds from the bow. Little John also flew toward the covert like a greyhound, while the Sheriff and his men gazed after him all bewildered with the sudden doing. But ere the yeoman had gone far the Sheriff roused himself. "After him!" he roared in a mighty voice; for he knew now who it was with whom he had been talking, and wondered that he had not known him before.

Little John heard the Sheriff's words, and seeing that he could not hope to reach the woodlands before they would be upon him, he stopped and turned suddenly, holding his bow as though he were about to shoot. "Stand back!" cried he, fiercely. "The first man that cometh a foot forward, or toucheth finger to bowstring, dieth!"

At these words the Sheriff's men stood as still as stocks, for they knew right well that Little John would be as good as his word, and that to disobey him meant death. In vain the Sheriff roared at them, calling them cowards, and urging them forward in a body; they would not budge an inch, but stood and watched Little John as he moved slowly away toward the forest, keeping his gaze fixed upon them. But when the Sheriff saw his enemy thus slipping betwixt his fingers he grew mad with his rage, so that his head swam and he knew not what he did. Then of a sudden he turned his horse's head, and plunging his spurs into its sides he gave a great shout, and, rising in his stirrups, came down upon Little John like the wind. Then Little John raised his deadly bow and drew the gray goose feather to his cheek. But alas for him! for, ere he could loose the shaft, the good bow that had served him so long, split in his hands, and the arrow fell harmless at his feet. Seeing what had happened, the Sheriff's men raised a shout, and, following their master, came rushing down upon Little John. But the Sheriff was ahead of the others, and so caught up with the yeoman before he reached the shelter of the woodlands, then leaning forward he struck a mighty blow. Little John ducked and the Sheriff's sword turned in his hand, but the flat of the blade struck the other upon the head and smote him down, stunned and senseless.

"Now, I am right glad," said the Sheriff, when the men came up and found that Little John was not dead, "that I have not slain this man in my haste! I would rather lose five hundred pounds than have him die thus instead of hanging, as such a vile thief should do. Go, get some water from yonder fountain, William, and pour it over his head."

The man did as he was bidden, and presently Little John opened his eyes and looked around him, all dazed and bewildered with the stun of the blow. Then they tied his hands behind him, and lifting him up set him upon the back of one of the horses, with his face to its tail and his feet strapped beneath its belly. So they took him back to the King's Head Inn, laughing and rejoicing as they went along. But in the mean time the widow's three sons had gotten safely away, and were hidden in the woodlands.

Once more the Sheriff of Nottingham sat within the King's Head Inn. His heart rejoiced within him, for he had at last done that which he had sought to do for years, taken Little John prisoner. Quoth he to himself, "This time tomorrow the rogue shall hang upon the gallows tree in front of the great gate of Nottingham Town, and thus shall I make my long score with him even." So saying he took a deep draught of Canary. But it seemed as if the Sheriff had swallowed a thought with his wine, for he shook his head and put the cup down hastily. "Now," he muttered to himself, "I would not for a thousand pounds have this fellow slip through my fingers; yet, should his master escape that foul Guy of Gisbourne, there is no knowing what he may do, for he is the cunningest knave in all the world,—

this same Robin Hood. Belike I had better not wait until tomorrow to hang the fellow." So saying, he pushed his chair back hastily, and going forth from the inn called his men together. Quoth he, "I will wait no longer for the hanging of this rogue, but it shall be done forthwith, and that from the very tree whence he saved those three young villains by stepping so boldly betwixt them and the law. So get ye ready straightway."

Then once more they sat Little John upon the horse, with his face to the tail, and so, one leading the horse whereon he sat and the others riding around him, they went forward to that tree from the branches of which they had thought to hang the poachers. On they went, rattling and jingling along the road till they came to the tree. Here one of the men spake to the Sheriff of a sudden. "Your worship," cried he, "is not yon fellow coming along toward us that same Guy of Gisbourne whom thou didst send into the forest to seek the outlaw, Robin Hood?"

At these words the Sheriff shaded his eyes and looked eagerly.

"Why, certes," quoth he, "yon fellow is the same. Now, Heaven send that he hath slain the master thief, as we will presently slay the man!"

When Little John heard this speech he looked up, and straightway his heart crumbled away within him, for not only were the man's garments all covered with blood, but he wore Robin Hood's bugle horn and carried his bow and broadsword in his hand.

"How now!" cried the Sheriff, when Robin Hood, in Guy of Gisbourne's clothes, had come nigh to them. "What luck hath befallen thee in the forest? Why, man, thy clothes are all over blood!"

"An thou likest not my clothes," said Robin, in a harsh voice like that of Guy of Gisbourne, "thou mayst shut thine eyes. Marry, the blood upon me is that of the vilest outlaw that ever trod the woodlands, and one whom I have slain this day, albeit not without wound to myself."

Then out spake Little John, for the first time since he had befallen into the Sheriff's hands. "O thou vile, bloody wretch! I know thee, Guy of Gisbourne, for who is there that hath not heard of thee and cursed thee for thy vile deeds of blood and rapine? Is it by such a hand as thine that the gentlest heart that ever beat is stilled in death? Truly, thou art a fit tool for this coward Sheriff of Nottingham. Now I die joyfully, nor do I care how

I die, for life is nought to me!" So spake Little John, the salt tears rolling down his brown cheeks.

But the Sheriff of Nottingham clapped his hands for joy. "Now, Guy of Gisbourne," cried he, "if what thou tellest me is true, it will be the best day's doings for thee that ever thou hast done in all thy life."

"What I have told thee is sooth, and I lie not," said Robin, still in Guy of Gisbourne's voice. "Look, is not this Robin Hood's sword, and is not this his good bow of yew, and is not this his bugle horn? Thinkest thou he would have given them to Guy of Gisbourne of his own free will?"

Then the Sheriff laughed aloud for joy. "This is a good day!" cried he. "The great outlaw dead and his right-hand man in my hands! Ask what thou wilt of me, Guy of Gisbourne, and it is thine!"

"Then this I ask of thee," said Robin. "As I have slain the master I would now kill the man. Give this fellow's life into my hands, Sir Sheriff."

"Now thou art a fool!" cried the Sheriff. "Thou mightst have had money enough for a knight's ransom if thou hadst asked for it. I like ill to let this fellow pass from my hands, but as I have promised, thou shalt have him."

"I thank thee right heartily for thy gift," cried Robin. "Take the rogue down from the horse, men, and lean him against yonder tree, whilst I show you how we stick a porker whence I come!"

At these words some of the Sheriff's men shook their heads; for, though they cared not a whit whether Little John were hanged or not, they hated to see him butchered in cold blood. But the Sheriff called to them in a loud voice, ordering them to take the yeoman down from the horse and lean him against the tree, as the other bade.

Whilst they were doing this Robin Hood strung both his bow and that of Guy of Gisbourne, albeit none of them took notice of his doing so. Then, when Little John stood against the tree, he drew Guy of Gisbourne's sharp, double-edged dagger. "Fall back! fall back!" cried he. "Would ye crowd so on my pleasure, ye unmannerly knaves? Back, I say! Farther yet!" So they crowded back, as he ordered, many of them turning their faces away, that they might not see what was about to happen.

"Come!" cried Little John. "Here is my breast. It is meet that the same hand that slew my dear master should butcher me also! I know thee, Guy of Gisbourne!"

"Peace, Little John!" said Robin, in a low voice. "Twice thou hast said thou knowest me, and yet thou knowest me not at all. Couldst thou not tell me beneath this wild beast's hide? Yonder, just in front of thee, lie my bow and arrows, likewise my broadsword. Take them when I cut thy bonds. Now! Get them quickly!" So saying, he cut the bonds, and Little John, quick as a wink, leaped forward and caught up the bow and arrows and the broadsword. At the same time Robin Hood threw back the cowl of horse's hide from his face and bent Guy of Gisbourne's bow, with a keen, barbed arrow fitted to the string. "Stand back!" cried he, sternly. "The first man that toucheth finger to bowstring dieth! I have slain thy man, Sheriff; take heed that it is not thy turn next." Then, seeing that Little John had armed himself, he clapped his bugle horn to his lips and blew three blasts both loud and shrill.

Now when the Sheriff of Nottingham saw whose face it was beneath Guy of Gisbourne's hood, and when he heard those bugle notes ring in his ear, he felt as if his hour had come. "Robin Hood!" roared he, and without another word he wheeled his horse in the road and went off in a cloud of dust. The Sheriff's men, seeing their master thus fleeing for his life, thought that it was not their business to tarry longer, so, clapping spurs to their horses, they also dashed away after him. But though the Sheriff of Nottingham went fast, he could not outstrip a clothyard arrow. Little John twanged his bowstring with a shout, and when the Sheriff dashed in through the gates of Nottingham Town at full speed, a gray goose shaft stuck out behind him like a moulting sparrow with one feather in its tail. For a month afterwards the poor Sheriff could sit upon nought but the softest cushions that could be gotten for him.

Thus the Sheriff and a score of men ran away from Robin Hood and Little John; so that when Will Stutely and a dozen or more of stout yeomen burst from out the covert, they saw nought of their master's enemies, for the Sheriff and his men were scouring away in the distance, hidden within a cloud of dust like a little thunder-storm.

Then they all went back into the forest once more, where they found the widow's three sons, who ran to Little John and kissed his hands. But it would not do for them to roam the forest at large any more; so they promised that, after they had gone and told their mother of their escape, they would come that night to the greenwood tree, and thenceforth become men of the band.

Thus end the bravest adventures that ever befell Robin Hood and Little John. So next we shall hear how stout King Richard of the Lion's Heart visited Robin in Sherwood Forest.

$$2$$

KING RICHARD COMETH TO SHERWOOD FOREST

NOT MORE THAN TWO MONTHS HAD PASSED AND GONE SINCE these stirring adventures that have just been told of befell Robin Hood and Little John, when all Nottinghamshire was in a mighty stir and tumult, for King Richard of the Lion's Heart was making a royal progress through merry England, and every one expected him to come to Nottingham Town in his journeying. Messengers went riding back and forth between the Sheriff and the King, until at last the time was fixed upon when his majesty was to stop in Nottingham, as the guest of his worship.

And now came more bustle than ever; a great running hither and thither, a rapping of hammers and a babble of voices sounded everywhere through the place, for the folk were building great arches across the streets, beneath which the King was to pass, and were draping these arches with silken banners and streamers of many colors. Great hubbub was going on in the Guild Hall of the town, also, for here a grand banquet was to be given to the King and the

nobles of his train, and the best master carpenters were busy building a throne where the King and the Sheriff were to sit at the head of the table, side by side.

It seemed to many of the good folk of the place as if the day that should bring the King into the town would never come; but all the same it did come in its own season, and bright shone the sun down into the stony streets, which were all alive with a restless sea of people. On either side of the way great crowds of town and country folk stood packed as close together as dried herring in a box, so that the Sheriff's men, halbreds in hands, could hardly press them back to leave space for the King's riding.

"Take care whom thou pushest against!" cried a great, burly friar to one of these men. "Wouldst thou dig thine elbows into me, sirrah? By 'r Lady of the Fountain, an thou dost not treat me with more deference I will crack thy knave's pate for thee, even though thou be one of the mighty Sheriff's men."

At this a great shout of laughter arose from a number of tall yeomen in Lincoln green that were scattered through the crowd thereabouts; but one that seemed of more authority than the others nudged the holy man with his elbow. "Peace, Tuck," said he; "didst thou not promise me, ere thou camest here, that thou wouldst put a check upon thy tongue?"

"Ay, marry," grumbled the other, "but I did not think to have a hard-footed knave trample all over my poor toes as though they were no more than so many acorns in the forest."

But of a sudden all this bickering ceased, for a clear sound of many bugle horns came winding down the street. Then all the people craned their necks and gazed in the direction whence the sound came, and the crowding and the pushing and the swaying grew greater than ever. And now a gallant array of men came gleaming into sight, and the cheering of the people ran down the crowd as the fire runs in dry grass.

Eight and twenty heralds in velvet and cloth of gold came riding forwards. Over their heads fluttered a cloud of snow-white feathers, and each herald bore in his hand a long silver trumpet, which he blew musically. From each trumpet hung a heavy banner of velvet and cloth of gold, with the royal arms of England emblazoned thereon. After these came riding fivescore noble knights, two by two, all fully armed, saving that their heads were uncovered. In their hands they bore tall lances, from the tops of which fluttered pennons of many colors and devices. By the side of each knight walked a page clad in rich clothes of silk and velvet, and each page bore in his hands his master's helmet, from which waved long, floating plumes of feathers. Never had Nottingham seen a fairer sight than those fivescore noble knights, from whose armor the sun blazed in dazzling light as they came riding on their great war-horses, with clashing of arms and jingling of chains. Behind the knights came the barons and the nobles of the midcountry, in robes of silk and cloth of gold, with golden chains about their necks and jewels at their girdles. Behind these again came a great array of men-at-arms, with spears and halberds in their hands, and, in the midst of these, two riders side by side. One of the horsemen was the Sheriff of Nottingham in his robes of office. The other, who was a head taller than the Sheriff, was clad in a rich but simple garb, with a broad, heavy chain about his neck. His hair and beard were like threads of gold, and his eyes were as blue as the summer sky. As he rode along he bowed to the right hand and the left, and a mighty roar of voices followed him as he passed; for this was King Richard.

Then, above all the tumult and the shouting a great voice was heard roaring, "Heaven, its saints bless thee, our gracious King Richard! and likewise Our Lady of the Fountain, bless thee!" Then King Richard, looking toward the spot whence the sound came, saw a tall, burly, strapping priest standing in front of all the crowd with his legs wide apart as he backed against those behind.

"By my soul, Sheriff," said the King, laughing, "ye have the tallest priests in Nottinghamshire that e'er I saw in all my life. If Heaven never answered prayers because of deafness, methinks I would nevertheless have blessings bestowed upon me, for that man yonder would make the great stone image of Saint Peter rub its ears and hearken unto him. I would that I had an army of such as he."

To this the Sheriff answered never a word, but all the blood left his cheeks, and he caught at the pommel of his saddle to keep himself from falling; for he also saw the fellow that so shouted, and knew him to be Friar

Tuck; and, moreover, behind Friar Tuck he saw the faces of Robin Hood and Little John and Will Scarlet and Will Stutely and Allan a Dale and others of the band.

"How now," said the King hastily, "art thou ill, Sheriff, that thou growest so white?"

"Nay, your majesty," said the Sheriff, "it was nought but a sudden pain that will soon pass by." Thus he spake, for he was ashamed that the King should know that Robin Hood feared him so little that he thus dared to come within the very gates of Nottingham Town.

Thus rode the King into Nottingham Town on that bright afternoon in the early fall season; and none rejoiced more than Robin Hood and his merry men to see him come so royally unto his own.

EVENTIDE HAD COME; THE GREAT FEAST IN THE GUILD HALL at Nottingham Town was done, and the wine passed freely. A thousand waxen lights gleamed along the board, at which sat lord and noble and knight and squire in goodly array. At the head of the table, upon a throne all hung with cloth of gold, sat King Richard with the Sheriff of Nottingham beside him.

Quoth the King to the Sheriff, laughing as he spoke, "I have heard much spoken concerning the doings of certain fellows hereabouts, one Robin Hood and his band, who are outlaws and abide in Sherwood Forest. Canst thou not tell me somewhat of them, Sir Sheriff? for I hear that thou hast had dealings with them more than once."

At these words the Sheriff of Nottingham looked down gloomily, and the Bishop of Hereford, who was present, gnawed his nether lip. Quoth the Sheriff, "I can tell your majesty but little concerning the doings of those naughty fellows, saving that they are the boldest law-breakers in all the land."

Then up spake young Sir Henry of the Lea, a great favorite with the King, under whom he had fought in Palestine. "May it please your majesty," said he, "when I was away in Palestine I heard ofttimes from my father, and in most cases I heard of this very fellow, Robin Hood. If your majesty would like I will tell you a certain adventure of this outlaw."

Then the King laughingly bade him tell his tale, whereupon he told how Robin Hood had aided Sir Richard of the Lea with money that he had borrowed from the Bishop of Hereford. Again and again the King and those present roared with laughter, whilst the poor Bishop waxed cherry red in the face with vexation, for the matter was a sore thing with him. When Sir Henry of the Lea was done, others of those present, seeing how the King enjoyed this merry tale, told other tales concerning Robin and his merry men.

"By the hilt of my sword," said stout King Richard, "this is as bold and merry a knave as ever I heard tell of. Marry, I must take this matter in hand and do what thou couldst not do, Sheriff, to wit, clear the forest of him and his band."

That night the King sat in the place that was set apart for his lodging whilst in Nottingham Town. With him were young Sir Henry of the Lea and two other knights and three barons of Nottinghamshire; but the King's mind still dwelt upon Robin Hood. "Now," quoth he, "I would freely give a hundred pounds to meet this roguish fellow, Robin Hood, and to see somewhat of his doings in Sherwood Forest."

Then up spake Sir Hubert of Bingham, laughing: "If your majesty hath such a desire upon you it is not so hard to satisfy. If your majesty is willing to lose one hundred pounds, I will engage to cause you not only to meet this fellow, but to feast with him in Sherwood."

"Marry, Sir Hubert," quoth the King, "this pleaseth me well. But how wilt thou cause me to meet Robin Hood?"

"Why, thus," said Sir Hubert; "let your majesty and us here present put on the robes of seven of the Order of Black Friars, and let your majesty hang a purse of one hundred pounds beneath your gown; then let us undertake to ride from here to Mansfield Town tomorrow, and, without I am much mistaken, we will both meet with Robin Hood and dine with him before the day be passed."

"I like thy plan, Sir Hubert," quoth the King merrily, "and tomorrow we will try it and see whether there be virtue in it."

So it happened that when early the next morning the Sheriff came to where his liege lord was abiding to pay his duty to him, the King told him what they had talked of the night before, and what merry adventure they were set upon undertaking that morning. But when the Sheriff heard this he smote his forehead with his fist. "Alas!" said he, "what evil counsel is this that hath been given thee! O my gracious lord and king, you know not what you do! This villain that you thus go to seek hath no reverence either for king or king's laws."

"But did I not hear aright when I was told that this Robin Hood hath shed no blood since he was outlawed, saving only that of that vile Guy of Gisbourne, for whose death all honest men should thank him?"

"Yea, your majesty," said the Sheriff, "you have heard aright. Nevertheless"—

"Then," quoth the King, breaking in on the Sheriff's speech, "what have I to fear in meeting him, having done him no harm? Truly, there is no danger in this. But mayhap thou wilt go with us, Sir Sheriff."

"Nay," quoth the Sheriff hastily, "Heaven forbid!"

But now seven habits such as black friars wear were brought, and the King and those about him having clad themselves therein, and his majesty having hung a purse with a hundred golden pounds in it beneath his robes, they all went forth and mounted the mules that had been brought to the door for them. Then the King bade the Sheriff be silent as to their doings, and so they set forth upon their way.

Onward they travelled, laughing and jesting, until they passed through the open country; between bare harvest fields whence the harvest had been gathered home; through scattered glades that began to thicken as they went farther along, till they came within the heavy shade of the forest itself. They travelled in the forest for several miles without meeting any one such as they sought, until they had come to that part of the road that lay nearest to Newstead Abbey.

"By the holy Saint Martin," quoth the King, "I would that I had a better head for remembering things of great need. Here have we come away and brought never so much as a drop of anything to drink with us. Now I would give half a hundred pounds for somewhat to quench my thirst withal."

No sooner had the King so spoken, than out from the covert at the roadside stepped a tall fellow with yellow beard and hair and a pair of merry blue eyes. "Truly, holy brother," said he, laying his hand upon the King's bridle rein, "it were an unchristian thing to not give fitting answer to so fair a bargain. We keep an inn hereabouts, and for fifty pounds we will not only give thee a good draught of wine, but will give thee as noble a feast as ever thou didst tickle thy gullet withal." So saying he put his fingers to his lips and blew a shrill whistle. Then straightway the bushes and branches on either side of the road swayed and crackled, and threescore broad-shouldered yeomen in Lincoln green burst out of the covert.

"How now, fellow," quoth the King, "who art thou, thou naughty rogue? Hast thou no regard for such holy men as we are?"

"Not a whit," quoth merry Robin Hood, for the fellow was he; "for in sooth all the holiness belonging to rich friars, such as ye are, one could drop into a thimble and the good wife would never feel it with the tip of her finger. As for my name, it is Robin Hood, and thou mayst have heard it before."

"Now out upon thee!" quoth King Richard. "Thou art a bold and naughty fellow and a lawless one withal, as I have often heard tell. Now, prythee, let me, and these brethren of mine, travel forward in peace and quietness."

"It may not be," said Robin, "for it would look but ill of us to let such holy men travel onward with empty stomachs. But I doubt not that thou hast a fat purse to pay thy score at our inn since thou offerest freely so much for a poor draught of wine. Show me thy purse, reverend brother, or I may perchance have to strip thy robes from thee to search for it myself."

"Nay, use no force," said the King sternly. "Here is my purse, but lay not thy lawless hands upon our person."

"Hut, tut," quoth merry Robin, "what proud words are these? Art thou the King of England, to talk so to me? Here, Will, take this purse and see what there is within."

Will Scarlet took the purse and counted out the money. Then Robin bade him keep fifty pounds for themselves, and put fifty back into the purse. This he handed to the King. "Here, brother," quoth he, "take this half of thy money, and thank Saint Martin, on whom thou didst call before, that thou hast fallen into the hands of such gentle rogues that they will not strip thee bare, as they might do. But wilt thou not put back thy cowl? for I would fain see thy face."

"Nay," said the King, drawing back, "I may not put back my cowl, for we seven have vowed that we will not show our faces for four and twenty hours."

"Then keep them covered in peace," said Robin, "and far be it from me to make you break your vows."

So he called seven of his yeomen and bade them each one take a mule by the bridle; then, turning their faces toward the depths of the woodlands, they journeyed onward until they came to the open glade and the green-wood tree.

Little John, with threescore yeomen at his heels, had also gone forth that morning to wait along the roads and bring a rich guest to Sherwood glade, if such might be his luck, for many with fat purses must travel the roads at this time, when such great doings were going on in Nottinghamshire; but though Little John and so many others were gone, Friar Tuck and twoscore or more stout yeomen were seated or lying around beneath the great tree, and when Robin and the others came they leaped to their feet to meet him.

"By my soul," quoth merry King Richard, when he had gotten down from his mule and stood looking about him, "thou hast in very truth a fine lot of young men about thee, Robin. Methinks King Richard himself would be glad of such a body guard."

"These are not all of my fellows," said Robin, proudly "for threescore more of them are away on business with my good right-hand man, Little John. But, as for King Richard, I tell thee, brother, there is not a man of us all but would pour out our blood like water for him. Ye churchmen cannot rightly understand our King; but we yeomen love him right loyally for the sake of his brave doings which are so like our own."

But now Friar Tuck came bustling up. "Gi' ye good den, brothers," said he. "I am right glad to welcome some of my cloth in this naughty place. Truly, me-thinks these rogues of outlaws would stand but an ill chance were it not for the prayers of Holy Tuck, who laboreth so hard for their well being." Here he winked one eye slyly and stuck his tongue into his cheek.

"Who art thou, mad priest?" said the King in a serious voice, albeit he smiled beneath his cowl.

At this Friar Tuck looked all around with a slow gaze. "Look you now," quoth he, "never let me hear you say again that I am no patient man. Here is a knave of a fair calleth me a mad priest, and yet I smite him not. My name is Friar Tuck, fellow,—the holy Friar Tuck."

"There, Tuck," said Robin, "thou hast said enow. Prythee, cease thy talk and bring some wine. These reverend men are athirst, and sin' they have paid so richly for their score they must e'en have the best."

Friar Tuck bridled at being so checked in his speech, nevertheless he went straightway to do Robin's bidding; so presently a great crock was brought, and wine was poured out for all the guests and for Robin Hood. Then Robin held his cup aloft. "Stay!" cried he. "Tarry in your drinking till I give you a pledge. Here is to good King Richard of great renown, and may all enemies to him be confounded."

Then all drank the King's health, even the King himself. "Methinks, good fellow," said he, "thou hast drunk to thine own confusion."

"Never a whit," quoth merry Robin, "for I tell thee that we of Sherwood are more loyal to our lord the King than those of thine order. We would give up our very lives for his benefiting, whilst ye are content to lie snug in your abbeys and priories, let reign who will."

At this the King laughed. Quoth he, "Perhaps King Richard's welfare is more to me than thou wottest of, fellow. But enough of that matter. We have paid well for our fare, so canst thou not show us some merry entertainment? I have oft heard that ye are wondrous archers; wilt thou not show us somewhat of your skill?"

"With all my heart," said Robin; "we are always pleased to show our guests all the sport that is to be seen. As Gaffer Swanthold sayeth, ' 'Tis a hard heart that will not give a caged starling of the best'; and caged starlings ye are with us. Ho, lads! set up a garland at the end of the glade."

Then, as the yeomen ran to do their master's bidding, Tuck turned to one of the mock friars. "Hearest thou our master?" quoth he, with a sly wink. "Whenever he cometh across some poor piece of wit he straightway layeth it on the shoulders of this Gaffer Swanthold,— whoever he may be,—so that the poor goodman goeth travelling about with all the odds and ends and tags and rags of our master's brain packed on his back." Thus spake Friar Tuck, but in a low voice so that Robin could not hear him, for he felt somewhat nettled at Robin's cutting his talk so short.

In the mean time the mark at which they were to shoot was set up at sixscore paces distance. It was a garland of leaves and flowers two spans in width, which same was hung upon a stake in front of a broad tree-trunk. "There," quoth Robin, "yon is a fair mark, lads. Each of you shoot three arrows thereat; and if any fellow misseth by so much as one arrow, he shall have a buffet of Will Scarlet's fist."

"Hearken to him!" quoth Friar Tuck. "Why, master, thou dost bestow buffets from thy strapping nephew as though they were love taps from some bouncing lass. I warrant thou art safe to hit the garland thyself, or thou wouldst not be so free of his cuffing."

First David of Doncaster shot, and lodged all three of his arrows within the garland. "Well done, David!" cried Robin, "thou hast saved thine ears from a warming this day." Next Midge, the Miller, shot, and he, also, lodged his arrows in the garland. Then followed Wat, the Tinker, but alas for him! for one of his shafts missed the mark by the breadth of two fingers.

"Come hither, fellow," said Will Scarlet, in his soft, gentle voice; "I owe thee somewhat that I would pay forthwith." Then Wat, the Tinker, came forward and stood in front of Will Scarlet, screwing up his face and shutting his eyes tightly, as though he already felt his ears ringing with the buffet. Will Scarlet rolled up his sleeve, and, standing on tiptoe to give the greater swing to his arm, he struck with might and main. "*Whoof!*" came his palm against the Tinker's head, and down went stout Wat to the grass, heels over head, as the wooden image at the fair goes down when the skillful player throws a cudgel at it. Then, as the Tinker sat up upon the grass, rubbing his ear and winking and blinking at the bright stars that danced before his eyes, the yeomen roared with mirth till the forest rang. As for King Richard, he laughed till the tears ran down his cheeks. Thus the band shot, each in turn, some getting off scot free, and some winning a buffet that always sent them to the grass. And now, last of all, Robin took his place, and all was hushed as he shot. The first shaft he shot split a piece from the stake on which the garland was hung; the second shaft lodged within an inch of the other. "By my halidom," said King Richard to himself, "I would give a thousand pounds for this fellow to be one of my guard!" And now, for the third time Robin shot; but, alas for him! the arrow was ill-feathered, and, wavering to one side, it smote an inch outside the garland.

At this a great roar went up, those of the yeomen who sat upon the grass rolling over and over and shouting with laughter, for never before had they seen their master so miss but Robin flung his bow upon the ground with vexation. "Now, out upon it!" cried he. "That shaft had an ill feather to it, for I felt it as it left my fingers. Give me a clean arrow, and I will engage to split the wand with it."

At these words the yeomen laughed louder than ever. "Nay, good uncle," said Will Scarlet, in his soft, sweet voice, "thou hast had thy fair chance and hast missed thine aim out and out. I swear the arrow was as good as any that hath been loosed this day. Come hither; I owe thee somewhat, and would fain pay it."

"Go, good master," roared Friar Tuck, "and may my blessing go with thee. Thou hast bestowed these love taps of Will Scarlet's with great freedom. It were pity an thou gottest not thine own share."

"It may not be," said merry Robin. "I am king here, and no subject may raise hand against the king. But even our great King Richard may yield to the holy Pope without shame, and even take a tap from him by way of penance; therefore I will yield myself to this holy friar, who seemeth to be one in authority, and will take my punishment from him." Thus saying, he turned to the King, "I prythee, brother, wilt thou take my punishment into thy holy hands?"

"With all my heart," quoth merry King Richard, rising from where he was sitting. "I owe thee somewhat for having lifted a heavy weight of fifty pounds from my purse. So make room for him on the green, lads."

"An thou makest me tumble," quoth Robin, "I will freely give thee back thy fifty pounds; but I tell thee, brother, if thou makest me not feel grass all along my back, I will take away every farthing thou hast for thy boastful speech."

"So be it," said the King, "I am willing to venture it." Thereupon he rolled up his sleeve and showed an arm that made the yeoman stare. But Robin, with his feet wide apart, stood firmly planted, waiting the other, smiling. Then the King swung back his arm, and, balancing himself a moment, he delivered a buffet at Robin that fell like a thunderbolt. Down went Robin headlong upon the grass, for the stroke would have felled a stone wall. Then how the yeomen shouted with laughter till their sides ached, for never had they seen such a buffet given in all their lives. As for Robin, he presently sat up and looked all around him, as though he had dropped from a cloud and had lit in a place he had never seen before. After a while, still gazing about him at his laughing yeomen, he put his finger-tips softly to his ear and felt all around it tenderly. "Will Scarlet," said he, "count this fellow out his fifty pounds; I want nothing more either of his money or of him. A murrain seize him and his buffeting! I would that I had taken my dues from thee, for I verily believe he hath deafened mine ear from ever hearing again."

Then, while gusts of laughter still broke from the band, Will Scarlet counted out the fifty pounds, and the King dropped it back into his purse again. "I give thee thanks, fellow," said he, "and if ever thou shouldst wish for another box of the ear to match the one thou hast, come to me and I will fit thee with it for nought."

So spake the merry King; but, even as he ended, there came suddenly the sound of many voices, and out from the covert burst Little John and threescore men, with Sir Richard of the Lea in the midst. Across the glade they came running, and, as they came, Sir Richard shouted to Robin: "Make haste, dear friend, gather thy band together and come with me! King Richard left Nottingham Town this very morning, and cometh to seek thee in the woodlands. I know not how he cometh, for it was but a rumor of this that reached me; nevertheless, I know that it is the truth. Therefore hasten with all thy men, and come to Castle Lea, for there thou mayst lie hidden till thy present danger passeth. Who are these strangers that thou hast with thee?"

"Why," quoth merry Robin, rising from the grass, "these are certain gentle guests that came with us from the high-road over by Newstead

Abbey. I know not their names, but I have become right well acquaint with this lusty rogue's palm this morning. Marry, the pleasure of this acquaintance hath cost me a deaf ear and fifty pounds to boot!"

Sir Richard looked keenly at the tall friar, who, drawing himself up to his full height, looked fixedly back at the knight. Then of a sudden Sir Richard's cheeks grew pale, for he knew who it was that he looked upon. Quickly he leaped from off his horse's back and flung himself upon his knees before the other. At this, the King, seeing that Sir Richard knew him, threw back his cowl, and all the yeomen saw his face and knew him also, for there was not one of them but had been in the crowd in the good town of Nottingham, and had seen him riding side by side with the Sheriff. Down they fell upon their knees, nor could they say a word. Then the King looked all around right grimly, and, last of all, his glance came back and rested again upon Sir Richard of the Lea.

"How is this, Sir Richard?" said he, sternly. "How darest thou step between me and these fellows? and how darest thou offer thy knightly Castle of the Lea for a refuge to them? Wilt thou make it a hiding-place for the most renowned outlaws in England?"

Then Sir Richard of the Lea raised his eyes to the King's face. "Far be it from me," said he, "to do aught that could bring your majesty's anger upon me. Yet, sooner would I face your majesty's wrath than suffer aught of harm that I could stay to fall upon Robin Hood and his band; for to them I owe life, honor, everything. Should I, then, desert him in his hour of need?"

Ere the Knight had done speaking, one of the mock friars that stood near the King came forward and knelt beside Sir Richard, and throwing back his cowl showed the face of young Sir Henry of the Lea. Then Sir Henry grasped his father's hand and said, "Here kneels one who hath served thee well, King Richard, and, as thou knowest, hath stepped between thee and death in Palestine; yet do I abide by my dear father, and here I say also, that I would freely give shelter to this noble outlaw, Robin Hood, even though it brought thy wrath upon me, for my father's honor and my father's welfare are as dear to me as mine own."

King Richard looked from one to the other of the kneeling knights, and at last the frown faded from his brow and a smile twitched at the corners of his lips. "Marry, Sir Richard;" quoth the King, "thou art a bold-spoken knight, and thy freedom of speech weigheth not heavily against thee with me. This young son of thine taketh after his sire both in boldness of speech and of deed, for, as he sayeth, he stepped one time betwixt me and death; wherefore I would pardon thee for his sake even if thou hadst done more than thou hast. Rise all of you, for ye shall suffer no harm through me this day, for it were pity that a merry time should end in such a manner as to mar its joyousness."

Then all arose and the King beckoned Robin Hood to come to him, "How now," quoth he, "is thine ear still too deaf to hear me speak?"

"Mine ears would be deafened in death ere they would cease to hear your majesty's voice," said Robin. "As for the blow that your majesty struck me, I would say that though my sins are haply many, methinks they have been paid up in full thereby."

"Thinkest thou so?" said the King with somewhat of sternness in his voice. "Now I tell thee that but for three things, to wit, my mercifulness, my love for a stout woodsman, and the loyalty thou hast avowed for me, thine ears, mayhap, might have been more tightly closed than ever a buffet from me could have shut them. Talk not lightly of thy sins, good Robin. But come, look up. Thy danger is past, for hereby I give thee and all thy band free pardon. But, in sooth, I cannot let you roam the forest as ye have done in the past; therefore I will take thee at thy word, when thou didst say thou wouldst give thy service to me, and thou shalt go back to London with me. We will take that bold knave Little John also, and likewise thy cousin, Will Scarlet, and thy minstrel, Allan a Dale. As for the rest of thy band, we will take their names and have them duly recorded as royal rangers; for methinks it were wiser to have them changed to law-abiding caretakers of our deer in Sherwood than to leave them to run at large as outlawed slayers thereof. But now get a feast ready, for I would fain see how ye live here in the leafy woodlands."

So Robin bade his men make ready a grand feast; and straightway great fires were kindled and burned brightly, at which fires savory things roasted sweetly. While this was going forward, the King bade Robin Hood call Allan a Dale for he would hear him sing. So word was passed for Allan, and presently he came, bringing his harp.

"Marry," said King Richard, "if thy singing match thy looks it is fair enough. Prythee strike up a ditty and let us have a taste of thy skill."

Then Allan touched his harp lightly, and all words were hushed while he sang thus:—

> *"Oh where hast thou been, my daughter?*
> *Oh where hast thou been this day,*
> *Daughter, my daughter?*
> *'Oh, I have been to the river's side,*
> *Where the waters lie all gray and wide,*
> *And the gray sky broods o'er the leaden tide,*
> *And the shrill wind sighs a straining.'*
>
> *" 'What sawest thou there, my daughter?*
> *What sawest thou there this day,*
> *Daughter, my daughter?'*
> *'Oh, I saw a boat come drifting nigh,*
> *Where the quivering rushes hiss and sigh.*
> *And the water soughs as it gurgles by,*
> *And the shrill wind sighs a straining.'*
>
> *" 'What sailed in the boat, my daughter?*
> *What sailed in the boat this day,*
> *Daughter, my daughter?'*
> *'Oh, there was one all clad in white,*
> *And about his face hung a pallid light,*
> *And his eyes gleamed sharp like the stars at night,*
> *And the shrill wind sighed a straining.'*
>
> *"'And what said he, my daughter?*
> *What said he to thee this day,*
> *Daughter, my daughter?'*
> *'Oh, said he nought, but did he this:*

Thrice on my lips did he press a kiss,
And my heartstrings shrunk with an awful bliss,
And the shrill wind sighed a straining.'

" 'Why growest thou so cold, my daughter?*
Why growest thou so cold and white,
Daughter, my daughter?'
Oh never a word the daughter said,
But she sat all straight with a drooping head,
For her heart was stilled and her face was dead:
And the shrill wind sighed a straining."

All listened in silence; and when Allan a Dale had done King Richard heaved a sigh. "By the breath of my body, Allan," quoth he, "thou hast such a wonderous sweet voice that it strangely moves my heart. But what doleful ditty is this for the lips of a stout yeoman? I would rather hear thee sing a song of love and battle than a sad thing like that. Moreover, I understand it not; what meanest thou by the words?"

"I know not, your majesty," said Allan, shaking his head, "for ofttimes I sing that which I do not clearly understand mine own self."

"Well, well," quoth the King, "let it pass; only I tell thee this, Allan, thou shouldst turn thy songs to such matters as I spoke of, to wit, love or war; for in sooth thou hast a sweeter voice than Blondell, and methought he was the best minstrel that ever I heard."

But now one came forward and said that the feast was ready; so Robin Hood brought King Richard and those with him to where it lay all spread out on fair white linen cloths which lay upon the soft green grass. Then King Richard sat him down and feasted and drank, and when he was done he swore roundly that he had never sat at such a lusty repast in all his life before.

That night he lay in Sherwood Forest upon a bed of sweet green leaves, and early the next morning he set forth from the woodlands for Nottingham Town, Robin Hood and all of his band going with him. You may guess what a stir there was in the good town when all these famous outlaws came marching into the streets. As for the Sheriff, he knew not what to say nor where to look when he saw Robin Hood in such high favor with the King, whilst all his heart was filled with gall because of the vexation that lay upon him.

The next day the King took leave of Nottingham Town; so Robin Hood and Little John and and Will Scarlet and Allan a Dale shook hands with all the rest of the band, kissing the cheeks of each man, and swearing that they would often come to Sherwood and see them. Then each mounted his horse and rode away in the train of the King.

THUS END THE MERRY ADVENTURES OF ROBIN HOOD; FOR, in spite of his promise, it was many a year ere he saw Sherwood again.

After a year or two at court Little John came back to Nottinghamshire, where he lived in an orderly way, though within sight of Sherwood, and where he achieved great fame as the champion of all England with the quarterstaff. Will Scarlet after a time came back to his own home, whence he had been driven by his unlucky killing of his father's steward. The rest of the band did their duty as royal rangers right well. But Robin Hood and Allan a Dale did not come again to Sherwood so quickly, for thus it was:—

Robin, through his great fame as an archer, became a favorite with the King, so that he speedily arose in rank to be the chief of all the yeomen. At last the King, seeing how faithful and how loyal he was, created him Earl of Huntingdon; so Robin followed the King to the wars, and found his time so full that he had no chance to come back to Sherwood for even so much as a day. As for Allan a Dale and his wife, the fair Ellen, they followed Robin Hood and shared in all his ups and downs of life.

Thus all things have an end, but not such a lucky ending as befell Robin Hood and his band of stout yeomen in famous Sherwood Forest.

EPILOGUE

Telling how Robin Hood came back again to Sherwood Forest, and how Sir William Dale was sent against him to take him. Likewise it is told how Robin Hood died by the treachery of his cousin, the Prioress of the Nunnery of Kirklees.

AND NOW, DEAR FRIEND,—YOU WHO HAVE JOURNEYED WITH me in all these merry doings,—I will not bid you follow me further, but will drop your hand here with a "good den," if you wish it; for that which cometh hereafter speaks of the breaking up of things, and shows how joy and pleasures that are dead and gone can never be set upon their feet to walk again. I will not dwell upon the matter over long, but will tell as speedily as may be of how that stout fellow, Robin Hood, died as he had lived, not at court as Earl of Huntingdon, but with bow in hand, his heart in the greenwood, and he himself a right yeoman.

KING RICHARD DIED UPON THE battlefield, in such a way as properly became a lion-hearted king, as you yourself, no doubt, know; so, after a time, the Earl of Huntingdon—or Robin Hood, as we will still call him as of old—finding nothing for his doing abroad, came back to merry England again. With him came Allan a Dale and his wife, the fair Ellen, for these two had been chief of Robin's household ever since he had left Sherwood Forest.

It was in the spring-time when they landed once more on the shores of England. The leaves were green and the small birds sang blithely, just as they used to do in fair Sherwood when Robin Hood roamed the woodland shades with a free heart and a light heel. All the sweetness of the time and the joyousness of everything brought back to Robin's mind his forest life, so that a great longing came upon him to behold the woodlands once more. So he went straightway to King John and besought leave of him to visit Nottingham for a short season. The King gave him leave to come and to go, but bade him not stay longer than three days at Sherwood. So Robin Hood and Allan a Dale set forth without delay to Nottinghamshire and Sherwood Forest.

The first night they took up their inn at Nottingham Town, yet they did not go to pay their duty to the Sheriff, for his worship bore many a bitter grudge against Robin Hood, which grudges had not been lessened by Robin's rise in the world. The next day at an early hour they mounted their horses and set forth for the woodlands. As they passed along the road it seemed to Robin that he knew every stick and stone that his eyes looked upon. Yonder was a path that he had ofttimes trod of a mellow evening, with Little John beside him; here was one, now nigh choked with brambles, along which he and a little band had walked when they went forth to seek a certain curtal friar.

"Look, Allan!" cried Robin. "Dost thou not see the scar on yonder beechen tree? That was made when thine arrow stripped away a piece of the bark the day thy shaft missed the noble hart so sadly. That was the same day that we were caught by the storm, and had to lodge over night at the old farmer's house—he who had the three buxom daughters."

Thus they rode slowly onward, talking about these old, familiar things; old and yet new, for they found more in them than they had ever thought of before. Thus at last they came to the open glade, and the broad, wide-spreading greenwood tree which was their home for so many years. Neither of the two spoke when they stood beneath that tree. Robin looked all about him at the well known things, so like what they used to be and yet so different; for, where once was the bustle of many busy fellows was now the quietness of solitude; and, as he looked, the woodlands, the greensward, and the sky all blurred together in his sight through salt tears, for such a great yearning came upon him as he looked on these things (as well known to him as the fingers of his right hand) that he could not keep back the water from his eyes.

That morning he had slung his good old bugle horn over his shoulder, and now, with the yearning, came a great longing to sound this bugle once more. He raised it to his lips, he blew a blast. "Tirila, lirila," the sweet, clear notes went winding down the forest paths, coming back again from the more distant bosky shades in faint echoes of sound,—"Tirila, lirila, tirila, lirila," until it faded away and was lost.

Now it chanced that on that very morn Little John was walking through a spur of the forest upon certain matters of business, and as he paced along, sunk in meditation, the faint, clear notes of a distant bugle horn came to his ear. As leaps the stag when it feels the arrow at its heart, so leaped Little John when that distant sound met his ear. All the blood in his body seemed to rush like a flame into his cheeks as he bent his head and listened. Again came the bugle note, thin and clear, and yet again it sounded. Then Little John gave a great, wild cry of yearning, of joy, and yet of grief, and, putting down his head, he dashed into the thicket. Onward he plunged, crackling and rending, as the wild boar rushes through the underbrush. Little recked he of thorns and briars that scratched his flesh and tore his clothing, for all he thought of was to get, by the shortest way, to the greenwood glade whence he knew the sound of the bugle horn came. Out he burst from the covert, at last, a shower of little broken twigs falling about him, and, without pausing a moment, rushed forward and flung himself at Robin's feet. Then he clasped his arms around the master's knees, and all his body was shaken with great sobs; neither could Robin nor Allan a Dale speak, but stood looking down at Little John, the tears rolling down their cheeks.

Whilst they thus stood, seven royal rangers rushed into the open glade and raised a great shout of joy at the sight of Robin; and at their head was Will Stutely. Then, after a while, came four more, panting with their running, and two of these four were Will Scathelock and Midge, the Miller; for all of these had heard the sound of Robin Hood's horn. All these ran to Robin and kissed his hands and his clothing, with great sound of weeping.

After a while Robin looked around him with tear-dimmed eyes, and said, in a husky voice, "Now, I swear that never again will I leave these dear woodlands. I have been away from them and from you too long. Now do I lay by the name of Robert, Earl of Huntingdon, and take upon me once again that nobler title, Robin Hood, the Yeoman." At this a great shout went up, and all the yeomen shook one another's hands for joy.

The news that Robin Hood had come back again to dwell in Sherwood as of old spread like wildfire all over the countryside, so that ere a se'ennight had passed nearly all of his old yeomen had gathered about him again. But when the news of all this reached the ears of King John, he swore both loud and deep, and took a solemn vow that he would not rest until he had Robin Hood in his power, dead or alive. Now there was present at court a certain knight, Sir William Dale, as gallant a soldier as ever donned harness. Sir William Dale was well acquainted with Sherwood Forest, for he was head keeper over that part of it that lay nigh to good Mansfield Town; so to him the King turned, and bade him take an army of men and go straightway to seek Robin Hood. Likewise the King gave Sir William his signet ring to show to the Sheriff, that he might raise all his armed men to aid the others in their chase of Robin. So Sir William and the Sheriff set forth to do the King's bidding and to search for Robin Hood; and for seven days they hunted up and down, yet found him not.

Now, had Robin Hood been as peaceful as of old, everything might have ended in smoke, as other such ventures had always done before; but he had fought for years under King Richard, and was changed from what he used to be. It galled his pride to thus flee away before those sent against him, like a chased fox flees from the hounds; so thus it came about, at last, that Robin Hood and his yeomen met Sir William and the Sheriff and their men in the forest, and a bloody fight followed. The first man slain in that fight was the Sheriff of Nottingham, for he fell from his horse with an arrow in his brain ere half a score of shafts had been sped. Many a better man than the Sheriff kissed the sod that day, but at last, Sir William Dale being wounded and most of his men slain, he withdrew, beaten, and left the forest. But scores of good fellows were left behind him, stretched out all stiff beneath the sweet green boughs.

But though Robin Hood had beaten off his enemies in fair fight, all this lay heavily upon his mind, so that he brooded over it until a fever seized upon him. For three days it held him, and though he strove to fight it off, he was forced to yield at last. Thus it came that, on the morning of the fourth day, he called Little John to him, and told him that he could not shake the fever from him, and that he would go to his cousin, the Prioress of the nunnery near Kirklees, in Yorkshire, who was a skilful leech, and he would have her open a vein in his arm and take a little blood from him, for the bettering of his health. Then he bade Little John make ready to go also, for he might perchance need aid in his journeying. So Little John and he took their leave of the others, and Robin Hood bade Will Stutely be the captain of the band until they should come back. Thus they came by easy stages and slow journeying until they reached the nunnery of Kirklees.

Now Robin had done much to aid this cousin of his; for it was through King Richard's love of him that she had been made prioress of the place. But there is nought in the world so easily forgot as gratitude; so, when the Prioress of Kirklees had heard how her cousin, the Earl of Huntingdon, had thrown away his earldom and gone back again to Sherwood, she was vexed to the soul, and feared lest her cousinship with him should bring the King's wrath upon her also. Thus it happened that when Robin came to her and told her how he wished her services as leech, she began plotting ill against him in her mind, thinking that by doing evil to him she might find favor with his enemies. Nevertheless, she kept this well to herself, and received Robin with seeming kindness. She led him up the winding stone stair to a room which was just beneath the eaves of a high, round tower; but she would not let Little John come with him.

So the poor yeoman turned his feet away from the door of the nunnery, and left his master in the hands of the women. But, though he did not come in, neither did he go far away; for he laid him down in a little glade near by, where he could watch the place that Robin abided, like some great, faithful dog turned away from the door where his master has entered.

After the women had gotten Robin Hood to the room beneath the eaves, the Prioress sent all of the others away; then, taking a little cord, she tied it tightly about Robin's arm, as though she were about to bleed him. And so she did bleed him, but the vein she opened was not one of those that lie close and blue beneath the skin; deeper she cut than that, for she opened one of those veins through which the bright red blood runs leaping from the heart. Of this Robin knew not; for, though he saw the blood flow, it did not come fast enough to make him think that there was anything ill in it.

Having done this vile deed, the Prioress turned and left her cousin, locking the door behind her. All that livelong day the blood ran from Robin Hood's arm, nor could he check it, though he strove in every way to do so. Again and again he called for help, but no help came, for his cousin had betrayed him, and Little John was too far away to hear his voice. So he bled and bled until he felt his strength slipping away from him. Then he arose, tottering, and bearing himself up by the palms of his hands against the wall, he reached his bugle horn at last. Thrice he sounded it, but weakly and faintly, for his breath was fluttering through sickness and loss of strength; nevertheless, Little John heard it where he lay in the glade, and, with a heart all sick with dread, he came running and leaping toward the nunnery. Loudly he knocked at the door, and in a loud voice shouted for them to let him in; but the door was of massive oak, strongly barred, and studded with spikes, so they within felt safe, and bade Little John begone.

Then Little John's heart was mad with grief and fear for his master's life. Wildly he looked about him, and his sight fell upon a heavy stone mortar, such as three men could not lift now-a-days. Little John took three steps forward, and, bending his back, heaved the stone mortar up from where it stood, deeply rooted. Staggering under its weight, he came forward and hurled it crashing against the door. In burst the door, and away fled the frightened nuns, shrieking, at his coming. Then Little John strode in, and never a word said he, but up the winding stone steps he ran till he reached the room wherein his master was. Here he found the door locked also, but, putting his shoulder against it, he burst the locks as though they were made of brittle ice.

There he saw his own dear master leaning against the gray stone wall, his face all white and drawn, and his head swaying to and fro with weakness. Then, with a great, wild cry of love and grief and pity, Little John leaped forward and caught Robin Hood in his arms. Up he lifted him as a mother lifts her child, and carrying him to the bed, laid him tenderly thereon.

And now the Prioress came in hastily, for she was frightened at what she had done, and dreaded the vengeance of Little John and the others of the band; then she stanched the blood by cunning bandages, so that it flowed no more. All the while Little John stood grimly by, and after she had done he sternly bade her to begone, and she obeyed, pale and trembling. Then, after she had departed, Little John spake cheering words, laughing loudly, and saying that all this was a child's fright, and that no stout yeoman would die at the loss of a few drops of blood. "Why," quoth he, "give thee a se'en-night and thou wilt be roaming the woodlands as boldly as ever."

But Robin shook his head and smiled faintly where he lay. "Mine own dear Little John," whispered he, "Heaven bless thy kind, rough heart. But, dear friend, we will never roam the woodlands together again."

"Ay, but we will!" quoth Little John, loudly. "I say again, Ay—out upon it—who dares say that any more harm shall come upon thee? Am I not by? Let me see who dares touch—" Here he stopped of a sudden, for his words choked him. At last he said, in a deep, husky voice, "Now, if aught of harm befalls thee because of this day's doings, I swear by Saint George that the red cock shall crow over the roof-tree of this house, for the hot flames shall lick every crack and cranny thereof. As for these women,"—here he ground his teeth,—"it will be an ill day for them!"

But Robin Hood took Little John's rough, brown fist in his white hands, and chid him softly, in his low, weak voice, asking him since what time Little John had thought of doing harm to women, even in vengeance. Thus he talked till, at last, the other promised, in a choking voice, that no ill should fall upon the place, no matter what happened. Then a silence fell, and Little John sat with Robin Hood's hand in his, gazing out of the open window, ever and anon swallowing a great lump that came in his throat. Meantime the sun dropped slowly to the west, till all the sky was ablaze with a red glory. Then Robin Hood, in a weak, faltering voice, bade Little John raise him, that he might look out once more upon the woodlands; so the yeoman lifted him in his arms, as he bade, and Robin Hood's head lay on his friend's shoulder. Long he gazed, with a wide, lingering look, whilst the other sat with bowed head, the hot tears rolling one after another from his eyes, and dripping upon his bosom, for he felt that the time of parting was near at hand. Then, presently, Robin Hood bade him string his stout bow for him, and choose a smooth fair arrow from his quiver. This Little John did, though without disturbing his master or rising from where he sat. Robin Hood's fingers wrapped lovingly around his good bow, and he smiled faintly when he felt it in his grasp; then he nocked the arrow on that part of the string that the tips of his fingers knew so well. "Little John," said he, "Little John, mine own dear friend, and him I love better than all others in the world, mark, I prythee, where this arrow lodges, and there let my grave be digged. Lay me with my face toward the east, Little John, and see that my resting-place be kept green, and that my weary bones be not disturbed."

As he finished speaking, he raised himself of a sudden and sat upright. His old strength seemed to come back to him, and, drawing the bowstring to his ear, he sped the arrow out of the open casement. As the shaft flew, his hand sank slowly with the bow till it lay across his knees, and his body likewise sank back again into Little John's loving arms; but something had sped from that body, even as the winged arrow sped from the bow.

For some minutes Little John sat motionless, but presently he laid that which he held gently down, then, folding the hands upon the breast and covering up the face, he turned upon his heel and left the room without a word or a sound.

Upon the steep stairway he met the Prioress and some of the chief among the sisters. To them he spoke in a deep, quivering voice, and said he, "An ye go within a score of feet of yonder room, I will tear down your rookery over your heads so that not one stone shall be left upon another. Bear my words well in mind, for I mean them." So saying, he turned and left them, and they presently saw him running rapidly across the open, through the falling of the dusk, until he was swallowed up by the forest.

The early gray of the coming morn was just beginning to lighten the black sky toward the eastward when Little John and six more of the band came rapidly across the open toward the nunnery. They saw no one, for the sisters were all hidden away from sight, having been frightened by Little John's words. Up the stone stair they ran, and a great sound of weeping was presently heard. After a while this ceased, and then came the scuffling and shuffling of men's feet as they carried a heavy weight down the steep and winding stairs. So they went forth from the nunnery, and, as they passed through the doors thereof, a great, loud sound of wailing arose from the glade that lay all dark in the dawning, as though many men, hidden in the shadows, had lifted up their voices in sorrow.

Thus died Robin Hood, at Kirklees Nunnery, in fair Yorkshire, with mercy in his heart toward those that had been his undoing; for thus he showed mercy for the erring and pity for the weak through all the time of his living.

His yeomen were scattered henceforth, but no great ill befell them thereafter, for a more merciful sheriff and one who knew them not so well succeeding the one that had gone, and they being separated here and there throughout the countryside, they abided in peace and quietness, so that many lived to hand down these tales to their children and their children's children.

A certain one sayeth that upon a stone at Kirklees is an old inscription. This I give in the ancient English in which it was written, and thus it runs:—

> Hear undernead dis laitl stean
> lais robert earl of huntingtun
> near arrir ver as hie sae geud
> an pipl kauld im Robin Heud
> sick utlaws as hi an is men
> vil England nider si agen.
>
> obiit 24 kal. dekembris 1247

And now, dear friend, we also must part, for our merry journeyings have ended, and here, at the grave of Robin Hood, we turn, each going his own way.

QUESTIONS, QUESTIONS, QUESTIONS

by Arthur Pober, Ed.D.

PART OF THE JOY OF READING AND REREADING CLASSIC BOOKS is the opportunity to immerse ourselves in exciting adventures—visiting and revisiting friends and stories. Whether this is the first time you have read this story or the tenth time, the questions below will generate ideas about the story you never thought of before.

Questions don't have to provide answers. Questions can springboard into new thoughts, ideas, and interpretations of our favorite books. There are no right answers. Rather, here are opportunities to rethink your initial impressions of a character, event, or storyline—whether it's a book you've just encountered or one you first read many years ago.

◆

1. Most of Robin's men have special names or nicknames. Do these names have meaning, or do they appear to be randomly selected? Do you have a special name that you use with your friends?

2. Robin becomes an outlaw because he killed a man and poached one of the King's deer. Do you think it is unfair that this made him an outlaw? What would happen to Robin if he did these things today?

3. What did Robin like about the Sheriff's shooting contest? How did he participate without being caught? How quickly did you discover Robin's disguise?

4. The Sheriff says of Robin's men, "I would sooner lose mine office than my life, so I will trouble them no more." Do you think he left the merry men alone for the right reasons, or was the Sheriff just being cowardly? What would you have done in his place?

5. Why do you think Robin reacted so strangely to Little John's teasing about his fight with Will Scarlet? Do you think Little John acted appropriately? What might happen if people found out that Will Scarlet beat Robin?

6. Robin and Will Scarlet both became outlaws because they killed someone. How are the two deaths similar and how are they different?

7. Although Little John and Robin are excellent fighters, they both lose their fights; John to Arthur a Bland and Robin to Will Scarlet. Why do you think they lost? Have you ever lost at something you were certain you could win?

8. Robin makes Friar Tuck carry him across the river on his shoulders. How do you feel about Robin's behavior? Do you think he got what he deserved from the Friar?

9. Robin tells Sir Richard "The proud I strive to bring low, but those that walk in sorrow I would aid if I could." What do you think he means?

10. Sir Richard gives Robin his knightly word. What do you think this means? Is there an equivalent of that today?

11. Robin says to the Bishop, "thy pride may have a fall ere thou wottest of it." What does he mean by this? Does Robin's prediction come true?

12. Where do you think the terms knave, bray, quiver, and Lincoln green come from? What do you think they mean? Are there any terms that we use today that would seem odd in another time or place?

13. Robin claims that killing Guy of Gisbourne is justified. Why does he believe this? Is killing ever justified?

14. Robin can sometimes be self-centered. Do you agree? In what parts of the story do you see this behavior? Do you know anyone like Robin?

15. What is the difference between fact and legend? In what ways do you believe Robin's story is fact? What parts of Robin's life became legend?

ARTHUR POBER, ED.D.

Dr. Pober has spent over twenty years in the areas of early childhood and gifted education. He has been the principal of one of the world's oldest laboratory schools for gifted youngsters, Hunter College Elementary School, and was Director of Magnet Schools for the Gifted and Talented for over 25,000 youngsters in New York City.

Dr. Pober is a recognized authority in the areas of media and child protection and is currently the U.S. representative to the European Institute for the Media and European Advertising Standards Alliance.

ABOUT THE AUTHOR

Howard Pyle was born in Wilmington, Delaware on March 5, 1853. Primarily an artist, his illustrations appeared in *Harper's Weekly* as well as several other magazines. In 1883 Pyle published his first children's book, *The Merry Adventures of Robin Hood*. Throughout the course of his career, Pyle published more than fifteen additional books including *The Wonder Clock, The Garden Behind the Moon,* and *The Story of King Arthur and His Knights*. In 1894 Pyle was named director of illustration at the Drexel Institute in Philadelphia, and in 1900 he opened the Howard Pyle School of Art in Wilmington.

The illustrations for this series were created by Scott McKowen, who, with his wife, Christina Poddubiuk, operates Punch & Judy Inc., a company specializing in design and illustration for theater and performing arts. Their projects often involve research into the visual aspects of historical settings and characters. Christina is a theater set and costume designer and contributed advice on the period clothing for the illustrations.

Scott created these drawings in scratchboard—an engraving medium that evokes the look of popular art from the period of these stories. Scratchboard is an illustration board with a specifically prepared surface of hard, white chalk. A thin layer of black ink is rolled over the surface, then lines are drawn by hand with a sharp knife by scraping through the ink layer to expose the white surface underneath. The finished drawings are then scanned and the color added digitally.

Explore these wonderful stories in our classics library.

THE MERRY ADVENTURES OF ROBIN HOOD
Howard Pyle

THE ADVENTURES AND
THE MEMOIRS OF SHERLOCK HOLMES
Arthur Conan Doyle

THE ADVENTURES OF TOM SAWYER
Mark Twain

ANNE OF GREEN GABLES
L. M. Montgomery

BLACK BEAUTY
Anna Sewell

THE CALL OF THE WILD and WHITE FANG
Jack London

A LITTLE PRINCESS
Frances Hodgson Burnett

LITTLE WOMEN
Louisa May Alcott

THE SECRET GARDEN
Frances Hodgson Burnett

TREASURE ISLAND
Robert Louis Stevenson

SPANISH AMERICAN WRITING
SINCE 1941

SPANISH AMERICAN WRITING SINCE 1941
A Critical Survey

George R. McMurray

UNGAR ● NEW YORK

1987
The Ungar Publishing Company
370 Lexington Avenue, New York, N.Y. 10017

Printed in the United States of America

Library of Congress Cataloging-in-Publication Data

McMurray, George R., 1925–
  Spanish American writing since 1941.

  Bibliography: p.
  Includes index.
  1. Spanish American literature—20th century—
      History and criticism. I. Title.
PQ7081.M373   1986   860′.9′98   86–6908
ISBN 0–8044–2623–6

To my wife, Doris

CONTENTS

3 ▪ POETRY   146

4 ▪ DRAMA 202

PREFACE

Spanish American Writing since 1941: A Critical Survey presents an overview of the vast volume of literary works produced by the eighteen Spanish-speaking nations of the Western Hemisphere plus Puerto Rico. Although this study may be useful to the specialist, it is intended primarily for readers of English who wish to learn more about the rich culture of their southern neighbors. An in-depth discussion of such a broad subject would require far more space than that allotted here. Therefore, I have not attempted to include every author worthy of attention, but rather have selected those I consider the most significant and representative. My choices have at times been extremely difficult, especially in the sections on Mexico and Argentina, two nations with long rosters of fine writers.

Chapters 2, 3, and 4 (Fiction, Poetry, and Drama) are divided into discussions of the major, internationally known figures, after which important, but less prominent, authors are treated under the following headings: Mexico, the Caribbean (Cuba, the Dominican Republic, and Puerto Rico), Central America (Costa Rica, El Salvador, Guatemala, Honduras, Nicaragua, and Panama), Colombia and Venezuela, The Andean Highlands (Bolivia, Ecuador, and Peru), and The Southern Cone (Argentina, Chile, Paraguay, and Uruguay). The authors of each country are presented in the order of their dates of birth, and their works—here again I have had to be selective—are also discussed in chronological order.

The dates of authors are inserted only the first time they are mentioned in the text. The publication dates of all literary works appear immediately after their Spanish titles. If they have been translated to English, the English titles and publication dates are also given. The titles of untranslated works have been rendered in English and printed in lower-case letters.

I should like to express my gratitude to the following individuals for their invaluable help in the preparation of this book: Rita Stein, the editor, for her numerous suggestions and careful reading of the manuscript; my wife, Doris, who not only typed the manuscript but also made many suggestions for improvements; Professors Frank Dauster, Evelio Echevarría, David William Foster, Roberto González Echevarría, José Otero, Margaret Sayers Peden, and George W. Woodyard, all of whom were kind enough to supply information and/or advice; and Emily Taylor and Ron DeWaal, Colorado State University librarians, whose expertise proved most helpful on many occasions.

1 ■ PATTERNS
AND CHANGE

If most residents of the United States and Canada are woefully
ignorant of Spanish American history and political institutions,
their knowledge of their southern neighbors' cultural life is
even more deficient. Thus, it has been said that the Rio Grande
is wider than the Atlantic Ocean. This volume aims to acquaint
readers of English with some major figures and trends of a
literature that in recent years has transcended national borders and attracted worldwide recognition and critical acclaim.
Although Spanish America has a common language, religion,
and colonial past, the vast geographical and cultural differences among the nineteen Spanish-speaking countries (including the Commonwealth of Puerto Rico) of the region today
underscore the magnitude of the task at hand. The year 1941
offers an appropriate point of departure because, as will be
seen, it represents a watershed not only in the maturation of
Spanish American fiction but also in the economic development
of the continent. (Although Spanish America spreads over parts
of two continents and the Caribbean, critics often allude to the
region collectively as a single continent.)

During World War II Spanish Americans were obliged to
curtail their imports from Europe and the United States, a
situation that enhanced their own industrial capability and
contributed to their prosperity. Profits also zoomed with the
demand for raw materials to fuel the war machines of the more
active combatants, especially the United States. The changes
brought about by this economic upswing include the now well-
known population explosion and the rampant urbanization so

1

evident throughout much of the continent. The cultural climate of the war era was enriched by the arrival of well-educated European refugees, many of whom continued their careers in the academic institutions and business communities of their newly chosen lands. And the publishing industry, so vital to any developing society, benefited from the accelerated construction of schools and the larger, better-educated reading public whose purchases of books, newspapers, and magazines grew at a steadily increasing rate.

In the political arena most countries of Spanish America have been plagued since independence by tyrannical dictators, military coups, and inept civilian leaders. Prior to 1941 only Mexico had experienced a true revolution (1910–20) resulting in profound alterations in its system of government. Argentina and Colombia perhaps best illustrate the political ferment immediately following World War II. In Argentina, Juan Perón, a populist demagogue of the Mussolini mold, could do no wrong in the eyes of the laboring masses during the nine years he wielded power (1946–55); at the same time, the former oligarchy held him and his powerful wife Evita in utter contempt. This polarization of social classes in Argentina was reflected in Colombia with the outbreak of *la violencia*, a civil war between conservatives and liberals that began in 1948 and lasted well into the 1960s, resulting in the death of between 200,000 and 300,000 citizens.

The triumph of the Cuban revolution (1959) is unquestionably the most significant political event in Spanish America since 1941, not only because it installed the first communist regime in the region but also because of Castro's defiance of the United States, which galvanized public opinion against decades of gringo imperialism and support of right-wing dictators. During the 1960s radical dissidents challenged the bourgeois "establishment," the most notable confrontation culminating in the Tlatelolco massacre of several hundred students in the Mexican capital on the eve of the 1968 Olympic Games. About this same time the army overthrew the democratically elected government of Peru. Instead of the ultra-conservative orientation of the typical military regime, however, the newly formed junta, which lasted more than a decade, adopted a socialistic platform based on land reform and the nationalization of basic industries. In 1970 the election of Marxist Salvador Allende as president of Chile was hailed by workers and leftist intellectuals as a major victory, but after three years of economic decline and social discontent, General Augusto Pinochet, perhaps with the aid of the CIA, overthrew the Allende government and installed a repressive military dictatorship. Thousands of liberal Chileans, including many writers and intellectuals, fled into exile; others less fortunate were jailed, tortured, or murdered. In the latter part of the decade just the opposite occurred in Nicaragua, where the corrupt right-wing regime of Anastasio Somoza was overthrown by the revolutionary socialist party known as the Sandinistas.

Economic prosperity in most of Spanish America lasted throughout the 1960s and into the late 1970s, when it was brought to a halt by the worldwide recession. The result was a shrinking market for exports and the inability of many countries to service the debts they had incurred for ambitious development projects. Still, surprisingly enough, the political atmosphere gives cause for optimism as repressive dictatorships find themselves being replaced by democratic governments or besieged by citizens demanding their rights. Thus, although the future of Central America remains clouded, the majority of South American nations are finally being governed by elected officials, and chinks have appeared even in Mexico's monolithic political establishment.

Perhaps because of the region's monumental problems, Spanish American writers have traditionally been strongly committed to the cause of social justice. Thus the essay, a vehicle for airing political and philosophical issues, has been a major literary genre as well. *Ariel* (1900; *Ariel*, 1922), by José Enrique Rodó (1872–1917) of Uruguay, has been called the gospel of Spanish American culture, its principal message being that Spanish Americans should not abandon the spiritual values of their Latin heritage for the steadily encroaching utilitarianism exemplified by the United States.

Most of the leading twentieth-century essayists, who tend

to be Marxist-oriented and anti-U.S., are products of three
countries: Peru, Argentina, and Mexico. "The father of Peruvian radicalism," Manuel González Prada (1848–1918), who
assailed Peru's festering social, economic, and religious institutions, inspired an entire generation of political writers, including José Carlos Mariátegui (1895–1930), Raúl Haya de la
Torre (1895–1982), and Luis Alberto Sánchez (b. 1910). Mariátegui based his harsh criticism on the Marxist ideology he
acquired during his studies in Europe, but he never abandoned
his deep-rooted Catholicism. Haya de la Torre is best known
as the founder of APRA (Alianza Popular Revolucionaria Ameri-
cana), a radical party that solidified the Peruvian left for many
years but eventually broke with the communists. The multifaceted Sánchez remains active today as a prominent *aprista*
legislator, journalist, historian, and literary critic.

Argentine essayists reflect not only a nation of high hopes
dashed by a chaotic political climate but also a society in search
of its identity. Prominent practitioners of the genre include
Ricardo Rojas (1882–1957), Carlos Alberto Erro (b. 1899), Francisco Romero (1899–1962), Ezequiel Martínez Estrada (1895–
1964), Héctor A. Murena (1923–1975), and Eduardo Mallea
(1903–1982). Unlike Domingo Faustino Sarmiento (1811–1888),
whose famous essay *Facundo* (1845; *Facundo*, 1868) contrasted
European civilization with gaucho barbarism, Rojas views European culture as exotic and "Indianism" as the fundamental
ingredient of the American ethos. He also believes that in Argentina European culture has undergone a process of "nationalization," a transformation wrought by the telluric forces of
the pampa. Although some of Rojas's ideas have been dismissed
as romantic mysticism, his writings have served as a point of
departure for the succeeding generation. Erro, for example, is
concerned primarily with the meaning of *criollismo*, i.e., the
identity of the *criollo*, or native Latin American, his investigations having led him to conclude that the essence of the
criollo spirit is forever evolving and that it must continue to
evolve free from the slavish imitation of European models.

An idealistic existentialist influenced by the Spanish philosophers Miguel de Unamuno and José Ortega y Gasset, Romero

stressed freedom above all other aspects of life. Not surprisingly he found himself in conflict with Perón's totalitarian regime, for which he suffered economic hardships and imprisonment. Though younger than both Erro and Romero, Mallea shares many of their existential concerns. His *Historia de una pasión argentina* (1937; history of an Argentine passion) delineates the distinction between the "visible" and the "invisible" Argentina, the former characterized by egoism, insincerity, and mediocrity, the latter by introspection, communion with nature, and dedication to the good of humanity. Mallea concludes that the "invisible" Argentina will eventually prevail.

In sharp contrast to the optimistic Mallea, Martínez Estrada stands out as a harsh critic of twentieth-century Argentine life. His fascinating *Radiografía de la pampa* (1933; *X-ray of the Pampa*, 1971) reflects a profound sense of futility, more than likely because of the nation's political and economic woes at the time of its writing. A leftist radical, he is vitriolic in his attacks against the bourgeoisie, but he is also repelled by violence and condemns any society, capitalist or Marxist, that relegates the individual to the position of a cog in a machine. Because of his uncanny insight into the ills of modern existence, Martínez Estrada has been called the embodiment of the Latin American conscience.

In Mexico the essay has represented an exceptionally rich source of political and cultural enlightenment since the Atheneum of Youth was formed early in the present century. This group included such masters as the philosopher Antonio Caso (1883–1946), who inspired the younger generation to abandon positivistic materialism for spiritual values; the political activist and mystical thinker José Vasconcelos (1882–1959), whose treatise *La raza cósmica* (1925; the cosmic race) describes Latin America as a melting pot for the emergence of a new race; and Alfonso Reyes (1889–1959), the brilliant stylist and cosmopolitan humanist who envisions a future synthesis of the indigenous Latin American and the more intellectual Old World cultures.

The first in a series of attempts to explain the Mexican character was *El perfil del hombre y la cultura en México* (1934;

Profile of Man and Culture in Mexico, 1962), by Samuel Ramos (1897–1959). A student of psychology and anthropology, Ramos believes that Mexicans suffer from an inferiority complex, a condition rooted in history. The Mexican, he contends, should strive for a more universal culture, but at the same time, for a culture that expresses a national soul and will. Ramos inspired a group of thinkers known as the Hyperion, which, under the leadership of the well-known philosopher Leopold Zea (b. 1912), continued his investigations of what it means to be Mexican. The most significant examination of this subject, however, is Octavio Paz's (b. 1914) *El laberinto de la soledad* (1950; *The Labyrinth of Solitude*, 1961), a penetrating analysis of the effects of the past on his fellow countrymen's search for identity in the twentieth century. Paz is also a perceptive observer of Mexican politics, his most original pieces on the subject having appeared in *Posdata* (1970; *The Other Mexico*, 1972).

Carlos Fuentes (b. 1928), Mexico's brilliant contemporary novelist and one of Paz's ardent admirers, has written prolifically on both Mexican and international issues. Fuentes views Spain's legacy to Spanish America as a kind of feudal ballast that has impeded progress throughout much of the region. Thus, in his opinion, the capitalistic industrialization imposed on Spanish America during the last half century has merely created a dual society: the modern capitalistic society of the city and the feudal society of the countryside. He pessimistically concludes that Spanish America is a "collapsed feudal castle with a cardboard capitalistic façade."

The poetry and fiction of Spanish America have also reflected the milieu of their origin, often in the form of strong social protest. Romanticism, with its Manichaean depictions of civilization versus barbarism, dominated most of the nineteenth century, but two very different literary movements appeared soon after 1880 and lasted for approximately thirty years. The first of these is *modernismo*,[1] whose leading figure, Rubén Darío (1867–1916) of Nicaragua, like the French sym-

---

1. Spanish American modernism has no connection with the subsequent avant-garde movement of the same name in Europe, the United States, and Brazil.

bolists and Parnassian poets, placed the quest for beauty and formal perfection above the depiction of sordid reality. Critics generally credit the *modernistas* with having enriched versification and achieved greater stylistic flexibility—also learned from the French—thus breaking ground for an equally brilliant generation of poets on the horizon. The second movement of this period is realism, which created pale, documentary imitations of novels by Émile Zola and Spain's Benito Pérez Galdós.

Spanish American poetry matured more rapidly than prose; the art-for-art's-sake stance of the *modernistas* was followed, during the 1920s and early 1930s, by a movement of avant-garde tendencies known as *vanguardismo*.[2] The *vanguardistas*, of whom César Vallejo (1892–1938) of Peru and Pablo Neruda (1904–1973) and Vicente Huidobro (1893–1948), both of Chile, are still the most esteemed today, sought absolute originality through the bold use of the metaphor and the surrealistic liberation of striking images from the subconscious. Their purpose was to shock their readers into experiencing new levels of awareness and, at the same time, to convey their disagreement with existing political and social institutions.

Postvanguardismo, the label often conferred on poetry from the late 1930s to the 1960s, retains many of the *vanguardistas'* formal innovations, but the more introspective *postvanguardistas* are afflicted by existential concerns, which they express in a simpler, more direct linguistic medium than that of their predecessors. The most important poets of this period are Neruda, whose left-wing ideology has become more strident, and Octavio Paz, who draws on surrealism to develop the subjects of loneliness, erotic love, and cosmic time.

Spanish American poetry of the past twenty-five years is extremely varied in both its formal and thematic aspects: revolutionary poets—many of them Cuban—express their Marxist ideology in down-to-earth, everyday language; history and myth provide the underpinnings of numerous poems; striking meta-

2. Spanish American *vanguardismo*, although limited to poetry, is similar in many respects to European and North American modernism.

phors and surrealistic imagery continue to inform many texts; and existential introspection characterizes still other, more philosophical works.

The novelists of the 1920s and 1930s, disenchanted with Europe after World War I but still adhering to the realist mode, set out to examine conditions in their own countries, focusing primarily on social problems such as political corruption and the mistreatment of the Indian. Thus began the movement known as regionalism, which spawned a series of didactic novels depicting man as a stereotyped victim of his cruel environment. The unfortunate result of this polemic stance was that righteous indignation and rhetorical abstractions often superseded intuitive art and psychological depth. Among the most memorable of these novels are: *Don Segundo Sombra* (1926; *Don Segundo Sombra: Shadows on the Pampa*, 1935), by Ricardo Güiraldes (1886–1927) of Argentina; *Doña Bárbara* (1929; *Doña Bárbara*, 1931), by Rómulo Gallegos (1884–1969) of Venezuela; and *Huasipungo* (1934; *The Villagers*, 1964), by Jorge Icaza (1906–1978) of Ecuador.

Since 1941 fiction has been revolutionized by a widely scattered group of gifted writers who, bored with regionalism, sought inspiration abroad in the works of, among others, James Joyce, Franz Kafka, Samuel Beckett, William Faulkner, Jean-Paul Sartre, and the surrealists. Although these "new novelists" are stylistically and perhaps even thematically indebted to the *vanguardista* and *postvanguardista* poets, they have elevated the contemporary novel to an art form that has overshadowed poetry as today's leading literary genre. The most important single influence on their works, however, is not a European or a North American, but rather the Argentine master Jorge Luis Borges (b. 1899). A poet and essayist as well as a writer of short stories, Borges is best known for his celebrated *Ficciones* (1944; *Ficciones*, 1962), a collection of highly sophisticated, metaphysical tales that challenged the tenets of realism, all but ignored the social-protest syndrome, and dazzled an increasing number of devotees with their infusions of fantasy and poetically stylized irony. It is often said that Borges not only taught a generation of writers how to write but also lib-

erated Spanish American literature from didactic documen-
tation and restored creative imagination as a major ingredient.

Two very different writers of Borges's generation are Alejo
Carpentier (1904–1980) of Cuba and Miguel Ángel Asturias
(1899–1974) of Guatemala, whose vibrant, surrealistic depictions of primitive cultures further expanded the dimensions of
the novel during the 1940s and 1950s. Still other "new novelists" of this period—leading figures include Agustín Yáñez
(1904–1980) of Mexico, Ernesto Sábato (b. 1911) of Argentina,
and Juan Carlos Onetti (b. 1909) of Uruguay—came under the
influence of Freudian psychology and existentialism, both recently brought to their shores by European immigrants. And
the repercussions of Juan Rulfo's (1918–1986) remarkable experimental novel *Pedro Páramo* (1955; *Pedro Páramo*, 1959)
have been felt far beyond the borders of his native Mexico.

The 1960s are frequently referred to as the decade of the
"boom," that is, the sudden appearance of numerous internationally acclaimed novels, some of which became best-sellers
almost overnight. The writers of the boom hardly constitute a
literary school, but they do indeed share a deep preoccupation
with language, a willingness to experiment with innovative
forms, and an emphasis on universal elements of the human
experience. Actually, there were two booms, the first one politically inspired by the Cuban revolution, which became a
catalyst for bringing Spanish American writers together and
publicizing their works. Of paramount importance in this respect was Casa de las Américas, a Cuban cultural agency that
published a wide variety of books, organized writers'
conferences—often more political than literary—and awarded
prizes annually for outstanding examples of each genre. Meanwhile, international publishing ventures were also launched in
Spain, Mexico, Argentina, and Venezuela in order to dissemi-
nate books and critical reviews to an ever-expanding reading
public. Literary reputations benefited, moreover, from the increase in translations of works by authors heretofore unknown
abroad.

The second, or literary, boom began with the publication
of major novels by Carlos Fuentes, Mario Vargas Llosa (b. 1936)

of Peru, and Julio Cortázar (1914–1984) of Argentina. Shortly thereafter other important novelists, including Chile's José Donoso (b. 1924), Cuba's Guillermo Cabrera Infante (b. 1929), and Argentina's Manuel Puig (b. 1932), emerged from obscurity. The boom reached its peak in 1967 when Gabriel García Márquez's (b. 1927)[3] masterpiece *Cien años de soledad* (*One Hundred Years of Solitude*, 1970) elicited unparalleled applause from the critics and within a year broke all records for its sales throughout the Spanish-speaking world. Early in the 1970s Fidel Castro's tyrannical treatment of Cuban writers and resultant loss of prestige coincided with the demise of the highly touted boom. Since that time a new generation of fiction writers has begun to emerge, but with the onset of the economic recession, the major figures of the 1960s, whose works are automatically assured of a wide distribution, have continued to dominate the literary scene.

The drama in Spanish America showed few signs of serious development prior to the 1930s, when several experimental theatrical groups appeared in Mexico City and Buenos Aires. Since 1941 the best examples of the genre have been characterized by existential themes, expressionist and surrealistic techniques, and thinly veiled messages of social protest. Interest has been stimulated in recent years by the proliferation of theater festivals, often organized by university students, and free street theaters, created for spectators unable to purchase tickets. Still, government censorship and the lack of large sophisticated audiences have prevented playwrights from achieving the degree of success enjoyed by recent novelists.

At the present moment of political ferment and economic turmoil Spanish American writers are reacting vigorously to the stark realities of their rapidly evolving societies and, at the same time, directing their voices of protest to the international community. Carlos Fuentes in many respects typifies the committed writer reared in an Anglo-Saxon-dominated hemi-

3. The year of García Márquez's birth is usually given as 1928. Recently, however, his father revealed convincing evidence that his son was born in 1927. García Márquez admits that he is uncertain of the year of his birth.

sphere; his commencement address at Harvard University on June 9, 1983 (published in the *Harvard University Gazette* of June 1983) reveals his long-standing love-hate relationship with his northern neighbors and is a passionate defense of his Latin culture. On the subject of the intervention of the United States in the current Central American conflict, Fuentes states that a land of democratic ideals and institutions should not be conducting itself like the Soviet Union, which he labels a brutal tyranny. He also invokes history in his support of the radical left in Central America: "You are not the Soviet Union. We shall be the custodians of your own true interests by helping you to avoid these mistakes. We have memory on our side. You suffer too much from historical amnesia. You seem to have forgotten that your own Republic was born out of the barrel of a gun: the American Revolutionaries also shot their way to power. We hope to have persuasion on our side, but also the body of international and inter-American law to help us."

North American readers of the literature created south of the Rio Grande will not only gain valuable insight into a vibrant culture whose recognition is long overdue, but will also acquire an alternate, and perhaps more objective, perspective of themselves and their nation's role in today's world.

2 ▪ FICTION

NEW DIRECTIONS

The year 1941 stands out as pivotal in the development of Spanish American fiction because it marks a well-defined transition from regionalism to a more universal outlook. In that year the Peruvian novel *El mundo es ancho y ajeno* (*Broad and Alien Is the World*, 1941), by Ciro Alegría (1909–1969), attracted a wide international audience when it won the Farrar and Rinehart Prize. A traditional example of social protest, it tells the story of Indian villagers who are driven from their ancestral lands by greedy whites and eventually annihilated during a rebellion. Despite its poetic depiction of a threatened primitive culture, the novel suffers by today's standards from antiquated literary techniques and obtrusive political didacticism typical of regionalism.

Two other regional novels of this same year are *El caballo y su sombra* (*The Horse and His Shadow*, 1943) by Enrique Amorim (1900–1960) of Uruguay, which describes the archetypal —in Spanish America—struggle between urban progress and rural backwardness; and *Nueva burguesía* (new bourgeoisie), by Mariano Azuela (1873–1952) of Mexico, a satirical account of Mexican middle-class opportunism emerging on the heels of the revolution.

In sharp contrast to these traditional protest novels are three well-known titles also published in 1941: *Tierra de nadie* (no-man's-land), by Juan Carlos Onetti; *Todo verdor perecerá* (*All Green Shall Perish*, 1966), by Eduardo Mallea; and the short-story collection *El jardín de los senderos que se bifurcan* (the garden of the forking paths), by Jorge Luis Borges, whose contents were later included in *Ficciones*, mentioned in the preceding chapter. (Each of these writers is discussed at greater length below.) Through its fragmented structure and lonely characters cast adrift, *Tierra de nadie* conveys a sense of chaos and nihilistic purposelessness that removes it from the parochial concerns of regionalism. Somewhat similarly, the characters of *Todo verdor perecerá* represent anguished human failures whose futile attempts to give meaning to their lives evokes Sartre's existential anguish of this same period. Borges's collection is quite different, and unquestionably more significant, because of his emphasis on an invented, fantastic reality replete with absurd situations and arcane philosophical postulations.

The innovative fiction of 1941, however, was not without its antecedents in the years immediately preceding. Of seminal importance are the works of four southern-cone writers: Horacio Quiroga (1878–1937) of Uruguay, Roberto Arlt (1900–1942) of Argentina, María Luisa Bombal (1910–1980) of Chile, and Adolfo Bioy Casares (b. 1914) of Argentina. Quiroga's tales of horror and death suggest the influence of Edgar Allan Poe, a well-known example being "El hombre muerto" (1920; "The Dead Man," in *The Decapitated Chicken, and Other Stories*, 1976), in which the protagonist experiences the onslaught of death thirty minutes after falling on his machete. Quiroga not only was the first Spanish American short-story writer to pay close attention to structure and impact on the reader, but he also relied on fantasy and archetypal human conflicts to transcend the regional settings—often the jungles of northern Argentina—that so dramatically framed his works.

Arlt depicts Argentina's disillusioned middle class along with an array of misfits on the fringe of society in his nation's capital. His best-known novel, *Los siete locos* (1929; *The Seven Madmen*, 1984), is the portrait of a tormented protagonist whose search for life's meaning in a bogus society of madmen prefigures the absurd irony so prevalent in subsequent Argentine fiction. Arlt's novels and short stories take his readers into an uncharted twilight zone of surrealistic hallucinations and fantasies scarcely glimpsed heretofore in Spanish American fiction.

Equally subjective and more introspective is Bombal's *La última niebla* (1935; *House of Mist*, 1947), which explores the subconscious of a young woman narrator whose husband's indifference obliges her to seek true love and passion in the world of dreams. A haunting leitmotif, the mist creates a timeless, surrealistic atmosphere of uncertainty that reduces reality to subliminal obsessions and activates the protagonist's fantasies. Bombal also spotlights the lack of communication among members of the upper class, whose lives are dominated by rigid, meaningless conventions.

The element of social commentary is entirely lacking in *La invención de Morel* (1940; *The Invention of Morel*, 1964), by Bioy Casares, who, like his friend and occasional co-author Borges, relies entirely on the subjective imagination to create his fictitious universe. *La invención de Morel* is an early example of Spanish American science fiction, its setting being a remote island inhabited by a small group of French-speaking individuals. After several enigmatic episodes, the narrator, a recent arrival, realizes that his fellow inhabitants of the island are not real but projections of an apparatus that recorded their visit many years ago and that now repeats their actions eternally. Bioy Casares's sophisticated fantasy emerges as a metaphor of fiction, which, unlike the practitioners of realism, he sees as a cerebral invention completely separate from the realm of objective, everyday reality.

The thirteen major writers discussed in the following pages appear in chronological order according to their dates of birth, the only exception being Borges, whose influence on contemporary Spanish American fiction mandates his initial position.

JORGE LUIS BORGES

Borges received much of his education in Switzerland during World War I, after which he returned to his native Buenos Aires with his upper-middle-class family. Although he began his literary career as a poet and essayist, he owes his international reputation primarily to his short stories, or, as he calls them, *ficciones*. These tales, which are characterized by fantastic plots, metaphysical themes, and stylistic innovations, have influenced European, North American, and most Spanish American writers of the younger generation. Indeed, he is generally considered the spiritual father of contemporary Spanish American letters.

Borges's first collection of stories, *Historia universal de la infamia* (1935; *A Universal History of Infamy*, 1973), attracted scant attention, but the previously mentioned *El jardín de los senderos que se bifurcan* and *Ficciones*, as well as *El Aleph* (1949; partial tr. in *The Aleph, and Other Stories*, 1970), are generally recognized as masterpieces. During the mid-1950s Borges's increasing blindness caused him to abandon the short story for poetry, but in 1970 he published *El informe de Brodie* (*Dr. Brodie's Report*, 1972), a collection of tales written in a direct, realistic vein reminiscent of the young Rudyard Kipling, one of Borges's favorite authors. *El libro de arena* (1975; *The Book of Sand*, 1977) marks a return to fantastic themes, although the style of these pieces remains straightforward, like that of the previous collection.

Borges is a sophisticated writer who views fiction not as an artistic representation of the real world, but rather as a poetic re-creation of the cultural labyrinths man has fabricated throughout history. He readily admits that his fictional universe stems from his varied and often esoteric readings in literature, philosophy, and theology, fields of human endeavor that, in his opinion, have analyzed and explained the world in fascinating but purely fictitious terms. His favorite authors, in addition to Kipling, include H. G. Wells, G. K. Chesterton, Robert Louis Stevenson, Thomas De Quincey, and Walt Whitman; the philosophical theories of Berkeley and Schopenhauer have greatly influenced his writings; and the mysterious theological labyrinths of gnosticism and the Cabala have reinforced many of his plots. As a result of these basic ingredients, his tales exude an aura of unreality that for him constitutes the very nature of art.

Borges considers man's quest for truth utterly vain. Philosophy and theology represent "provisional" systems of thought destined to be discredited and replaced by others, history evolves as a product of the imagination tempered by time, and psychology is denigrated as fakery because individual behavior depends on phenomena far too complex to be understood. Thus, Borges limits himself to the portrayal of faceless characters in archetypal situations that serve to conceptualize as well as to formalize his fictional world. Though spare, compact, and classically elegant in its overall design, Borges's style contains occasional baroque twists that, like his pseudo-erudite references, are often inserted for ironic effect.

Like many twentieth-century authors, Borges depicts the absurdity of mortal man's search for meaning and transcendence in an infinite universe beyond his intellectual comprehension. The absurd is illustrated not only by the vain quest for truth but also by the artist's persistent, though futile, efforts to achieve aesthetic perfection. Borges utilizes a symbolically evocative vocabulary and poetic devices such as the transferred epithet, the oxymoron, and metonymy in order to disintegrate concrete reality and thrust his reader into an abstract, hallucinatory world fraught with irony and paradox. He frequently dons the mask of the bungling narrator, contradicting himself or frankly admitting that he does not know all the facts surrounding the events he is relating. Another of his techniques is to combine elements of fiction and the essay, often resorting to the use of the footnote in order to feign authenticity or to mock erudition. The result is the collapse of certainties and an ever-increasing awareness that beneath outward appearances there exists an uncharted realm of endless contradictions, the probing of which is a major facet of Borges's art.

Borges's principal themes include the metaphysical problems of time and human destiny; the fusion of reality and dream; the identity of the self; and the world as a labyrinth. Though universal, his tales are often firmly anchored in Argentine reality, as demonstrated by his poetic evocations of the Argentine setting and his fascination with the machismo cult. His frequent use of the mirror as an image serves to create a fictive, dreamlike reality and, on occasion, to dramatize the disunity of the personality. Other major elements of Borges's works are his reinterpretations of old myths to convey contemporary themes and his preoccupation with the creative process, which often results in a kind of self-mocking style.

Two masterpieces among Borges's celebrated *ficciones* are "La muerte y la brújula" (1942; "Death and the Compass," 1962) and "El sur" (1953; "The South," 1962). A parody on reason, "La muerte y la brújula" portrays an excessively rational detective, Lönnrot, who finds himself trapped in a cerebral labyrinth of his own making while attempting to solve a series of crimes. Scharlach, the criminal, emerges not only as Lönnrot's antithetical double but also as a kind of diabolical deity who has been plotting Lönnrot's death from the beginning. In "El sur" Borges masterfully fuses reality and dream. Juan Dahlmann, the protagonist, is a cultured librarian who subconsciously yearns for the primitive life of the mythical Argentine gaucho. He probably dies in a hospital during an operation, but moments before his demise he dreams of a journey to the south—a metaphor of the Argentine past—where he bravely faces death in a knife fight. The story's bipartite, reflecting-mirror structure derives from the parallels and contrasts between the drab reality of Dahlmann's life in Buenos Aires and the surreality of his romantic dream. And the idealized macho that Dahlmann ultimately becomes represents his alter ego or an inverted mirror image of his real self.

Borges's stylistic genius is particularly evident in "Las ruinas circulares" (1941; "The Circular Ruins," 1962), about a wizard who dreams a man into existence. The structure of this tale serves to reinforce its central theme of philosophical idealism: that material objects are ideas in our minds, with no independent existence, and that, therefore, the whole of reality consists of ideas in the mind of God. The first sentence, "No one saw him [the wizard] disembark in the unanimous night," is likely to puzzle the reader because of the strange use of the adjective "unanimous." However, the climactic ending ("he [the wizard] understood that he also was an illusion, that someone else was dreaming him") suggests that the adjective "unanimous" was chosen, with typical Borgesian precision, to foreshadow the revelation that *unus animus* (one soul) was dreaming the wizard just as he had dreamed his own creation. The "unanimous night," then, is not only a metaphor of the epistemological blindness of all men, but also a link with the final line, underscoring the circular structure implied in the title.

Other of Borges's masterworks are "Tlön, Uqbar, Orbis Tertius" (1941; "Tlön, Uqbar, Orbis Tertius," 1962), a combination of essay and story describing the intrusion on the real world of a fictional world founded on pantheistic idealism; "La Biblioteca de Babel" (1941; "The Library of Babel," 1962), in which a symmetrically structured library represents the universe as it is conceived by rational man and the library's illegible books, man's basic ignorance; and "El Aleph" (1945; "The Aleph," 1970), an ingenious attempt to create an intuitive, simultaneous vision of the world in the lineal medium of language.

Borges's *Weltanschauung* has often been referred to as subversive because he mocks conventional modes of thinking, making his readers acutely aware that all doctrines are ephemeral creations of human reason and that concrete reality may consist only of mental perceptions. Although he depicts life as a labyrinth through which man wanders under the illusion of having organized and understood the chaotic, meaningless world, his unique oeuvre illustrates the triumph of art over the absurd human experience.

MANUEL ROJAS

Born in Buenos Aires of Chilean parents, Manuel Rojas (1896–1973) spent his youth wandering throughout much of Argentina and Chile earning his living from a wide variety of odd jobs. During the late 1920s and the 1930s he achieved a reputation in Chile as a regionalist, often being compared to Maxim Gorky and Sherwood Anderson. In reality, his early works differ from regionalism in their emphasis on man as a complex individual rather than as a stereotyped victim of his natural or social environment. In his literary essays, moreover, Rojas criticizes regionalism—he calls it *criollismo* and equates it with naturalism—as a picturesque, outmoded movement and advocates the use of innovative techniques to enhance psychological penetration and gain new perspectives on long-standing human problems.

Despite the differences separating him from his contemporaries, Rojas remained classified as a regionalist until the publication of his masterpiece, *Hijo de ladrón* (1951; *Born Guilty*, 1955), which brought him international acclaim as one of the early practitioners of the new novel. The narrator-protagonist is a seventeen-year-old named Aniceto Hevia, just released from prison in Valparaíso, Chile, after serving time for a burglary he did not commit. The foreground action, which lasts only a few days, involves his friendship with two drifters, their efforts to feed themselves by collecting scrap metal on a beach, and, in the final lines, their departure for another town, where they hope to be employed as house painters. Most of the novel, however, consists of fragmentary recollections of Aniceto's past: his mother's death; his father's imprisonment for theft (*Hijo de ladrón* means "son of a thief"); his arrest during a riot in Valparaíso.

Although Aniceto's monologues give the impression of spontaneity and randomness, they are in reality carefully arranged in order to link present events with the past and thus in their totality convey a unified mosaic of his life; they also reproduce artfully and simultaneously the multiple planes of reality perceived by a young mind under stress. Rojas makes use of leitmotifs in order to enhance the unity of the plot as well as the development of the protagonist, the best example of this device being the birth certificate Aniceto does not have but needs on various occasions. His obsession with this nonexistent document underscores his alienation from society and his resultant feelings of solitude and despair. But at the end of the novel his basic optimism finds renewed expression through his better knowledge of self (the quest for identity is a major theme) and, even more important, through his communication and solidarity with his newly found companions.

Several critics have pointed out the obvious picaresque elements in *Hijo de ladrón*, but unlike most examples of that popular Spanish genre, Rojas's novel does not satirize human foibles, nor does it convey a moral lesson. Rather, it is characterized by objectivity tempered with compassion for the downtrodden and social outcasts, whose dignity and pride remain intact even under the worst circumstances. Perhaps because of his broad experience with the lower strata of society, Rojas's portraits of wasted lives have a ring of authenticity that heightens their aesthetic value. In virtually all of his works he remains a realist who shuns sensationalism and explicit scenes of violence in the interest of art. Thus, by today's standards, he is hardly a member of the avant-garde. Seen in retrospect, though, *Hijo de ladrón* stands out as an early sample of the "new novel."

MIGUEL ÁNGEL ASTURIAS

Asturias's formative years were spent in Guatemala during the tyrannical regime (1898–1920) of Manuel Estrada Cabrera. In 1923 he began a ten-year sojourn in Paris, where he studied Mayan mythology at the Sorbonne with the eminent scholar Georges Raynaud and helped to translate into Spanish the sacred book of the Mayas, the *Popol Vuh*. During this period he also became acquainted with the leading French surrealists, whose exploration of the subconscious and theories on automatic writing furnished the keys for many of his works.

Asturias's first book was *Leyendas de Guatemala* (1930; legends of Guatemala), a compilation of tales he gleaned from the days of his youth in his native land. His most widely read novel is *El Señor Presidente* (1946; *El Señor Presidente*, 1964), written in France but not published, because of censorship, unitl more than a decade after his return to Guatemala. The overriding theme of this remarkable book is the terror felt by Guatemalans under the oppressive dictatorship of Estrada Cabrera, although neither the country nor the despot is mentioned by name.

Because they live under constant stress, the characters of *El Señor Presidente* resemble grotesque caricatures reacting irrationally to the horrors around them. The *Presidente* seldom appears on stage, but his sinister presence hovering in the wings dominates virtually every scene, affirming his role as the protagonist. Other major figures are Angel Face, the *Presidente*'s right-hand man; Angel Face's wife Camila; and Camila's father, Eusebio Canales, a general who leads an unsuccessful revolt against the *Presidente*. Rooted in ancient myths, the archetypal actions of these characters not only enrich the novel's literary texture but also strengthen its structural framework.

Perhaps the most striking aspect of *El Señor Presidente* is its style, which reflects avant-garde movements of the 1920s such as surrealism and expressionism. Dreams, nightmares, and hallucinations suggest the presence of the surrealists, whose explorations of the subconscious constitute the essence of their creations. The dreamlike atmosphere of the novel is heightened, moreover, by abrupt modal changes and sharply contrasting images, both visual and aural, reminiscent of surrealistic art.

Asturias relies on expressionistic techniques to capture irrational mental states in moments of panic. For example, after learning that his life is in danger, Canales hastens homeward, all the while planning his escape. His extreme fear, however, distorts his vision of reality, lengthening the distance to his destination and thus augmenting even more his agitation. Similarly, as Señora Carvajal, the wife of a man accused of treason, rushes to the prison to stay his execution, her overpowering anxiety causes her to imagine that the wheels of the coach in which she is riding have stopped turning, delaying her arrival. *El Señor Presidente* is obviously a novel of social protest anchored in historical reality, but its tense portrait of a society gripped by terror makes it a landmark in Spanish American fiction.

Many critics consider *Hombres de maíz* (1949; *Men of Maize*, 1975) Asturias's masterpiece. A vast mosaic of primitive Mayan culture, this loosely structured novel consisting of six weakly integrated parts is difficult to summarize; basically the plot centers on a conflict between traditional Indians and outside entrepreneurs who seek to exploit the land for economic gain. The Indians consider it a desecration to commercialize the grain because, as "men of corn" (the Mayans were said to have been created from corn), they view it as a gift offered to them only for their own use. *Hombres de maíz* thrusts the reader into the magical realm of Mayan cosmogony, a realm created by ancestral voices replete with rhythmic repetitions and incantations. As demonstrated by his linguistic virtuosity, Asturias recognized the need to revitalize the rigidly structured literary idiom inherited from Spain with the spontaneous vernacular of speech. His poetic sensitivity and intuitive insight provided him with the tools necessary not only to record the telluric voices of the Guatemalan landscape, but also to probe the mysteries of the Indian psyche.

Four of Asturias's works register protests against North American political and economic imperialism in Guatemala. Three of these, which form a trilogy, focus on the abuses of the United Fruit Company (now named United Brands) as it establishes its control over virtually every aspect of the country. *Viento fuerte* (1949; *Strong Wind*, 1968), about the clash between small banana growers and their powerful gringo antagonists, was followed by *El papa verde* (1954; *The Green Pope*, 1971), depicting the company's consolidation of its political influence; *Los ojos de los enterrados* (1960; *The Eyes of the Interred*, 1973), the last of the trilogy, dramatizes a general strike that succeeds in toppling the government and improving the lot of the company's employees. Asturias's collection of short stories entitled *Weekend en Guatemala* (1956; weekend in Guatemala) continues the theme of social protest, in this case inspired by political events in 1954 during the presidency of Jacobo Árbenz. A liberal leader who supported the expropriation of lands belonging to the United Fruit Company, Arbenz was overthrown by right-wing extremists with the aid of the United States. These topical stories convey the grisly carnage resulting from the coup as well as the outrage most Latin Americans felt over this episode of Yankee gunboat diplomacy.

Asturias gained worldwide recognition in 1967 when he was awarded the Nobel Prize for literature. In Spanish America he is viewed as an early practitioner of the "new novel," an innovator who abandoned the rational thought patterns of modern man and captured the magical reality of myth as it is experienced by the Mayan Indian of Guatemala. Through his extraordinary insight and linguistic genius, his readers find themselves immersed in an unreal, vibrant world previously unknown to them. Asturias stated that as a Spanish American attentive to the rampant exploitation in his native land, he was more inclined toward protest literature than toward European models of existential introspection. His lasting reputation, however, rests on his artistic treatment of myth and his revelation of psychic truths all but forgotten by the rational man of today.

LEOPOLDO MARECHAL

Leopoldo Marechal (1900–1970) of Argentina, like his contemporary Jorge Luis Borges, first achieved considerable success as a poet, but unlike Borges, he supported the Perón regime and for that reason found himself ostracized by Argentine literary circles during the 1940s and 1950s. His political views probably explain, at least in part, the critical indifference or hostility toward his seminal novel, *Adán Buenosayres* (1948; Adam Buenosayres). (Julio Cortázar was one of the few early critics to recognize the book's importance.) More recently, however, this and his other prose works have undergone a re-evaluation, and Marechal is now recognized, along with Borges, as one of the two major innovators of the new Argentine fiction.

The overriding theme of *Adán Buenosayres* is the spiritual search for salvation through human and divine love. This universal theme is reinforced by the protagonist's first name, Adán (Adam), representing universal man, and by his adventures in the Argentine capital, representing those of all men. As a poet and teacher—like Marechal—well acquainted with the city's intellectual life, Adán also represents Marechal's alter ego. The foreground action delineates forty-eight hours of Adán's life, but just as James Joyce captures the essence of Dublin through his portrait of Leopold Bloom in *Ulysses*, Marechal draws a vast mosaic of Buenos Aires through the portrait of his protagonist. The novel's structural complexity and linguistic experiments, however, have placed it beyond the comprehension of many readers, as have its lengthy discussions of philosophical and aesthetic questions. In addition, allusions to prominent personages (it is frequently called a roman à clef) have further obscured its meaning, especially to foreign readers. On the other hand, *Adán Buenosayres* is enlivened by hilarious black humor and satirical descriptions of café life, brothels, and literary coteries such as the elite Martín Fierro group in which Borges occupied a position of prominence—one character is supposedly a caricature of Borges.

Adán's adventures, like those of Leopold Bloom, also reflect the archetypal structures of ancient myths, although the alienation theme, the metaphysical search, and the metropolitan setting are thoroughly modern. Besides the influence of Joyce, and by extension that of Homer, echoes of Dante's *Divine Comedy* also resonate throughout Marechal's novel, the corrupt society of Buenos Aires ultimately emerging as another inferno. Adán's descent into this nightmarish underworld brings the story to an abrupt ending, but his religious fervor suggests the possibility of a future mystical catharsis.

In addition to representing its author's spiritual biography, *Adán Buenosayres* dramatizes a search for the essence of Argentina, a search reminiscent of Mallea's *Historia de una pasión argentina*. Marechal's work, however, represents a more radical break with literary tradition, primarily because of its grotesque, oneiric fantasies and its showcase of styles, ranging from the intellectual and poetic to the popular and obscene. Nevertheless, in the mythological history of the Argentine capital it looms midway between the works of Arlt and Onetti, on the one hand, and, on the other, those of Sábato and Cortázar. *Adán Buenosayres* may be a literary masterpiece or, as a few critics still believe, a colossal disaster. Most would agree, however, that its unfettered flights of imagination and unprecedented experiments with language make it a major precursor of the boom.

EDUARDO MALLEA

Like Borges, Mallea was born into a cultured, upper-middle-class family whose way of life was to have a profound effect on his oeuvre. In 1937, early in his literary career, Mallea published his seminal essay, *Historia de una pasión argentina* (mentioned in the previous chapter), in which he developed his concept of the two Argentinas: one visible, the other invisible. The visible Argentina refers to the materialistic, bourgeois society that Mallea sees as a kind of false veneer covering the genuine or invisible Argentina, which embodies the nation's hidden, spiritual values. Much of his subsequent work represents an impassioned attempt to reveal the invisible Argentina to his readers.

Mallea's first important novel, *Fiesta en noviembre* (1938; *Fiesta in November*, 1966), juxtaposes two seemingly unrelated plots: a fiesta in the mansion of an Argentine *grande dame* and the kidnapping and execution of an unnamed poet, more than likely a reference to the tragic fate of Federico García Lorca during the Spanish Civil War. The philosophical message— the triumph of luxury and violence over art and intellect— emerging from these contrasting plot threads illustrates the author's turning away from the predominantly regional concerns of the 1930s.

One of Mallea's most ambitious novels, *La bahía de silencio* (1940; *The Bay of Silence*, 1944), portrays a youthful writer named Martín Tregua—a thinly disguised Mallea—whose rambling, first-person narration represents a search for the real Argentina beneath the spiritual isolation and barren materialism of everyday life. The plot encompasses the thirteen years between 1926 and 1939, a period of deepening malaise in the Western world. After a brief interlude in Europe during the mid-1930s, Tregua returns to Argentina, where he ultimately fails in his attempts not only to awaken his nation to its state of moral inertia, but also to establish any meaningful relationships with other human beings. Written in the form of a confession, the novel is directed to a mysterious *Ud.* (you), perhaps a female counterpart or anima figure of the author himself. Whoever she may be, she remains just as elusive as the object of the idealistic Tregua's quest.

Perhaps the best known and most widely read of Mallea's works is the previously mentioned *Todo verdor perecerá*. The principal characters of this intense, compact novel are Nicanor

Cruz, a taciturn farmer embittered by many years of drought, and his wife Agata, whose reticence mirrors that of her husband. A reflection of the scorched fields they attempt to cultivate for fifteen years, their sterile relationship ends with Nicanor's death and Agata's all-too-brief taste of happiness in the city of Bahía Blanca. *Todo verdor perecerá* is steeped in total gloom, a mood artfully engendered by descriptions of parched, inhospitable landscapes, drawn-out moments of silence, and interior monologues filled with rancor, desolation, and despair. The final image of Agata's flight into darkness underscores the leitmotif of solitude so common throughout Mallea's works.

Of Mallea's numerous novels published during the past three decades, the most outstanding include *Chaves* (1953; *Chaves*, 1966) and *Simbad* (1957; Sinbad). The former depicts an antihero vaguely reminiscent of Meursault, the outsider-protagonist of Albert Camus's *The Stranger*. Implicit also in this finely wrought portrait is the failure of language to bridge the spiritual gap between solitary souls. Written during the oppressive Perón era, *Simbad* represented an escape for Mallea into the mysterious realm of artistic creativity. This massive novel recalls *La bahía de silencio*, its protagonist Fernando Fe emerging as a fictionalized projection of the author, a playwright-director striving for the elusive goal of aesthetic perfection. The title derives from the legendary figure of the *Arabian Nights*, whose search for the gift of happiness inspires the idealistic Fe.

Mallea's influence on Spanish American fiction stems from his existential themes, his psychological profundity, and his cosmopolitan literary tastes. Although inclined toward the abstract and the analytical, his prose style can also wax poetic, especially in his sketches of the vast Argentine landscape. His fascination with his native land bears little resemblance to that of the regionalists; rather it represents a quest for the spiritual essence of Argentina and, at the same time, an attack on the materialistic values and alienation afflicting much of the Western world. Despite the possible influence of Sartre's existentialism on his works, he rejects the French philosopher's atheism as well as the premise that man creates his own essence in the course of living. Instead, the introspective Mallea stresses contemporary man's need to regain the lost nobility of self and to fulfill his God-given potential as a human being. Mallea's influence began to wane under the Perón regime, and, perhaps because of his anti-Marxist views, he has been downgraded in recent years by the younger generation. His original probings of twentieth-century malaise have, nevertheless, guaranteed him a permanent place in both Argentine and Spanish American letters.

ALEJO CARPENTIER

The Cuban Alejo Carpentier is probably the most influential Spanish American fiction writer of his generation with the exception of Borges. The son of a French architect and Russian mother, he spent much of his life abroad, principally in France, where he fell under the spell of surrealism during the 1920s and 1930s, and in Venezuela, the setting of his novel *Los pasos perdidos* (1953; *The Lost Steps*, 1956). Carpentier's writings reveal a man of wide cultural interests ranging from journalism and literature to history, philosophy, and music. At the time of his death he was Fidel Castro's cultural envoy in Paris.

Carpentier's first major novel was *El reino de este mundo* (1949; *The Kingdom of This World*, 1957), which depicts events in Haiti during the late eighteenth and early nineteenth centuries. What animates this objectively written, scrupulously documented historical work is its masterful fusion of reality and fantastic myth, a technique often referred to in Spanish America as "magical realism."[1] In his prologue to the novel

1. Magical realism is a term critics of Spanish American literature have bandied about for more than twenty-five years, but because it has yet to be defined precisely and universally, some critics prefer not to use or even recognize the term. Still, it would be impossible in any survey discussion of recent Spanish American fiction to ignore this literary mode about which so much has been said. Basically, magical realism attempts to penetrate objective reality and to reveal the mysterious and poetic qualities underlying the daily lives of a community or people. With a few notable exceptions, it is found primarily in countries with large Indian or black populations, that is, wherever European civilization is only a veneer superimposed on hidden layers of primitive cultures.

Carpentier views European surrealism as artificial and decadent in comparison to magical realism—he calls it *lo real maravilloso*—which captures the fabulous aspects of a region rich in legends and geographical wonders. He also states that magical realism presupposes unquestioning faith in the truth of the supernatural occurrences depicted, a faith derived naturally from the ambience of primitive cultures. (Carpentier himself was struck by the power of voodoo myths in Haiti during his visit to that nation in 1943.) The plot of the novel focuses on a rebellion against the colonial French, the reign of the Haitian king Henri Christophe, and the overthrow of his brutal regime by the mulattoes. The never-ending struggle against tyranny and the cyclical repetitions of history emerge as the two major themes.

In *Los pasos perdidos* (1953; *The Lost Steps*, 1956) Carpentier all but abandons magical realism in order to portray his narrator-protagonist's odyssey back through time to the roots of civilization. A musician weary of his meaningless routine in New York, he is sent by a museum to Venezuela, where he travels to the source of the Orinoco River (the geographical setting is not named in the novel) in search of ancient musical instruments. His affair with Rosario, the embodiment of a kind of life-giving Earth Mother, increases his desire to shed the shackles of civilization, but he eventually comes to realize that the age of innocence lies beyond the reach of the modern urban intellectual. *Los pasos perdidos* can be interpreted in several different ways: as existential man's quest for individual authenticity; as a Jungian return to the unconscious prior to regeneration or rebirth; as an escape from tyrannical linear time; or as an artistic attempt to recapture the forgotten past.

Carpentier's tour de force in literary technique is his short novel *El acoso* (1956; the pursuit), whose protagonist is a political activist-turned-informer fleeing those he betrayed. He seeks refuge in a concert hall where, listening to Beethoven's Third Symphony, he evokes snatches of his life leading up to the moment of his murder, which coincides with the climactic end of the concert. Striking aspects of this work include the deft manipulation of interior monologues and the proliferation of narrative voices, techniques that disrupt the flow of time and create the impression of a static, emotion-packed present. Also woven into the literary texture are occasional allusions to biblical myths—the Fall is suggested by the fugitive's sinful past—and allegorical parallels between the dramatic chain of events and the development of a self-conscious text.

Guerra del tiempo (1958; *War of Time*, 1970) is a collection of stories depicting archetypal human behavior throughout the course of history. Typical of these finely wrought pieces is "Semejante a la noche" ("Like the Night"), in which a first-person narrator of shifting identities relates analogous episodes from six key moments in history: the Trojan War, the Crusades, the sixteenth-century Spanish conquest of America, the seventeenth-century French expedition to America, World War I, and World War II. The narrators are all young, inexperienced soldiers whose similar behavior prior to embarking on their dangerous missions suggests a striking circularity in time and, consequently, a negation of linear history and its implications of progress. The story's circular structure also implies a condemnation of war and a negation of the myth of the invincible hero, for through the repetition-with-variation technique, noble ideals and patriotic fervor gradually give way to skepticism and cynicism. "Semejante a la noche" encompasses much of Western civilization, the abrupt temporal dislocations, shifting points of view, and exotic vocabulary lending a magical, mirrorlike quality to the inexorable flow of events. The message conveyed by this montage of historical moments is that although man's immediate circumstances may vary from century to century, the human condition remains essentially unaltered.

Although Carpentier's masterpiece, *El siglo de las luces* (1962; *Explosion in a Cathedral*, 1963), is set in the period of the French Revolution and the Napoleonic era, its descriptive passages and vast philosophical scope also synthesize the twentieth-century experience. The protagonist is an opportunistic man of action named Victor Hugues, a footnote in French history who, having enriched himself as a merchant in the Caribbean, surfaces as a revolutionary leader in that part of the world. In Santiago de Cuba he befriends three members of an upper-class family: Sofía, who becomes his mistress; her brother Carlos; and their cousin Esteban, ultimately the disillusioned idealist. The action shifts intermittently from the Caribbean to France and Spain, where in the final pages Sofía and Esteban are killed in a riot, an ironic commentary on the Age of Enlightenment alluded to in the book's Spanish title, which means "the century of lights." *El siglo de las luces* was written during the late 1950s, but revised and published after the triumph of Fidel Castro's revolution. As in many of his works, Carpentier's attitude toward revolutionary movements is ambiguous. What this densely textured, intellectual novel seems to convey, however, is that although the participants of any given revolution may suffer defeat and death, the basic myths of the revolutionary experience endure and reemerge in subsequent generations with renewed vigor.

Carpentier's later novels underscore his obsession with the historical and cultural links between Europe and Spanish America. *El recurso del método* (1974; *Reasons of State*, 1976) is a satirical portrait of an aging Spanish American dictator living in France during and immediately following World War I. The Spanish title parodies Descartes's "Discourse on Method," the corrupt, pseudointellectual dictator-protagonist embodying the ironic opposite of the rational French philosopher. *Concierto barroco* (1973; baroque concerto) weaves into its involuted plot a mixture of European and American musicology over several centuries of history; the end result has been described as a sustained cacophony of warring resonances.

Carpentier's vast erudition and sweeping panoramas of space and time have made him a cosmopolitan writer at home on both sides of the Atlantic. However, he obviously preferred the intense vitality of primitive cultures, which he depicts in a sophisticated neobaroque style replete with sensual imagery. The first Spanish American novelist to attempt to synthesize the entire Spanish American experience, he weaves a dense linguistic texture reinforced by the universal elements of allegory, myth, and philosophy. As seen by Carpentier, today's world is a product of cyclical forces that have shaped history as well as human nature.

AGUSTÍN YÁÑEZ

Although best known as one of Mexico's leading novelists, Agustín Yáñez also achieved prominence in the fields of education, politics, and public administration. His works include scholarly studies on well-known Mexican figures, short-story collections, and novels, the most outstanding of which are *Al filo del agua* (1947; *The Edge of the Storm*, 1963), *La tierra pródiga* (1960; the prodigal land), and *Las tierras flacas* (1962; *The Lean Lands*, 1969).

Al filo del agua, Yáñez's masterpiece, marks a turning point in Spanish American fiction, primarily because it combines for the first time a variety of avant-garde literary techniques. The portrait of a small town in Jalisco (Yáñez's native state) just prior to the outbreak of the Mexican revolution of 1910 (hence the title), this novel juxtaposes scenes in the manner of John Dos Passos's *Manhattan Transfer*; it also utilizes Joycean interior monologues to reveal the inner lives of its characters and Freudian dream sequences to depict the atmosphere of religious and sexual constraints imposed by outmoded beliefs.

The "Overture" prefacing the novel is a poetic panoramic description of the town, with its hushed voices, black-clad women, monotonous quiescence, and total absence of joy. Although the entire community probably should be considered the protagonist, Father Dionisio Martínez, the senior parish priest, stands out as the unifying element and the most completely drawn character. His deep concern for his parishioners and his sincere efforts to protect them from sin end in futility with the onslaught of the revolution and the departure with the troops of his beloved niece, María. In the final scene Don Dionisio emerges as a tragic figure, a genuine martyr, whose self-doubt and failure to reverse the thrust of history are likely to elicit the reader's sympathy.

The novel's numerous plot threads and analytically portrayed characters serve to underscore the atmosphere of oppression and suppressed sexual desire, which eventually burst forth in various forms of violence. The fanatical Father Islas and Luis Gonzaga, a love-struck but deeply religious youth, experience attacks of madness rooted in sexuality. Micaela Rodríguez, who rebels against the suffocating traditions of the town, has an affair with Damián Limón, which eventually leads to her murder and that of Damián's father. The arrival of the beautiful, sophisticated Victoria introduces a disturbing element, but her influence on Gabriel, the talented church-bell ringer, represents another form of freedom, that of artistic expression. Because of its negative impact on the town, ecclesiastical dogma obviously comes under attack; the symbolic descriptions of Gabriel's musical artistry and the sympathetic portrayal of Don Dionisio, however, tend to mute the antireligious overtones.

Al filo del agua is one of several works of the 1940s that channeled Spanish American fiction into the mainstream of world literature. Unlike most of its predecessors, which pitted man against nature—often the real protagonist—Yáñez's novel focuses on the intimate lives of complex individuals, whose destinies are determined by their social and psychological acts. This modern view of man also suggests a dialectical view of the historic process. Thus, after a series of clashes between traditional and modern values, the novel conveys the certainty that dramatic, irreversible changes have occurred in Mexican life, but the open-ended structure leaves the future of both the town and the nation clouded in doubt. Although undoubtedly more positive than negative, Yáñez's attitude toward the revolution also remains in the realm of ambiguity. His masterpiece is firmly anchored in Mexican reality, but its artistic probing of the subconscious and its objective, albeit complex, world vision elevates it to the level of universal art.

Like *Al filo del agua*, *Las tierras flacas* is set in the arid, unproductive countryside of Jalisco. Instead of a town, however, this novel depicts an isolated rural area known as Tierra Santa (Holy Land), where the unscrupulous Epifanio Trujillo runs roughshod over his neighbors in his quest for land and power. A confirmed bachelor, he has many illegitimate children, of whom his favorite is Miguel Arcángel. Miguel incurs his father's wrath when he marries without his consent (Epifanio himself has his eye on the girl), adopts his mother's maiden name, and achieves success far from Tierra Santa. Many years later he returns to challenge his father's authority and eventually brings justice and progress to the region. Another major plot thread results from the death of Teófila Garabito, a beautiful, talented girl who had acquired the first sewing machine in Tierra Santa. Because he was in love with her, Epifanio resolves to take possession of the machine, which ultimately becomes a symbol of unity against the Trujillo clan and of technological progress in the region.

Las tierras flacas, also like *Al filo del agua*, displays a variety of styles and techniques, the most effective being the interior monologue. However, *Las tierras flacas* leans more heavily on superstitions and on sorcery, much of which stems from the episodes involving the witch doctor, Matiana. It is also saturated—at times to the point of tedium—with proverbs, perhaps intended to capture the mentality of rural Jalisco and, at the same time, to inject an element of local color. Though not without its moments of dramatic impact, this novel lacks the poetically drawn setting, psychological depth, and exciting historical backdrop that breathe life into *Al filo del agua*.

While Yáñez was governor of Jalisco during the 1950s, he had the opportunity to scrutinize economic development projects undertaken in various parts of the state. *La tierra pródiga* dramatizes the struggle between government bureaucrats and wealthy property owners in the tropical coastal region of the state. The two principal antagonists are Ricardo Guerra Victoria, the corrupt, charismatic leader of the local landholders, and Medellín, a competent government engineer sent to oversee the construction of a tourist resort. The plot reaches its climax with the victory of state capitalism, symbolized by Medellín, over unprincipled entrepreneurs bent on continuing the timeworn practice of local bossism. *Al filo del agua*, *Las tierras flacas*, and *La tierra pródiga* constitute a trilogy of insightful glimpses into Mexico's past, present, and future.

JUAN CARLOS ONETTI

Juan Carlos Onetti's relatively uneventful life and dour personality are perhaps best manifested by the spiritual biographies of his solitary, uncommunicative protagonists. A native of the Uruguayan capital Montevideo, he has also lived for long periods in Buenos Aires, the setting of some of his works. In addition to his reputation as a fine short-story writer and an important journalist, he is generally considered Uruguay's leading novelist. Since 1975 he has been living in exile in Spain.

Onetti has been called the lone wolf of Spanish American letters, but he is perhaps best known for having set the standards for the contemporary novel of alienation in his part of the world. Indeed, his characters illustrate the new kind of man created by urban sprawl, the rootless outsider cast adrift in the burgeoning Spanish American capitals. Like those of Eduardo Mallea, Onetti's introspective antiheroes suggest his affinity with Sartrean existentialism, but unlike his idealistic Argentine colleague, who seeks to effect a moral renovation of his countrymen, Onetti sees life as fundamentally absurd and man as a hopeless victim of the human condition.

The protagonist of Onetti's first novel, *El pozo* (1939; the pit), is a forty-year-old failure named Eladio Linacero, who relives his sordid past in the form of an autobiography written in a cheap boardinghouse. The moral degradation of the alienated Linacero and the fusion of dream and reality projected by his interior monologue make this one of Spanish America's first truly modern novels. More ambitious and complex is the above-mentioned *Tierra de nadie*, the technique of which recalls Dos Passos's *Manhattan Transfer*. Here Onetti attempts to capture the essence of Buenos Aires through a fragmented, multidimensional collage of scenes acted out by an array of amoral, disoriented characters. The most interesting of these include Casal, an aspiring artist; Aranzuru, a lawyer who gives up his profession for a useless bohemian existence; Larvi, a projection of the disillusioned Onetti; and Pablo Num, a taxidermist whose artistic medium, like Onetti's technique of simultaneity, defies chronology. Thus, the kaleidoscopic juxtaposition of objective and oneiric realities obliterates linear time and replaces it with carefully arranged spatial constructs. Though somewhat confusing and less than successful as a cohesive work of art, this novel merits recognition as a significant experiment in literary technique because it broke ground for the newer forms of fiction soon to appear.

About the time he published *Tierra de nadie* Onetti wrote "Un sueño realizado" (a dream come true), which was to become the title of a collection of tales published in 1951. In this story, a faded, middle-aged woman asks a theater director in a drab provincial town to stage a single performance of a play based on an absurd dream she describes to him. The story and the play end simultaneously when the woman, having portrayed a youthful version of herself in an empty theater, collapses and dies on the stage. As in several of his future works, Onetti suggests that the world of dreams—for him a metaphor of artistic creativity—enables man to transcend his immediate circumstances, but not the tragedy of his ineluctable mortality.

Onetti has written two masterpieces, *La vida breve* (1950; *A Brief Life*, 1976) and *El astillero* (1961; *The Shipyard*, 1968). *La vida breve*, which has been called a monument to evasion, unfolds in the mind of Juan María Brausen, a colorless employee for a publicity agency and an aspiring writer who seeks transcendence through the creation of two alter egos: Grey Díaz, a lonely middle-aged doctor living in the imaginary town of Santa María; and Juan María Arce, the lover of a prostitute residing in the apartment next to Brausen's. At the end of the novel Grey Díaz replaces Brausen as the narrator and Santa María replaces Brausen's apartment as the setting. And, somewhat like the protagonist of "Un sueño realizado," Brausen discovers that although he finds momentary liberation from his drab existence in the realm of fantasy, his imaginary creations only reflect his own meaningless reality. *La vida breve* is the first of Onetti's novels set in Santa María, a mythical microcosm often compared to Faulkner's Yoknapatawpha County.

The protagonist of *El astillero* is another of Onetti's middle-aged failures. Junta Larsen, a former brothel owner run out of Santa María five years earlier, returns to become the manager of a bankrupt shipyard owned by a mad local tycoon named Jeremías Petrus. Although Larsen realizes from the beginning that his job consists solely of inconsequential rituals to be carried out amid imaginary clients and rusting machinery, he dutifully performs his meaningless tasks as the only defense against advancing age, death, and nothingness. Moreover, he even courts Petrus's retarded daughter, Angélica Inés, in the vain hope of gaining access to the town's respectable society. In the final pages, when he comes upon an unattended pregnant woman in labor, he flees in panic, unable to act in a critical moment of existential reality. Onetti obliges the reader to choose between two possible endings, both of which relate Larsen's defeat.

On an existential level, the decaying shipyard represents the absurd world of compulsive daily routine that lulls man (Larsen) into a false sense of security. The novel also has been read as an allegory of Uruguay, a welfare state that fell victim to bureaucratic blight and economic stagnation during the years immediately following its publication. Onetti's sensitive portraits of urban alienation and twentieth-century anguish mark him as a major precursor of the boom.

JOSÉ MARÍA ARGUEDAS

The son of a white father and an Indian mother, José María Arguedas (1911–1969) was born in the Andean highlands of Peru; he spoke Quechua before learning Spanish. At the age of eighteen he left his home for Lima to study anthropology at the National University. Because of his left-wing political activities he was imprisoned briefly in 1937. Subsequently, having completed his studies in Indian folklore, he was named director of the Institute of Ethnological Studies at the National Museum of History. He committed suicide in 1969.

Arguedas's first works of prose fiction fit the regionalist mold of scenes from rural life and protest against social injustice. *Agua* (1935; water) is a collection of three stories depicting violent conflicts between Indians and white landowners who attempt to deprive them of their land and destroy their culture. *Yawar fiesta* (1941; *Yawar Fiesta*, 1985) also treats the expulsion of Indians from their communal lands, but, in addition, it contains picturesque folkloric elements such as scenes of bullfighting as practiced by natives of the region.

El sexto (1961; the sixth one) is Arguedas's most political work, its plot being based on episodes from the author's life. The protagonist, Gabriel, is a student who witnesses incredible scenes of brutality and bestiality while serving a prison sentence for antigovernment political activities. A bitter denunciation of Peruvian society, *El sexto* delineates not only the dichotomy between races and social classes, but also the hatred between communists and *apristas* (members of the moderate leftist party known as APRA).

Arguedas's masterpiece is *Los ríos profundos* (1958; *Deep Rivers*, 1978), a novel that retains many regionalist elements but, at the same time, achieves universal stature through its interiorized portrait of the protagonist and its mythical underpinnings. A transparent persona of the author, Ernesto is a sensitive fourteen-year-old who accompanies his father, an itinerant lawyer, through the Andean provinces of Peru before being sent to a Catholic boarding school to complete his education. Here the harsh environment of cruelty, violence, and moral corruption becomes a microcosm of the society outside the school, increasing Ernesto's sympathy for the Indian culture he prefers to that of the white race. The novel ends when an epidemic mandates the closing of the school and Ernesto sets out for the home of an uncle.

Los ríos profundos is a landmark in Spanish American fiction for several reasons. Its fluid temporal design is thoroughly modern, Ernesto's present and past being conveyed through a mélange of direct, first-person narration and poetic recollections of his childhood. An aura of magical realism pervades numerous passages, illustrated by Ernesto's arrival in Cuzco, where an ancient wall comes to life, and in the boarding school, where a spinning top assumes the form of a bird. Numerous Indian songs and legends are integrated into the plot, providing an escape from sordid reality and underscoring the narrator's cultural preferences. Equally important is Arguedas's simple but evocative style, which combines Quechuan syntax and Spanish vocabulary to simulate the thought patterns of his Indian characters and reveal with greater authenticity their unique vision of the cosmos.

The two most dramatic episodes of the novel involve the insurrection of the market women, whom Ernesto ardently supports, and the ravages of the epidemic, which leads to the climax and the protagonist's departure for his uncle's hacienda. A hypocritical priest's sermon teaching resignation to Indians suffering from white exploitation represents one of the many examples of social protest, but Ernesto's respect for the underdog and his pagan love of nature emerge as the novel's principal unifying elements.

Two additional novels worthy of mention are *Todas las sangres* (1964; every blood) and *El zorro de arriba y el zorro de abajo* (1971; the fox from above and the fox from below). *Todas las sangres*, which has also been called Arguedas's masterpiece, constitutes a vast mural of Peruvian society. Its principal concern, however, is the encroachment of foreign capitalists attempting to seize Indian communal lands containing valuable mineral deposits. The ensuing rebellion and brutal repression dramatize racial and economic issues still afflicting Peru in the 1980s.

Left incomplete and published posthumously, *El zorro de arriba y el zorro de abajo* is a collage of autobiographical diary entries, dialogues, and narrative passages depicting the invasion of a coastal community by impoverished highlanders. The foxes of the title symbolize the two principal regions of Peru (the Andean highlands and the coast), and their dialogues delineate the sharp division between them. The author's diary entries convey his deepening despair over the political and social conditions in his native land, thus foreshadowing, and perhaps explaining, his suicide.

Arguedas is often compared with Asturias and with his fellow Peruvian, Ciro Alegría. Like Asturias, he interprets the Indian mind with the subtle, avant-garde tools of his craft, although Asturias's works reveal a much greater awareness of European literary currents. Throughout his career, Alegría remained a regionalist writer, whose portraits of the suffering Indian inspired little more than compassion from his reading audience—he viewed Quechuan culture from the vantage point of a sympathetic white intellectual. As mestizos, both Asturias and Arguedas identified more readily with the Indian mentality. However, whereas Asturias, who did not speak the Mayan tongue, relied solely on intuition and artistic sensitivity to capture the speech and thought patterns of his protagonists, Arguedas possessed a thorough knowledge of the Quechuan language and culture, enabling him to impart rare insights into the Indian mind as well as poetic glimpses of Quechuan lore. His reputation both at home and abroad rests primarily on his authentic, lovingly drawn portraits of the Peruvian Indian, whose animistic vision of the world defies comprehension by the white urban dweller.

ERNESTO SÁBATO

Ernesto Sábato grew up in a small town on the Argentine pampa, where his Italian immigrant parents had settled. After graduating with a Ph.D. in physics in the late 1930s, he did postgraduate work in both France and the United States. His interest in surrealism, an adjunct to his studies in Paris, was probably instrumental in his increasing disillusionment with science. Nevertheless, upon his return to Argentina, he supported himself for several years as a professor of physics. Since the mid-1940s he has devoted his life entirely to literary pursuits.

Sábato has published only three novels to date, but he has written numerous collections of essays, the most important being *Uno y el universo* (1945; the self and the universe), *Hombres y engranajes* (1951; men and gears), and *El escritor y sus fantasmas* (1963; the writer and his ghosts). In his essays he states that he renounced science because it promoted a rational concept of man radically at variance with human experience. The way to understand the world, he came to believe, is not through the phantom of reason, but through the intimate knowledge of the self, knowledge gained only through introspection and art. Perhaps the most central concern expressed in his essays, however, is man's struggle to realize his spiritual potential as an individual in today's mechanized, materialistic society. He concludes that the threat to the individual is equally great in a capitalistic and a communistic society.

Sábato's first novel, *El túnel* (1948; *The Outsider*, 1950), is a tragedy of isolation and despair brought about by the narrator-protagonist's obsession with reason. Juan Pablo Castel is a well-known artist whose painting "Maternity" depicts a woman with a child and, in the upper left-hand corner, a woman standing alone on a beach gazing at the sea. This image of solitude captivates María Iribarne's imagination, leading to her tempestuous affair with Castel. Her enigmatic behavior, however, impels the increasingly jealous and domineering Castel to seek an explanation of her every act. The resultant breakdown in communication leads to María's murder and Castel's confinement in a mental hospital.

Narrated in a taut, lucid style, *El túnel* is fraught with episodes of existential anguish and absurdity reminiscent of Jean-Paul Sartre, whose first names are, perhaps not coincidentally, the French equivalents of the protagonist's. Freudian psychology is another major element, as evidenced by Castel's surrealistic dreams and his Oedipal relations with María—both her name and the painting would seem to define her role as a mother figure. And Castel's character also evokes well-known Jungian themes, his excessive emphasis on the rational side of life having destroyed his psychic equilibrium, and his portrayal of María (we see her only through his distorted vision) likening her to Jung's anima archetype. The demented Castel, then, emerges as a symbol of modern man, who, Sábato believes, finds himself enclosed in a metaphorical tunnel of solitude, ensnared by the phantom of reason, and incapable of spiritual or humanistic communication with his fellow beings.

Critics unanimously consider *Sobre héroes y tumbas* (1961; *On Heroes and Tombs*, 1981) Sábato's masterpiece. A kind of Argentine epic displaying an impressive array of styles, this existential novel dramatizes events in Buenos Aires during the last two years of the Perón era (1953–55), but its setting also ranges geographically from the northern to the southern regions of the country and, historically, as far back as the early nineteenth century. In addition, it probes the national psyche through the presentation of four major characters: Alejandra Vidal Olmos, the beautiful epileptic daughter of a patrician family, whose roots go back to the Wars of Independence; Fernando, her ruthless and demented father; Martín del Castillo, a sympathetic middle-class youth who becomes involved with Alejandra; and Bruno Bassán, a friend of Fernando's family and perhaps the author's persona.

The third part of this four-part novel is narrated by Fernando, who, convinced that a secret blind sect rules the world, sets out to discover its leaders. His surrealistic "Memorandum on the Blind," which chronicles his cloacal journey through the underground tunnels of Buenos Aires, represents not only his own mental deterioration, but also the decadence characteristic of the Argentine aristocracy. In the final section of the novel the apocalyptic fates of Fernando and Alejandra (they are consumed in a fire set by Alejandra) coincides with the end of the Peronist regime. And Martín's metaphorical odyssey to the south, juxtaposed with an account of General Lavalle's heroic march northward more than a century before, portends the kind of spiritual regeneration envisioned by Sábato's colleague, Eduardo Mallea. Although Sábato's hopes for the future of his native land remain unfulfilled today, his masterwork stands as a monument to a nation still struggling for its true identity.

Sábato's third and most recent novel, *Abaddón el exterminador* (1974; Abaddón the exterminator), has not received wide critical acclaim. A pastiche of his previous writings combined with autobiographical reminiscences and character spin-offs of his own psyche—Sábato himself is the protagonist—the novel charts the progress of evil, which, the reader is led to believe, will eventually dominate the world. (The title derives from the biblical angel of vengeance.) Although the setting is Buenos Aires in the early 1970s, the appearance of historical figures ranging from Hitler (the Antichrist) to Che Guevara (the idealized guerrilla fighter) expands temporal and spatial dimensions to encompass much of recent history. Sábato strongly believes in the Jungian concept of "synchronicity," i.e., the acausal linking of events that, Sábato believes, are directed by occult forces manipulating human existence. Moreover, his preoccupation with evil bears certain resemblances to gnosticism, a pre-Christian religion distinguished by the conviction that matter is evil and that emancipation comes through gnosis (knowledge). The novel ends with Sábato's death, and the word *paz* (peace) inscribed on his tombstone suggests that he has attained knowledge and, with it, emancipation from evil. *Abaddón el exterminador*, then, represents not only a journey of self-discovery, but also an investigation into the malign forces shaping twentieth-century life. In its entirety, Sábato's oeuvre demonstrates his grave concern for the fate of man in a world dominated by science, reason, and meaningless materialism. His imaginative treatment of this universal theme has won him considerable esteem in his native Argentina and abroad.

AUGUSTO ROA BASTOS

Born in rural Paraguay, Augusto Roa Bastos (b. 1917) attended military school in the capital city of Asunción and fought briefly in the Chaco War, a conflict between Paraguay and Bolivia (1932–36). Soon thereafter he began a career in journalism, which was interrupted in 1947 by a civil war and his exile to Argentina, where, except for several sojourns in Europe, he spent more than thirty years. In 1983, after several unsuccessful attempts to return to Paraguay, he was granted Spanish citizenship.

Like many well-known novelists, Roa Bastos first wrote poetry, but he soon discovered prose fiction to be a more appropriate medium for developing his talent. His first collection of short stories, *El trueno entre las hojas* (1953; thunder among the leaves), leans heavily on the depiction of injustice and violence and on poetic imagery to denounce social conditions in Paraguay. Its magical and mythical elements, however, indicate a basic repudiation of regionalism and an early awareness of avant-garde literary technique. Perhaps the best of these tales is "La excavación" ("The Excavation," in Darwin J. Flakoll and Claribel Alegría, eds., *New Voices in Hispanic America*, 1962), which has been described as a metaphor of man's struggle for spiritual liberation against tyranny. The protagonist is a political prisoner, Perucho Rodi, who many years previously fought in the Chaco War. While Rodi is digging an escape tunnel for his fellow prisoners and himself, the ground above him collapses, entombing him alive. As he frantically attempts to claw his way out, he loses consciousness, and just before he dies, he relives an episode during the war when he and other Paraguayan soldiers dug a tunnel behind enemy lines and massacred an entire unit of Bolivians.

"La excavación" can be read on several different levels, the most obvious being that of social protest. In addition to the shocking prison conditions, Roa Bastos depicts the atrocities of war and alludes to the exploitation of Paraguayans and Bolivians by foreign imperialists. On a symbolic level, the story reveals possible influences of Borges, for whom Roa Bastos has expressed the highest esteem. The two tunnels resemble Borgesian labyrinths, the first leading Rodi to his death rather than to freedom, and the second representing a conduit to the very center of his psyche, where he confronts his double in the form of a Bolivian soldier he killed during the Chaco War massacre. Now alive and armed with a machine gun, the Bolivian shoots Rodi exactly as he had been shot by Rodi many years before.

An additional dimension of "La excavación" is provided by its mythical underpinnings, which illuminate its overall meaning and enhance its structural unity. Rodi emerges as the representative of the Paraguayan people struggling against oppression, but unlike the mythical hero, he is doomed to lose because of his past sins against his fellow man. In his nightmare of the Chaco War, his Bolivian victims physically resemble his fellow prisoners, who in the final lines of the story, after Rodi's death, are enticed to escape through the unlocked prison doors and are then massacred by their guards. Rodi, then, is both a hero and a traitor, one who must sacrifice his life for the cause of freedom because the evil he committed in his past lives on in the present. This dichotomy within the human personality illustrates the ambiguity characterizing both Borges's and Roa Bastos's fiction.

Roa Bastos's subsequent short-story collections, which develop increasingly complex structures, include *El baldio* (1966; the vacant lot), *Madera quemada* (1967; burnt wood), and *Moriencia* (1969; slaughter). A fine example of his more recent short fiction is "Borrador de un informe" (draft of a report), first published in *El baldío*. The narrator-protagonist is a corrupt government official sent with a detachment of soldiers to maintain order in a town celebrating a religious festival. His official report to his superior is sprinkled with a series of parenthetical asides in the form of interior monologues that gradually reveal that the real objective of his mission is to seize the donations collected by the church from the pilgrims and deliver them to the government authorities in the capital. His report constitutes not only a cynical act of public betrayal but also, on a more personal level, an admission of his own weaknesses and guilt. Thus, his asides gradually reveal his epilepsy and sexual impotence, symbols of fissures in the political system, as well as his role in the premeditated murders of three individuals: the judge, the chief of police, and a prostitute and Mary Magdalene figure who pays with her life for her mocking discovery of the protagonist's sexual inadequacy. The irony and dramatic momentum generated by the dual points of view deftly unify the narrator's disjointed thought patterns. What makes this story a tour de force of literary technique, however, is its tantalizing withholding of details, its shifting temporal planes, and, above all, its ambiguity, which obliges the reader to become an active participant in the discovery of what actually happens. This is particularly true in the episodes involving the prostitute, who first appears as a pilgrim carrying a cross and whose death results from the bite of a venomous snake the official arranges to have left near her bed. Despite its evocative religious symbolism, "Borrador de un informe" is told in a direct style shorn of the excessive poetic figures found in some of Roa Bastos's early tales.

Hijo de hombre (1960; *Son of Man*, 1965) is generally considered Roa Bastos's masterpiece. This amalgam of history and myth depicts events in various parts of Paraguay between 1912 and 1936, but allusions are also made to historical figures and events of the nineteenth century. The two principal characters, antithetical by nature, are Cristóbal Jara, a Christ figure whose heroism and sacrifice during the Chaco War symbolize man's capacity for self-redemption, and Miguel Vera, the intellectual narrator whose commitment to social revolution is ultimately nullified by his inability to act and by his Judas-like betrayal of Jara. Another Christ figure is Gaspar Mora, a leper from the village of Itapé who carves a wooden image of Christ that, long after his death, reminds the villagers of their own suffering and becomes the stimulus for their revolt against oppression. This episode exudes an aura of myth because Vera relates it as it was told to him by an old derelict, an embodiment of Itapé's collective unconscious.

As the title *Son of Man* suggests, the Christ figures represent inversions of Christianity's traditional Savior, the author's intention being to demonstrate that man's salvation will result from his own secular, human capabilities rather than from a deity created by stagnant church doctrine. The novel's biblical underpinnings, however, give universal dimensions to a human tragedy that might otherwise have been limited to Paraguay.

Fourteen years after the publication of *Hijo de hombre* Roa Bastos published perhaps his most significant novel, *Yo el Supremo* (1974; *I the Supreme*, 1986). A portrait of Paraguay's first dictator, Dr. José Gaspar Rodríguez de Francia, who ruled from 1814 to 1840, this dense, experimental work presents a mélange of documents including letters, diaries, historic footnotes, and segments of Francia's "private notebook." In addition, the author invents dialogues and probes his protagonist's subconscious in order to project an original version of the xenophobic "perpetual dictator," whose specter casts a shadow over the country's entire history.

Despite its historical subject matter, *Yo el Supremo* differs sharply from the traditional historical novel. Instead of the chronological dramatization of events, time moves back and forth erratically as mandated by the dictator's musings and the scrambled order of the documents and dialogues. The historical theme is complemented, moreover, by aesthetic and philosophical questions such as the unreliability of language, the mysteries of the creative process, and the differences between truth and fiction. *Yo el Supremo* is one of several outstanding Spanish American novels about dictators published during the 1970s. In view of its structural complexities and somewhat controversial subject matter, it will undoubtedly intrigue the more sophisticated reading public for some time to come.

Roa Bastos is Paraguay's first major writer of prose fiction. Because of his mythical interpretations of the past and his manipulation of modern literary devices, he is often seen as a successor of Asturias and Arguedas. Like these and all the other precursors of the boom, he has sought to discover the core of humanity in the tragic Spanish American experience.

JUAN JOSÉ ARREOLA

Although the Mexican writer Juan José Arreola (b. 1918) received little formal education, he is a man of vast literary culture and a keen observer of human nature. His first collection of short stories, *Varia invención* (1949; *Various Inventions*, 1964) was followed by his masterpiece, *Confabulario* (1952; *Confabulario and Other Inventions*, 1964). The latter includes stories, parables, and vignettes displaying a broad range of themes, styles, and techniques. As its title suggests, *Bestiario* (1959; *Bestiary*, 1964) revives the art of mirroring human foibles in animal portraits. Arreola's only novel, *La feria* (1963; *The Fair*, 1977), represents a poetically conceived satirical mosaic of his hometown, Zapotlán, in the state of Jalisco. *Palindroma* (1971; palindrome) contains sundry short fiction as well as a one-act farce depicting the pitfalls of marriage.

Arreola has been called the Mexican Borges. Both he and Borges prefer universal to regional themes; both might be described as sophisticated eclectics, having read widely and utilized elements of their favorite books to create their own works; both have developed styles characterized by verbal precision and classical elegance; and both are masters at illuminating the absurdity of the human experience through irony, paradox, and fantasy. Arreola differs from Borges, however, in several respects. He is less intellectual and writes in a lighter, more satirical vein than his Argentine counterpart; unlike Borges, he has penned tales of social protest with moralizing overtones;

and he is far more preoccupied with sexual relations, a theme almost entirely absent from Borges's fiction.

In Arreola's best story, "El guardagujas" (1952; "The Switchman," 1964), a "stranger" with a heavy suitcase arrives promptly at a train station eager to begin his journey to "T." While waiting for his train, he has an amusing conversation with an old man (the switchman), who suddenly appears out of nowhere with a tiny toy lantern and tells the horrified outsider about the possible hazards of travel in "this country." The story ends with the arrival of the train, the mysterious disappearance of the switchman, and the statement by the stranger (now called "the traveler") that his destination is no longer "T," but "X."

"The Switchman" has been interpreted in a variety of ways: as a fantasy satirizing the inefficiency of the Mexican railroads, as an attack on political tyranny, and as a religious allegory. It can best be read, however, as a masterful portrayal of existential absurdity: the heavy suitcase represents the overly rational stranger's burden of reason; the hazardous journey he will undertake is a metaphor of life; the tiny toy lantern, which in the final lines swings precariously in front of the onrushing train, symbolizes the dim light of reason confronting the overwhelming vicissitudes of human existence; and the ironical switchman emerges as the alter ego of the stranger, who ultimately finds himself switched onto the track traveled by the absurd man.

Additional existential pieces include "Autri" (1959; "Autri," 1964), a reworking of Sartre's *No Exit*, and "El silencio de Dios" (1952; "God's Silence," 1964), an imaginary dialogue between the narrator and God, who turns out to be the narrator's alter ego. Perhaps influenced by Sartre's psychology, Arreola is convinced that true love is an unattainable ideal. Thus, in tales such as "El rinoceronte" (1952; "The Rhinoceros," 1964), male domination and female deception destroy marital bliss.

Arreola expresses his preoccupation with aesthetics in "El discípulo" (1952; "The Disciple," 1964), which demonstrates that the ideal work of art should remain open-ended, activating the imagination. He strikes a moralizing note in "Un pacto con el diablo" (1952; "A Pact with the Devil," 1964), a popular tale patterned after Stephen Vincent Benét's "The Devil and Daniel Webster." "El fraude" (1949; "The Fraud," 1964) parodies the Prometheus myth by adapting it to an absurd, contemporary situation. And "El prodigioso miligramo" (1952; "The Prodigious Milligram," 1964) chronicles allegorically the disintegration of Western civilization due to the destruction of tradition, the rise of individualism, and the power of human greed.

An outstanding craftsman, Arreola has left an indelible imprint on Mexican and Spanish American letters. He will undoubtedly be remembered for his linguistic virtuosity and his satirical presentations of human foibles tempered by parody, fantasy, and compassion.

JUAN RULFO

Juan Rulfo was born into a family of landowners that suffered financial ruin during the Mexican revolution (1910–20) and the *cristero* wars, a series of church-led rebellions against the government during the late 1920s. After completing a minimal education in Guadalajara, the capital of his native state of Jalisco, Rulfo moved to Mexico City, where he studied law and literature briefly. The bulk of his education, however, came from his wide reading. For approximately the last twenty years of his life he worked as an editor for the National Indian Institute and served as an adviser at the government-sponsored Mexican Writers' Center.

Although Rulfo was one of Spanish America's most esteemed authors, he published only two books: a collection of short stories, *El llano en llamas* (1953; *The Burning Plain, and Other Stories*, 1967), and a novel, *Pedro Páramo* (1955; *Pedro Páramo*, 1959). The setting of all his work is the southern part of Jalisco, an arid region inhabited by poverty-stricken peasants whose lives are marked by violence and the omnipresent threat of death. The hallmarks of Rulfo's style are his sparse, incisive language and his incursions into experimental techniques.

El llano en llamas consists of fifteen tales, whose protagonists are tormented by guilt, poverty, and despair. Reacting against the convention of authorial omniscience, Rulfo relies on dialogue and the interior monologue to create the impression of objectivity and enhance dramatic effect. He also utilizes flashbacks, shifting points of view, and circular structures, devices that lend a timeless, static quality to his fictional universe. Indeed, time all but stops in the minds of his characters, for whom the burdens of the past have absorbed the present and demolished all hope for the future. By probing the depths of their psyches Rulfo, like Faulkner, exposes the core of all humanity, thus transcending the borders of his rural microcosm and achieving universal status.

One of Rulfo's most memorable stories is "Es que somos muy pobres" ("We Are Very Poor"). The unnamed child narrator describes the disasters that have befallen his peasant family: the recent death of an aunt, a flood that carries away a cow given to his sister Tacha by her father for her dowry, and the ruin of two older sisters who have become prostitutes. In view of these events, the story's initial sentence, "Everything is going from bad to worse here," would seem to imply that for the narrator and his family, life is fraught with misfortunes even greater than death. This tragic vision of the world is underscored by their fatalistic acceptance of adversity, perhaps a result of their symbiotic relationship with hostile nature. A series of parallels serves not only to convey this intricate relationship, but to give aesthetic coherence to a narrative that might otherwise lack structural unity. Just as the river carries off the highly prized cow, her legs in the air, the two older sisters are led astray by sexual passion, "rolling around on the ground, all naked, and each one with a man on top of her"; on separate occasions the narrator and his mother utter the same phrase ("May God watch over them"), the narrator referring to his sister's cow and her missing calf, and his mother to her two wayward daughters. In the last scene the sobbing Tacha is linked to both her cow and her sisters, her face covered with streams of dirty water, "as if the river had gotten inside her," and her maturing breasts bouncing up and down, starting her "on the road to ruin."

The point of view in this story serves to re-create rather than merely to recount the feelings of the narrator, thus drawing the reader to the center of the action and involving him more directly. Rulfo's prose is sprinkled with regional expressions and concrete rural images that illuminate the bleak Jaliscan landscape and reflect the tragic lives of his protagonists. Although the interior monologue reproduces the disjointed thought patterns and rambling syntax of a bewildered adolescent, on closer examination it reveals a high degree of stylization for poetic effect, relying on abrupt temporal dislocations, repetitions with variation, and the deft use of conjunctions to render the impression of spontaneity and vitality. The end result is a dynamic but carefully measured portrait of dramatic human proportions that transcends the limits of rural Mexico.

Among Rulfo's other finely wrought tales are "El hombre" ("The Man"), which describes in contrapuntal monologues the relentless pursuit of a murderer; "No oyes ladrar los perros" ("No Dogs Bark"), the stark drama of a law-abiding old man carrying his wounded bandit son to a distant town for medical assistance; "Talpa" ("Talpa"), in which remorse plagues two lovers after they deliberately hasten the death of the woman's ailing husband; and "Anacleto Morones" ("Anacleto Morones"), a rare sample of black humor involving the efforts of ten crones to sanctify a scoundrel.

The setting of *Pedro Páramo*, Rulfo's undisputed masterpiece, is the ghost town of Comala, where a young man named Juan Preciado is sent to search for his father, Pedro Páramo. Anticipating a kind of paradise described to him by his mother, Juan Preciado is literally frightened to death by the eerie voices of phantoms who recount episodes from their sinful lives. Perhaps the two most salient features of this book are its fragmented structure and its colloquial but poetically stylized language. Pedro Páramo emerges as the prototype of the Latin American *cacique* (a corrupt small-town despot), whose character gradually takes shape through his own interior monologues and the dialogues of other characters. A curious blend of brutality and sentimentality, he is referred to at the beginning of the novel as the embodiment of pure hate, the possible reasons for which are numerous: the murder of his father; the death of his favorite son; the loss of his childhood sweetheart to another man; her madness after she becomes his (Pedro Páramo's) wife; and the disrespect shown by the citizens of Comala following her death.

The protagonist's murder by one of his numerous illegitimate sons can be read as the metaphoric demise of *caciquismo* (political bossism) in Mexico, but *Pedro Páramo* is much more than a vehicle for social protest. It is, as well, a lyrical novel with strong mythical overtones that utilizes plot, structure, and evocative images to convey the archetypal theme of man's fall from grace. And it also exemplifies the architectonic novel, that is, the novel whose montage composition spatializes time, substituting dynamic movement through space for linear chronology in order to suggest the simultaneous snatches of reality provided by communication technology in today's world.

Three of Spanish America's pivotal writers are natives of Jalisco. Agustín Yáñez broke new ground with his Freudian analyses of small-town characters. Juan José Arreola's humor and philosophical approach to literature gained him a reputation as a cosmopolitan observer of the human condition. Rulfo's portraits of the bleak Jaliscan landscape reflect the existential dilemma of twentieth-century man, whose vain search for self-fulfillment in a godless world has led him to solitude and despair. Although bordering on nihilism, Rulfo's view of man's fate is redeemed by the artistry in which it is cloaked.

MAJOR FIGURES OF THE BOOM

The boom, which is discussed at greater length in chapter 1, refers to a veritable explosion in the publication of exceptionally fine novels during the 1960s. Universal in themes and experimental by nature, these works were not only acclaimed internationally by literary critics but, in most cases, also became best-sellers very quickly. In addition to its primary literary aspect, the boom also exuded strong political overtones, having been inspired by the Cuban revolution and fostered by the

Cuban government, which, through its cultural agency, Casa de las Américas, funded the publication and dissemination of fiction, sponsored literary conferences, and awarded prizes for outstanding literary works. Of the many talented authors to emerge during the decade of the boom, the six discussed below stand out for their exceptional ability to capture the essence of life in their respective homelands in the most innovative and universal terms. The influence of these writers has been felt throughout Europe and the Western Hemisphere.

JULIO CORTÁZAR

Born in Belgium of Argentine parents, Julio Cortázar was raised and educated in Argentina. While teaching French literature at the University of Cuyo he was jailed briefly for his opposition to the Perón regime. In 1952 he emigrated to Paris, where he spent the rest of his life working as an interpreter and translator for UNESCO.

Cortázar is admired equally for his novels and short fiction. Important influences on his work include Alfred Jarry (the French precursor of surrealism), Sartre, Poe, and, in Argentina, Borges and Arlt. Although his writings are multidimensional, perhaps their most salient trait—especially evident in the stories—is their depiction of everyday reality, ingeniously subverted by fantasy. The result is a celebration of the irrational and the mysterious, which serve to undermine conventional logic and thrust the reader into a surrealistic realm of ambiguity. (Much of Cortázar's fiction was inspired by personal nightmares.) By integrating fantasy into humdrum, everyday reality, Cortázar's fiction makes us marvel, but, as one critic has observed, its meaning tends to slip through our fingers.

Cortázar's best and most widely acclaimed novel, *Rayuela* (1963; *Hopscotch*, 1966), represents a landmark in Spanish American fiction and, according to some observers, marks the real beginning of the boom. The protagonist, Horacio Oliveira, is a middle-class Argentine intellectual whose anguished quest for life's meaning amid what he sees as the void of Western culture remains frustrated to the end. The book is divided into

three parts: the first describes Oliveira's life in Paris with a
group of bohemians, including his Uruguayan mistress, La Maga;
the second takes place in Buenos Aires, where Oliveira is re-
united with his former sweetheart Gekrepten, his friend Traveler, and the latter's wife Talita; and the third consists principally
of the aesthetic commentaries and random clippings from the
notebook of Professor Morelli, a friend of Oliveira's. Parts 1
and 2 (the first fifty-six chapters) constitute a novel to be read
linearly, whereas part 3—in reality a second book—contains
a table of instructions designed to guide the reader nonchron-
ologically through all of the one hundred fifty-five chapters.

The novel's title symbolizes the game of life, which man
(Oliveira) plays by hopping from one square (situation) to another in the course of his existential pilgrimage. The title also
illustrates Cortázar's playfulness, which emerges not only
through the novel's structure, but also through its iconoclastic
language, a form of revolt against the stilted literary idiom
inherited from previous generations. Derisive of everyday routine, Cortázar delights in creating absurd episodes designed to
amuse and, at the same time, to reveal the solitude, precar-
iousness, and lack of visible purpose in human existence.

The most dramatic example of the absurd describes Talita's
trek across a plank placed between Oliveira's and Traveler's
apartments—located on opposite sides of the street, several
stories above ground level—in order to deliver some tea and
nails to Oliveira. As she moves slowly across the chasm in order
to accomplish her meaningless mission, she suddenly realizes
that should she fall, life would continue unchanged for everyone
except her, a realization underscored by the idle chatter between Oliveira and Traveler during her ordeal.

Because of its mockery of literary conventions, *Rayuela*
emerges as an antinovel par excellence and Oliveira as the
prototype of the frustrated, indecisive antihero. The four major
characters represent doubles, Oliveira and his pragmatic foil,
Traveler, complementing each other, and La Maga and Talita
becoming one and the same for Oliveira, who ultimately finds
himself confined in an insane asylum. In the final lines of the
novel he contemplates a suicidal leap from his window in order

to reach the ultimate square of a hopscotch board he sees far
below, but the dénouement remains unclear.

More than any previous Spanish American novel, *Rayuela*
challenges the reader to come to grips with technical complexities and thematic ambiguities. Thus, Oliveira's unresolved on-
tological quest not only determines the novel's labyrinthine,
open-ended structure, but also obliges the reader to abandon
his traditional role as a passive spectator and become an active
participant—Morelli uses the term "accomplice"—in the creative process. Oliveira's repeated failures would seem to convey
a pessimistic outlook on the part of the author, but his revolt
against accepted values and his ambiguous fate suggest a glimmer of hope. Like other existentialists, Cortázar sees man as
an undefined animal with goals yet to be achieved. The reader
suspects, however, that in addition to the conventions of traditional fiction, *Rayuela* mocks the existential ethos of the preceding generation and, perhaps, even its own literary pretensions.

Cortázar's collections of short stories contain numerous
masterpieces, many of which introduce fantasy into the everyday world in order to disrupt or violate what he considers the
stifling, rational order of bourgeois life. Unique among these
collections is *Historia de cronopios y de famas* (1962; *Cronopios
and Famas*, 1969), a series of sketches of mythical creatures
invented by the author. Here wry humor and sophisticated
irony serve to isolate absurd elements of human behavior and
to depict easily recognizable social prototypes. The *cronopios*,
for example, are impractical, disorganized people whose unbounded joie de vivre, optimism, and artistic sensitivity elicit
both guffaws and sympathy from the reader. The *famas*, on the
other hand, are stodgy, pragmatic individuals, devoid of imagination and governed by ludicrous but rigidly observed rituals.
Cortázar's amusing portraits of the *cronopios* illustrate his affinity for the absurd man who, though ridiculous, assumes heroic proportions through his display of resilience and good humor
in the face of adversity.

One of the best examples of Cortázar's absurd short fiction
is "La autopista del sur" ("The Southern Thruway") in *Todos
los fuegos el fuego* (1966; *All Fires the Fire, and Other Stories*,

1973), which dramatizes a massive traffic jam beginning on a Sunday afternoon in August and lasting until the following spring. The travelers on the six-lane highway leading to Paris gradually form communes consisting of the cars in their immediate vicinity, and thus manage to deal with everyday problems such as the procurement of food and water, the treatment of ailing travelers, and the inevitable friction between individuals and communes. The leading character of this heroless tale is an engineer driving a Peugeot 404, who, when the bottleneck is finally eliminated, finds himself fondly recalling the daily routine of the preceding months. Meanwhile, the other drivers speed toward Paris, presumably to continue the meaningless, repetitious existence they led prior to their confrontation with the absurd.

Cortázar's first story, "Casa tomada" (1947; "House Taken Over," in *End of the Game, and Other Stories*, 1967, republished as *Blow-up, and Other Stories*, 1968), depicts a middle-aged bachelor who shares a large home with his sister until their routine existence is shattered by mysterious, unnamed invaders. "Verano" (1974; "Summer," in *A Change of Light, and Other Stories*, 1980) is in some respects a reworking of the earlier tale, the protagonists here being a childless couple, Mariano and Zulma, who, while vacationing in their cabin, agree to keep a friend's small daughter overnight. Late that evening a neighing horse gallops around the cabin, frightening the couple and arousing their erotic instincts. The next morning the appearance of normality is restored.

"Verano" can be read as a psychological fantasy, the elements of Freudian and Jungian thought reinforcing those of the fantastic genre. The child's unexpected arrival at the country home of Mariano and Zulma disrupts the pattern of their existence, which is characterized by inflexible repetitions, lack of spontaneity, and alienation from each other. The little girl, who remains anonymous throughout the story, embodies imagination, her childlike innocence triggering Mariano's speculation that his and his wife's daily rituals are merely adult defense mechanisms against the chaos of death and nothingness. The horse probably symbolizes lust, but it also evokes the blind cosmic forces of chaos and, as Jung has stated, the magic, intuitive side of man, all of which in the present context suggests the rebellion of instinct and imagination against the banality of the protagonists' lives.

The influence of surrealism on Cortázar's oeuvre is nowhere more evident than in "La noche boca arriba" (1956; "The Night Face Up," in *End of the Game, and Other Stories*, 1967), the tale of a youth injured in a motorcycle accident as he speeds through a modern city, presumably in Mexico. While recovering after surgery, he dreams that he is a Motec Indian fleeing from the Aztecs, who capture him and prepare to sacrifice him to their gods. His dream is frequently interrupted, however, by welcome moments of awareness of his hospital surroundings. In the nightmarish climax, he finds himself on the steps of a pyramid waiting to be sacrificed when he realizes with horror that dream and reality have been reversed.

The fluctuations between reality and dream generate abrupt changes in mood that are intensified by the emotionally charged atmosphere and sensual imagery of both the modern hospital and the ancient Mexican setting. In a brief interlude of lucidity the feverish protagonist recalls that between the initial impact of his accident and the moment when he was picked up from the pavement he seemed to sink into a black pit of nothingness for what appeared to be an eternity. This initial dislocation in time is, in a sense, repeated throughout the story as he is wrenched again and again from the comfort of his hospital bed into the horror of his nightmare. Still, numerous parallels between his conscious and unconscious states create a unifying, reflecting-mirror structure that renders the surrealistic dénouement more convincing to the reader.

Many of Cortázar's works represent the search for the surrealist absolute, a kind of intermediate gray zone between objective and subjective realms where opposites come together and antinomies are abolished. In "La noche boca arriba" Cortázar goes a step further, transforming objective reality into an insane dream and the terrible nightmare of Aztec savagery into reality, but he nevertheless accomplishes something akin to the surrealists' goal. The final lines of the story jolt the reader into a keen awareness of the precarious balance between the rational consciousness and the unconscious, an awareness that undermines faith in reason and creates an expanded, multidimensional surreality.

Another of Cortázar's masterpieces is "Las babas del diablo" (1958; "Blow-up," in *End of the Game, and Other Stories*), on which Michelangelo Antonioni based his famous film *Blow-up* (1966). The protagonist of this story is Robert Michel, a French-Chilean translator and amateur photographer who takes a snapshot of a woman and a boy on the Île Saint-Louis in Paris, surmising that what he has witnessed is the woman's attempted seduction of her young companion. Immediately thereafter Michel is confronted by the hostile woman and a man who approaches from a car parked nearby. Meanwhile the boy has taken flight. Several days later Michel enlarges the snapshot and once again finds himself drawn into the scene, which takes on a new meaning. To his horror, he now realizes that the agent of seduction was not the woman but the man. Thus in his imagination he relives the episode of the photograph, this time focusing his camera on the man and again giving the boy the opportunity to escape.

"Las babas del diablo" has elicited various interpretations, but like several of Cortázar's other tales, it is primarily an example of self-conscious metafiction, that is, an account of the author's ordeal in creating the story. In the opening lines, the narrator refers to his predicament over how to relate the events he has witnessed, and throughout his narration he repeatedly alludes to the clouds drifting across the sky, symbols of an evanescent reality neither snapshots nor words can reproduce. The analogies between photography and fiction serve to illuminate the metafictional theme, that is, that the camera and the typewriter are lifeless tools capable only of freezing fragments of the ever-changing world by means of static images and words. However, if the photograph is good (and we are told that this one is), it can act like an explosion on the viewer, disclosing a dynamic, open-ended reality, just as the artistically conceived story often points to something beyond itself. Thus, Michel's enlargement takes on a life of its own, revealing a new element in the drama he witnessed. Similarly, his story assumes new dimensions as he reworks it and acquires additional insight into the motivations of his three actors. Like "La noche boca arriba," which transforms the real world into a surrealist nightmare, "Las babas del diablo" alters the reality of a snapshot, the enlargement of which becomes a metaphor of a creative process.

Deshoras (1983; late hours), Cortázar's last collection of short fiction, contains eight surrealistically structured tales, some reminiscent of his earlier masterpieces. Although the tone of these stories reflects the author's darkening outlook, they emit occasional flashes of the old joyous brilliance made even more striking by the twilight in which they occur. They also illustrate his dictum that the writer's duty is to hurl himself toward an unexplored, unsettling reality, a feat Cortázar deftly performs in "Pesadilla" (nightmare), which recalls the dual, intersecting realms of "La noche boca arriba."

Cortázar's death on February 12, 1984, shocked and saddened readers throughout the Western world. One of the major literary figures of the twentieth century, he left an aesthetic legacy equaled by few of his contemporaries. The Mexican poet Octavio Paz paid the ultimate tribute to his longtime friend by alluding to his stylistic genius as follows: "Cortázar was one of the renovators of Spanish prose. He gave it facility, grace, agility, and naturalness. Prose made of air . . . with great powers of seduction and evocation . . . prose that enlivens the language, making it bounce, dance, and fly." (*El País*, Madrid, February 13, 1984, p. 19)

JOSÉ DONOSO

The son of a physician, José Donoso was born in Santiago, Chile, into an upper-middle-class family of Spanish and Italian descent. He was educated at an English school in Santiago and at Princeton University, from which he received a B.A. in 1951. He lectured for two years (1965–67) at the Writers' Workshop at the University of Iowa and subsequently lived in Spain. For the past few years he has resided in Chile.

During the 1960s Donoso emerged as one of Latin America's most important writers of fiction, and with the death of Pablo Neruda in 1973 he became, and remains today, Chile's most universally admired man of letters. Although he is known primarily as a novelist, he has also published short stories, all written between 1950 and 1962. These artistically drawn, psychologically penetrating studies of middle-class mores present in embryonic form many of the themes developed in his novels. Donoso's major themes include the decay of modern social institutions, the conflict between reason and instinct (or between order and chaos), the interplay of domination and dependence in human relations, the disunity of the personality (frequently illuminated by the display of masks), and the absurd futility of human existence.

Two of Donoso's best stories, both translated in *Charleston, and Other Stories* (1977), are "Paseo" (1959; "The Walk," 1977), the portrait of a spinster named Matilde, whose rigidly structured existence is shattered by the entrance of a stray dog into her household; and "Santelices" (1962; "Santelices," 1977), in which a timid office clerk living in a drab boardinghouse attempts to save a girl from imaginary lions and tigers. Both of these tales reveal elements of Jungian psychology: in "Paseo" the dog's emerging as Matilde's shadow, in "Santelices" the dramatization of the archetypal hero's—in this case antihero's—dragon fight.

Donoso's first two novels, *Coronación* (1957; *Coronation*, 1965) and *Este domingo* (1966; *This Sunday*, 1967), have much in common, but at the same time they reveal fundamental differences that demonstrate his maturation as an artist. Both depict the sterile lives of upper-middle-class families whose deteriorating mansions symbolize the decline of bourgeois society. Both novels also capture the nightmarish forces of instinct and irrationality lurking beneath the placid surface of the social order. *Este domingo* is aesthetically superior, however, because it adroitly introduces avant-garde stylistic techniques and structural devices that effect a more exacting scrutiny of human relationships and the explosive situations they engender.

El lugar sin límites (1966; *Hell Has No Limits*, in *Triple Cross*, 1972) is a grotesque depiction of the absurd human condition based on the biblical myths of the Creation and the Fall. The action takes place in a stagnating community founded approximately twenty years earlier by a corrupt politician, Don Alejo, who emerges as an ironic god figure when he plots the death of the town. The homosexual protagonist, La Manuela, dances in a ramshackle bordello run by his frigid, unattractive daughter. His dreams of light and glory contrast strikingly with his sordid environment and tragic fate, creating a chiaroscuro ambience that reinforces the theme of absurdity and makes this one of Donoso's most powerful and poetic creations.

With the publication of his masterpiece, *El obsceno pájaro de la noche* (1970; *The Obscene Bird of Night*, 1973), Donoso enhanced his growing international reputation. An antinovel combining many of his previous themes and obsessions, it also displays an impressive array of styles and techniques. The two settings are a luxurious estate (La Rinconada), designed as a bastion of order against the forces of chaos, and a dilapidated home for retired servants (La Casa), whose mental aberrations reflect the labyrinthine disarray of the structure. The grotesque fantasies and multiple identities of the schizophrenic protagonist, an aspiring writer named Humberto Peñaloza, alternate between these two diametrical opposites, creating tensions that reach a climax with the dissolution of Humberto's multipersonality. Other major characters whose antithetical natures inform the novel include Don Jerónimo Azcoitía, the handsome aristocratic founder of La Rinconada; his beautiful but frigid wife Doña Inés; their deformed son Boy; and Doña Inés's crafty old servant Peta Ponce.

The numerous interpretations to which this masterfully executed novel lends itself attest to its ambiguity, an aesthetic element Donoso holds in high esteem. On a superficial level it depicts the collapse of outmoded social and political institutions in today's world. Examined from a metaphysical point of view, it conveys an absurd, unstable reality in which man appears doomed to suffer terror, death, and nothingness. The rambling interior monologues, the dream sequences, and the juxtaposition of incongruous images suggest the surrealists' probings of the uncharted psychic realm beyond the confines of rational consciousness. And the plot might be read as the nightmarish account of Humberto's ongoing creative endeavor, the end result of which is a novel that drives him mad and baffles his readers. If this interpretation is correct, the above-mentioned characters represent spinoffs of Humberto's schizophrenic self (Don Jerónimo, his persona; and Boy, his repressed shadow), or other projections of his unconscious (Doña Inés, his anima; and Peta Ponce, the terrible-mother archetype).

In 1973, three years after finishing his surrealistic masterpiece, Donoso published *Tres novelitas burguesas* (*Sacred Families*, 1977). Although these three novellas contain many of his previous obsessions, they introduce new elements of humor and fantasy into the author's tormented vision of the world; they also reflect his residency in Barcelona, the setting of all three pieces. The collection achieves a measure of unity through the reappearance of the same characters, the most important of whom are three couples belonging to Spain's professional upper middle class. Although the vanity and superficiality of this milieu are treated satirically, the themes of social injustice and decay have been virtually abandoned. Rather, the emphasis here is on the complexity of human relations, the search for identity, and the subtle delineation of setting and atmosphere.

"Chattanooga ChooChoo" ("Chattanooga Choo-Choo"), the lightest and most amusing of the collection, represents a hilarious spoof of women's liberation. "Átomo verde número cinco" ("Green Atom Number Five") combines comedy and grotesque tragedy to depict the disintegrating psychic world of a well-to-do, childless couple. The best of the three novellas is "Gaspard de la nuit" ("Gaspard de la Nuit"), whose title derives from a composition by Maurice Ravel. Like several of Donoso's works, "Gaspard" lends itself to Jungian analysis, the sixteen-year-old Mauricio's enigmatic behavior emerging as a metaphor of the dragon fight, the archetypal confrontation of the mythic hero with a monster in order to set free the captive princess. A form of rebirth, the dragon fight represents the ego's perilous task of venturing into the depths of the unconscious and re-deeming from it elements crucial to psychic renewal and growth. At the beginning Mauricio is a shy adolescent who subcon-sciously seeks liberation from his mother (the dragon), a nec-essary step in the development of his own authentic personality. His search for identity ends when he meets his double in the form of a nameless beggar—in reality his unconscious self—who, upon becoming Mauricio, infuses new life into the con-scious side of his psyche and strengthens his sense of aware-ness. The only element lacking in Mauricio's rite of passage is his heroic feat of liberating the princess. His goal is not heroism, however, but adjustment to a bourgeois society characterized by material wealth and antiheroes.

More romance than novel, Donoso's prize-winning *Casa de campo* (1978; *A House in the Country*, 1984) is a massive piece of literary artifice replete with historical, philosophical, and aesthetic implications. The action begins when the adult mem-bers of the aristocratic Ventura family set out on a day's ex-cursion, leaving their lively progeny unattended on their country estate, Marulanda. The magical elasticity of fictional time, how-ever, stretches the day into a year, thus making possible the rise of a new social order that brings about the apocalyptic destruction of Marulanda and the Ventura dynasty. (The chil-dren's perverse games and the invasion of cannibals from the other side of the spiked iron fence surrounding the property are but two of the provocations of the cataclysmic dénouement.) *Casa de campo* repeats the motif of the decaying mansion Do-noso has utilized in his previous writings to represent the dis-integration of family ties, the decline of bourgeois institutions in Latin America, and, on a more universal scale, the surrender of rigid order and tradition to sensitivity, passion, and the dark forces of chaos. Heretofore unseen in his work, however, is the injection of a first-person authorial voice, vaguely reminiscent of Borges, that again and again stresses the fictive nature of the world being invented—an obvious repudiation of realism—and the obstacles encountered in the course of the creative process. This device, coupled with occasional allusions to other literary works, indicates a shift on the part of the author from a tragic to a more playful, deliberately contrived art form.

El jardín de al lado (1981; the garden next door), perhaps Donoso's most autobiographical novel, relates the struggles of an aging Spanish American writer, living with his wife in Spain, to achieve success in the petty circle of publishers and literary critics. Noteworthy for its satirical tone and intuitive insights into the complexities of human relations, this novel resembles *Casa de campo* in its emphasis on the self-conscious author's attempts to transform everyday existence into an artificial visualization of a dreamlike reality. Readers familiar with Donoso's private life will recognize in the intricate chain of events many parallels between the author and his protagonist. For those unacquainted with Donoso's career, his *Historia personal del "boom"* (1972; *The Boom in Spanish American Literature: A Personal History*, 1977) provides not only an engaging account of his formation as a writer, but also an informative critique of the literary scene during the decade of the 1960s.

In its entirety Donoso's work depicts a desperate play of masks donned by faceless figures confronting a chaotic, indecipherable universe. Perhaps because of this timely world outlook he is attracting increasing interest throughout Latin America, Europe, and the United States. His dark view of human nature and repeated insinuations of impending doom may seem overly pessimistic to some readers, but few will fail to appreciate his astonishing imagination, artistic sensitivity, and profound insight into the perils of life in the twentieth century.

GABRIEL GARCÍA MÁRQUEZ

Gabriel García Márquez spent the first eight years of his life in the village of Aracataca, near Colombia's Atlantic coast, in the home of his grandparents, whose store of myths, legends, and superstitions had a profound influence on him. After studying law at the University of Bogotá, he worked in several Colombian cities as a journalist, in Europe as a correspondent for the Bogotá daily *El Espectador*, and in New York City for the Cuban news agency Prensa Latina. During most of the 1960s he lived in Mexico, where he wrote his most famous book, *Cien años de soledad* (1967; *One Hundred Years of Solitude*, 1970). From 1967 until 1975 he resided in Barcelona, and in recent years he has spent considerable time in Mexico and Colombia. He was awarded the Nobel Prize for literature in 1982. Although he has expressed an avid interest in a multitude of writers, the most important influences on his fiction are Hemingway and Faulkner, the former for his detached, succinct mode of expression, and the latter for his creation of a single microcosmic universe populated by human failures.

The setting of several of García Márquez's works is Macondo, a small town modeled after Aracataca. His first novel, *La hojarasca* (1955; *Leaf Storm*, 1972), depicts life in Macondo during the first three decades of the twentieth century, a period covering the town's founding by refugees from the Colombian civil wars (1899–1902), its economic boom brought on by the banana industry, and its subsequent decline. The interwoven plots and subplots are narrated in the form of monologues by three characters, all of whom are attending a wake following the suicide of the town's doctor. (The similarities between *La hojarasca* and Faulkner's *As I Lay Dying* have not gone unnoticed by the critics.) A man of mysterious origin and questionable character, the deceased seems to embody the forces of guilt and evil threatening a community on the brink of chaos. *La hojarasca* suffers from monotony and flatness because its three narrative voices lack individuality, but it does succeed in evoking the oppressive, fatalistic atmosphere of moral decay and physical stagnation afflicting Macondo. The novel nevertheless ends on a positive note when the highly respected colonel (one of the narrators and the protagonist of García Márquez's next novel) fulfills his promise to bury the doctor despite the opposition of the town's citizenry.

Set in the 1950s against the backdrop of Colombia's civil strife known as *la violencia*, *El coronel no tiene quien le escriba* (1961; *No One Writes to the Colonel*, 1968) is a masterfully written novella about a retired colonel (inspired by García Márquez's grandfather) who waits in vain for his government pension. Impoverished and ailing, he falls victim to illusion when he inherits a gamecock from his recently slain son and decides to enter it in a contest with a bird from a neighboring community. The contrast between the naïve, good-natured protagonist and his skeptical, embittered wife provides a vein of humor that highlights the poignancy of the old man's plight. His unflagging determination in the face of adversity, moreover, characterizes him as an absurd hero whose valor is symbolically illuminated by the gamecock. This work's combination of stylistic precision, verbal economy, and psychological insight has rarely, if ever, been surpassed in Latin American fiction.

La violencia plays a more important role in *La mala hora* (1962; *In Evil Hour*, 1979), in which the citizens of *el pueblo*, already nervous because of political tensions, find themselves on the verge of panic when slanderous posters of unknown origin begin to appear in their midst. Ensuing events unveil a society of morally corrupt citizens whose irrational impulses and collective guilt find expression in the posters. The novel's spare, elliptical prose, disjointed montage structure, and random injections of black humor serve to intensify the atmosphere of uncertainty and fear enveloping the community.

In his first collection of short stories, *Los funerales de la Mamá Grande* (1962; *Big Mama's Funeral*, in *No One Writes to the Colonel, and Other Stories*, 1968), García Márquez resumed his realistic sketches of Macondo, often leaving the details of his protagonist's interior drama to the reader's imagination, as, for example, in "La siesta del martes" ("Tuesday Siesta"), the tale of a courageous woman and her young daughter who stoically confront the hostile curiosity of an entire town. The alienation and moral superiority of the artist emerge as major themes of "La prodigiosa tarde de Baltazar" ("Baltazar's Marvelous Afternoon"), in which the protagonist makes an elaborate bird cage for the son of a greedy, affluent bourgeois and, when the latter refuses to pay for the "piece of junk," gives it to the boy free of charge. Objective reality is abandoned, however, in the title story, which makes use of myth, fantasy, and hyperbole to satirize a feudal society ruled by an avaricious ninety-two-year-old matriarch.

The shift to a more subjective plane of vision becomes increasingly evident in *Cien años de soledad*, a recapitulation of all García Márquez's previous works. This exceptionally fine novel, which has been acclaimed as a masterpiece throughout

Latin America, Europe, and the United States, relates the founding of Macondo by José Arcadio Buendía, the adventures of six generations of his descendants, and, ultimately, the town's destruction. It also presents a vast synthesis of social, economic, and political evils plaguing much of Latin America. Even more important from a literary point of view is its aesthetic representation of a world in microcosm, that is, a complete history, from Eden to Apocalypse, of a world in which miracles such as people riding on flying carpets and a dead man returning to life tend to erase the thin line between objective and subjective realities. The resultant impression of totality is further strengthened by the novel's ingeniously conceived spiral structure as well as by its narrative technique. In the final pages the narrator turns out to be not an omniscient author viewing the action from afar, as the reader has been led to believe, but one of the characters (the old gypsy Melquíades), whose manuscript and the fictional universe therein are obliterated by the hurricane "full of voices from the past." The illusion is thus conveyed of an all-encompassing novelistic world, both engendered and consumed from within.

The title—*Cien años de soledad*—alludes to the mental state of the characters, whose irrational single-mindedness and intense struggles against a hostile natural and social milieu leave them frustrated, alienated, and, as in the case of the last two adult Buendías, condemned to beget a baby with a pig's tail. Nevertheless, despite its dramatizations of endless civil wars, gringo imperialism, and violent labor disputes, *Cien años de soledad* is not primarily a novel of social protest. Rather it is a poetic depiction of man's solitude in a labyrinthine universe he can never understand or dominate. García Márquez takes his cue from Borges, who stresses the fictive nature of literature because language reflects only the mind of the author, not objective reality. Thus the obliteration of Macondo in the final lines of the novel could be read as a sleight-of-hand disappearance of a purely imaginary world that ceases to exist when it is no longer perceived by the reader.

The fantasy so characteristic of *Cien años de soledad* is even more prevalent in *La increíble y triste historia de la cán-*

dida Eréndira y su abuela desalmada (1972; *Innocent Eréndira, and Other Stories*, 1979), a collection of seven delightful tales, several of which were written for children. "Un señor muy viejo con unas alas enormes" ("A Very Old Man with Enormous Wings") describes an amusing sequence of events unleashed by an aging winged creature's fall to earth in a seaside village, but on a more intellectual level it assails capitalistic exploitation, parodies religion, and suggests the demise of innocence. The collection's title story displays themes, characters, and an organizational framework strongly reminiscent of Grimm's fairy tales. And "El ahogado más hermoso del mundo" ("The Handsomest Drowned Man in the World") is a fable about the physical and spiritual renovation of a drab seaside village when the corpse of a gigantic young man is washed ashore and accorded elaborate funeral rites.

El otoño del patriarca (1975; *The Autumn of the Patriarch*, 1976), a novel eagerly anticipated by readers of *Cien años de soledad*, portrays an unnamed dictator (the patriarch), who, at the time of his death, is somewhere between 107 and 232 years of age. The patriarch embodies the archetypal evils of despotism, but even more significant is his extreme, and often pathetic, solitude, which becomes increasingly evident with his advancing age and which emerges as the principal theme. Despite its political and psychological overtones, *El otoño del patriarca* can best be described as a lyrical novel, whose plot and character development are subordinate to formal design and symbolic imagery. The work's narrative content is conveyed by a wide variety of rhetorical devices, including its figurative language, rambling syntax, and constantly shifting point of view. In addition, frequent infusions of fantasy, hyperbole, and grotesque absurdities further enrich its texture and elicit reader reactions ranging from hilarity to horror. Hailed as a masterpiece by many critics, this brilliantly stylized portrait of solitude resulting from tyranny stands out as an unforgettable tour de force of experimental fiction.

Crónica de una muerte anunciada (1981; *Chronicle of a Death Foretold*, 1983) has also been widely acclaimed by the critics and reading public. A concise, emotion-packed mélange of fiction and journalism—the plot is based on a newspaper report—the novel details step by step the events leading up to the murder of Santiago Nasar, the youth accused of having seduced the sister of his two assassins. Santiago's probable innocence and his assassins' reluctance to commit their blood-curdling deed only reinforce García Márquez's condemnation of the rigid, outmoded code of honor imposed on all males in Latin American society. The author's intrinsic artistry as a storyteller is demonstrated by his ability to rivet the reader's attention on the portentous chain of events surrounding the ill-fated victim, whose murder is revealed in the opening lines of the novel but, nevertheless, anxiously anticipated up to the climax.

García Márquez's unwavering support of Marxist regimes throughout the world is well known; still, he has steadfastly refused to subordinate art to left-wing propaganda, having stated on several occasions that the duty of the revolutionary writer is to write well. At present Latin America's most widely known and admired novelist, he imparts in his fiction not only the stark reality of a rapidly evolving, strife-torn continent but, through the humanistic and universalizing elements of myth, imagination, and aesthetic perception, an original vision of man and his world.

CARLOS FUENTES

The son of a Mexican diplomat, Carlos Fuentes lived in several capitals of the Western Hemisphere as a child. He received a law degree from the National University of Mexico and subsequently studied economics at the Institute of International Studies in Geneva. He has held a number of posts in the Mexican government, including the ambassadorship to France during the late 1970s. Although he frequently visits Mexico, in recent years he has resided in Europe and the United States, where he has lectured on literary and political topics in many universities.

Fuentes is known above all as a novelist, but he has also published three fine collections of short stories, three plays, and several books of essays. His first novel, *La región más transparente* (1958; *Where the Air Is Clear*, 1960), is a mosaic of Mexico City during the 1950s. An experimental work reminiscent of John Dos Passos's *Manhattan Transfer*—Fuentes admits to the strong influence of this writer—it portrays a broad spectrum of characters from all levels of society by means of a temporal and spatial montage of clashing, multivocal scenes. Two of the basic themes emerging from this complex structure are the lingering resonances of Indian myth in modern Mexico and the betrayal of the Mexican revolution of 1910 by the rising middle class at the expense of the declining aristocracy and the poverty-stricken masses. The major characters include Federico Robles, a mestizo of peasant origin who acquires vast financial holdings; his wife, Norma, a cold, selfish white woman who perishes in a fire; his blind mistress, Hortencia Chacón, whose love effects his moral regeneration after the collapse of his empire; and a ubiquitous Indian named Ixca Cienfuegos, symbolizing the mysterious forces of the pre-Hispanic past that take vengeance on, or control the destinies of, even the most affluent and powerful. (Federico and Norma Robles are two cases in point.) Fuentes's dynamic fusion of present and past via the juxtaposition of dialogues, interior monologues, and unidentified voices represents a quest for national identity unique in Mexican fiction, a quest conveyed by the collective unconscious of a modern metropolis superimposed on a vibrant, ancient civilization.

A year after the publication of his avant-garde panorama of Mexico City, Fuentes published *Las buenas conciencias* (1959; *The Good Conscience*, 1961), a more traditional *Bildungsroman* about a young man's clash with the conservative upper-class society in the provincial city of Guanajuato. At first Jaime Ceballos's awakening to the hypocrisy and corruption in his midst takes the form of rebellion, but he ultimately abandons his youthful idealism and conforms to the pressures of wealth and social prestige. As might be expected, the irony of the title reflects the tone and *Weltanschauung* of the entire novel.

In 1962 Fuentes published two major works: *Aura* (*Aura*, 1968) and *La muerte de Artemio Cruz* (*The Death of Artemio Cruz*, 1964). The former can be described as a gothic novella with strong historical underpinnings, but it is also an example of magical realism with intriguing allusions to Jungian psychology. The protagonist, a young historian who goes to the home of Consuelo de Llorente to edit the memoirs of her deceased husband, finds himself captivated by Consuelo's beautiful niece, Aura. The ensuing revelations of sorcery, involuted time, and double identities make this one of Fuentes's most engrossing pieces of fiction.

La muerte de Artemio Cruz is generally considered Fuentes's best novel to date. One of Mexico's wealthiest and most powerful men, the protagonist is seen on his deathbed on the first page, and before his death in the final lines, he relives twelve crucial moments of his past—all involving important decisions on his part—the sum total of which represents the essence of his existence. Like *La región más transparente*, *La muerte de Artemio Cruz* depicts a search for national identity, but the latter concentrates more on Mexican history than on myth, dramatizing conflicts of the nineteenth century as well as the revolution of 1910 and major events prior to 1959, the year of the foreground action. The existential theme of man's anguished confrontation with death is reinforced by the related concepts of freedom, responsibility, and bad faith, all of which haunt the semiconscious protagonist as he takes stock of the legacy he will leave behind and recognizes, or attempts to deny, his guilt.

La muerte de Artemio Cruz is divided into twelve chapters, each of which has three parts; the first part of each chapter, written in the first-person singular and the present tense, conveys the protagonist's random perceptions as he approaches death; the second part, written in the second-person singular (*tú*) and the future tense, relives episodes of the past as if they were to occur in the future, thus assuming that the protagonist's choices are still open; and the third part of each chapter narrates in the third-person singular an episode from the protagonist's past. These episodes are not arranged linearly, however, but rather are scrambled to enhance compositional unity and dramatic impact. For example, the chapter dealing with Captain Cruz's capture by the forces of Pancho Villa in 1915 occupies the center of the novel because these events mark a turning point in Cruz's life. The 1941 episode, which depicts Cruz at the peak of his power, occurs at the beginning, thus impelling the reader to discover how he reached the pinnacle of success. And the 1913 and 1924 episodes are juxtaposed in order to contrast Cruz's passionate love affair with Regina during the revolution and his complex marital relations with the embittered Catalina eleven years later.

Another of Fuentes's major novels is *Cambio de piel* (1967; *Change of Skin*, 1968), a showcase of experimental techniques and stylistic virtuosity geared to jar the reader into new areas of awareness. The plot centers on four residents of Mexico City, Elizabeth, Javier, Franz, and Isabel, who are traveling to Veracruz to spend the 1965 Easter holidays. Elizabeth, the daughter of a Jewish family in New York City, has been married for twenty years to Javier, a Mexican poet of brief renown, now employed by the United Nations. Franz is a Sudetenland German and former architect from Prague who, during World War II, collaborated with the Nazis by designing a concentration camp. Isabel, Franz's mistress, is the twenty-three-year-old daughter of a wealthy Mexican family. While the two couples are visiting some Aztec ruins in Cholula (about halfway to Veracruz), they are obliged, due to car trouble, to spend the night in a hotel, where they exchange bed partners. Meanwhile, they have been followed to Cholula by the narrator, a cab driver and self-styled intellectual named Freddie Lambert, and a group of six American hippies known as the Monks. These youths eventually hold a mock trial of Elizabeth, Javier, and Franz, condemning Franz to death for his war crimes. The climax is reached when Isabel leads her three companions deep into the interior of a pyramid. What happens then is not entirely clear, but in this eerie atmosphere Franz is either crushed during an earthquake or executed by the Monks, who have followed the group into the monument. The reader is ultimately led to believe that the others have escaped and that the narrator is confined in the Cholula insane asylum.

Although the foreground action takes place in less than twenty-four hours, the author, by means of dialogues, flashbacks, and interior monologues, depicts the heterogeneous backgrounds of the four characters, greatly expanding temporal and spatial dimensions. One of the book's major themes is its interpretation of present-day Mexican reality based on what the author calls *el mito mexicano*, that is, his homeland's historic and legendary past, reduced in a synthesis of fact and fiction to more human proportions. In myth Fuentes seeks clues to explain the complex nature of a contemporary Mexico plagued by poverty, ostentation, excessive pride, cruelty, and feelings of inferiority. A gigantic condemnatory fresco of Western civilization, *Cambio de piel* examines the spiritual cancer of twentieth-century society, often in the most irreverent terms. The result is a masterful interpretation of man's restless search for identity in a crisis-ridden world in which the old makes way for the new—thus the title—at a steadily accelerating pace.

   Terra nostra (1975; *Terra Nostra*, 1976) and *Una familia lejana* (1980; *Distant Relations*, 1982) are Fuentes's most significant later novels. Highly sophisticated works placing considerable demands on the reader, both treat the complex cultural ties between old and new worlds, with special emphasis on literature, history, and the visual arts. The leading figure of *Terra nostra*, the temporal scope of which ranges from the Roman empire to 1999, is a Spanish king named Felipe who in many respects recalls Philip II. For example, he is building an enormous religious structure dedicated to his ancestors, bringing to mind El Escorial; he is also shy, retiring, and possesses facial features similar to those of the homely Philip II. His father, however, is not Charles V, but Philip I (Felipe el Hermoso), who was in reality Philip II's grandfather. Thus Fuentes molds history to suit his own purposes. He likewise alters fiction, as in the case of Don Quixote, who is portrayed as the seducer of Dulcinea with the help of the famous go-between, Celestina. And many of the descriptions of historical figures assume grotesque proportions reminiscent of Goya's paintings. Fuentes views history as a gigantic jigsaw puzzle, an accumulation of contradictions almost as fictive as the realm of fiction. He thus condenses centuries of time into one reign, his portrait of Felipe representing all the Spanish Hapsburgs and the Golden Age of literature, the sum total of Spain's vast cultural legacy. Although more than half of the novel is set in Spain, large sections depict events in the New World, which, as a symbol of freedom, poses a threat to the rigid political hierarchy of the mother country. Given Fuentes's left-wing convictions, it is not surprising that *Terra nostra* strongly condemns Spain for transporting her political and social institutions to her colonies, where the same patterns of injustice continued for centuries.

In *Una familia lejana* an aging French count named Branly relates to the narrator, who ultimately turns out to be Carlos Fuentes, a series of events involving two Heredia families, one French and one Mexican. The mysterious parallels between the two families on different sides of the world eventually come to symbolize, by extension, the "distant relations" between all peoples as well as the keenly perceived parallels between historical moments, continents, and even well-known works of fiction. Like other Spanish American novels, such as Cortázar's *Rayuela* and Donoso's *Casa de campo*, Fuentes's text is self-conscious, reflecting his obsession with narrative technique and the burden of the literary past on the contemporary author who finds himself in the throes of creating an original work of art for an increasingly critical reading public. The author's problem, then, becomes a major subject of his text, and, in the case of *Una familia lejana*, the cultured Count Branly's tale could symbolize the baggage of European letters weighing on the New World innovator, Carlos Fuentes.

Fuentes's three collections of stories display a wide range of subjects, but, as in his novels, an important concern in many of his tales is the lingering influence of Mexico's colorful past, both pre-Columbian and colonial, on present-day reality. Perhaps his most popular tale is "Chac Mool" ("Chac-Mool," in *Burnt Water: Stories*, 1980), published in the collection *Los días enmascaradas* (1954; the masked days); the story is about an idol representing the Mayan and Toltec rain god that comes to life and claims the protagonist, an educated inhabitant of the Mexican capital, as his sacrificial victim. The colonial period is evoked in "Estos fueron los palacios" ("These Were Palaces," in *Burnt Water*), published in the collection *Agua quemada* (1981; all four stories included in *Burnt Water*); this story portrays a lonely retired servant, Manuela, and a crippled fourteen-year-old youth named Luisito, both of whom live in a tenement near the Zócalo in Mexico City. A sensitive realist, Manuela feeds the stray dogs in the neighborhood and treats them when they are hurt, whereas the more romantically inclined Luisito spends his days envisioning the majestic past of his once-wealthy family and that of colonial Mexico, when the tenements around the Zócalo were beautiful palaces. A mysterious, intuitive understanding develops between the two protagonists, who need and complement each other in a variety of ways. Luisito not only replaces, in Manuela's mind, the daughter she has lost to prostitution, but also induces her to imagine the grandeur of past centuries instead of reliving her own sordid life as a servant in the household of a general. Manuela's spiritual strength compensates for Luisito's physical infirmity, making him more aware of life around him and thus causing him to achieve a greater sense of identity. The tenement and the dogs symbolize legacies of the past, the former having derived from an affluent social class condemned to decay, and the latter representing the base of Mexico's societal pyramid built up through generations of poverty, cruelty, and injustice.

The final episodes of the story are especially revealing. In the surreal atmosphere of a moonlit night—this episode is more than likely dreamed or imagined by one or both of the protagonists—Manuela and Luisito descend the main staircase of their "palace" to the sounds of the barking dogs, a symbol of the present, and of beautiful music out of the remote past. Manuela evokes her former lover and tells Luisito to imagine that he is embracing her beautiful daughter Lupe Lupita. The fading of the music and the increasingly strident barking of the dogs, whom Manuela and Luisito vow they will always care for, propel the action into the present and suggest a social message. In the final lines, Luisito enters the kitchen unaccompanied in search of food, an indication of nascent initiative and maturity. Unlike "Chac Mool," whose protagonist is victimized by the indigenous past, "Estos fueron los palacios" conveys a message of hope despite the crippling legacy Mexicans have inherited from history.

Gringo viejo (1985; *The Old Gringo*, 1985) is a lyrical and philosophical tale about the well-known writer Ambrose Bierce ("the old gringo"), who disappeared in Mexico in 1914. Fuentes speculates that the unconventional Bierce, having joined the troops of a young revolutionary general, Tomás Arroyo, was killed by him in an altercation over some historical documents Bierce burned. This ingeniously conceived, self-conscious novel (Fuentes never lets his readers forget that his tale is pure invention) also suggests that Mexico and the United States are doomed never to bridge their vast cultural differences.

GUILLERMO CABRERA INFANTE

As a product of the poor working class of Cuba, Guillermo Cabrera Infante enthusiastically supported Fidel Castro's revolution and held important editorial posts for over a year after the end of the conflict. In 1961 he was sent to Belgium as Cuba's cultural attaché, but in 1965, disillusioned by government bureaucracy and the turn of events in his native land, he chose political exile in London. Since then he has lived in England and other parts of Europe.

In 1960 Cabrera Infante published *Así en la paz como en la guerra* (in peace as in war), a collection of fourteen stories interspersed with fifteen objectively sketched vignettes depicting the political injustice and violence of the Batista regime before it was overthrown by Castro in 1959. Although the stories of this collection are more traditionally structured than his masterpiece, *Tres tristes tigres* (1967; *Three Trapped Tigers*, 1971), they do, like his most successful novel, suggest an undercurrent of malaise in Cuban society, hinting at the possibility of radical change.

One of the best tales is "En el gran Ecbo" (1961; at the great Ecbo), in which a young, sophisticated bourgeois couple attends a religious ceremony of blacks worshiping their god of purity. During the ceremony an old black woman speaks briefly to the young lady, who immediately thereafter terminates her relationship with her male companion. Cabrera Infante's technique is reminiscent of Hemingway's, that is, his laconic dialogue, sparse descriptions of surface reality, and flat, deadpan tone. The story owes its tautness to two sets of opposites: the antithetical natures of the couple and the gulf between the white middle-class and black African cultures. The man is rationalistic and arrogant, viewing the religious ceremony as an exotic, after-lunch diversion, while his companion emerges as a more sensitive individual, deeply moved by the primitive fervor of the participants and the magic-charged atmosphere of the ceremony. She also appears to have arrived at a point of crisis in her life, having come to feel both bored with and guilty about her illicit relationship with the man. The dénouement dramatizes the vulnerability of the educated middle class, which feels threatened by the Jungian shadow—the dark, misunderstood side of the psyche embodied in the more instinctual lower classes.

Unique among the many fine novels of the boom, *Tres tristes tigres* depends on humor, tragedy, and avant-garde strategies to recapture the nostalgic, bygone ambience of Havana in 1958, only months before Castro's triumph. The leading characters, several of whom are first-person narrators, include La Estrella, an obese black chanteuse who sings without accompaniment in a voice embodying pure, primordial sound; Arsenio Cué, a well-known television actor; Silvestre, a frustrated writer of dubious talent; Eribó, who plays drums in a nightclub band; Códac, a newspaper photographer assigned to cover Havana's flamboyant nightlife; and a splenetic figure named Bustrófedon, who delights in creating puns, anagrams, palindromes, and other types of word games.

If, as some critics contend, the true protagonist of *Tres tristes tigres* is language, Bustrófedon looms as the hero who utilizes the word as *prima materia* to help create and inform the novel. (His name derives from a Greek rhetorical device, the procedure of writing one line in one direction and the next in the opposite direction.) Bustrófedon not only punctures the inflated literary idiom, but also brilliantly parodies seven well-

known Cuban writers, each of whom allegedly describes the
death of Leon Trotsky in his own unique style. The nineteenth-
century poet José Martí (1853–1895) uses the outdated linguistic embellishments typical of his modernist generation; José
Lezama Lima's (1910–1976) display of erudition stands out as
his most salient characteristic; moral and ethical concerns dominate Virgilio Piñera's (1912–1979) version; Lydia Cabrera (b.
1900) and Nicolás Guillén (b. 1902) stress exotic vocabulary
and native rhythms; the colloquial style of one of Lino Novás
Calvo's (1905–1983) most famous tales characterizes his efforts; and, perhaps most notable of all, the baroque, verbose
prose attributed to Alejo Carpentier describes in labored, labyrinthine detail the events leading up to the historic assassination.

Although the initial impression of *Tres tristes tigres* is one
of chaos, its parallels with biblical myth serve to delineate
structure and clarify meaning. The prologue consists of the
inane chatter of a master of ceremonies in the famous Tropi-
cana nightclub filled with wealthy Cubans and U.S. tourists
on a weekend fling. His invitation to enjoy the spectacle about
to be staged, along with his repeated calls for lights, represents
the Book of Genesis, that is, the advent of a world about to be
created. As the plot evolves, the reader becomes increasingly
aware that Bustrófedon symbolizes a kind of redemptive mes-
siah, whose genius is directed toward the restoration of language just as Christ was sent for the salvation of mankind.
And after his death from a brain tumor, Bustrófedon achieves
immortality through his legacy of words, poems, and other verbal creations.

The apocalypse is evoked in the final part of *Tres tristes
tigres* when the fortunes of the leading characters decline and
a sense of foreboding, often expressed by symbolic dreams, becomes increasingly pervasive. Allusions to the political drama
about to unfold include Castro's uprising in the Sierra Maestra,
the subject of occasional satirical remarks, and Bustrófedon's
fanciful theory that the Russian language may be nothing but
Spanish in reverse and thus identical to Spanish when viewed
in a mirror. Inasmuch as Bustrófedon sees language as the

basic expression of culture, his theory would seem to anticipate the reversal of cultural values—Russian for Latin—soon to occur in Cuba. A series of dreams interspersed throughout the novel also implies impending disaster as, for example, one in which an apocalyptic blast levels Havana and the sole survivor, a naked woman on a gray horse, turns out to be Marilyn Monroe. And the epilogue, which consists of the incoherent ravings of a madwoman, leaves the reader with a hint of both moral and physical disintegration.

In addition to its pervasive mythical elements, *Tres tristes tigres* depicts the gritty realities of Cuban life, often in the form of amusing, offhand comments. The poverty Cabrera Infante knew as a child more than likely inspired his descriptions of the struggle for survival in a country whose underdevelopment is repeatedly ridiculed. The author's sharp ear for dialogue accurately records the street Spanish spoken in Havana during the 1950s, his purpose being to give literary status to the "human voice on the wing." Other realistic elements emerge from the injected tale of Mr. Campbell, a U.S. citizen who spends a weekend in Havana with his wife. From the moment of their arrival by boat, the patronizing Mrs. Campbell finds everything "enchanting," while her sarcastic mate typifies the U.S. tourist who criticizes all aspects of life on the island except those that mirror life at home.

Because of its stylistic virtuosity and multifaceted portrait of a city, *Tres tristes tigres* invites comparison with Joyce's *Ulysses*, but Cabrera Infante's tone, unlike Joyce's, is one of nostalgia shaded by skepticism. This yearning to recapture the Havana of the 1950s recalls Cortázar's wistful evocation of Buenos Aires in *Rayuela*; a major difference, however, is that the abstract, philosophical themes of *Rayuela* attract the intellectual reader, whereas *Tres tristes tigres*, with its emphasis on pop culture and the vernacular, is likely to appeal to a wider audience. Cabrera Infante has repeatedly expressed his admiration for Lewis Carroll, a writer with whom he shares a fascination with word games and, as suggested above, with mirrors. The movement through the looking glass in Carroll's famous novel is brought to mind in *Tres tristes tigres* when

Bustrófedon, the embodiment of immortal art, passes from life to death, synthesizing the two mutually reflecting realms. (The reader is reminded that Bustrófedon, who never actually appears in the novel, is first portrayed through the eyes of his friends and then, after his demise, through their collective memory of his creativity.) Bustrófedon also considers the palindrome (eye, nun, kayak, level, sexes, radar, civic, gag, boob) the perfect verbal entity because it looks the same from either side of the mirror and is thus, he believes, unchangeable and immortal.

In their entirety the characters of *Tres tristes tigres* embody the frenzied search for order and permanence in a world on the verge of disintegration and oblivion. A possible escape from this existential void is provided by the creative process of the novel itself, a process in which the reader is obliged to become an active participant. Bustrófedon's destruction and renovation of language, then, can be interpreted not only as the harbinger of the new linguistic order engendered by the literary boom, but also as a metaphor of imminent political and social change. The total chaos conveyed by the epilogue, however, could represent the author's disillusionment with the outcome of the most far-reaching political and social experiment of the century in Latin America.

Tres tristes tigres is an entertaining, exhilarating novel that runs the gamut from madcap humor to tragedy and despair. It also challenges the reader to discover a kind of mythical order embedded within its baffling framework and frequently unruly style. Though limited in its setting to Cuba during the 1950s, it achieves universal stature because its fictional world evolves not through the eyes of a single, detached observer, but through the minds of its major characters, who, like most people today, find themselves buffeted simultaneously by the forces of destruction and re-creation.

Cabrera Infante returns to the same setting in *La Habana para un infante difunto* (1979; *Infante's Inferno*, 1984), a phantasmagoric novel about the sexual misadventures of a young unnamed journalist, the author's alter ego, in the Cuban capital over a period of several decades. A parody of the *Künstlerroman* and autobiographical writing, this book relies above all on Dante's *Divine Comedy* and Lezama Lima's *Paradiso* for its thematic and structural underpinnings. The protagonist's recollections of, and imaginary exploits in, Havana represent his search for identity, which ends with the realization that the quest itself is an act of deception. Thus, the final image of his descent into the maelstrom of the womb suggests that his desire for immortality can be fulfilled only through the creation of the novel he is writing. Like *Tres tristes tigres*, *La Habana para un infante difunto* displays a mélange of melancholic nostalgia, literary puns, and hilarious humor, demonstrating that the author's greatest gift to contemporary literature is the zest he brings to the act of writing.

MARIO VARGAS LLOSA

The youngest of the leading figures of the boom, Mario Vargas Llosa is Peru's most prestigious writer. He was born into a middle-class family and has degrees from the University of San Marcos in Lima and the University of Madrid. After having lived abroad for many years, he returned to Peru, where he still resides, in the mid-1970s.

Although Vargas Llosa is well known as a political leftist strongly committed to social justice, he has steadfastly refused to compromise aesthetic goals for revolutionary propaganda. In his essays on the creative process, he has set forth the theory that literary themes are an author's demons or obsessions emanating from his irrational unconscious. He sees the formal elements of style, technique, and structure, however, as products of the rational consciousness that should be conceived and organized in a logical manner to reinforce theme.

Vargas Llosa's first novel, *La ciudad y los perros* (1962; *The Time of the Hero*, 1966), exploded onto the literary scene with its experimental form and exciting plot, and today, in retrospect, some critics consider it, along with Cortázar's *Rayuela*, an initiator of the boom. The story takes place in the Leoncio Prado military academy in Lima, where Vargas Llosa himself once studied. In the opening pages of the novel a chemistry exam is stolen, unleashing a series of events that culminate in the murder of an informer and the refusal of upper-echelon officers to conduct an investigation for fear of damaging the academy's reputation. By means of temporal dislocations, scrambled points of view, and other literary devices, the fictional dimensions are expanded in order to reveal the heterogeneous backgrounds of the cadets. Thus the academy emerges as a microcosm of Peruvian society, and the book as a scathing condemnation of the vice and violence engendered by an obsolete social system.

Whereas *La ciudad y los perros* reflects the naturalistic tenets of social determinism, *La casa verde* (1966; *The Green House*, 1966) enters the realms of myth and metaphor. Considered by many as Vargas Llosa's masterpiece, this vast, complicated novel has two major settings: the first, a provincial city (Piura) located in the northwestern Peruvian desert, where a series of highly dramatic events unfolds in a brothel (the green house); and the second, a community called Santa María de Nieva, in the Amazonian wilderness, where traders, government officials, military personnel, missionaries, and primitive Indians vie for a livelihood and for supremacy over a hostile environment.

The leading figure of the Piura setting is Don Anselmo, a harp player who in his youth builds the green house just outside the city and draws a clientele from a wide area. Anselmo falls in love with and kidnaps a blind orphan girl, Antonia, and when it becomes known that she has died giving birth to his child, the enraged Padre García and the women of Piura burn down the green house. Years later La Chunga, Anselmo's daughter by Antonia, builds a second green house, where her now aging father leads a popular orchestra. As the years pass, the original green house becomes a kind of myth, which Anselmo and others of his generation refuse to discuss or even admit ever existed. The only links between Piura and the Amazonian jungle are provided by Sergeant Lituma, a native of Piura who served in the northeast, and his Indian wife Bonifacia, a resident of Santa María de Nieva whom he brings back to Piura. Lituma is subsequently arrested, and Bonifacia, alone and with no other means of support, becomes a prostitute in the green house.

Like most of Vargas Llosa's fictional creations, the characters of *La casa verde* appear to be trapped by the immediacy of each situation, which causes them to react instinctively and propels them toward tragedy or defeat. They reveal themselves principally through their actions, dialogues, and interior monologues, usually set forth in fragmentary form on intersecting temporal and spatial planes. The complex novelistic framework conveys an ambiguous view of reality enriched by evocative motifs, mythical allusions, and veiled character identities. For its exotic appeal, ingeniously interwoven plot threads, and graphic depiction of man pitted against an environment he can neither comprehend nor control, *La casa verde* is truly an unforgettable literary experience.

Conversación en La Catedral (2 vols., 1969; *Conversation in The Cathedral*, 1975) once again demonstrates Vargas Llosa's consummate craftsmanship, its primary focus being the political vicissitudes of Peruvian dictator Manuel Odría's regime (1948–56). The action is set in motion by the fortuitous meeting of Santiago Zavala, a disenchanted idealist estranged from his upper-class family, and Ambrosio Pardo, an indigent black who years before worked for Santiago's father. The ensuing conversation between the two men in a Lima bar (La Catedral) provides the occasion for the meticulously arranged flashbacks dramatizing the destinies of individuals from diverse social classes. Like all of Vargas Llosa's fiction, *Conversación en La Catedral* at first baffles, then ensnares, and finally thrusts its reader into a world torn by violence and threatened by moral decay.

Because of its rollicking, farcical humor, *Pantaleón y las visitadoras* (1973; *Captain Pantoja and the Special Service*, 1978) is perhaps Vargas Llosa's most popular novel to date. Pantoja is a diligent young army officer who is sent to Peru's remote Amazonian region to organize a squadron of prostitutes and thus make life more bearable for the lonely soldiers stationed there. Because of his puritanical nature and zealously analytical approach to his assignment, Pantoja elicits the reader's guffaws from the beginning, but ultimately he comes to typify the absurd hero who continues to struggle against overwhelming odds. The theme of absurdity is underscored, moreover, by the hilarious parodies of military procedures, the clashing

montage of incompatible episodes, and generous doses of irony
and the grotesque.

Comic situations also abound in *La tía Julia y el escribidor*
(1977; *Aunt Julia and the Scriptwriter*, 1982), which draws on
memories of Vargas Llosa's youth during the 1950s, namely
his marriage to an "aunt" (the ex-wife of a blood-related uncle)
despite strong family opposition. A second plot centers on a
mad scriptwriter, Pedro Camacho, who churns out an incredible string of action-packed soap operas for a Lima radio station
where Mario, the narrator and protagonist, is also employed.
The novel's overriding irony stems from the juxtaposition of
the two plots, the first based on fact and the second on imaginary events. Camacho's preposterous scenarios somehow con-
taminate Mario's affair with his Aunt Julia, likening their
romantic capers—intrigues, heated arguments, separations,
reconciliations—to the sentimental melodramas that captivate
such a large radio audience. The end result is a kind of metanovel in which the line between reality and imagination becomes blurred and the creative process itself becomes an
important aspect of the book.

Vargas Llosa has described *La guerra del fin del mundo*
(1981; *The War of the End of the World*, 1984) as his most
ambitious novel to date. Another ingenious fusion of fiction and
reality, it depicts the rebellion of a group of fanatical Catholic
monarchists against the recently established republic in late-
nineteenth-century Brazil. To suppress this refractory movement centered in the remote northeastern town of Canudos,
the Brazilian government sent four separate expeditions to-
taling six thousand men who, after incredible hardships and
losses, reduced the heavily fortified redoubt to rubble and
slaughtered the vast majority of its inhabitants. In 1902 the
Brazilian writer Euclides da Cunha published his classic *Os
sertões* (translated as *Rebellion in the Backlands*), which describes, in addition to the bloody campaign, Brazil's exotic
northeast and its primitive inhabitants.

Although Vargas Llosa consulted numerous historical
sources and imagined the novel's most dramatic scenes, *La
guerra del fin del mundo* obviously relies on *Os sertões* for its
narrative framework. The action begins in October 1896, when

a company of soldiers is sent to quell the incipient uprising, and it ends several months after the conclusion of the year-long conflict. The most important single figure of the saga is the rebel leader, a demented ascetic known as the Consejero. The story of his past and that of many of his followers, some hardened criminals mesmerized by their leader, constitute major segments of the novel. Vargas Llosa also vividly portrays the most important military leaders of the campaign as well as the political intrigues swirling around the rebellion. For example, the liberal party of Bahía, the state where the action takes place, accuses the conservatives of instigating the rebellion with the aid of the English crown in order to restore the monarchy. But the most memorable scenes are those dealing with the bitterly contested battles during the days prior to the fall of Canudos.

The technical brilliance characteristic of Vargas Llosa's previous works is lacking in *La guerra del fin del mundo*, which, for the most part, evolves via traditional narrative procedures. Still, the abrupt temporal and spatial dislocations between sections and the occasional juxtaposition of dialogues separated in time—techniques familiar to Vargas Llosa's devotees—enrich the literary texture by obliging the reader to link episodes, supply missing bits of information, and thus assume a more active role in reconstructing the novel. The constant shifts between the primitive rebels and their more "civilized" adversaries, moreover, underscore the themes set forth by both Cunha and Vargas Llosa: the struggle between civilization and barbarism and its detrimental effect on Brazil's national unity. Ironically, the soldiers and politicians from the more progressive coastal areas eventually prove to be just as cruel and unyielding as their "barbarous" enemies.

The novel's principal defect is its length, the result of the excessive details reminiscent of regionalist fiction. Still, there are masterfully written, action-packed pages that illuminate tense moments of the historical drama. An episode in the final pages not only underscores the sociogeographical schism in nineteenth-century Brazil, but also suggests the myth-generating power of the popular imagination. Here an army colonel from the Northeast takes brutal vengeance on a young lieutenant from the coast who makes the mistake of casting doubt on the backlanders' patriotism. And when the same colonel inquires about the fate of a local bandit whose heroic exploits inspired the rebels, an elderly woman taken prisoner in Canudos replies, "The archangels carried him up to heaven. . . . I saw them."

In *Historia de Mayta* (1984; *The Real Life of Alejandro Mayta*, 1986) Vargas Llosa once again finds inspiration in recent Peruvian history, namely, in the events surrounding the unsuccessful armed uprising of a Trotskyite, Alejandro Mayta, in the Andean highlands during the late 1950s. The novel dramatizes the sordid daily life of a revolutionary in search of the utopian dream, but it also comes to grips with the author's dilemma as he attempts to create fiction from the multilayered labyrinths of historical fact, Marxist ideology, and subjective imagination.

As one of Latin America's finest literary critics, Vargas Llosa has often alluded to, or written at length about, his favorite authors, the most important of whom are Flaubert, Sartre, and Camus. His admiration for the French nineteenth-century master stems from Flaubert's stylistic precision and technical perfection; Vargas Llosa's development of plot and character reflect the existential thought of Sartre and Camus. Perhaps another major influence is García Márquez, whose life and works are the subject of *García Márquez: Historia de un deicidio* (1971; García Márquez: history of a deicide). Before writing this monumental critique, Vargas Llosa had never included humor as a major ingredient in his fiction. *Pantaleón y las visitadoras* and *La tía Julia y el escribidor*, however, suggest that the amusing capers and grotesque absurdities he observed in García Márquez's novels may have inspired the abrupt turn toward comedy in his own oeuvre.

AND MANY OTHERS

Spanish America represents a vast array of diverse nations that are, nevertheless, often grouped by historians, economists, and literary scholars according to geographical regions. Despite a few exceptions (Paraguay and Argentina, for example), the nations of each region do indeed display striking similarities that can be detected in their fiction. Thus, many Caribbean writers have been influenced by the African culture in that region; Central Americans often fuse magical realism based on local native folklore with social protest elements; though different in many respects, Colombian and Venezuelan letters depict two neighboring nations evolving from tyrannical dictatorships into major bastions of capitalism and democracy; Andean literature portrays the exploited Indian as well as life in the violence-ridden urban setting; and the fiction of Argentina, Chile, and Uruguay reflects these nations' predominantly European ancestry, treating universal themes such as existential loneliness and the decay of middle-class values.

MEXICO

During the 1940s well-known Mexican novelists such as Mariano Azuela, Gregorio López y Fuentes (1897–1966), and Mauricio Magdaleno (b. 1906) continued to publish the kind of realistic, regionalist fiction that had prevailed prior to 1941. As indicated above, however, the contemporary period—from the 1950s to the present—has been dominated by more universal writers, the most influential of whom are Agustín Yáñez, Juan Rulfo, Juan José Arreola, and Carlos Fuentes. The list of other fine writers to emerge since midcentury indicates that, along with Argentina, Mexico has led Spanish American nations in both the quantity and quality of its literary production.

Many critics believe that José Revueltas (1914–1970), a social activist who spent much time in prison, has been undeservedly neglected. The author of seven novels and four collections of short stories, Revueltas utilized experimental techniques before most members of his generation in order to dramatize his Marxist convictions and existential concerns. His best novels are *El luto humano* (1943; *The Stone Knife*, 1947), which presents, through interior monologues and other innovative strategies, a fragmented and depressing, but richly textured, vision of rural Mexico from the pre-Columbian era to the 1930s; *Los errores* (1964; the errors), an urban novel critical of Soviet communism—Revueltas was eventually expelled from the Party—with a dual plot involving crime and political violence; and *El apando* (1969; the isolation cell), a stylistic tour de force based on the author's stay in Mexico City's infamous Lecumberri prison after he was arrested for his role in the antigovernment demonstrations in 1968.[2]

Elena Garro (b. 1920) has also published several novels, but she is best known for *Los recuerdos del porvenir* (1963; *Recollections of Things to Come*, 1969), a dazzling display of magical realism depicting a town caught in the grips of the *cristero* wars of the 1920s. (The *cristeros* were devout Catholics who rebelled against the Plutarco Elías Calles regime [1924–28] when he attempted to enforce the constitution's anticlerical laws.) Garro's best short story is "La culpa es de los tlaxcaltecas" ("It's All the Fault of the Tlaxcaltecas," in *Colorado State Review*, VIII, 2, 1981), in her collection *La semana de colores* (1964; the week of colors), about an upper-middle-class Mexican woman who believes that in a previous existence she was the wife of an Aztec warrior fighting against the Spanish conquerors. When her dual role becomes unbearable, she renounces the modern world and fades into the still vibrant substrata of Mexico's mythical past.

Rosario Castellanos (1925–1974) created memorable Indian portraits of her native state of Chiapas, near the Guatemalan border. In her first novel, *Balún Canán* (1957; *The Nine Guardians*, 1959), Castellanos captured the magical wonder of the Indian culture as seen through the eyes of a seven-year-

2. The year 1968 is crucial in recent Mexican history. Influenced by the antigovernment protests in France, the United States, and elsewhere, Mexican students began a series of demonstrations that culminated on October 2, just prior to the Olympic Games in Mexico City, with the army's massacre of several hundred students in Tlatelolco, a large square containing pre-Columbian ruins, a Spanish colonial church, and many modern buildings. (Tlatelolco is also known as *la Plaza de las Tres Culturas* [the Square of Three Cultures].) As demonstrated by the frequent mention of the Tlatelolco tragedy in recent Mexican fiction, this event has become permanently embedded in the nation's collective unconscious.

old girl, the author's persona. Her second novel, *Oficio de ti-nieblas* (1962; business of thunder), also poeticizes the native customs Castellanos observed as a child, but it encompasses a greater time span, evoking historical events from the nineteenth century to the era of land reforms promulgated by President Lázaro Cárdenas during his regime (1934–40). Castellanos's sympathy for and intuitive understanding of the Indian psyche are reinforced by her pleas for social justice and improved communication between races.

One of Mexico's most popular novelists was Luis Spota (1925–1985), a former journalist who exposed the most sordid aspects of Mexican society. Spota's direct and often crude realism prevails in *Murieron a mitad del río* (1948; they died in the middle of the river), about the unjust treatment of wetbacks by Texans and Mexican border police; *Más cornada da el hambre* (1952; *The Wounds of Hunger*, 1957), which depicts the corrupt, brutal world of bullfighting; *El tiempo de la ira* (1960; *The Time of Wrath*, 1962), the portrait of a ruthless military dictator; and *La plaza* (1972; the square), based on the aftermath of the Tlatelolco massacre of students in 1968. Spota's most widely acclaimed novel, however, is *Casi el paraíso* (1956; *Almost Paradise*, 1963), a cleverly structured, devastating satire of Mexico's frivolous and often naïve nouveaux riches who are duped by a handsome Italian "prince," in reality the son of a prostitute.

Although more profound than Spota, Sergio Galindo (b. 1926) and Jorge Ibargüengoitia (1928–1984) also rank among the most popular contemporary novelists. Galindo's two best works are *El bordo* (1960; *The Precipice*, 1969) and *El nudo* (1970; the knot). *El bordo* focuses on various members of a provincial family and an intriguing chain of events culminating in tragedy. The narrative strategies of *El nudo* are considerably more complicated, the principal subject matter here being the relationship between a middle-aged couple and a younger man. Galindo stands out as an astute observer of human nature and an inspired creator of tense, dramatic situations.

Ibargüengoitia's salient traits are humor and irony, elements scarce in social protest literature. *Los relámpagos de*

agosto (1965; *The Lightning of August*, 1986) and *Maten al león*
(1969; kill the lion) represent highly amusing satires of a revolutionary general, whose memoirs inadvertently reveal his
opportunism and incompetence; and a depraved, aging dictator
a group of conspirators attempt to overthrow. In *Estas ruinas
que ves* (1975; these ruins you see) Ibargüengoitia deftly fuses
irony and nostalgia to twit provincial customs in his native city
of Guanajuato. *Dos crímenes* (1979; *Two Crimes*, 1984) is a sus-
penseful tale of an innocent man who, upon being accused of
terrorism, takes refuge in his wealthy uncle's home, where his
unwitting involvement in a plot to obtain an inheritance from
the old gentleman reveals much about the corrupt social structure of present-day Mexico. The author taps the rich vein of
Mexican history for the subject matter of *Los conspiradores*
(1981; the conspirators), which dramatizes in human, day-to-
day terms the independence movement Father Miguel Hidalgo
led against the Spaniards in 1810.

In 1965 sophisticated readers were intrigued and bewildered with the appearance of *Farabeuf; o, La crónica de un
instante* (Farabeuf; or, the account of one moment), by Salvador
Elizondo (b. 1932). An experiment in narrative technique with
no precedent in Spanish American fiction, this disconcerting
antinovel attempts to capture a climactic moment of orgasm
and death. The characters are Dr. Farabeuf (a fictionalized
version of a nineteenth-century anatomist) and his mistress, a
woman of shifting identities whom we suspect he is preparing
to dissect alive. The themes of eroticism and sadism are intensified by a style reminiscent of the French New Novel, which
presents reality not in terms of logical cause and effect relationships, but rather as fleeting phenomenological sensations
produced by perceptions of opaque objects. Repeated in kaleidoscopic patterns, these sharply defined images give the
impression of a haunting nightmare. Elizondo's other works
include *Narda; o, El verano* (1966; Narda; or, summertime), a
collection of adroitly structured, surrealistic tales; *El hipogeo
secreto* (1968; the secret hypogeum), a novel in which the
labyrinthine creative process parallels the linguistic philosophy
of Ludwig Wittgenstein; and *Cámara lúcida* (1982; camera lu-

cida), a series of erudite and often witty reflections on the nature of art and the frustration and anguish of the would-be author.

Juan García Ponce (b. 1932) is another of Mexico's prolific novelists and short-story writers. Like Sergio Galindo, García Ponce explores the complexities of human relations in virtually all of his works. His style, however, tends to be more intricate, more analytical than Galindo's, and he is more concerned with the vagaries of sexual passion than his elder colleague. García Ponce's best works include *La cabaña* (1969; the cabin), a slow-moving but engrossing love story; *El libro* (1970; the book), in which the analysis of a novel by the Austrian writer Robert Musil leads to an affair between a professor and one of his students; *Figuraciones* (1982; figurations), a collection of finely honed erotic tales; and *Crónica de la intervención* (1982; chronicle of the intervention), a two-volume narration of erotic encounters and political maneuvers leading up to the Tlatelolco tragedy.

Vicente Leñero (b. 1933) stands out as one of contemporary Mexico's most admired and influential intellectuals. His masterpiece, *Los albañiles* (1964; the bricklayers), has the outward form of a detective story, but the investigator's unsuccessful search for the murderer of a night watchman (Don Jesús) represents a metaphor of modern man's vain quest for salvation and truth. Leñero utilizes a wide range of avant-garde techniques designed to eliminate the omniscient narrator and create a multidimensional work of art, thus underscoring the complexities of an evil and indecipherable world. Even more structurally complex, *Estudio Q* (1965; studio Q) parodies television soap operas and shatters the myth of the unified personality by portraying an actor who confuses reality with fiction while making a film based on his own life. *El garabato* (1967; the squiggle) emerges as an antinovel about the author's struggle to create a plausible and captivating work of art. Like *Los albañiles*, it takes the form of a detective story, but the parallel plot of a critic seeking the solution to a moral dilemma while he reads a mediocre mystery suggests the underlying literary theme. Leñero's more recent novels include *Los periodistas* (1978;

the journalists), a documentary account of a dispute between *Excelsior*, Mexico's most prestigious newspaper, and then President Luis Echeverría; and *El evangelio según Lucas Gavilán* (1979; the gospel according to Lucas Gavilán), a display of technical virtuosity linking social issues in contemporary Mexico with both historical and biblical events.

A well-known journalist as well as a novelist, Elena Poniatowska (b. 1933) attained prominence with the publication of *La noche de Tlatelolco* (1971; *Massacre in Mexico*, 1975), a series of interviews with witnesses of Tlatelolco and prisoners incarcerated by then President Gustavo Díaz Ordaz for participating in the antigovernment protests. To date this moving testimonial has been printed in more than forty editions, an indication of the impact the tragedy has had on the national psyche. Poniatowska's *Hasta no verte Jesús mío* (1969; until I see you my Jesus) appeared two years before *La noche de Tlatelolco* and today still ranks as one of the best Mexican novels of its decade. Based on conversations she had with an old peasant woman, the book represents a vivid record of the revolution of 1910 as recalled by an unlettered participant. A somber tone of muted passion characterizes the novella *Querido Diego, te abraza Quiela* (1978; dear Diego, Quiela embraces you), consisting of a series of imaginary love letters written to the painter Diego Rivera by his Russian mistress Angelina Beloff, who remained in Paris after World War I when Rivera returned to Mexico.

Arturo Azuela (b. 1938) is the grandson of Mariano Azuela, the most famous fiction writer of the Mexican revolution, and the author of several fine novels. The first of these, *El tamaño del infierno* (1973; the size of hell), portrays four generations of a family similar to the Azuelas, beginning in the late nineteenth century and ending soon after the Tlatelolco massacre of 1968. The central figure is Jesús, who, having killed a man in his youth, flees to Cuba and over the years becomes an omnipresent family legend. Certain parallels between Jesús and the young Santiago, who almost dies during the cataclysmic events of 1968, exemplify the many cyclical recurrences unifying the complex plot. Azuela's second novel, *Un tal José*

Salomé (1975; a fellow named José Salomé), describes the destruction of a town's identity when it is absorbed by a burgeoning nearby city. *Manifestación de silencios* (1979; *Shadows of Silence*, 1985), perhaps Azuela's best work to date, portrays a close-knit circle of beleaguered intellectuals who gravitate toward the fringes of radical politics but, out of justifiable fear, remain for the most part in the "shadows of silence." When one of the group, José Augusto Banderas, commits a senseless murder and is forced into exile, his life as a left-wing fugitive abroad provides an additional dimension to the novel. A professor of mathematics at Mexico's National University, where both the student body and faculty are highly politicized, Azuela limns his characters and milieux with assurance and authenticity.

Another important figure on the Mexican literary scene is José Emilio Pacheco (b. 1939), whose novels and short fiction encompass both national and universal concerns. Two stories typical of his style are "Parque de diversiones" (amusement park), in *El viento distante* (1963; the distant wind), a story consisting of a grouping of sketches inverting the roles of men and animals in order to underscore the absurdity of the human experience; and "Fiesta brava" (bullfight [lit., fierce fiesta]), in *El principio del placer* (1972; the pleasure principle), a sophisticated example of self-conscious fiction with subtle parallels between U.S. imperialism and Aztec sacrifices. Pacheco's fascination with history and circular time underpins his novels *Morirás lejos* (1968; you will die far away) and *Las batallas en el desierto* (1981; the battles in the desert). The subject of the former is the persecution of Jews by the Romans and, more recently, again by the Nazis. In *Las batallas en el desierto*, a short *Bildungsroman*, Pacheco strikes a poignant note of nostalgia, modified by irony and increasing social awareness, as he recalls episodes from his adolescence during the years of Miguel Alemán's presidency (1946–52).

In the mid-1960s Mexican fiction was profoundly altered by a movement of young writers known as *La Onda* (the Wave), which was closely related to the worldwide student rebellion of this decade, and which reflected the nonconformity of youth and its rejection of bourgeois values. The leading writers of the

Wave were Gustavo Sainz (b. 1940) and José Agustín (b. 1944), both of whom remain major literary figures in Mexico today. Sainz's first novel, *Gazapo* (1965; *Gazapo*, 1968), portrays a teenager named Menelao who has left home because of a quarrel with his stepmother. During his own mother's absence from the Mexican capital he and his friends gather in her apartment, where they can give vent to their frustrations and fantasies. The novel's structural configuration is a montage of real and imagined scenes, often erotic, which take the forms of tape recordings, telephone conversations, letters, and diaries. Deftly manipulated for dramatic effect, these devices freeze moments of time, capturing the immediacy of events as well as the humor and spontaneity of adolescent behavior. Apparent also is the author's indictment of social institutions for their failure to achieve their alleged purposes in today's world.

Whereas *Gazapo* exudes a comic air of youthful exuberance, Sainz's *Obsesivos días circulares* (1969; rev. ed., 1979; obsessive circular days) emerges as a complex metanovel about the narrator-protagonist's endeavor to create fiction from the recalcitrant raw materials of language and the chaotic reality he confronts. A paranoiac, introspective intellectual, Terencio works as a caretaker in a girls' school owned by a powerful underworld figure. The loosely organized plot is generated by Terencio's terror of physical violence, his erotic fantasies, and his sophisticated literary tastes, which provide a refuge of stability in his existence. The protagonist of *La princesa del Palacio de Hierro* (1974; the princess of the Iron Palace) is a frivolous young woman who narrates a series of escapades with her hedonistic friends. At first her compulsive, rambling monologue conveys a carefree, effervescent quality, but as disillusion sets in, her flow of words boils down to a vain attempt to fill the void in her meaningless existence. *Compadre Lobo* (1978; friend Lobo) is replete with scenes of gratuitous cruelty and violence, which, the author implies, owe their origin to the Aztec rituals of human sacrifice. Thus, while the artist-protagonist Lobo (wolf) is strangely drawn to death, his bohemian companions engage in endless sprees, brawls, and sexual orgies. The novel achieves aesthetic balance by means of two contrasting styles: the vernacular of the dialogues and the sparse, stylized idiom of the narrator, a writer friend of Lobo's. Sainz's fascination with his nation's mythic past and its impact on the present also motivated him to write *Fantasmas aztecas: Un pre-texto* (1982; Aztec phantoms: a pre-text), a brilliant piece of self-conscious fiction based on the recent excavation of the Aztec Templo Mayor (Main Temple) in the heart of Mexico City.

José Agustín's *La tumba* (1964; the tomb) is generally regarded as the earliest manifestation of the Wave. Its seventeen-year-old narrator belongs to a group of wealthy juveniles whose dissolute conduct derives at least in part from their debauched, hypocritical elders. The disrespectful tone and racy slang of the novella lend authenticity to the plot and, at the same time, slash at traditional syntax, an arm of the "establishment." *De perfil* (1966; from the side), Agustín's second fictional endeavor, is also narrated by a teenager; it is longer and much funnier than the first. Furthermore, it makes use of a greater variety of structural devices to involve the reader more intimately with the narrator and to focus on the hazards of growing up, the principal theme. *Inventando que sueño* (1968; imagining that I dream) is a collection of short stories, the most significant of which is "Cuál es la onda" ("What's Cool," in Seymour Menton, ed., *The Spanish American Short Story*, 1980). More than any other piece of fiction, this story typifies the Wave. The leading characters are a young drummer, Oliveira, and a girl, Requelle, who initiate their friendship at a dance. They spend the night in a series of sleazy hotels, mocking virtually every aspect of the middle class in the iconoclastic, juvenile jargon that constitutes both the medium and the message of the story. The name Oliveira more than likely derives from the protagonist of Cortázar's *Rayuela*, a novel Agustín greatly admires. Like his Argentine counterpart, Agustín creates a spontaneous language of colloquial words, puns, and foreign phrases, which in their entirety react against the rigid linguistic patterns and, by implication, the outmoded institutions of the status quo. "Cuál es la onda" also reveals the impact on Mexican youth of rock music groups such as the Beatles and the Rolling Stones, whose rhythms Agustín projects through the hilarious banter of his protagonists. Occasionally he shifts the narrative perspective, abruptly directing an offhand, and at times insulting, remark to the reader or an amusing authorial comment on his own writing assignment. The ironic tone engendered by these techniques becomes a major unifying element of the story.

During the 1970s and early 1980s Agustín lectured in many universities throughout the United States. His most recent novel, *Ciudades desiertas* (1982; deserted cities), reflects his experiences in, and attitudes toward, this country. A harsh satire of what he sees as a narrow, insipid culture north of the Mexican border, *Ciudades desiertas* depicts a young couple from Mexico City involved in the International Writing Program at the University of Iowa. Like "Cuál es la onda," *Ciudades desiertas* is characterized by grotesque humor, explicit sexual scenes, and obscenities generated by violent, pent-up emotions. Agustín's stylistic evolution during the fourteen years between these two works reflects the inevitable disillusionment that accompanies maturity, but it also suggests an increasing tension between neighboring cultures briefly drawn together by the international youth movement of the 1960s.

THE CARIBBEAN

Cuba

In the Spanish-speaking Caribbean, Cuba has been the most productive in the field of contemporary fiction. This is due in part to Fidel Castro's revolution; despite censorship and the imprisonment of some writers in Cuba, the regime has fostered the publication and distribution of books to a population increasingly more literate. As mentioned in chapter 1, the Cuban revolution also became a major focal point of the boom, having brought together left-wing Latin American intellectuals through the creation of international literary congresses—often more political than literary—and the sponsorship of prizes for each literary genre.

The three most significant Cuban writers of the twentieth

century are Alejo Carpentier (discussed above), Lino Novás Calvo, and José Lezama Lima, the last two mentioned above in the discussion of Cabrera Infante's *Tres tristes tigres*. Along with Carpentier, Novás Calvo helped to establish a modern tradition in Cuban prose fiction by introducing such innovative procedures as the shifting narrative perspective and poetically stylized, colloquial language reminiscent of Juan Rulfo. His world vision, which stems from tragic and existential concerns, displays universal rather than regional dimensions. Novás Calvo is better known for his short stories than for his novels. Typical of the stories are "La noche de Ramón Yendía" ("The Dark Night of Ramón Yendía," in Seymour Menton, ed., *The Spanish American Short Story*, 1980), in *La luna nona, y otros cuentos* (1942; the ninth moon, and other stories) and "¡Trínquenme ahí a ese hombre!" (tie that man down!) in *Cayo Canas* (1946; Palm Key). The former portrays a taxi driver caught in the vagaries of a coup d'état against the regime (1925–33) of the Cuban dictator Geraldo Machado. Forced by his police torturers to turn informer, Yendía ends his life tragically, believing he is being pursued by the revolutionaries he betrayed. The story's multiple layers of irony serve to underscore the protagonist's existential anguish and the underlying absurdity of his plight. An individual response to a given situation is also the subject of the latter story, an ambiguous tale parodied in *Tres tristes tigres*. The first-person narrator presents his version, probably unreliable, of a chain of events involving an old man, his dying wife, a farmhand, and a sensuous girl hired to care for the ailing woman. Although the narrator proclaims his innocence in the theft of the old man's cache of money, we suspect that the latter's fury directed against the narrator may be entirely justified.

José Lezama Lima's masterpiece, *Paradiso* (1966; *Paradiso*, 1974), looms as one of the most significant novels of the boom. A parody of the nineteenth-century *Bildungrsroman* with numerous autobiographical elements and resounding echoes of Proust and Dante, *Paradiso* depicts the life of José Cemí, an intellectual student rebel during the regime of Geraldo Machado. The novel also juxtaposes real and phantasmagorical

passages to examine the protagonist's progression from adolescence to maturity in a crisis-ridden social environment. On
an allegorical level, *Paradiso* can be interpreted as an exploration of the world of homosexuality, a subject examined in
historical depth by Cemí and others, but almost equally important are the lengthy discussions, set forth in a dense, figurative
prose, of a wide variety of subjects, including history, music,
mythology, religion, and death. Despite the central position
occupied by Cemí, some critics have seen language as the true
protagonist and, this being the case, the novel's poetic creativity
(Lezama Lima is also a highly esteemed poet) as a metaphor
of man's resurrection or reentry into the Paradise he has lost
through his rational, learned responses to the universe.

Though less known than Carpentier, Novás Calvo, and
Lezama Lima, Virgilio Piñera nevertheless made unique contributions to the novel, short story, and theater. His fiction
reveals an anguished, pessimistic *Weltanschauung*, occasionally tinged with irony and grotesque humor. He was also one
of the relatively few successful practitioners of the fantastic
short story in Cuba. Two of Piñera's most widely read novels
are *Pequeñas maniobras* (1963; little maneuvers) and *Presiones
and diamantes* (1967; pressures and diamonds), the former a
portrait of existential solitude, and the latter, an absurd representation of decadent capitalism, seen in sharp contrast to
the socialistic society of the future.

The most highly acclaimed, and probably the least understood, member of the younger Cuban generation is Severo Sarduy (b. 1937) who, in 1960, after supporting Castro's revolution,
left his homeland for Paris to study art criticism and never
returned. During the 1960s, in addition to launching his literary career, he joined Roland Barthes and other structuralist
critics on the staff of the prestigious journal *Tel Quel*. His experimental novels, which have been called the subconscious of
Spanish American fiction, evolve an original pictorial style that
parodies modern literary conventions such as the development
of believable, recognizable characters and the shopworn search-
for-identity theme. His first novel, *Gestos* (1963; gestures), synthesizes Cuban slang and phenomenological images in the

manner of the French New Novel to dramatize guerrilla warfare in Havana during the prerevolutionary regime of General Fulgencio Batista. In *De donde son los cantantes* (1967; *From Cuba with a Song*, in *Triple Cross*, 1972), Sarduy invents three dynamically skewed plots involving the Chinese, African, and white segments of the Cuban population. The first plot is set in Havana's Chinese district, where a transvestite entertainer named Lotus Flower is pursued and eventually murdered by a Spanish general; the second limns the tragic fate of a black woman from rural Cuba who marries a politician in Batista's congress; and the third retraces Cuban history, culminating in the trek of two white transvestites who carry a statue of Christ symbolic of Castro from Santiago to Havana. As illustrated by this and subsequent novels, Sarduy sees Spanish American culture as a caldron of contradictory forces embodied in bizarre, sexually driven protagonists, more theatrical than real.

Cobra (1972; *Cobra*, 1975) portrays a transvestite who, having undergone a sex-change operation, becomes the star of a plush theater-brothel, the hangout of an array of weirdos. The latter include La Cadillac, Cobra's antithetical double who also has undergone a sex change, but in reverse; a motorcycle gang of tattooed drug pushers; and a sect of exiled Tibetan monks, suppliers of the gang's drugs. The final section of the novel is a quote from Columbus's diary, his voyage being seen as the first example of Western man's search for the mythic, utopian East to resolve the violent contradictions of Western civilization. (Sarduy himself is a Buddhist and frequent visitor to India and Tibet.)

Two additional novels by Sarduy are *Maitreya* (1978; Maitreya) and *Colibrí* (1982; Hummingbird). A Cuban-Chinese cook named Luis Leng becomes the reincarnation of Buddha in *Maitreya*, the settings of which include Tibet, revolutionary Cuba, Miami, New York, and finally, Iran. Replete with historical, ideological, and philosophical allusions, this timely work describes the attempts of Westerners to destroy Eastern religions, after which the East exacts its vengeance by purging itself of Western doctrines. The setting of *Colibrí* is the Big House, a luxurious brothel run by an aging transvestite (La Señora), where oil barons satisfy their sexual fantasies. The title is the nickname of a handsome young wrestler who, after La Señora's death, burns down the brothel, rebuilds it, and runs it himself. A parody of the jungle novel—Mario Vargas Llosa's *La casa verde* comes to mind—*Colibrí* also allegorizes the Spanish American experience, La Señora representing the archetypal dictator, the oil barons the corrupt upper classes, and Hummingbird the more polished but equally corrupt modern establishment. That the Big House ultimately becomes an insane asylum indicates the author's negative view of the continent of his origin. According to some critics, Sarduy has emerged as Spanish America's most original and influential writer of the post-boom period, his tragicomic world of clashing colors and mock solemnity serving to dismantle previous styles and chart new directions.

Three of Cuba's dynamic portrayers of the revolution are Jesús Díaz Rodríguez (b. 1941), Eduardo Heras León (b. 1941), and Norberto Fuentes (b. 1943). Díaz Rodríguez is best known for his collection of emotion-packed tales entitled *Los años duros* (1966; the hard years). Heras León's descriptions of battles and revolutionary heroes are found in two volumes of stories: *La guerra tuvo seis nombres* (1968; the war had six names) and *Los pasos en la hierba* (1970; the steps in the grass). And Norberto Fuentes, perhaps the most gifted of this group, has attracted wide recognition for his straightforward accounts of Castro's extermination of insurgent counterrevolutionaries in 1962. Two of Fuentes's finest collections of stories are *Condenados de Condado* (1968; the condemned of Condado) and *Cazabandido* (1970; bandit hunter).

Mention must also be made of Reinaldo Arenas (b. 1943), who, with Severo Sarduy, is one of the most original Cuban writers of his generation. Arenas, however, is more accessible to the reading public than Sarduy. *Celestino antes del alba* (1967; Celestino before dawn), Arenas's first novel, reveals the dual influence of William Faulkner and Miguel Ángel Asturias. Like Benjy in *The Sound and the Fury*, the narrator of *Celestino antes del alba* is a retarded child who describes the sordid life of a poor farm family; in addition, the narrator and his cousin,

Celestino, imagine a world of fantasy, resulting in a typical example of magical realism reminiscent of Asturias. A similar technique characterizes *El mundo alucinante* (1969; *Hallucinations*, 1971), an experimental novel based on the *Memorias* of an eighteenth-century Mexican friar, Servando Teresa de Mier. In this unique historical work, chronological time is all but erased by the appearance of contemporary figures, both real and fictional, alongside Simón Bolívar, Napoleon, Alexander von Humboldt, Chateaubriand, and others. Increasingly unhappy in Cuba because of the government's harassment of writers, Arenas emigrated to the United States in 1980. Two years later he published *Otra vez el mar* (1982; *Farewell to the Sea*, 1985), which has been called a litany of despair and one of the most horrifying descriptions to date of life in a communist country. The protagonists are a disenchanted revolutionary poet and his wife whose failing marriage parallels the descriptions of the intolerable living conditions under the Castro regime. *El palacio de las blanquísimas mofetas* (1983; the palace of the snow-white skunks) is based on the life he knew as a child in rural, pre-Castro Cuba, but like his previous works, it combines reality and fantasy, present and past, rationality and madness to convey his peculiar surrealistic vision of the world.

Dominican Republic

Juan Bosch (b. 1909) of the Dominican Republic is considered a master of the short story, but he is also well known in his native land as a politician, having been elected president in 1962 (his government was overthrown the following year by a military coup). Bosch depicts peasant life in a realistic vein with occasional injections of dreams and fantasies reminiscent of Horacio Quiroga. Although his tales are replete with aimless violence, they are tempered with irony and compassion for the exploited lower classes. His collections include *Ocho cuentos* (1947; eight stories), *La muchacha de La Guaira* (1955; the girl from La Guaira), *Cuentos de Navidad* (1956; Christmas stories), and *Más cuentos escritos en el exilio* (1964; more stories written in exile). The Dominican Republic's best-known novelist is J. M. Sanz-Lajara (b. 1917), whose *Viv* (1961; Viv) and

Los rompidos (1963; the broken ones) represent, respectively, a tragic love story and an impressionistic portrait of country life. Of the nation's younger generation, Marcio Veloz Maggiolo (b. 1936) is admired for his novels entitled *El buen ladrón* (1960; the good thief) and *Judas* (1962; Judas), both based on biblical themes; and *Los ángeles de hueso* (1967; the angels made of bone), about a group of frustrated idealists and their search for God.

Puerto Rico

Puerto Rican literature experienced a veritable renaissance with the appearance of the generation of 1940, a group of writers who continued their literary pursuits for decades thereafter. Their predominant themes include the industrialization of the island, the problems engendered by urban life, and the existential dilemmas first dramatized by French, English, and U.S. writers. Although some members of this generation were influenced by the direct, unadorned language of Hemingway and Camus, others made use of more complex techniques such as the stylistic involutions and interior monologues perfected by Faulkner. The most prominent member of his generation and still Puerto Rico's best-known man of letters was René Marqués (1919–1979), whose basic preoccupation as a writer was Puerto Rico's political future. An outspoken advocate of independence instead of the current commonwealth status of the island, he abhorred the domination of his homeland by the United States, which has led to the industrialization of a basically agricultural economy, and to the contamination of the Hispanic culture. Although Marqués published two novels, he is better known for his theater and his short fiction. Typical of the latter is his "Purificación en la calle del Cristo" ("Purification on Christ Street," in Kal Wagenheim, ed., *Cuentos: An Anthology of Short Stories from Puerto Rico*, 1978), in *En una ciudad llamada San Juan* (1960; in a city called San Juan), about three elderly, upper-class sisters whose lives reflect the trajectory of Puerto Rican history since the latter part of the nineteenth century.

Other prominent members of the generation of 1940 are

Abelardo Díaz Alfaro (b. 1919), who is best known for *Terrazo* (1948; landscapes), a book of poetically conceived tales depicting the conflicts of rural life; José Luis González (b. 1926), the Marxist author of *En este lado* (1954; on this side) and of numerous other stories set in various parts of the world (González lived for many years in Europe, Mexico, and the United States); Pedro Juan Soto (b. 1928), whose famous collection *Spiks* (1957; *Spics*, 1973) describes the lives of impoverished Puerto Rican immigrants in New York; and Emilio Díaz Valcárcel (b. 1929), a veteran of the Korean War, about which he wrote in several of the best tales in *El asedio* (1958; the siege).

One of the most popular of the younger generation of Puerto Rican writers is Luis Rafael Sánchez (b. 1936), whose *La guaracha del macho Camacho* (1980; *Macho Camacho's Beat*, 1980) caused a sensation because of its adroit use of street slang, raw humor, and explicit sexual scenes. A devastating satire of the island's corrupt political institutions and cultural dependence on the United States, this novel portrays an array of characters snared in absurd situations containing just enough truth to be taken seriously. The freewheeling linguistic medium, moreover, emerges as a metaphor of the radical transformation advocated by the author in all spheres—political, social, and moral—in order to rid Puerto Rico of its colonial mentality. The novel's title stems from a popular form of dance music (*la guaracha*) with repetitive lyrics proclaiming "Life is a phenomenal thing," a phrase that becomes a leitmotif and reinforces the pervasive tone of irony.

CENTRAL AMERICA

Costa Rica

Three of Costa Rica's leading literary figures are Carlos Luis Fallas (1909–1966), Yolanda Oreamuno (1916–1956), and Fabián Dobles (b. 1918). Fallas's best-known novel is *Mamita Yunai* (1941; Mamita Yunai), which protests against political fraud and economic imperialism (*Yunai* is a phonetic rendition in Spanish of "United," for the United Fruit Company). More avant-garde than either Fallas or Dobles, Oreamuno exploits psychological themes through a wide variety of Joycean techniques as, for example, in *La ruta de su evasión* (1949; the route of her evasion). Dobles is Costa Rica's most prolific writer of short stories, his best-known collection being *Historias de Tata Mundo* (1955; stories of Tata Mundo), a grouping of carefully structured portraits of rural life.

El Salvador

Outstanding representatives of the contemporary fiction of El Salvador include Álvaro Menéndez Leal (b. 1931), who occasionally signs his name Álvaro Menén Desleal, and Manlio Argueta (b. 1935). Known above all for his stories, Menéndez Leal reveals the possible influence of Kafka, Borges, and Arreola in tales such as "Una cuerda de nylon y oro" (a rope of nylon and gold), in *Una cuerda de nylon y oro, y otros cuentos maravillosos* (1969; a rope of nylon and gold, and other marvelous stories), an absurd science fiction tale fraught with anti-U.S. overtones based primarily on the war in Vietnam. Argueta has recently emerged as one of Central America's leading novelists. His first two novels, *El valle de las hamacas* (1968; the valley of the hammocks) and *Caperucita en la zona roja* (1977; Little Red Ridinghood in the red zone), are not only showcases of literary technique, but also portraits of young dissidents seeking to overthrow recent dictatorial regimes in El Salvador. Argueta's best work, however, is *Un día en la vida* (1980; *One Day of Life*, 1983), which dramatizes in direct, unadorned language a Salvadoran family's growing awareness of the injustice in their country just prior to the outbreak of the current hostilities. The protagonist and principal narrator of this moving social-protest document is an intelligent but illiterate peasant woman, Lupe Fuentes, whose suffering involves the reader in, and increases his understanding of, a tragic conflict that has devastated Central America's smallest nation since 1980.

Guatemala

Guatemala's Miguel Ángel Asturias (discussed above) is the only Central American man of letters to reach a wide in-

ternational audience since 1941. Two Guatemalans deserving
of recognition are Mario Monteforte Toledo (b. 1912) and Augusto Monterroso (b. 1921). Monteforte Toledo has written traditional but very different novels such as *Entre la piedra y la
cruz* (1948; between the stone and the cross) and *Una manera
de morir* (1954; a way of dying). The former focuses on the
unjust treatment of the Guatemalan Indian by the government
in order to effect social reform; the latter portrays an idealistic
communist who gives way to total despair after having become
disillusioned with party corruption and dogmatism. Augusto
Monterroso, a long-time resident of Mexico, stands out as Guatemala's leading satirist in the field of short fiction. One of his
most amusing stories is "Mr. Taylor" (Mr. Taylor) in *Obras
completas, y otros cuentos* (1959; complete works, and other
stories), about a gringo who attains wealth and power in an
unnamed Latin American country by exporting the shrunken
heads of natives to U.S. collectors of folkloric objets d'art.

Honduras

The best Honduran fiction does not take the form of the
novel but rather that of the short story. Of the older generation,
Víctor Cáceres Lara (b. 1915) excels in highly symbolic dramatizations of rural life, especially in his collection entitled *Humus* (1952; humus). "Paludismo" (malaria), perhaps the finest
piece in this volume, depicts the past of a dying woman who,
many years before, was enticed from her village by a drifter
promising her a bright future. The quality of her life in a coastal
city deteriorated steadily with her lover's unemployment and
death, her turn to prostitution, and her present bout with malaria. Although the author alludes briefly to the exploitation
of workers by the United Fruit Company, the adverse fate of
his characters is due primarily to their all-too-human weaknesses. Two other Honduran short-story writers of note are
Marcos Carías (b. 1938) and Eduardo Bahr (b. 1940). A satire
of middle-class mores, Carías's tragicomic "Día de boda" (1970;
wedding day) highlights the culture shock experienced by a
Latin American couple who travel to Spain for their son's wedding, which, because of their outrage over his marriage to a

foreigner, turns out disastrously. Bahr's *Fotografía del peñasco* (1969; photograph of the crag) inveighs against political repression, the subject of "Yo sería incapaz de tirarle una piedra" (I would be incapable of throwing a stone at you). Written in the form of a letter to the nation's president, this story appeals to the president's sense of humanity by describing the sensation of being caught in a murderous fusillade during a peaceful demonstration.

Nicaragua

Nicaragua's Sergio Ramírez (b. 1942), recently elected vice president of the country in the Sandinista regime, has published numerous short stories; two of his best, both presented in *Charles Atlas también muere* (1976; Charles Atlas also dies), are the title story of this collection, about the demythification of the fabled strong man, and "El centerfielder" (the centerfielder), the portrait of a political prisoner whose impending execution parallels, with tragic and ironic resonances, several aspects of his failed baseball career many years before. Ramírez's novel ¿*Te dio miedo la sangre?* (1977; *To Bury Our Fathers*, 1984) dramatizes a series of uprisings between 1930 and 1961, mostly against the Somoza dictatorship. This book displays a baroque style evocative of Carpentier and six intricately interwoven plot threads suggesting the influence of Vargas Llosa. Referred to as *el hombre* (the man), Somoza assumes a kind of mythic presence which serves as a background for the portrait of an entire nation in travail.

Panama

Among Panamanian fiction writers Rogelio Sinán, a pseudonym for Bernardo Domínguez Alba (b. 1904), and Joaquín Beleño (b. 1921) emerge as the most widely read and admired. Considering its early date of publication, Sinán's introspective, Freudian novel, *Plenilunio* (1947; full moon), is unique in Central American literature prior to 1950. Beleño's *Luna verde* (1951; green moon) registers a vehement protest against the humiliating conditions the author witnessed while working as a day laborer for gringo bosses in the Canal Zone.

COLOMBIA AND VENEZUELA

With the exception of Gabriel García Márquez (discussed above), no Colombian or Venezuelan author has achieved an international reputation since 1941. There are, nevertheless, gifted Colombians and Venezuelans who have been unjustly neglected by both the critics and the reading public. One possible explanation for this neglect, especially in the case of Colombia, is the lack of well-established publishing houses in the two countries prior to, and even during, the boom. Thus, fine works of fiction have appeared in limited editions and without the publicity accorded literary figures in, for example, Mexico and Argentina.

Colombia

Although Colombia's Hernando Téllez (1908–1962) published little during his lifetime, his stories of *la violencia* are some of the best dealing with this tragic episode. A classic in Spanish American short fiction, his "Espuma y nada más" (lather and nothing more), in *Cenizas para el viento, y otras historias* (1950; ashes for the wind and other stories), is narrated by a village barber who, as a secret informer for the rebel cause, describes his distraught state of mind while shaving, and wanting to kill, an army captain known to have tortured scores of guerrilla fighters. The story ends with an ironic macho flourish that alters its aesthetic form as well as its meaning.

Eduardo Caballero Calderón (b. 1910), one of Colombia's most admired writers, has utilized *la violencia* as a backdrop for his dramatic treatment of social and psychological problems. His novel *El Cristo de espaldas* (1952; backs turned on Christ) depicts a priest-Christ figure victimized by the bitter conflicts he encounters in a village he has been sent to serve. Equally dramatic is this author's *Siervo sin tierra* (1954; Siervo without land), in which a peasant (Siervo) struggles for his entire life to obtain a plot of ground, only to die shortly before he is to take possession of it. *Manuel Pacho* (1962; Manuel Pacho) is more experimental in technique, its existential plot dealing with the inner life of a retarded boy who has witnessed the

murder of his parents. Two additional novels by Caballero Calderón are *El buen salvaje* (1966; the noble savage), about a
Colombian student's life in the "civilized jungle" of Paris, and
Caín (1969; Cain), which combines the classical love triangle
with the themes of fratricide and *la violencia*.

Another Colombian who has focused on human problems
created by *la violencia* is Jesús Zárate Moreno (1915–1967),
an author almost totally ignored by the critics until recently.
In Zárate Moreno's best collection of stories, *El día de mi muerte*
(1955; the day of my death), the most memorable are "Un árbol
en el camino" (a tree on the road) and "Un perro aúlla en la
noche" (a dog howls in the night). In the former, a tale with
existential overtones, the protagonist thinks he has saved his
brother from his political enemies only to find he has brought
about his death under the most absurd, fortuitous circumstances.
The latter also describes a tragic family situation generated by
political conflict when a man endangers his wife and children
in an attempt to save his father's honor.

Manuel Zapata Olivella (b. 1920) based his political novel
La calle 10 (1960; Tenth Street) on the events that initiated *la
violencia*, that is, the assassination of the popular politician
Jorge Eliécer Gaitán on April 9, 1948, and the *bogotazo*, or
bloody uprising, that raged for several days in Bogotá immediately thereafter. A very different set of circumstances informs
En Chimá nace un santo (1964; in Chimá a saint is born), a
portrayal of an isolated community of peasants dominated by
a crippled youth believed to be a miracle worker. *Changó, el
gran putas* (1984; Changó, the great son of a bitch) is a structurally complex, carefully researched epic of the Latin American blacks' struggles for justice since their arrival from Africa.

A prominent innovator in contemporary Colombian fiction
is Héctor Rojas Herazo (b. 1922), whose novels *Respirando el
verano* (1962; breathing the summer) and *En noviembre llega
el arzobispo* (1967; in November the archbishop arrives) invite
comparisons with Faulkner, García Márquez, and Onetti. *Respirando el verano* is the nonchronological tale of a family torn
by bitter disputes during the civil wars of the late nineteenth
and early twentieth centuries. More avant-garde than its pred-

ecessor, *En noviembre llega el arzobispo* captures both the sordid, everyday reality and the mythical fantasies of a community on the Atlantic coast, where the monotony of daily life is relieved by memories of the past and an anticipated visit of the archbishop. The shifts in time and narrative focus, moreover, create a fragmented, dynamic structure highlighted by such varied themes as love, hate, repression, adultery, and violence.

La violencia is also the theme of *El día señalado* (1964; the appointed day), by Manuel Mejía Vallejo (b. 1923), one of Colombia's best-known writers. Here two basic plot threads are interwoven, one involving the presence of unwelcome government troops in a town victimized by fear, and the other, the arrival of a youth seeking to take vengeance on his father. The hatred and brutality so prevalent in the town are balanced by the spiritual strength of the priest, who manages to blunt the forces of violence through love and human understanding. Despite the somber tone, Mejía Vallejo's message is that, collectively, man possesses the inner strength to triumph over his evil instincts. Very different is *Aire de tango* (1973; tango atmosphere), a homage both to the era of the tango and to the city of Medellín, the novel's setting. One of the principal characters is the famous Argentine singer Carlos Gardel, who died in Colombia during the 1930s and who is still remembered there with nostalgia. Mejía Vallejo succeeds in transforming a past reality into fiction by mythicizing a popular art form along with the colorful ambience it has come to represent.

La casa grande (1962; the big house), by Alvaro Cepeda Zamudio (1926–1972), develops Faulknerian themes and techniques that make it another landmark in contemporary Colombian fiction. The two predominant subjects of this novel are the gradual downfall of a family and the massacre of striking banana workers by the Colombian army in 1928 (the same strike dramatized in *One Hundred Years of Solitude*). Each of the ten segments introduces, with appropriate stylistic variations, a different character, the end result being a dynamic, balanced work of art that involves the reader in the lives of the characters and rivets his attention on the central conflict.

In recent years the Colombian literary scene has been enlivened by a growing list of successful writers born after 1930. Representative of this group are Plinio Apuleyo Mendoza (b. 1932), Fernando Soto Aparicio (b. 1933), Héctor Sánchez (b. 1940), and Gustavo Álvarez Gardeazábal (b. 1945). Apuleyo Mendoza's novel *Años de fuga* (1979; years of flight) deserves praise both for its innovative form and its confrontation with Colombian reality since the historic year 1948. The protagonist, Ernesto Melo, leaves Colombia for Paris immediately after the *bogotazo*, sensing that his generation's revolutionary ideals have suffered a decisive defeat in his homeland. The foreground action occurs in the 1970s when Ernesto, now middle-aged, recalls his life in Paris, his return to Colombia, and, years later, his second visit to Paris, where he encounters a generation of youths devoted to drugs and individual fulfillment rather than to political ideals and social reform. The novel's fluid temporal planes and shifting points of view serve not only to contrast two very different generations, but also to convey Ernesto's confrontation with his inner self, his visit to Paris constituting a search for values that elude him. Although, as one critic has observed, Ernesto's existential emphasis on choice may strike the contemporary reader as a case of déjà vu, it successfully illustrates recent intellectual trends in Colombia and other developing countries.

More than any of his contemporaries, the prolific novelist Soto Aparicio reveals the strong influence of naturalism. *La rebellión de las ratas* (1963; the rebellion of the rats), for example, though technically superior to the traditional naturalistic art form, protests against the exploitation of workers by a mining company. In *Viaje a la claridad* (1971; voyage to clarity), Soto Aparicio leans heavily on analytical psychology to explore the reactions of an adolescent who has been violated by her stepfather. This novel's subtle use of the interior monologue and the shifting narrative perspective breathe life into the victim, who emerges as an artistically drawn, well-rounded protagonist.

Héctor Sánchez has written several novels set in small towns similar to the one in which he was raised. He has expressed his admiration for Juan Carlos Onetti, and indeed his fiction—short stories as well as novels—exudes the monotony and purposelessness one finds in the Uruguayan's mythical community of Santa María. *Sin nada entre las manos* (1976; with empty hands), one of Sánchez's best creations to date, repeats with subtle variations subjects already familiar to his readers. Nontraditional in its plot and structure, this novel consists of a series of seemingly unrelated segments that, through parallel events and character associations organized by the reader, gradually assume a circular, unified form.

Álvarez Gardeazábal is the most talented of the younger generation and possibly the most widely read contemporary Colombian writer with the exception of García Márquez. His *Cóndores no entierran todos los días* (1972; condors don't bury every day) became a best-seller in Colombia because of its gripping treatment of *la violencia*. *Dabeiba* (1972; Dabeiba) presents a chronicle of events in a town where rumors and gossip highlight the threat of an impending tragedy. Perhaps this author's most sensational novel is *El bazar de los idiotas* (1974; the bazaar of the idiots), which parodies religious miracles by portraying two idiots as heroes who heal the infirm through the prohibited act of masturbation. And *El titiritero* (1977; the puppeteer) sets forth conflicting versions of the death of a university student fifteen years after the fact, illuminating the unreliability of official communications and the elusiveness of historical truth. Álvarez Gardeazábal's contribution to the contemporary literary scene includes his remarkable ability to sustain reader interest and, at the same time, to adapt new narrative forms to his peculiar vision of the world.

Venezuela

Contemporary Venezuelan fiction has, in general, lagged behind that of other major Spanish American nations. The country's leading twentieth-century man of letters, Rómulo Gallegos, published his best works in the 1920s and 1930s. Another member of the older generation, Arturo Uslar Pietri (b. 1906), who, like Gallegos, has played an active role in political life, published some of his best-known works in the 1930s, although he has continued to write very readable historical fiction: *El camino de El Dorado* (1948; the road to El Dorado), a fictionalized biography of a tyrannical conquistador; *Treinta hombres y sus sombras* (1949; thirty men and their shadows), a collection of tales based on legends; *Un retrato en la geografía* (1962; a portrait in geography), about political events in Venezuela in the mid-1930s; and *Oficio de difuntos* (1976; office for the dead), a vivid portrayal of the archetypal Latin American dictator. The most striking characteristics of Uslar Pietri's prose are its complete mastery of poetic forms and its ingenious fusion of fantasy, folklore, and history.

One of the early innovators of Venezuelan fiction was Miguel Otero Silva (1908–1985), an idealist of strong social conscience who sought to renovate what he viewed as his spiritually decadent homeland. *Casas muertas* (1955; dead houses) ranks as one of the best Spanish American "new novels" to appear during the two decades prior to the boom. The setting and protagonist of this poetically conceived tragic work is the formerly prosperous but now dying town of Ortiz, a victim of the ruinous political regime (1908–35) of the dictator Juan Vicente Gómez and a microcosm of Venezuela during his last years in power. More optimistic in tone but less effective as a work of art, *Oficina No. 1* (1961; office number 1) describes a booming oil town during the presidency (1952–58) of Marcos Pérez Jiménez. The Pérez Jiménez regime comes under strong attack, however, in *La muerte de Honorio* (1963; Honorio's death), narrated by five political prisoners via a broad range of literary devices. Structural techniques also express the political theme in *Cuando quiero llorar no lloro* (1970; when I want to weep I don't), the alternating accounts of three youths of different social classes, each of whom is victimized by the established political order.

The two best Venezuelan fiction writers to emerge during the boom are Salvador Garmendia (b. 1928) and Adriano González León (b. 1931). The underlying theme of Garmendia's stories and novels is man's alienation in the urban environment, especially the poorer districts of Caracas. His first novel, *Los pequeños seres* (1959; the little beings), is considered a landmark because it not only introduces the problems of urban life into Venezuelan literature, but also makes effective use of modern techniques. The protagonist is an unsuccessful, anguished office worker whose efforts to reconstruct his life through memories and interior monologues ultimately lead to despair, madness, and suicide. A somewhat similar situation informs *Los habitantes* (1961; the inhabitants), which depicts the inner lives of an unemployed truck driver and various members of his family. And another human failure, a frustrated writer named Miguel Antúnez, is portrayed in *Día de ceniza* (1964; day of ashes). This carefully crafted novel, replete with startling images and swift cinematic sequences, traces Antúnez's past life spent in bars, bordellos, and rented rooms, the "ashes" of the title emerging as a symbol of his self-destruction and despair. As demonstrated in his entire oeuvre, Garmendia's hallmarks are his command of form and his ability to create convincing, well-defined characters.

Like Garmendia, González León is an innovator in both language and technique. His short-story collection *Las hogueras más altas* (1957; the highest blazes) presents solitary characters driven to commit unexpected acts of violence, usually motivated by rejection or hate. *Asfalto-infierno* (1963; asphalt hell) is González León's first urban novel of alienation, but of much greater importance is his masterpiece, *País portátil* (1969; portable country), which relates the story of the Barazarte family through the mind of one of its members (Andrés), a young revolutionary. As he carries a bomb through Caracas on a bus, Andrés evokes not only the feudal life of his family on their country estate and events from Venezuela's remote past, but also his arrival in Caracas and his subsequent involvement in radical politics. His journey through the noisy, congested capital, however, and his intense feelings of doubt, uncertainty, and fear constitute an odyssey of self-discovery not unlike that of many disillusioned youths of the 1960s throughout the Western world. The novel's universality also stems from its adept probings of the protagonist's subconscious, a realm of emotions he shares with much of humanity.

Other Venezuelans acclaimed by the critics and reading public are Rodolfo Izaguirre (b. 1931), Argenis Rodríguez

(b. 1935), José Balza (b. 1939), and Francisco Massiani (b. 1944). Izaguirre's best-known novel, *Alacranes* (1968; scorpions), takes the form of a nightmarish portrait of a decadent family, a metaphor of contemporary society. Rodríguez's *La fiesta del embajador* (1969; the ambassador's party) is a grotesque satire of Venezuelan officials attending a New Year's Eve party; Balza's *Largo* (1968; largo) chronicles the final days of the demented narrator, a young artist, before his suicide; and Massiani's *Piedra de mar* (1968; sea stone) emerges as a self-conscious novel about the act of creating fiction, the characters of which are teenagers involved in a search for meaning both within themselves and in the world around them.

THE ANDEAN HIGHLANDS

Bolivia

Contemporary Bolivian fiction is characterized by the dramatization of violent conflict on virtually all levels of national life, a direct result of the country's extreme poverty and political instability. Jesús Lara (b. 1898) vehemently defended the exploited Indian in his novels, typical of which is *Yanakuna* (1952; serfdom), about an uprising against landowners and the terrible ensuing reprisals. The best known of the older generation of Bolivian writers is Augusto Céspedes (b. 1904), who has written both long and short fiction. His widely acclaimed *Metal del diablo* (1946; the devil's metal) depicts the wretched working conditions in the tin mines and the exploitation of workers by owners and operators. Céspedes's political novels include *El dictador suicida* (1956; the suicidal dictator) and *El presidente colgado* (1966; the hanged president).

A leading figure of the younger generation, Marcelo Quiroga (b. 1931) introduced the existential themes of alienation, loneliness, and anguish into Bolivian fiction with his landmark novel *Los deshabitados* (1959; the empty ones). Also belonging to this generation are Adolfo Cáceres Romero (b. 1937) and Renato Prada Oropeza (b. 1937), who in 1967 collaborated on an important collection of short stories entitled *Argal-Lagar*

(Argal-Lagar). Like Quiroga's novels, these stories cultivate existential themes, thus contributing to a trend toward greater universality in Bolivian letters. Perhaps the best piece of this collection is Cáceres Romero's "La emboscada" (the ambush), an ingeniously structured account of an incident involving Che Guevara's sole surviving comrade after the famous Argentine revolutionary's death. Prada Oropeza's *Los fundadores del alba* (1969; *The Breach*, 1971) was also inspired by Che Guevara. This moving, innovative novel, presented in a nonlinear montage of temporal and spatial fragments, details the tragic fate of an ex-seminary student who becomes involved in the guerrilla movement and dies after a confrontation with the Bolivian army. The message conveyed by the plot is that "the founders of a new day" (the literal translation of the title) must replace bitterness with love and understanding if their mission is to be accomplished. Two additional titles worthy of note are *Tirinea* (1969; Tirinea), by Jesús Urzagasti (b. 1941), an antinovel of alienation, and *Los habitantes del alba* (1969; the inhabitants of the dawn), by Raúl Teixico (b. 1943), a collection of three psychological tales about love, hope, and friendship.

Ecuador

Despite its relatively small population, Ecuador has produced a surprisingly large number of fine writers in this century, many of whom belong to the so-called Generation of 1930. This group of committed left-wing intellectuals, whose best works have yet to be equaled by later arrivals on the Ecuadorian literary scene, vowed to provoke reforms in their native land by documenting political and social injustices for their fellow countrymen. The leading members of this generation are Jorge Icaza, mentioned in chapter 1, Alfredo Pareja Diez-Canseco (b. 1908), Demetrio Aguilera Malta (1909–1981), Humberto Salvador (b. 1909), Joaquín Gallegos Lara (1911–1947), Enrique Gil Gilbert (b. 1912), and Adalberto Ortiz (b. 1914).

Jorge Icaza, Ecuador's most prestigious regionalist, published his best social-protest works during the 1930s, but he wrote significant fiction until only a few years before his death. His *Huairapamushcas* (1948; children of the evil wind) continues the delineation of the struggles between Indian and white seen in the earlier works, ending symbolically with the survival of *cholo* (half-breed) twins who represent a bridge between the white and Indian cultures. *El chulla Romero y Flores* (1958; the good-for-nothing Romero y Flores), which some critics consider Icaza's masterpiece, analyzes the protagonist's search for identity in the Ecuadorian capital and his gradual coming to terms with the dichotomy in his racial background. Icaza's last novel, *Los atrapados* (1972; the trapped ones), combines fictional and autobiographical elements, including his own struggles to achieve success as a writer, in order to demonstrate that man is a prisoner of his political, economic, and social environment. *Los atrapados* also reveals a greater awareness of stylistic innovations together with a deep interest in the relationship between reality and fiction. A major defect in Icaza's oeuvre is his tendency to portray the Indian as a brutish stereotype rather than as a complex human being with the potential for controlling his own destiny. Nevertheless, in its entirety his fiction presents the most vivid protest to date against social injustice in the Andean highlands of Ecuador.

Pareja Diez-Canseco's *Hombres sin tiempo* (1941; men without time) describes the hair-raising conditions in a prison where the author was incarcerated for political reasons. In *Las tres ratas* (1944; the three rats), the lives of three sisters inform the plot, which also incorporates naturalistic themes such as drugs, sex, and political corruption. Pareja Diez-Canseco's more recent novels parallel the history of his homeland from the July 9, 1925, revolution to the early 1940s. The best of these, *Las pequeñas estaturas* (1970; the small statures), emerges as a kind of roman à clef about the complexities of Ecuadorian politics; it also displays elements of magical realism and an impressive array of modern literary techniques.

With the exception of Icaza, Aguilera Malta is Ecuador's most renowned writer of fiction. Like Icaza and Pareja Diez-Canseco, he published much of his work during the 1930s, but his literary career spans several decades. *La isla virgen* (1942; the virgin island) dramatizes a white man's struggles to develop a tropical island, a struggle that causes his madness. Aguilera

Malta has also written novels dealing with a broad spectrum of history: *Una cruz en la Sierra Maestra* (1960; a cross on the Sierra Maestra), about the Cuban revolution; *Manuela la caballeresa del sol* (1964; *Manuela la Caballeresa del Sol*, 1967), based on Manuela Saenz's relations with Simón Bolívar; and *Un nuevo mar para el rey: Balboa, Anayansi y el Océano Pacífico* (1965; a new sea for the king: Balboa, Anayansi and the Pacific Ocean), a fictional account of Balboa's historic exploit and his love affair with an Indian girl. This author's most widely acclaimed novel is *Siete lunas y siete serpientes* (1970; *Seven Serpents and Seven Moons*, 1979), which has been described as an excellent example of magical realism. An ingenious admixture of legends, witchcraft, and modern everyday concerns, it depicts the perennial contest between good and evil in the community of Santorontón, where a lustful *cacique* (political boss) named Candelario Mariscal reigns supreme. The mythically based themes and magical realism of this novel are continued in *El secuestro del general* (1973; *Babelandia*, 1985), in which the town of Laberinto provides the backdrop for oppression and revenge when a despotic general is imprisoned in a cage and lowered into a volcano. More fantastic than real, *El secuestro del general* expresses the fertile imagination of a people under the spell of diabolical passions and overpowering myths. Like its predecessor, this novel has been labeled a total fictional experience by one of Latin America's leading creators of fiction.

Humberto Salvador condemns a wide range of social evils, but he stands out among his contemporaries for his Freudian analyses of human relations in novels such as *Prometeo* (1943; Prometheus), *La fuente clara* (1946; the clear fountain), and *Viaje a lo desconocido* (1967; voyage into the unknown). His most memorable work, *Silueta de una dama* (1964; silhouette of a lady), represents an ironically drawn portrait of a vain beauty whose interior monologues recall her love affairs before and after her marriage. Enrique Gil Gilbert's masterpiece is *Nuestro pan* (1942; *Our Daily Bread*, 1943), a sensitive novel about the fears, hopes, and struggles of rice-paddy workers in the hot coastal region of Ecuador. Two of the many problems described in this exceptionally fine work are the oppressive social structure and the cruel natural environment confronting those attempting to eke out a living in the tropics. *Cruces sobre el agua* (1946; crosses on the water), by Gallegos Lara, is generally considered as one of Spanish America's most outstanding proletarian novels. Although its central subject matter is a 1922 strike in the coastal city of Guayaquil, this work presents a vast panorama of Ecuadorian life.

The youngest of the Generation of 1930 is Adalberto Ortiz, Ecuador's first major black writer. His most successful novel is *Yuyungo* (1942; Yuyungo), the portrayal of a black's search for identity in a society plagued by racial injustice. Yuyungo, whose name is a disparaging Indian term for black man, is first seen as a child, then in various social situations showing his relations with blacks, Indians, and whites, and finally as a soldier dying in defense of his country during the 1941 Peruvian invasion. This novel's strong social-protest theme links it to the regionalist movement, but its poetic presentation of the introspective Yuyungo's personal quest places it somewhere between the traditional and the "new novel." *El espejo y la ventana* (1967; the mirror and the window) also portrays an introverted protagonist, but its plot is even more closely related to events in Ecuador's past, in this case the decades of the 1920s and 1930s.

Two younger Ecuadorian writers whose works have elicited critical acclaim are Alsino Ramírez Estrada (b. 1930) and Miguel Donoso Pareja (b. 1931). *El testimonio* (1967; the testimony), by Ramírez Estrada, turns on two spheres of interest that act as narrative counterpoints. The first of these is the protagonist's restricted family circle, which is described by letters he receives from his mother, and the second consists of the protagonist's broader world of social activities and responsibilities. In this novel the creative process becomes a source of irony when the narrator confesses that the dénouement represents his own subjective, rather than objective, reality. Donoso Pareja, a long-time resident of Mexico, imparts Marxist ideals in his collection of traditionally structured stories entitled *El hombre que mataba a sus hijos* (1968; the man who killed his sons). His novel *Henry Black* (1969; Henry Black), however, resembles a surrealistic nightmare in its portrait of the schizo-phrenic protagonist whose inability to communicate with oth-ers derives at least in part from the cruel ambience in which he is condemned to live.

In sharp contrast to Donoso Pareja's pessimistic *Weltan-schauung*, Vicente Cabrera's (b. 1944) novelettes in *La noche del té; El gabán* (1984; the night of the tea; the overcoat) rep-resent a surge of fresh vitality in Ecuadorian letters. Cabrera's hallmarks are his intriguing, carefully woven plots, his con-vincing sense of character, and his vigorous, elegant prose. *La noche del té* describes the paradox of a middle-class urban fam-ily's efforts to cure a mentally ill daughter by consulting a witch doctor in a remote pueblo. The initial setting of *El gabán* is a boardinghouse, where a student is arrested on flimsy evidence for his alleged participation in a political demonstration. The unexpected ending is fraught with irony and conspicuously de-void of protest. A professor of Spanish literature in the United States for many years, Cabrera recently returned to Ecuador in order to renew his contact with his native tongue and write fiction.

Peru

Of the three Andean countries treated in this section, Peru stands out as the leader in the field of contemporary fiction, perhaps because of its larger population. Although the inter-national reputations of Ciro Alegría, José María Arguedas, and Mario Vargas Llosa (all discussed above) have tended to over-shadow other Peruvian writers of recent years, these outstand-ing men of letters have nevertheless stimulated their compatriots' interest in literature and, at the same time, inspired their lesser-known colleagues to sublimate their critical world visions into engrossing works of art. During the 1950s a group of talented young Peruvian writers gave new directions to the national literature, often shifting their focus from rural to urban settings while establishing a balance between regional and universal themes. Although they continued to protest against social in-justice, they also relied on technical innovations and stylistic artistry to dramatize the alienation and violence increasingly characteristic of life in Peru's burgeoning capital.

The two eldest of this generation, Sebastián Salazar Bondy (1924–1965) and Eleodoro Vargas Vicuña (b. 1924), are very different in their approaches to literature. Salazar Bondy is interested not only in the city dweller, but also in the political vicissitudes and the philosophical implications of modern man's existence. His collection of stories *Náufragos y sobrevivientes* (1954; shipwrecks and survivors) shows how human values have been distorted and happiness made unattainable by the frenetic pace of urban life. His posthumous novel, *Alférez Arce, Teniente Arce, Capitán Arce* (1969; Ensign Arce, Lieutenant Arce, Captain Arce), utilizes flashbacks and a shifting point of view to delineate a political prisoner's altered state of mind— his ambition is reduced to fear—moments before his execution for his role in an unsuccessful attempted coup. Vargas Vicuña excels in the short story, a medium he cultivates in order to focus on his characters' psychological reactions to unusual sit- uations in rural, rather than urban, life. He is also a master of the subtle suggestion, which frequently appears only in the final lines of his tales, jolting his reader into new areas of awareness. Some of his finest stories are found in *Nahuin* (1953; Nahuin) and *Taita Cristo* (1964; Taita Cristo).

Another interpreter of the rural Peruvian setting is Carlos Eduardo Zavaleta (b. 1928), who, like Vargas Vicuña, is known primarily as a writer of short stories. In *La batalla* (1954; the battle), one of his best collections, he relies on striking, sur- realistic images to depict the cult of violence in traditional Indian life. The title story, for example, describes in gory detail the grotesque life-and-death struggle of a drunken Indian with a condor during a fiesta. Zavaleta's most important novel, *Los Ingar* (1955; the Ingars), dramatizes the rivalry and hatred between two families, resulting in a series of violent clashes and a tragic climax.

Manuel Scorza (1928–1984) wrote a series of *indigenista* novels, i.e., depictions of Indians as victims of landowners, mine operators, or government officials. As in most works of this type, Scorza's frequently end with the rebellion and massacre of the persecuted protagonists. What distinguishes this writer from most of his *indigenista* colleagues, however, is his use of magical realism (the fusion of realism and fantasy) to convey his urgent social message in more poetic and imaginative terms. Thus, wild animals fight alongside the Indian in his struggles against the oligarchy, heroes of the past mingle with present-day fictional characters, and a river becomes a symbol of mourning. Perhaps Scorza's best novel is *La tumba del relámpago* (1979; the tomb of lightning), which, unlike his previous works, discloses hidden layers of meaning through the adroit manipulation of innovative literary devices.

With the exception of Vargas Llosa, Peru's most prestigious living writer is Julio Ramón Ribeyro (b. 1929). Although his fame is owed above all to his short fiction, Ribeyro has also written exceptional novels, two examples of which are *Crónica de San Gabriel* (1960; chronicle of Saint Gabriel), about a decadent family of landowners; and *Los geniecillos dominicales* (1965; Sunday temper), a multilayered, satirical portrait of Lima presented through the life of the alienated protagonist. This author's most widely acclaimed collection of short stories is *Los gallinazos sin plumas* (1955; the featherless buzzards), the title story of which has become a classic in modern Peruvian letters. In this hair-raising tale, two young brothers living in a slum are obliged by their grandfather to collect garbage to fatten his pig, Pascual, which he intends to sell for a handsome profit. When the boys are unable to work for several days because of illness, their grandfather throws their pet dog into the pigsty to satisfy the voracious animal. The theme of "Los gallinazos sin plumas" is effectively conveyed by Marxist symbolism: The insatiable, monstrous Pascual represents the capitalistic system based on economic growth through exploitation; the grandfather emerges as the exploiter who nurtures the system for his own gain; and the boys (the "featherless buzzards") stand for the exploited, alienated proletariat that Marx encouraged to revolt against oppression. In his more recent fiction, Ribeyro has tended to veer toward the realm of the fantastic.

Like Ribeyro, Enrique Congrains Martín (b. 1932) excels as a writer of short stories, limning the more sordid aspects of life in the Peruvian capital. Of special interest in his first collection, *Lima, hora zero* (1954; Lima, zero hour), is the depiction of the plight of uprooted rural migrants seeking a better life in the city where they ultimately confront chaos, despair, and alienation in the outlying *barriadas* (slums). The title story of this collection details the efforts of slum dwellers to survive in the face of everyday problems such as the lack of water and the threat of expulsion from the land on which they are settled. Congrains Martín's second collection, *Kikuyo* (1955; Kikuyo), dramatizes similar themes but concentrates more heavily on the economic struggles of the lower middle class. His novel *No una, sino muchas muertes* (1957; not one but many deaths) treats surrealistically the criminal elements in Lima, which he likens to "a beast with a million heads."

The youth crisis of the 1960s looms as a major theme in the works of Oswaldo Reynoso, or Reinoso (b. 1932). *Los inocentes* (1961; the innocents), this author's first collection of tales, is characterized by juvenile slang, a vehicle for assaulting the establishment and expressing the alienation of the younger generation. Reynoso's novel *En octubre no hay milagros* (1965; in October there are no miracles) advocates political action by developing two plot threads, one set in a poverty-ridden proletarian milieu, and the other involving a decadent upper-class family of exploiters. *El escarabajo* (1970; the beetle) is a scatological allegory of the adverse conditions in Peru, language once again emerging as a weapon to attack the established order and, the author hopes, to effect social reform.

Six additional Peruvians meriting recognition are Luis Loayza (b. 1934), Alfredo Bryce Echenique (b. 1939), Miguel Gutiérrez (b. 1940), Luis Urteaga Cabrera (b. 1940), Eduardo González Viaña (b. 1941), and Isaac Goldemberg (b. 1945). Loayza is best known for his novel *Una piel de serpiente* (1964; a snake skin), which, like Reynoso's works, deals with rebellious youth. *Una piel de serpiente*, however, ends with the defeat of the rebels by the bourgeois government. Set in the northern city of Piura, Gutiérrez's novel *El viejo saurio se retira* (1969; the old saurian retires) represents a scathing indictment of outmoded institutions in Peru, its principal characters being a group of unruly teenagers whose obscene language represents the novel's medium as well as its message. *Los hijos del orden* (1973; the sons of order), by Urteaga Cabrera, constitutes another condemnation of the Peruvian status quo, but ironically the "sons of order" are violent youths acting out their frustrations in a Lima rehabilitation center for juvenile delinquents. Here Urteaga Cabrera demonstrates his mastery of Vargas Llosa's techniques, his purpose being to capture the immediacy of events and, at the same time, to convey his urgent social message in gruesome detail. By contrast, González Viaña emerges as the most poetic of his generation. His tales, collected in *Los peces muertos* (1964; the dead fish) and *Batalla de Felipe en la casa de palomas* (1970; Felipe's battle in the dovecote), depict rural life with a flair for fantasy and a wealth of irony and stylistic artistry reminiscent of Juan José Arreola. Goldemberg, the youngest of this group, has elicited praise for his novel *La vida a plazos de don Jacobo Lerner* (1979; *The Fragmented Life of Don Jacobo Lerner*, 1976)—the English translation appeared before the Spanish version—which chronicles the past of a Jewish immigrant to Peru, his economic hardship, and, above all, his struggle to maintain his cherished identity as a Jew in an alien society. The identity crisis of a Jewish protagonist is narrated in a much lighter vein in *Tiempo al tiempo* (1984; *Play by Play*, 1985). The product of a Russian Jewish father and a Peruvian Catholic mother, Marcos undergoes the rites of initiation in a military school and, in a hilarious surrealistic dream, on a soccer field where his mother appears as a goalie. Goldemberg's poignant portrait is enlivened by his skillful manipulation of literary technique—Marcos's sexual successes and defeats are told by a television announcer as if they were a soccer game—and his bizarre but engaging sense of humor.

The best of the younger generation of novelists on the Peruvian literary scene after Vargas Llosa is Alfredo Bryce Echenique. This remarkable author, who has also published several volumes of fine short stories, is probably best known for his novel *Un mundo para Julius* (1971; a world for Julius), a sympathetically drawn portrait of the scion (Julius) of a wealthy Peruvian family and of the decadent milieu in which he is raised. Although the plot is conveyed by a variety of modern narrative techniques, the young protagonist is the principal narrator and witness of events, a strategy that generates ironic overtones and implies a sharp criticism of Lima's elite. This same type of criticism becomes the warp and woof of Bryce Echenique's short stories, most of which have been published in *Huerto cerrado* (1968; closed orchard), *Muerte de Sevilla en Madrid* (1972; death of Seville in Madrid), and *La felicidad ja ja* (1974; happiness ha ha). His novel *La vida exagerada de Martín Romaña* (1981; the exaggerated life of Martín Romaña) is set in Paris during the 1960s, which Romaña, a fledgling Peruvian writer, describes in his memoirs (the novel). The inimitable ironic tone of *Un mundo para Julius* remains intact in *La vida exagerada de Martín Romaña*, as does the author's ability to sustain reader interest throughout the more than six hundred pages of text (*Un mundo para Julius* is approximately this same length).

THE SOUTHERN CONE

Argentina

As mentioned previously, Argentina and Mexico lead the rest of Spanish America in volume of literary works published, both nations having not only large numbers of educated readers, but also more well-established publishing firms and better avenues of distribution. Argentina's most influential writers of fiction since 1941 have been Jorge Luis Borges, Ernesto Sábato, Julio Cortázar, and, to a somewhat lesser degree, Leopoldo Marechal and Eduardo Mallea (all discussed above). Nevertheless, a host of others, far too numerous to include here, have achieved national and, in some cases, international reputations. The eldest of these is Bernardo Verbitsky (b. 1907), who has been called Argentina's best social realist of the twentieth century. The action of most of his numerous books takes place in the gray, gritty working-class districts of Buenos Aires between 1930 and 1960. Representative of his fiction are *Un noviazgo* (1956; an engagement), which describes Argentina's economic decline of the 1930s under a military dictatorship and its disastrous effects on the proletariat; and *Villa miseria tam-*

bién es América (1957; poverty town also is America), a panoramic view of the continent, which Verbitsky pessimistically envisions as a vast spiritual slum.

Entirely different is Verbitsky's contemporary José Bianco (b. 1908), a penetrating psychological novelist who, though admired by other writers, has yet to receive the public recognition he merits. Two of his finest works, *Las ratas* (1943) and *Sombras suele vestir* (1944), have been published in English translations in a single volume entitled *Shadow Play; The Rats: Two Novellas* (1984). Narrated in the first person by a disillusioned neurotic named Delfín, *Las ratas* chronicles the confusing events leading up to Delfín's murder (by poisoning) of his half-brother. Like its predecessor, *Sombras suele vestir* depicts a series of complex family relations, the protagonist here being a prostitute whose actions upon the death of her mother oblige the reader to become an active participant in interpreting and organizing the plot. Through his creative genius Bianco demonstrates that reality is never simple, but rather ambiguous, contradictory, and intriguing.

Bianco's prolific contemporary Manuel Mujica Láinez (1910–1984) dissects the upper strata of present-day Argentine society while often seeking inspiration for his mythical creations in the remote, exotic past. Three of his most significant novels are *La casa* (1954; the house), about the gradual decline of an aristocratic Argentine family; *Bomarzo* (1962; *Bomarzo*, 1969), which portrays a duke's search for immortality during the Italian Renaissance; and *El unicornio* (1965; *The Wandering Unicorn*, 1983), a masterful combination of medieval history, fable, romance, and adventure, with allegorical allusions to present-day issues. An imaginative intellectual of broad interests more than a technical innovator, Mujica Láinez was one of Argentina's most original and universal writers.

Adolfo Bioy Casares was discussed briefly at the beginning of this chapter as a precursor of the "new novel," but he has continued to write prolifically and, along with Borges, is considered one of the leading creators of fantasy in Argentina. The similarity of his works to those of Borges, one might add, is very likely due to his collaboration on several books with his older, more renowned colleague. Bioy Casares's best novels subsequent to 1941 are *Plan de evasión* (1945; plan of evasion), which postulates the ability of men—in this case inmates on an island prison—to escape from confinement through the drastic alteration of sensory perceptions; *El sueño de los héroes* (1954; the dream of the heroes), an account of the protagonist's mental excursion into the past only to discover that the distance covered is an illusion because present and past exist side by side; and *Diario de la guerra del cerdo* (1969; *Diary of the War of the Pig*, 1972), an expressionistic allegory of man's tenuous existence and acute awareness of the self, as illustrated by a war of extermination between the young (the killers) and the old (the willing victims). Like Borges, Bioy Casares compels his readers to examine the fine line between illusion and reality, an exercise fraught with irony that tends to undermine the myths formulated by human logic.

One of Argentina's leading female writers, Silvina Bullrich (b. 1915) has published numerous realistic novels about the role of women in her native land (Bullrich is an outspoken feminist) and the vices permeating all levels of Argentine society. Two of her most ambitious works are *Los burgueses* (1964; the bourgeois) and *La creciente* (1965; the flood). The first and best of a trilogy, *Los burgueses* is narrated by an unidentified member of the landed gentry during a birthday celebration held on a country estate. The characters emerge as vain, frivolous individuals from various segments of a society Bullrich treats, not without irony, as unredeemably decadent. *La creciente* continues the satirical tone of its predecessor by depicting a city under the threat of a natural disaster, a metaphor of political and social corruption. Bullrich's portraits of rebellious, emancipated women include *Bodas de cristal* (1952; crystal wedding) and *Teléfono ocupado* (1955; busy signal).

Antonio di Benedetto (b. 1922) and Marco Denevi (b. 1922) have created sharply contrasting fictional worlds. Di Benedetto is a first-rate writer who merits wider recognition than he has received, whereas Denevi may have achieved greater prominence than he deserves. Often compared to Sábato, Cortázar, and the French creators of the New Novel, di Benedetto portrays anguished protagonists searching for the meaning of existence in an unresponsive universe. Two examples are *Zama* (1956; Zama), about an eighteenth-century politician whose aggressive behavior masks his obsessive fear of death; and *El silenciero* (1964; the silencer), the protagonist of which is a city dweller unable to cope with the unbearable noise in his surroundings. Denevi achieved instant fame in 1955 for his enormously popular *Rosaura a las diez* (Rosaura at ten o'clock), a cleverly structured murder mystery narrated by four different characters. Besides his other successful detective novel, *Ceremonias secretas* (1960; secret ceremonies), he has published very readable short fables railing against the evils of technology in an absurd, depersonalized world.

A well-known essayist as well as a short-story writer and novelist, Héctor A. Murena, mentioned in chapter 1, also describes the absurdity of modern existence, but he is more profound than Denevi, and his criticism of Argentine institutions tends to be more sarcastic and acerbic. His most significant novels include *La fatalidad de los cuerpos* (1955; the fatality of bodies), *Las leyes de la noche* (1958; the laws of the night), *Los herederos de la promesa* (1965; the heirs of the promise), and *Epitalámica* (1969, epithalamic). The first three of these form a trilogy describing the dismal, melancholy, and, at times, nightmarish life in Argentina during the Perón regime of the 1940s and 1950s; *Epitalámica* relies on absurd fantasy, grotesque humor, and baroque language to satirize a decadent society headed for destruction.

An Argentine living in Mexico, Humberto Costantini (b. 1924) won the Casa de las Américas prize for his *De dioses, hombrecitos y policías* (1979; *The Gods, the Little Guys and the Police*, 1984), a bitter but hilarious allegory of the torture and disappearance of liberals under an Argentine military regime during the 1970s. The plot deals with Greek gods who concern themselves with the hapless members of an apolitical group of poets suspected by the police of subversive activities. The danger of being an intellectual, no matter how insignificant, in a totalitarian society emerges as the novel's principal theme. A similar setting frames *La larga noche de Francisco Sanctis*

(1984; *The Long Night of Francisco Sanctis*, 1985), which depicts a prosaic, apolitical accountant who immerses himself in music as a means of retreat from a crass society. Sanctis's dilemma arises when a former university classmate entrusts him with the mission of warning two innocent citizens of their imminent arrest for political reasons. The fluctuations of the protagonist's state of mind over a ten-hour period and his inevitable moral choice form the warp and woof of this taut, compassionate novel.

Harold Conti (b. 1925) and Beatriz Guido (b. 1925) have achieved wide recognition among Argentine readers. Occasionally compared to Juan Carlos Onetti, Conti portrays alienated outsiders whose lives are physically and psychologically restricted by drab settings—usually the poorer sections of Buenos Aires—and monotonous, everyday life. His many prize-winning novels include *Alrededor de la jaula* (1967; around the cage), in which a homeless boy comes to identify his own life with that of a confined mongoose; and *En vida* (1971; while alive), about a man who abandons his wife for a prostitute and ultimately rejects even his own son. Guido, like Bullrich, indicts Argentine society in the realistic mode, but she is more interested in adolescent psychology than her elder colleague. *La casa del ángel* (1954; the angel's house), for example, presents a young female protagonist oppressed by religious fanaticism and the sexual role imposed on her by her family. *El incendio de las vísperas* (1964; the fire of vespers), perhaps her best and most controversial work, deals with the moral decay of the Argentine oligarchy under Perón's government.

Dalmiro Sáenz (b. 1926) has achieved considerable fame in Argentina for both his short stories and novels. An existentialist concerned with moral and ethical rather than social issues, he depicts characters suffering from anguish and solitude primarily because of the responsibility they feel for the evil in their midst. In his collections of short stories such as *No* (1960; no) and *Treinta-treinta* (1962; thirty-thirty) Sáenz presents episodes with explicit naturalistic details in order to link sexual and divine love, both of which he invests with metaphysical dimensions. His novels, reminiscent of André Malraux's, include *Hay hambre dentro de tu pan* (1963; there is hunger inside your bread), in which a remorseful government official bears the blame for political oppression; and *El pecado necesario* (1964; the necessary sin), an ironic detective tale about a police investigator who, while attempting to solve a crime, discovers the prime suspect to be his own double.

Another first-rate storyteller and novelist, Daniel Moyano (b. 1928) has demonstrated an uncanny ability to illuminate the mysterious facets of everyday reality in a style freighted with symbols and evocative imagery. His collections of tales, some of which deal with the awakening of adolescents to the complexities of the world around them, include *La lombriz* (1964; the worm), *Los monstruos, y otros cuentos* (1967; the monsters, and other stories), and *Mi música es para esta gente* (1970; my music is for these people), the last enhanced aesthetically by avant-garde literary devices. Moyano's most impressive novel to date is *El oscuro* (1968; the dark one), a deeply penetrating, brooding portrait of a police chief who, through his interior monologues, peers into the recesses of his own soul in an attempt to exorcise an unpleasant memory involving his wife and a younger man. In the process he not only exposes his own weakness, but also acquires literary stature as a symbol of the spiritual malaise affecting contemporary Argentina. *El trino del diablo* (1974; the devil's trill) strikes a more satirical note, forcefully indicting the Argentines for their corrupt institutions and decaying ethical values.

David Viñas (b. 1929) is probably Argentina's best known and most competent Marxist social realist. An ardent critic of the military, the oligarchy, and the Perón dictatorship, he has written novels, essays, and literary criticism in which he demythicizes much of the "heroic" past embedded in his homeland's collective unconscious. Viñas's most successful novels include *Cayó sobre su rostro* (1955; he fell on his face) and *Los dueños de la tierra* (1958; the lords of the land), both of which condemn the central government's role in the colonization of Patagonia, the southern part of Argentina; *Los años despiadados* (1956; the pitiless years), an assault on, among other things, the corruption and exaggerated machismo in Argentine society during the Peronist years; and *Los hombres de a caballo* (1967; the men on horseback). The latter, perhaps Viñas's best novel, emerges as a complex, artistically conceived account of the Argentine army's efforts to quell a guerrilla revolt in Peru, but a series of flashbacks evokes the wars of independence, when the army fought for, not against, the common man.

A contemporary of Viñas, Pedro Orgambide (b. 1929) also takes Argentine society to task, but like that of Sáenz, his world outlook is more existential than Marxist. His *Memorias de un hombre de bien* (1964; memoirs of an honest man) presents a highly amusing portrait of an upper-class *pícaro* who has lost his family fortune. His best novel, however, *El páramo* (1965; the wasteland), appropriately set in the barren stretches of Patagonia, looms as an allegory of twentieth-century existence. The narrator and protagonist of this depressing work is an idealistic medical doctor who sets up practice in the remote southern region in order to escape the confines of the city, only to discover that life there also impedes his quest for freedom. Although his anguish resembles that of other existential anti-heroes, the influence of the physical environment represents a remnant of naturalism, a movement that has never entirely vanished from the Spanish American literary scene.

Marta Lynch (1930–1985), another militant leftist, shaped her pessimistic vision of Argentine life into a steady stream of well-crafted, coherent works of art. Her first novel, *La alfombra roja* (1962; the red carpet), considered by some readers as a roman à clef, depicts an unscrupulous bourgeois politician's rise to power, his dehumanization, and, ultimately, his mythification. In *Al vencedor* (1965; to the victor) Lynch sharpened her critical focus on a frustrated society, her protagonists being two young men whose disillusion with the conditions they encounter after their discharge from the army induces them to turn to violent crime. *La señora Ordóñez* (1968; Mrs. Ordóñez) also depicts a strife-torn milieu, in this case that of a woman in search of social justice during the Peronist years and her erotic involvement with politically active men. In *El cruce del río* (1972; the river crossing) maternal love becomes the energizing agent for the protagonist's revolutionary fervor; and in her collection of stories *Los años de fuego* (1980; the years of fire) Lynch continued to probe the lives of women whose emotional experiences illustrate evolving female roles in her native land.

Of the growing list of Argentine writers born since 1930, Manuel Puig, mentioned in chapter 1, is perhaps the most gifted and certainly the most innovative and widely read. His first novel, *La traición de Rita Hayworth* (1968; *Betrayed by Rita Hayworth*, 1971), is the story of a boy growing up in a drab Argentine town and his escape from this reality by going to the movies. A complex montage of interior monologues, dialogues, diaries, and letters describes the beauty and romance of pop art as an ironic counterpoint to the barren lives of its characters. *Boquitas pintadas* (1969; *Heartbreak Tango*, 1973) is Puig's most popular book, having sold well over 100,000 copies in Argentina alone. Acclaimed by the critics as well, it portrays via cinematic techniques a working-class woman who longs to become involved with a Don Juan, her unrealized dreams perhaps representing the frustrations of an entire nation. In Puig's third novel, *The Buenos Aires Affair* (1973; *The Buenos Aires Affair*, 1976)—the original title is in English—the abduction of a sculptress by an art critic provides the background action for an entertaining parody, replete with experimental literary capers and baroque distortions, of the detective thriller. Subsequent novels include *El beso de la mujer araña* (1976; *Kiss of the Spider Woman*, 1979), which dramatizes the homosexual relationship between two prisoners in a Buenos Aires jail; *Pubis angélical* (1979; angelic pubis), the chronicle of an ailing Argentine woman's traumatic past in a repressive environment and her attempts to escape through her private fantasies; and *Maldición eterna a quien lea estas páginas* (1980; *Eternal Curse on the Reader of These Pages*, 1982), a series of dialogues between an old and a young man, revealing much about the dynamics of language and, ironically, its vitiation of true communication. Puig has perhaps been best described as a camp novelist, i.e., a collagist of comic episodes expressed in clichés and other conventions of cheap popular culture. On the surface his books resemble trivial soap operas destined for the unsophisticated, but a more exacting scrutiny of them reveals an authentic, sensitively conceived reality based on human truths and the poetic parameters of myth.

Five additional Argentine writers of the younger generation are Tomás Eloy Martínez (b. 1934), Eduardo Gudiño Kieffer (b. 1935), Luisa Valenzuela (b. 1938), Enrique Medina (b. 1942), and Mario Szichman (b. 1945). Martínez's highly acclaimed anti-novel *Sagrado* (1969; sacred) consists of monologues by the three protagonists describing the absurdity of their lives in the provincial city of Tucumán. *Para comerte mejor* (1968; the better to eat you), Gudiño Kieffer's best-selling experimental novel, has been favorably compared to Cortázar's *Rayuela*, although its sole setting is Buenos Aires. Other books by Gudiño Kieffer are *Guía de pecadores* (1972; sinners' guide), a mosaic of alienated characters vainly searching for meaning in the congested Argentine capital; and *Será por eso que la quiero tanto* (1975; that's probably why I love her so much), about a provincial family's adverse fate in a Buenos Aires slum.

Luisa Valenzuela, who obviously has been influenced by Borges and Cortázar, has emerged as one of the most popular of the younger generation. A prolific practitioner of both the novel and the short story, she owes her reputation to books such as *Aquí pasan cosas raras* (1975; *Strange Things Happen Here*, 1979), a collection of tragicomic tales reflecting the sinister political repression and absurd atmosphere created by an Argentine military regime; *Cambio de armas* (1982; *Other Weapons*, 1985), a grouping of sophisticated, self-reflecting stories concentrating on the interplay of power and dependence in male-female relationships in a world where real events and fantasy coalesce; and *Cola de lagartija* (1983; *The Lizard's Tail*, 1983), a profoundly disturbing portrait of José López Rega, Isabel Perón's diabolical minister of social welfare.

Perhaps the angriest and the most prolific of Argentina's young novelists, Enrique Medina has been condemned as a pornographer by conservative readers, but he has grown steadily in literary stature with the publication of his powerful depictions of the dark side of his nation's society. His first novel, *Las tumbas* (1972; the tombs), attacks the juvenile reformatory system through the direct language and brutal behavior of its young protagonist. The target of *Sólo ángeles* (1973; only angels) is the political repression in Uruguay during the early 1970s. In *El Duke* (1976; *The Duke: Memories and Anti-Memories of a Participant in the Repression*, 1985), an ex-prizefighter reminiscent of Arlt's seedy figures recalls in desultory fashion his activities with labor union thugs; the result is a mosaic of a social milieu that transforms decent human beings into destructive beasts. *Perros de la noche* (1977; night dogs) has been called the novelistic equivalent of the theater of cruelty because of its descriptions of repulsive behavior and degradation. Here an abandoned brother and sister duplicate the evil they observe around them, their violent, incestuous relationship emerging as a metaphor of a depraved society. Additional novels by Medina include *Las muecas del miedo* (1981; the grimaces of fear), in which the narrator shows his expatriate fellow painter the festering wounds, crumbling institutions, and bureaucratic chaos of the Argentine capital; *Con el trapo en la boca* (1983; with the rag in her mouth), the first-person account of a lower-middle-class adolescent who rebels against male domination by castrating her boyfriend with a razor blade; and *Los asesinos* (1984; the murderers), a series of vignettes about life in contemporary Buenos Aires where decency is seen as a deviance and an aberration amid documentary evidence of moral decay. In its entirety Medina's oeuvre presents a horrifying panorama of life in his homeland during the 1970s and early 1980s. That this enfant terrible's works were not banned by the repressive military regime that governed Argentina between 1976 and 1983 is in itself a major accomplishment.

Mario Szichman is a well-known critic and journalist as well as the author of *A las 20:25 la señora entró en la inmortalidad* (1981; *At 8:25 Evita Became Immortal*, 1983), in which Eva Perón's death in 1952 serves as the point of departure for a poignant but often hilariously grotesque chronicle of a Jewish immigrant family living in Argentina.

Chile

Chile is more famous for its poetry than for its prose fiction, having produced two Nobel Prize-winning poets since 1941.

Nevertheless, in recent years the relative position of the Chilean novel has been enhanced by the emergence of many fine practitioners of the genre, the most talented of whom is José Donoso (discussed above as a prominent figure of the boom). Also discussed above is Manuel Rojas, Chile's outstanding contributor to the "new novel" of the 1940s and 1950s. Two major precursors of this "movement" are Eduardo Barrios (1884–1963) and Marta Brunet (b. 1901). An introspective, psychological writer, Barrios published his most memorable works before 1941, but he also created one of Spanish America's best regional novels, *Gran señor y rajadiablos* (1948; great lord and hellion), about a land baron and his role in the struggle between civilization and barbarism. His last important novel, *Los hombres del hombre* (1950; the men in man), represents a penetrating study of a man who, in a moment of crisis, contemplates the hidden facets of his own personality. Brunet initiated her career as a regionalist, often depicting women protagonists against a backdrop of picturesque country landscapes. In her works published after the mid-1940s, however, she abandoned her regionalist stance in order to explore the interior worlds of her characters and their existential problems. Her more modern novels include *Mampara* (1946; screen), *Raíz del sueño* (1949; root of the dream), and *María Nadie* (1957; Mary Nobody), all of which present lonely female protagonists whose dreams of happiness remain unfulfilled; and *Amasijo* (1962; Amasijo), a tragic psychological portrait of a homosexual writer.

During the 1930s many young Chilean intellectuals became dissatisfied with regionalism, which they felt no longer reflected the realities of a country undergoing fundamental social changes wrought by immigration, industrialization, and urbanization. A school of left-wing writers who had come together at the Pedagogical Institute of the University of Chile took advantage of the political ferment of 1938—the year Pedro Aguirre Cerda of the liberal Popular Front Party was elected president—to proclaim their opposition to the regionalists' outmoded methods and advocate a new type of fiction, often referred to as neorealism. This so-called Generation of 1938 shifted the literary focus from the country to the city and, inspired by Marx and Freud, strove to achieve social and political reforms by portraying the miserable lot of the downtrodden masses. Outstanding members of the group include Juan Godoy (b. 1911), Nicomedes Guzmán (1914–1964), Carlos Droguett (b. 1915), Guillermo Atías (1917–1981), and Fernando Alegría (b. 1918).

Godoy is known above all for his *Angurrientos* (1940; the insatiable ones), which describes the futile attempts of a young, idealistic leftist to instill social consciousness in his country-men and improve the life of the *roto*, the poverty-stricken Chilean laborer. Similar themes, occasionally reinforced by surrealistic techniques, appear in his later works, including *La cifra solitaria* (1945; the solitary number) and *Un inspector de sanidad* (1950; a health inspector). Guzmán also paints the *roto* with sympathy, but in addition to describing his vice-ridden environment, as does Godoy, Guzmán shows the confrontation between classes, often in the form of strikes and their violent aftermath. Two of his most readable novels are *La sangre y la esperanza* (1942; blood and hope), about a strike organizer and police brutality in a Santiago slum; and *La luz viene del mar* (1951; the light comes from the sea), which takes place in a mining district of northern Chile.

Carlos Droguett is vitally concerned with social conditions in his homeland, but he tends to be more sensational in his subject matter, more pessimistic in his world outlook, and more experimental in his techniques than Godoy or Guzmán. *Sesenta muertos en la escalera* (1953; sixty dead on the staircase) focuses on a massacre of Chilean students and the psychic reactions of the survivors. *Eloy* (1960; Eloy), perhaps his best book, sets forth the rambling memories of a bandit hours prior to his death in a hail of bullets fired by the police. Three other well-known titles by Droguett are *Patas de perro* (1965; dog's paws), *El compadre* (1967; the friend), and *El hombre que había olvidado* (1968; the man who had forgotten). *Patas de perro* portrays a boy with dog's paws, a symbol of the social nonconformity present in every individual; the protagonist of *El compadre* is an alcoholic who, while laboring on a scaffold, recalls his sordid, unhappy past; and *El hombre que había olvidado* emerges as an allegory of the bleak human experience, its protagonist being a messianic madman who cuts off the heads of newborn babies.

Two of Guillermo Atías's best-known novels are *El tiempo*

banal (1955; the banal era) and *A la sombra de los días* (1965; in the shadow of the days). The former, which reveals the influence of John Dos Passos, presents a broad mosaic of middle-class life in Santiago, while the latter depicts a political conflict between fascists and moderates in Chile during the 1930s.

A well-known critic as well as a prolific creator of fiction, Fernando Alegría has lived for many years in the United States, but instead of merely evaluating his native land from afar, as have many of his Latin American colleagues, he uses his "exile" to depict the cultural differences between the Anglo-Saxon and Latin cultures. This aspect of his work is evident in his highly entertaining, carefully plotted novel *Caballo de copas* (1957; *My Horse González*, 1964), which concerns the adventures of Chilean racing fans in California and their efforts to win a fortune with their prize stallion. Another of Alegría's impressive novels is *Los días contados* (1968; the numbered days), about the poverty and alienating conditions—narrated with stylistic authenticity and flashes of humor—faced by a prizefighter in a Santiago slum. In his short fiction, Alegría stresses social-protest themes, but in this genre he reveals in addition a fondness for Kafkaesque fantasy. For example, as suggested by its title, "El poeta que se volvió gusano" (the poet who turned into a worm), in *El poeta que se volvió gusano, y otras historias verídicas* (1956; the poet who turned into a worm, and other true stories), shows the grotesque dehumanization of a writer, here a writer accused of subversive activities by a right-wing investigating committee.

The Chilean Generation of 1950 differs from the Generation of 1938 by its comparative indifference to political and social issues and by its turn inward in search of new values. Better educated and more sophisticated than their predecessors, the members of the later group found inspiration abroad in the writings of Joyce, Woolf, Faulkner, Sartre, and Camus. And, through their estranged protagonists, they convey their existential concerns over the absurdity of life in a world without absolute values. In addition to José Donoso, the most outstanding writers of this generation are Jaime Laso (1926–1969), Enrique Lafourcade (b. 1927), and Jorge Edwards (b. 1931).

Laso's *El cepo* (1958; the trap), a highly regarded existential novel about bored office workers caught in the web of a stifling bureaucracy, suggests the influence of Camus's statement on the absurd human condition. This author draws on his own life as a sailor in *El acantilado* (1962; the cliff) to depict the final voyage of an aging sea captain. Lafourcade's early novels include *Pena de muerte* (1952; death penalty), a tragic study of homosexuality; *Para subir al cielo* (1954; in order to ascend to heaven), an allegory of love and existential anguish with implications of social criticism; and *La fiesta del Rey Acab* (1959; the fiesta of King Acab), the portrait of an archetypal Latin American dictator. Two of Lafourcade's more experimental novels are *Invención a dos voces* (1963; invention for two voices) and *Frecuencia modulada* (1968; modulated frequency). *Invención a dos voces* satirizes United States materialism (Lafourcade has spent considerable time in the United States) and its lack of respect for the idealist. *Frecuencia modulada* evolves a complex montage of contrasting scenes that in their entirety coalesce into a multifaceted mosaic of a modern metropolis. Lafourcade's most popular novel is *Palomita blanca* (1971; little white dove), a poor-girl–rich-boy romance set against a backdrop of Salvador Allende's 1970 election campaign and the youth crisis of that era. Also political by nature is one of this author's most recent pieces of fiction, *Adiós al Fuehrer* (1982; good-bye to the Führer), a grotesque account of the vestiges of Nazism in present-day Chile.

A member of the Chilean diplomatic corps for a number of years, Edwards is perhaps best known for his *Persona non grata* (1973; *Persona Non Grata*, 1977), which describes his break with Castro after having spent several months in Cuba in early 1971 as the Allende government's chargé d'affaires.[3] His first novel, *El peso de la noche* (1964; the weight of night), is reminiscent of Donoso's early writings, its central concern being the decline of an upper-middle-class matriarchal family. In *Los*

3. In 1970 the socialist candidate Salvador Allende was elected president of Chile. His government immediately resumed relations with communist Cuba, the raison d'être of Edwards's mission. Allende was killed during the military takeover of his government in September 1973.

convidados de piedra (1978; the stone guests) Edwards brilliantly dissects contemporary Chilean society and the forces that have shaped it in recent years. Akin to a vast mosaic, this novel has as its foreground action a fiesta in the home of Sebastián Agüero during the month of October 1973. Although it is Sebastián's forty-fourth birthday, the real occasion for the celebration is the recent (September 11) overthrow of the socialist government of Salvador Allende, whose policies the host and his guests, all arch-conservatives, detest. The "stone guests" of the title are former friends of those present, some dead, others imprisoned, and still others living in exile because of their liberal political convictions. The fiesta lasts an entire night during which the celebrators evoke in desultory fashion scenes from the past, re-creating dialogues not only of the *convidados de piedra*, but also of a wide array of other characters from all levels of society.

In 1978 Edwards returned to Chile from his five-year self-imposed exile and wrote *El museo de cera* (1981; the wax museum), a political allegory vivified by surrealistic dreams and flights of fantasy. Although the setting is never identified, the plot parallels events in Chile during the years prior to and immediately after the fall of the Allende regime. Edwards creates an oneiric atmosphere in which frustrated intellectuals are censored and subjected to terror under the harsh military government. He also presents Chile as a kind of wax museum where legacies of Spain have continued to exist anachronistically as if frozen in time. The protagonist of *El museo de cera*, for example, is a *marqués* whose defense of the old against the rising tide of social change is represented by the novel's title.

The setting of *La mujer imaginaria* (1985; the imaginary woman) is Chile in the early 1980s, a period of economic prosperity and, immediately thereafter, of devastating depression. More realistic than *El museo de cera*, this novel portrays the aging matriarch of a conservative upper-middle-class family who suddenly decides to satisfy the artistic bent of her youth. As a painter and active member of the intellectual community, she thus becomes a symbol of liberation in a country dominated by political reactionaries. Edwards has also published several collections of finely honed short stories, including *El patio* (1952; the patio), *Gente de la ciudad* (1961; people of the city), *Las máscaras* (1968; the masks), and *Temas y variaciones* (1969; themes and variations).

Many of Chile's best writers, particularly those of the younger generation, fled into exile after the army's coup against the Allende government in 1973. The most outstanding of this talented group is Antonio Skármeta (b. 1940). A resident of West Berlin, where he holds a faculty position in the Academy of Cinema, Skármeta has written short stories, novels, and film scripts. His collections of stories, which include *El entusiasmo* (1967; enthusiasm), *Desnudo en el tejado* (1969; naked on the roof), and *Tiro libre* (1973; free shot), often portray youthful protagonists who seek freedom from social restraints as a means of understanding both the world and the inner self. "Primera preparatoria" (first grade), in *Tiro libre*, for example, deals with a young man's departure for Australia, ostensibly because of his objections to Allende's left-wing government. The night before he leaves he has a violent quarrel with his father, a supporter of the liberal cause, who calls him a reactionary and refuses to bid him farewell. The story's irony is multilayered: the usual pattern of liberal youth versus conservative old age is reversed; the author was in his youth, and remains today, an ardent supporter of Allende's ideals; and, though cloaked in ambiguity, the motives of the departing son are probably not political, as initially suggested, but psychological.

The first of Skármeta's novels, *Soñé que la nieve ardía* (1975; *I Dreamt the Snow Was Burning*, 1985), is a moving chronicle of events leading up to and immediately following the violent overthrow of the Allende regime. The protagonist is a young, ambitious soccer player named Arturo, who comes from the backwaters of Chile to Santiago, where he hopes to make a fortune in a professional sports career. His materialistic values soon clash with those of a group of idealistic Allende supporters living in the same boardinghouse where Arturo resides. The ensuing military coup snuffs out the lives of many socialists, Arturo's sweetheart included, and restores to power those who, like Arturo, dream of wealth and power. Skármeta's other novels are *No pasó nada* (1980; nothing happened), a kind of *Bildungsroman* about a fourteen-year-old Chilean boy in Germany who hopes to become a writer; *La insurrección* (1982; *The Insurrection*, 1983), which depicts the recent Nicaraguan revolution, emphasizing its impact on the lives of ordinary people; and *Ardiente paciencia* (1985; ardent patience), a charming tale about Pablo Neruda's friendship with his mailman, who uses Neruda's verses to win the woman he loves.

Perhaps better known as an essayist than as a novelist, Ariel Dorfman (b. 1942) was a professor of journalism and literature during the Allende presidency. His novel *Viudas* (1981; *Widows*, 1983), which he wrote while in exile in the United States, takes place in Greece at some undefined moment in the twentieth century, but in reality it alludes to the tragic disappearance of thousands of people arrested by the secret police under the dictatorial regime of General Augusto Pinochet immediately after the overthrow of Allende. Another fictional portrait of the Chilean political situation is *La casa de los espíritus* (1982; *The House of the Spirits*, 1985), by Isabel Allende (b. 1942), a relative of Salvador Allende. This accomplished first novel depicts the rise and fall of three generations of a family of landowners whose lives constitute a microcosm of modern Chile, although the country is never mentioned by name. The political and social realities of a nation divided by economic injustices and bitter ideological disputes—a socialist government is overthrown by a military coup with the help of the CIA—are laced with poetic flights of fantasy reminiscent of *One Hundred Years of Solitude*. Like Dorfman, Allende left Chile after the 1973 military takeover. She has lived in Venezuela since her self-imposed exile.

Paraguay

Paraguay has produced few first-rate writers other than Augusto Roa Bastos (discussed above), perhaps because of the repressive military regimes that have governed the country throughout most of its history. Paraguay's second most important novelist is Gabriel Casaccia (pseudonym of Benigno Casaccia Bibolini, 1907–1980), who, like Roa Bastos, lived for many years in Argentina. Unlike his more famous compatriot, however, Casaccia preferred traditional literary forms to the innovative or the experimental. Casaccia's three most significant novels are *La babosa* (1952; the gossip [lit., the driveler]), *La llaga* (1963; the wound), and *Los exiliados* (1966; the exiles). Considered a landmark in Paraguayan fiction, *La babosa* emerges as the first novel of merit to attack the nation's political and social evils. The finely woven plot unfolds in a pueblo near Asunción (the capital), where the stifling atmosphere of petty vice and corruption is illustrated by two major characters, a gossipy spinster known as *La Babosa* and a vulgar, unscrupulous writer. The two plot threads of *La llaga* trace a conspiracy to overthrow a Paraguayan dictator and the Oedipus complex of a boy whose jealousy of his mother's lover brings about the defeat of the conspirators. Several characters of *La llaga* reappear in *Los exiliados*, in which generations of indolent, depraved Paraguayans plot in vain from Argentina to overthrow their government. *Los herederos* (1975; the heirs) and the posthumous *Las Huertas* (1981; the Huertas) continue Casaccia's depiction of Paraguay's deteriorating social structure.

Three additional Paraguayan writers, each of a different generation, are Jorge Rodolfo Ritter (b. 1914), Rubén Bareiro Saguier (b. 1930), and Lincoln Silva (b. 1945). Ritter's traditional social-protest novel *El pecho y la espalda* (1962; the chest and the back) describes the wretched conditions of ignorant, poverty-stricken peasants as seen through the eyes of a physician. Bareiro Saguier, a professor of Spanish American literature at the Sorbonne, is the author of a volume of poetically stylized stories entitled *Ojo por diente* (1973; eye for tooth), about repression and fear in contemporary Paraguay. And Silva has received critical acclaim for his *Rebelión después* (1970; rebellion afterward), a political novel replete with fantasy and black humor mocking the exaggerated nationalism of his compatriots.

Uruguay

Uruguay, one of Latin America's smallest nations, has produced more than its share of first-rate contemporary writers of fiction, among whom Juan Carlos Onetti (discussed above) stands out as the most significant. Enrique Amorim is mentioned briefly as a regionalist at the beginning of this chapter, but his subsequent novels serve as a bridge between regionalism and the more sophisticated urban, existential fiction of the 1950s. The previously noted *El caballo y su sombra* of 1941 confronts conservative traditions of the Uruguayan countryside with progressive economic forces introduced by European immigrants. The resultant agrarian reform and fusion of bloods, it is implied, will bring about progress in an isolated, backward nation. Additional novels by this prolific author include *Nueve lunas sobre Neuquén* (1945; nine moons over Neuquén), about political tensions caused by Nazi elements in Argentina during World War II; *La victoria no viene sola* (1952; victory doesn't come by itself), which treats a communist conspiracy to gain political power; *Corral abierto* (1956; open corral), a shocking portrayal of juvenile delinquency; and *Eva Burgos* (1960; Eva Burgos), an attack on legalized prostitution.

An intriguing contemporary of Onetti's was Felisberto Hernández (1902–1964), a concert pianist whose innovative short stories and novels contributed to the trend away from regionalism. "El cocodrilo" (the crocodile), in *Las hortensias* (1949; the hydrangeas), one of his most anthologized pieces, portrays a concert pianist who finds himself obliged to sell ladies' stockings in order to supplement his income, but even in this more remunerative occupation he must resort to compulsive weeping, a metaphor of defeat and alienation, in order to gain sympathy and support for his endeavor. Hernández was a master at creating absurd situations imbued with ambiguity, surrealistic symbolism, and demented logic. His musical prose, moreover, engages all the senses, revealing his unique perception of exterior reality and its effects on the mental processes. As illustrated by *El caballo perdido* (1943; the lost horse) and the posthumous *Tierras de la memoria* (1965; lands of memory), his novels evoke the subconscious past of his boyhood, often in the guise of humorous or fantastic anecdotes.

Uruguay's two finest contemporary writers, aside from Onetti, are Carlos Martínez Moreno (b. 1917) and Mario Benedetti (b. 1920). A critic, journalist, and lawyer as well as a distinguished man of letters, Martínez Moreno has published several collections of short stories in addition to the novels that have earned him his reputation. Much of *Paredón* (1963; execution wall) takes place in revolutionary Cuba, where a Uruguayan journalist is sent to cover a political execution. The major thrust of the book, however, is the sharp contrast it shows between the vitality of Cuba in the early stages of the Castro regime and the lethargy of Uruguay during this same period.[4] This theme also emerges from *Con las primeras luces* (1966; with the first lights), which describes the death of its decadent protagonist, a symbol not only of the Uruguayan aristocracy, but of the entire country. Another excellent example of Martínez Moreno's work is *Coca* (1970; cocaine), which narrates in retrospect the adventures of three drug pushers after they are caught in Montevideo. And in his more recent semidocumentary *El color que el infierno me escondiera* (1981; the color that hell concealed from me), Martínez Moreno marshals his considerable arsenal of narrative strategies to dramatize the nightmarish violence perpetrated by the military government of his besieged homeland. In their entirety these novels reveal a mature, consummate artist who has yet to receive the intercontinental critical accolades he deserves.

Benedetti has much in common with Martínez Moreno, but he is even more versatile—poet, essayist, and literary historian as well as short-story writer and novelist—and more militant than his colleague. He also appears to be more closely aligned with existential literature, as demonstrated by his portraits of solitary middle-class office workers (he himself was one) whose lives are devoid of meaning and purpose. Benedetti is perhaps best known for his compact, finely crafted short fiction, his most widely acclaimed collections being *Esta Mañana, y otros cuen-*

4. For many years Uruguay was a stable, prosperous democracy, often touted as the Switzerland of Latin America. In the late 1950s, however, the nation's vitality was sapped by a sagging economy, and a decade later its very foundations were shaken by a group of urban guerrillas known as the Tupamaros, all of which led to brutal repression and the establishment of a dictatorial regime.

tos (1949; this morning, and other stories), characterized by violence, irony, and occasional acerbity; *Montevideanos* (1959; Montevideans), which describes middle-class frustrations in a static social ambience; and *La muerte y otras sorpresas* (1968; death and other surprises), more universal in its incursions into fantasy and the darker side of the human psyche. Benedetti's best-known novels are *La tregua* (1960; *The Truce*, 1969) and *Gracias por el fuego* (1965; thanks for the light). Written in the form of a diary, the former exposes the inner world of a bored, middle-aged office worker approaching retirement. A widower with several grown children, he is granted a "truce" in his struggle against solitude in the form of an affair with a younger woman, but his brief happiness ends tragically with her sudden death. *Gracias por el fuego* strikes a similar chord of pessimism through its depiction of a newspaper magnate's son whose weakness and ultimate suicide reflect a bourgeois establishment unable or unwilling to cope with the nation's mounting problems. Benedetti's own revolutionary fervor comes to light in his more recent novels: *El cumpleaños de Juan Ángel* (1971; Juan Ángel's birthday), a powerful, poetically conceived account of the Tupamaro uprising; and *Primavera con una esquina rota* (1982; spring with a broken corner), about a conspirator who serves five years in prison for attempting to overthrow the government, and who, upon his release, discovers the impossibility of resuming previous personal relationships. *Geografías* (1984; geographies) is another of Benedetti's first-rate collections of short stories, the principal topics of these pieces being the fears, frustrations, and haunting memories of Uruguayan political exiles, most of whom fled their homeland after the military takeover in 1973.

Two promising Uruguayans of the younger generation are Eduardo Galeano (b. 1940) and Cristina Peri Rossi (b. 1941). A precocious journalist during his youth in both Montevideo and Buenos Aires, Galeano achieved international recognition for his best-selling historical overview of Latin American underdevelopment entitled *Las venas abiertas de América Latina* (1971; *Open Veins of Latin America*, 1973). His collections of stories, which also stress social and political themes, include

Los fantasmas del día del león (1967; the phantoms of the day of the lion) and *Vagamundos* (1973; wanderworld). Galeano's most significant novels to date are *La canción de nosotros* (1975; our song) and *Días y noches de amor y de guerra* (1978; *Days and Nights of Love and War*, 1983). Like so much recent Uruguayan fiction, *La canción de nosotros* attempts to define the acute political and economic crisis in the country, in this case by juxtaposing plot threads and historical fragments describing the horrors of life under a brutal dictatorship. *Días y noches de amor y de guerra* utilizes a similar technique, consisting of disjointed accounts of the author-narrator's experiences as a political activist throughout Latin America. Galeano not only denounces oppression but also eulogizes the exploits of revolutionary heroes like, for example, those of Che Guevara in Cuba, Guatemala, and Bolivia. This passionately written book is impressive in its broad narrative scope and moving in its plea for solidarity against the forces of tyranny. In the first part of a projected trilogy, *Memoria del fuego: I, Los nacimientos* (1983; *Memory of Fire: I, Genesis*, 1985), Galeano combines essay, history, and fiction to depict the violently jolting traditions of the New World, from indigenous myths to the savage conquest by the Spaniards who, masking their lust for gold under the guise of Christian fervor, enslaved the Indians and destroyed their cultures.

Peri Rossi is more poetic than Galeano but equally militant and iconoclastic. Better known as a short-story writer than a novelist, she prefers the artistic concentration and compactness of the shorter genre. Her first volume of tales, *Viviendo* (1963; living), traces the lives of three female protagonists, all of whom suffer from lack of will to act and thus influence their own destinies. The end result in all three cases is estrangement and loneliness. *Los museos abandonados* (1969; the abandoned museums), Peri Rossi's second collection, describes objects in empty museums as metaphors of a rotten, mummified past that must be erased; indeed, in the title story two young lovers destroy statues and desecrate treasures of ancient civilizations. Another piece from this same collection, "Los extraños objetos voladores" (the strange flying objects), describes in realistic detail the appearance in the sky of a large brown mass symbolizing the nihilistic forces threatening Uruguay. Peri Rossi's surrealistic and overtly political novel *El libro de mis primos* (1969; the book of my cousins) has been praised by critics as one of the most imaginative works of fiction ever published by a Uruguayan.

3 ▪ POETRY

Prior to the 1960s Spanish America's literary achievements were, in general, greater in poetry than in prose fiction. Many possible reasons for this phenomenon have been suggested, including the passionate, lyrical nature of the Latin, the spectacular landscape of the continent, and the compelling need to escape from the harsh political and economic realities of the region. In addition, Spanish American poets have traditionally been rewarded with posts in the diplomatic and consular services of their countries, so that they were brought into contact with new ideas and perhaps inspired to create universal works of art years before the demise of regionalism in the novel. Poetry in Latin America, then, has been, and probably still is, a more respected form of cultural expression than it is in the United States.

Although the ivory-tower, art-for-art's-sake stance of Spanish American *modernismo*, which dominated poetry for almost three decades prior to World War I, revitalized the language and expanded literary horizons, its excessive ornamentation was soon to give way to *postmodernismo*, marked by a trend toward simplicity and greater concern for the here and now. Another movement, known as *vanguardismo*, appeared almost simultaneously, but its practitioners were more radical in their rejection of the past, finding inspiration in contemporary European movements such as cubism, dadaism, surrealism, and expressionism. In the Hispanic world this avant-garde school became known by a variety of names: *ultraísmo* in Spain and Argentina, *estridentismo* in Mexico, *creacionismo* in Chile. The *vanguardistas* broke with previously established verse forms and made the metaphor the key to poetic expression. They also abandoned rhyme, anecdote, and logical syntax for the free association of ideas and images, and, especially in Argentina, they advocated the omission of conjunctions, connective phrases, and superfluous adjectives. Like dadaism and surrealism, moreover, *vanguardismo* is characterized by occasional doses of grotesque humor and sadistic violence. Other *vanguardistas*, usually Marxists or anarchists, wrote in a more realistic vein, assailing social evils and stressing the necessity of reform. Thus, during the 1920s and 1930s numerous literary coteries throughout the continent, each with its own journalistic forum, expressed not only a common striving for a new poetics, but also a commitment to social justice.

In their entirety the various poetic currents between the 1930s and the 1960s are often referred to as *postvanguardismo*. As stated in chapter 1, this broadly based label encompasses many elements carried over from *vanguardismo*, including most of the latter's formal innovations as well as its emphasis on surrealistic imagery, free association, and, on occasion, automatic writing. The *postvanguardistas* also introduced existentialist themes such as solitude, anguish over the passing of time, and absurdity, all of which they conveyed in styles ranging from the simple and direct to the philosophically abstract and obscure. Another type of poetry that came into its own during this period derives from the popular Afro-Caribbean culture, with its primitive myths, exotic sounds, and sensual rhythms. And the practitioners of *poesía pura* (pure poetry) emphasized stylistic precision, intellectual control over emotion, and the elimination of verbosity, ornamentation, and anecdote.

Although, as stated above, the quality of Spanish American poetry prior to the 1960s surpassed that of prose fiction, the novel and short story have enjoyed greater prestige since the advent of the boom. The poetry of the past two decades is difficult to categorize, not only because of its large volume and variety, but also because of its constant and rapid evolution, which differs from country to country. Nevertheless, one can clearly distinguish several groups: the revolutionary Marxist poets, based primarily in Cuba; the surrealists, with their emphasis on incongruous, dreamlike images; the more introspective, abstract existentialists; and the absurdists, who mock reason by depicting irrational or chaotic situations in concrete, unpoetic language.

The two most important twentieth-century poets who ended their careers prior to 1941 are Nicaragua's Rubén Darío and Peru's César Vallejo. The leader of the *modernista* school, Darío epitomizes this group's formal innovations—often inspired by the French Parnassians and symbolists—and its quest for sensual, exotic beauty. In his youth Vallejo, Spanish America's *vanguardista* poet par excellence, felt the influence of the *modernistas*, but even in his first published collection, *Los heraldos negros* (1918; the black messengers), he began to discard the decorative, sonorous verses and opulent rhetoric of the *modernistas* for popular speech patterns, indigenous themes, and episodes based on everyday life. *Trilce* (1922; *Trilce*, 1973) shattered all traditions in Spanish American poetry with its tortured view of Peru and, by implication, of the world. One year after its publication Vallejo abandoned his native land for France, where he spent the rest of his life, except for a two-year sojourn in Spain and visits to the Soviet Union and other East European countries. He joined the Communist Party in 1931 and during the Spanish Civil War lent his support to the Republican cause. His best poetry written in Europe, most of which was published posthumously, appears in *Poemas humanos* (1939; *Poemas humanos/Human Poems*, 1968) and *España, aparte de mí este cáliz* (1939; *Spain, Take This Cup From Me*, 1974).

Throughout his work one of Vallejo's major recurring themes is his search for love, justice, and permanent values in a world with which he remains perpetually at odds. Bitterly ironic and, on occasion, darkly humorous, *Trilce* conveys a sense of neurotic frustration, urgency, and pent-up emotion engendered by violent inner conflicts and reflected by syntactical distortions, irregular rhythms, and hermetic imagery. Vallejo displays the height of his poetic powers in his masterful posthumous works, which move away from the self-absorption and stylistic obscurity of *Trilce* to express his pleas for social justice and fraternal love in more accessible forms. Despite his avowed allegiance to Marxism, he never uses his art to impart communist dogma; rather he suggests that man's salvation can occur only through a basic transformation of human nature. Critics generally agree that his legacy to subsequent generations of Spanish American poets has been immeasurable.

MAJOR POETS

Eight Spanish American poets of the post-1941 period have emerged as the most significant practitioners of the genre. Exceptionally talented, innovative, and highly acclaimed by literary critics and the reading public, they have irreversibly altered the course of Spanish American poetry, achieved wide international recognition, and entered the mainstream of contemporary world literature. These poets are discussed below in chronological order according to their dates of birth.

GABRIELA MISTRAL

A rural schoolteacher, university professor, and educational administrator for many years before she gained international recognition, the Chilean Gabriela Mistral (pseudonym of Lucila Godoy Alcayaga, 1889–1957) was invited to Mexico in the early 1920s as a consultant for the education reform being implemented on the heels of the Mexican revolution. Soon thereafter she joined the diplomatic service, representing the Chilean government in countries throughout Europe and the Western Hemisphere. In 1945 she became the first Latin American to be awarded the Nobel Prize for literature. Her most significant collections of poems include *Desolación* (1922; desolation), *Ternura* (1924; tenderness), *Tala* (1938; devastation), and *Lagar* (1954; wine press).

The principal theme of *Desolación* is the author's anguish over the suicide of the young man she had hoped to marry, but in these poems she also describes the spectacular Chilean landscape and expresses her faith in God, often in terms of biblical images. *Ternura* presents a series of unadorned, finely crafted verses for children, for whom Mistral showed special affection throughout her life. The grief she felt at the death of her mother inspired many of the poems in *Tala*, and *Lagar*, her last book, contains her most metaphysical verses, the overriding themes here being the passing of time and the escape from its physical and mental ravages through insanity or death.

Usually cited as prime examples of *postmodernismo*, Mistral's poems express her love—spiritual rather than sensual—for all humanity, especially children and the humble, as well as for God and nature. Her style is characterized by lyrical intimacy, frank simplicity, and a wealth of metaphors which serve to illuminate her innermost subjective world.

VICENTE HUIDOBRO

Along with César Vallejo and Pablo Neruda, Vicente Huidobro is considered among the three most influential Spanish American poets of the twentieth century. Born into a wealthy Chilean family, he learned French as a child from French governesses. In 1916 he traveled to Paris, where he collaborated with Guillaume Apollinaire, Pierre Reverdy, Tristan Tzara, and others in the publication of the avant-garde literary journal *Nord-Sud*. A prolific, cosmopolitan author of some thirty collections of poems—several written in French—as well as novels, plays, and essays, Huidobro became the principal propagator of avant-garde ideas and techniques throughout Latin America. In defense of his ardent political liberalism, he also fought for the Republican cause in the Spanish Civil War and served with distinction as a captain in the French army during World War II. His death in Chile several years later probably resulted from head wounds suffered in combat.

Huidobro is perhaps best known for his aesthetics of *creacionismo* (creationism), which he sets forth in his essay *Non serviam* (1914; I shall not be a slave) and in his famous poem "Arte poética" (poetic art), in *El espejo de agua* (1916; the mirror of water). In these literary manifestos he compares the poet to a god whose task is to create reality, not to imitate it. Thus, just as nature utilizes its resources to create a tree, the poet should create a poem by making exhaustive use of figurative language, especially the metaphor. The end result of *creacionismo*, he contends, should be an original, autonomous reality, free of the constraints of literary rules and conventions.

Canciones en la noche (1913; songs in the night) and *Adán* (1916; Adam) both contain experimental poems arranged on the page in the form of pictographs, perhaps visual conceits of a fragmented civilization suggested by cubistic paintings. Also experimental by nature were *Poemas árticos* (1918; *Arctic Poems*, 1974) and *Ecuatorial* (1918; equatorial), the former representing futuristic visual images of modern technology, and the latter depicting the ravages of war-torn Europe in absurd but strikingly original metaphors. In these works, too, words are arranged spatially in order to link poetry with painting and thus heighten its visual and emotional impact. Like that of Huidobro's previous poetry, the style of these collections is characterized by the use of humorous puns, neologisms, reiteration, and onomatopoeia.

Critics generally consider *Altazor; o, El viaje en paracaídas* (1931; Altazor; or, the trip in a parachute) as Huidobro's masterpiece. An existential quest not only for personal identity and salvation, but also for a new poetic language, this experimental work alludes to man's archetypal Fall, the protagonist's name representing a combination of *alto* (high) and *azor* (goshawk). In reality, the description of Altazor's downward flight, a literary tour de force lasting through seven cantos, emerges as a metaphor of the poet's descent into the depths of his own psyche and his confrontation with death and nothingness. The spiritual anguish of Altazor (Huidobro's alter ego) derives from his realization that despite his innovative efforts, he is unable to free himself completely from the tyranny of traditional language and thought patterns.

Huidobro's last two major books, *Ver y palpar* (1941; see and touch) and *El ciudadano del olvido* (1941; the citizen of oblivion), both convey a tone of despair brought about by the threat of death. In its entirety, his oeuvre represents the annihilation of objective reality and the creation, in its place, of a new, ideal world of art envisioned by the poet. Despite his admiration for the surrealists, Huidobro rejects their theory of automatic writing, preferring to exert rational control over the creative process, even in his most experimental writings. As Spanish America's first avant-garde poet, he is perhaps more universal than Chilean in his world outlook. His universality is demonstrated by his desire to renovate modern poetry and his militant concern for the welfare of humanity.

JORGE LUIS BORGES

Borges's short fiction, which established his international reputation, is discussed in the preceding chapter. His poetry also represents an important segment of his oeuvre, not only because it stands on its own merit—Borges himself believes he is more likely to be remembered first as a poet—but also because its themes and stylistic devices reappear in the short stories. Borges joined the avant-garde *ultraísta* poets in Spain immediately after World War I and brought *ultraísmo* to Argentina in 1921 upon his return home after seven years in Europe. The movement was of short duration in Argentina, perhaps because Borges himself never completely succumbed to its cult of the startling metaphor. Instead, he concentrated on his nostalgia for the Argentine past and his aesthetic and philosophical preoccupations in his first three collections of poems: *Fervor de Buenos Aires* (1923; fervor of Buenos Aires), *Luna de enfrente* (1925; moon across the way), and *Cuadernos de San Juan* (1929; San Juan notebooks). Highlights of these collections include three poems in *Fervor de Buenos Aires*: "Patio" ("Patio"), which describes the serene, comforting refuge of a patio at sundown; "Amanecer" ("Daybreak"), based on the idealist-inspired premise that Buenos Aires is in danger of disappearing because few, if any, of the city's inhabitants are sufficiently awake to preserve it in the mind's eye; "El general Quiroga va en coche al muere" ("General Quiroga Rides to His Death in a Carriage"), about the assassination of a well-known Argentine gaucho general of the nineteenth century; and one in *Luna de enfrente*: "Jactancia de quietud" ("Bragging of Stillness"), a statement on the inadequacy of language to reproduce reality. (The translations of these poems appear in *Selected Poems, 1923–1967*, 1973.)

After concentrating primarily on the essay and the short story for well over two decades, Borges returned to poetry after he lost his sight in the mid-1950s. Although his more recent poems treat metaphysical themes similar to those of his youth, he has tended to utilize a simpler, more conversational vocabulary and syntax and has shown a preference for classical meters, which are easier for him to memorize than blank verse. One also detects in his later poems a more intimate tone, underscoring his philosophical meditations on time, death, solitude, and daily frustrations. Borges's collections during the second phase of his poetry include *El hacedor* (1960; *Dreamtigers*, 1964) and *Elogio de la sombra* (1969; *In Praise of Darkness*, 1974), both of which contain short prose pieces; *El otro, el mismo* (1969; the other, the self); *El oro de los tigres* (1972; *The Gold of the Tigers*, 1977); *La rosa profunda* (1975; the deep rose); *La moneda de hierro* (1976; the iron coin); and *Rosa y azul* (1977; pink and blue).

One of Borges's most famous poems, "El otro tigre" ("The Other Tiger"), in *El hacedor*, expresses his despair over the limitations of language as a means of capturing reality when he realizes that the tiger he envisions, the one depicted in his poem, and the real animal are three entirely different creatures. "Los espejos" ("Mirrors"), also from *El hacedor*, describes his well-known horror of mirrors because they disintegrate concrete reality and make him feel like "a reflection and a mere vanity." "Laberinto" ("Labyrinth"), in *Elogio de la sombra*, sketches his view of the world as a mazelike prison through which man wanders, victimized by chance, until he meets his ironbound fate. And in "El remordimiento" (remorse), in *La moneda de hierro*, Borges laments his failure to achieve true happiness, the result, he believes, of his single-minded, lifelong dedication to literature.

NICOLÁS GUILLÉN

Nicolás Guillén is a mulatto whose works reflect the Afro-Cuban culture as well as his vehement protest against all forms of oppression. He was born in the province of Camagüey, the son of a politician who was murdered when Guillén was still a teenager. After studying law for a short time in Havana, he worked as a printer and journalist while writing verses inspired by romanticism and by the *modernista* poet Rubén Darío. His literary reputation was established by his first three collections of poems: *Motivos de son* (1930; Cuban dance motifs), *Sóngoro Cosongo* (1931; Sóngoro Cosongo), and *West Indies Ltd*. (1934; English title). After joining the Communist Party in 1937, Guillén traveled widely throughout the Western world and the Soviet Union. Because of his left-wing political activities, he lived in exile for many years prior to the Cuban revolution, but in 1959 he returned to his homeland, where he has been an ardent supporter of Fidel Castro. He is generally considered Cuba's best living poet and the poet laureate of the Cuban revolution.

Motivos de son captures the rhythm, humor, and sensuality of the *son* (a popular Cuban dance) in the Afro-Cuban dialect, many words of which have lost their meanings but survive solely for their musical sounds. Although the poems of *Sóngoro Cosongo* contain many of the same elements, here the author's voice also rises in vigorous protest against oppression throughout the world. The protest theme becomes even more strident in *West Indies Ltd.*, which cries out for the solidarity of all downtrodden people. In *España: Poema en cuatro angustias y una esperanza* (1937; Spain: poem in four anguishes and one hope) Guillén demonstrates his support for the Spanish Republic, and *Cantos para soldados y sones para turistas* (songs for soldiers and dances for tourists), which was published the same year, portrays soldiers as blind instruments of imperialism and rich American tourists as ludicrous revelers who visit Cuba only to drink, gamble, and engage in illicit sex.

Guillén's more recent collections include *La paloma de vuelo popular* (1958; the dove of popular flight), a grouping of political poems about injustice, racism, and right-wing fanaticism, with special emphasis on the desegregation issue in the United States; *Elegías* (1958; elegies), which evokes episodes from the author's youth in Camagüey and the awakening of his idealistic fervor; *Tengo* (1964; *Tengo*, 1974), a celebration of the Cuban revolution's accomplishments—education, employment, and medical programs—and the simple pleasures that have accrued to the common man since the departure of the foreign imperialist; and *El gran zoo* (1967; *Patria o Muerte! The Great Zoo, and Other Poems*, 1972), a series of poeticized fables satirizing human conduct.

In its initial stages Guillén's oeuvre resonates with primitive sounds and rhythms, giving artistic expression to the Afro-Cuban culture via poetic devices such as onomatopoeia, alliteration, and counterpoint phrasing. As it evolves, however, his poetry becomes more universal in both form and content. A revolutionary at heart, Guillén chides his compatriots for their submission to exploitation and goads the Cuban blacks into demanding racial equality. Though humorous, colorful, and seemingly unsophisticated for the benefit of a wide reading public, his works are the product of a serious man of letters who has successfully fused folk art with an impassioned commitment to social justice.

JORGE CARRERA ANDRADE

Jorge Carrera Andrade (1903–1978), Ecuador's best twentieth-century poet, studied law in Quito and then, during the 1920s, attended universities in England, Spain, Germany, and France. He became particularly fond of French literature after reading the romantic and symbolist writers and had a personal acquaintance with many of the surrealists. Upon his return to Ecuador he entered the diplomatic service, representing his country for many years throughout Latin America, the United States, Europe, and the Orient. He was also Ecuador's ambassador to the United Nations and its representative to UNESCO.

Carrera Andrade's early poems display the decorative trappings of the modernist school, but he is usually associated with *postmodernismo* and *vanguardismo*. His mature works reveal three basic ingredients: the ubiquitous, striking metaphor, usually a vehicle for illuminating the visual reality of nature and everyday life; a strong note of social protest, indicating his compassionate concern for the downtrodden; and a tragic awareness of his own solitude, underscored by his search for spiritual values. Carrera Andrade's first major collection is *La guirnalda del silencio* (1926; the wreath of silence), which was published on the eve of his departure for Europe. *Boletines de mar y tierra* (1930; bulletins of sea and land) reflects his sojourn in Europe as well as his increasingly universal outlook. The plight of the Ecuadorian Indian and the approaching world crisis emerge as major preoccupations in *Tiempo manual* (1935; manual time). The author turns inward in *País secreto* (1940; secret country), revealing for the first time the introspective side of his nature and his acute sense of loneliness. And *El hombre planetario* (1959; the planetary man), considered by many readers as his masterpiece, seems to renew his faith in the fraternal bonds cementing human relations. Another theme presented in this and subsequent collections is the threat of modern mechanization to individual freedom and self-fulfillment.

Although Carrera Andrade's use of the metaphor links him to the *vanguardistas*, he eschews the contrived, obscure image typical of *vanguardismo* and seldom, if ever, deforms reality. One of his favorite leitmotifs is the window, a representation of the perspective from which he, the author, views his poetically stylized world. Despite his admiration of the surrealists, he rejects their concentration on subconscious states, preferring instead to dissolve conscious sensory experience into brilliantly lucid metaphors. He also maintains that Europeans can afford to deny reason but that Latin Americans, coming from chaos, must strive to give order to the universe.

Fundamentally Carrera Andrade's works reveal an optimist who, despite mounting world tensions, envisions the future as a utopia destined to evolve from human goodness and reason. He disapproves of existentialism and antiliterature because of their excessive emphasis on anguish and absurdity. The serenity and hope that characterize much of his work are especially evident in his ingeniously conceived "micrograms," poems of one short stanza, usually consisting of a single metaphor. The numerous translations of his poems attest to his recognition as a universal man of letters. Indeed, it has been said that Carrera Andrade began his career with the province as his world and ended it with the world as his province.

PABLO NERUDA

Born and raised in southern Chile, Pablo Neruda (pseudonym of Neftalí Reyes Basualto) studied at the University of Chile in Santiago, where he published several volumes of neoromantic lyric poetry. The most successful of these, *Veinte poemas de amor y una canción desesperada* (1924; *Twenty Love Poems and a Song of Despair*, 1969) established his reputation as an important talent among the young generation of Chilean writers. Another major work, *Tentativa del hombre infinito* (1926; attempt of the infinite man) represents a transitional phase between the lucid *Veinte poemas* and the dense, hermetic style characteristic of Neruda's next phase. In 1927 Neruda joined the diplomatic corps and for five years represented his nation's government in various parts of the Orient. During this time he wrote the first volume of his famous surrealistic masterwork, *Residencia en la tierra* (1933; *Residence on Earth*, 1946). (The second and third volumes of *Residencia en la tierra* appeared in 1935 and 1947, and their respective English translations in 1946 and 1973.) He served his country in Spain during the mid-1930s and, upon witnessing the Civil War, published *España en el corazón* (1937; *Spain in the Heart*, in *Residence on Earth, and Other Poems*, 1946). Heretofore Neruda's poetry had been narcissistically concerned with himself, but in *España en el corazón* he gave vent to his impassioned political beliefs, assailing General Franco and his followers for betraying the Republic and committing unwarranted acts of cruelty.

In 1943 Neruda visited Macchu Picchu, the ancient Inca fortress city in Peru, and wrote his moving surrealist poem *Alturas de Macchu Picchu* (1943; *The Heights of Macchu Picchu*, 1967), in which he attempts to discover links with his indigenous ancestors, lost during the Spanish conquest. Increasingly active in politics during World War II, he joined the Communist Party in 1945 and the following year was elected to the Chilean senate. In 1949 he was forced into exile for a period of three years, during which time he wrote what some critics consider his best work, *Canto general* (1950; general song). This baroque, Marxist-oriented epic of Latin America traces the sins of history from the continent's paradisiacal, pre-

Columbian past to the present, emphasizing the heroic struggle for freedom against political tyranny, but also describing the spectacular beauty and grandeur of the region.

Odas elementales (1954; *Elementary Odes*, 1961) represents another phase in Neruda's oeuvre; here he abandons the grandiose tone of the epic for a more straightforward, down-to-earth mode of expression in order to describe, not without jocular irony, everyday objects such as a pair of socks, an artichoke, an onion, and an orange. Written for the enjoyment of all types of readers, these odes not only express the author's sense of wonder at the architectural precision of the most commonplace things, but also suggest the brotherhood of all men, each of whom can share Neruda's appreciation of nature.

Neruda's more recent works include *Nuevas odas elementales* (1956; new elementary odes); *Tercer libro de las odas* (1957; third book of odes); *Estravagario* (1958; *Extravagaria*, 1972), a return to the more personal themes of love and solitude; the five-volume, autobiographical *Memorial de la Isla Negra* (1964; *Isla Negra: A Notebook*, 1981); and a political essay, *Incitación al Nixoncidio y alabanza de la revolución chilena* (1973; *A Call for the Destruction of Nixon and Praise for the Chilean Revolution*, 1980). Soon after the election of Salvador Allende to the presidency in 1970 Neruda was named Chile's ambassador to France, a post he held until illness forced his return to Chile two years later. He died in Santiago less than two weeks after the September 11, 1973, military coup.

The author of more than thirty books, Neruda possessed a protean ability always to be in the vanguard of change. Indeed, he has been called the Picasso of modern poetry, a poet in perpetual revolt against his own previous work and in constant search for new modes of expression. Still, one can detect throughout the course of his career a fundamental conflict between his hermetic surrealism, which waxes and wanes periodically, and his desire to be a popular, politically committed spokesman for the common man. Amid his vast array of styles, moods, and cycles one can detect the following recurring themes and techniques: the sensual enjoyment of erotic love, nature, and the material world; the poet as an exponent of social change;

and the use of surrealistic imagery to capture subconscious states of mind.

As might be expected, numerous symbols and leitmotifs illuminate Neruda's imaginary world and serve as guideposts for his readers. Birds and butterflies, for example, represent liberation and hope; the sea suggests all-encompassing life; waves, however, symbolize the relentless flow of time, leading inevitably to devastation or death; bells are conveyors of optimism; the concept of fertility is expressed by a variety of concrete nouns including horses, bees, bread, and grapes; and swords stand for virility, heroism, and adventure. Negative motifs include ashes, dust, salt, the suspended wheel going nowhere, and dampness, which evokes a cloying, intangible menace.

Neruda's wide variety of styles is illustrated by *Residencia en la tierra*. In the first volume the poem entitled "Galope muerto" ("Dead Gallop") sets the underlying pessimistic tone, with its somber metaphors and chaotic syntax depicting man's headlong dash toward oblivion. The second volume of *Residencia en la tierra* utilizes a more direct, almost narrative technique to convey the author's gradual resignation to the impending catastrophe. And in the third volume his political and social commitment glimmers with a ray of hope unseen heretofore in this masterpiece.

In the course of his literary career Neruda alternated between classical meters, free verse, and experimental forms to express moods ranging from the lyrical and the didactic to the ironic and the absurd. Because he has left his personal mark on virtually every major trend in modern Spanish American poetry, he is generally regarded as the continent's leading twentieth-century practitioner of the genre.

OCTAVIO PAZ

Octavio Paz, Mexico's most esteemed man of letters and a frequent candidate for the Nobel Prize, strikes the reader as healthy and well-adjusted in comparison to the neurotic Vallejo and the deeply troubled Neruda of *Residencia en la tierra*. The son of a left-wing lawyer, Paz studied at the National University in Mexico City and, with the publication of *Luna silvestre* (1933; wild moon) and *¡No pasarán!* (1937; they shall not pass), emerged as a leading poet of the younger generation. While attending an international literary conference in Spain in 1937, he witnessed the Civil War, lending his support to the Republican cause. Back in Mexico, he helped to found two literary journals, *Taller* (workshop) and *El hijo pródigo* (the prodigal son), and in 1944 received a Guggenheim Fellowship for study in the United States. He spent the following year in France, where he met André Breton and other surrealists, who were to have a profound influence on his poetry. In 1946 he entered Mexico's diplomatic corps, representing his government in many different countries, including India, where he served as ambassador for six years. There he immersed himself in Indian philosophy, literature, and art. He resigned his ambassadorship, however, in protest against the Tlatelolco massacre in 1968. Since that time he has lectured at many foreign universities, published numerous collections of poems and essays, and won an impressive number of literary prizes. In recent years he has also edited two Mexican journals, *Plural* (plural) and *Vuelta* (return).

Paz has been influenced by a wide variety of movements, philosophies, and religions: Marxism (which he abandoned after the Hitler-Stalin pact of August 23, 1939), surrealism, existentialism, structuralism, Buddhism, and Hinduism. Still an ardent political liberal, he is equally critical of communism, capitalism, Mexico's monolithic one-party system, and all right-wing dictatorships. Perhaps the single most important theme in his poetry is his existential solitude, which he strives to overcome through erotic love and aesthetic creativity. A major cause of human solitude, he believes, is chronological time, because it traps man in its unrelenting flow and carries him ever further from his paradisiacal past. Thus Paz seeks to capture an all-encompassing moment of dizzying ecstasy outside of time, a moment of epiphany that will annul humdrum reality and germinate a vast, magnificent realm in which, like the one envisioned by the surrealists, opposites are synthesized and

contradictions eliminated. Much of Paz's poetry, then, represents a search for liberation from the baggage of history in
order to permit the emergence of the suppressed self and the
creation of a new aesthetic.

Two of Paz's major surrealistic collections are *Libertad bajo
palabra* (1949; freedom under the word) and *¿Águila o sol?* (1951;
Eagle or Sun?, 1970); the former fuses objective reality and
dream in disciplined classical meters, and the latter achieves
similar results by exploring Mexico's mythical past in a grouping of brief prose poems. Paz's most famous poetic creation is
Piedra de sol (1957; *Sun Stone*, 1963), the title of which refers
to the massive Aztec stone calendar on display in the Museum
of Anthropology in Mexico City. The embodiment of the infinite
Aztec universe, this circular calendar is reflected in the circular
structure of the poem whose task, according to Paz, is to awaken
dormant, time-laden matter (the stone) through contact with
liberating light (the sun) and, in so doing, resuscitate an ancient
civilization shrouded in darkness. Also integrated into the poem
are elements of the author's personal life and metaphysical
questions about man's place in the universe.

Blanco (1967; *Blanco*, 1971) is generally considered Paz's
most difficult work. Patterned according to structuralist principles, this poem draws comparisons between the creative process and the sex act and, simultaneously, conveys the author's
haunting desire to express the inexpressible and remake the
world on his own terms. Like Borges, Paz is obsessed with the
image of the mirror, which, he believes, reminds us that we
are both real and insubstantial. He also states that the poet
can discover the other self—and thus achieve self-re-creation
—in the body of the woman he loves as well as in the poem he
strives to create. *Ladera este* (1969; in *Configurations*, 1971)
reflects Paz's sojourn in India and his fascination with Oriental
philosophy, especially Hinduism. (The literal translation of the
title is "east slope.") Perhaps the outstanding poem of this
collection and one of the author's best is "Viento entero" ("Whole
Wind"), which arrests the flow of time by juxtaposing images
of contrasting civilizations, resulting in a dynamic synthesis of
cultural opposites. Two of Paz's more recent collections, *Pasado*

en claro (1975; *A Draft of Shadows*, 1979) and *Vuelta* (1976; return), restate his preoccupations with language, love, and metaphysical questions. Like many of his previous works, these also place considerable demands on the reader, obliging him to re-create obscure passages and, at times, entire poems.

Paz's many books of literary criticism and theory include *El arco y la lira* (1956; *The Bow and the Lyre*, 1973), an exceedingly perceptive analysis of poetry as language and social phenomenon; *Las peras del olmo* (1956; the pears of the elm), studies of several Mexican authors; and *Cuadrivio* (1965; quadrivium), which elucidates the works of four Hispanic poets. In both his poetry and his poetics he presents an ennobling vision of twentieth-century existential man, who has become separated from his true self in an intimidating, technological world. Paz's utopian dream of restoring wholeness and unity to the psyche through the dialectics of love and creativity illustrates his fundamental optimism. His brilliant use of imagery to evolve concepts relevant to the present-day human experience makes him Spanish America's most admired living poet.

NICANOR PARRA

During the years between Mistral's death in 1957 and Neruda's in 1973 only Nicanor Parra (b. 1914) was able to withstand Neruda's suffocating dominance of Chilean poetry. Since Neruda's demise, Parra has been his nation's leading poetic voice as well as one of Spanish America's most popular and esteemed men of letters. He was born in southern Chile, the son of a schoolteacher, and graduated in 1938 from the University of Chile in Santiago with a degree in mathematics and physics. After teaching in high school for several years, he attended graduate school at Brown and Oxford universities. Since 1952 he has been a professor of mathematics at his alma mater. A committed leftist, he has visited the Soviet Union, other countries of Eastern Europe, and Cuba. In recent years he has also emerged as a vociferous environmentalist, warning his compatriots of the dire consequences of pollution and the nuclear arms race.

Cancionero sin nombre (1937; songbook without a name), many of whose poems have been set to music, combines lyricism and humor to evoke real-life scenes occasionally shaded by fantasy. Of far greater significance is *Poemas y antipoemas* (1954; *Poems and Antipoems*, 1967), which initiated the author's career as a nontraditional antipoet. *La cueca larga* (1958; the long *cueca* [Chile's national dance]) suggests not only the musical rhythms of the *cueca* and the coarse humor and sensuality of the Chilean peasant, but also the latter's frustration and anguish. Other major collections of Parra's antipoems are *Versos de salón* (1962; drawing-room verses), *Canciones rusas* (1962; Russian songs), and *Artefactos* (1972; artifacts). His *Sermones y prédicas del Cristo de Elqui* (1977) and *Nuevos sermones y prédicas del Cristo de Elqui* (1979), both translated in *Sermons and Homilies of the Christ of Elqui* (1985), present the ironic thoughts and oratory of a twentieth-century itinerant preacher.

More than any other major Spanish American, Parra epitomizes the practitioner of antipoetry, which, as the term implies, rejects traditional poetic forms and signals a reexamination of the purpose and nature of the genre. Thus, his language tends to be unadorned, concrete, and direct; he has also reinstated the anecdote, relating everyday occurrences in a conversational tone, deliberately devoid of grandiloquence, solemnity, and sentimentalism. Parra's themes are basically existential in nature: the absurdity of routine daily life; the failure of the bourgeois establishment and man-made institutions; the impossibility of lasting love; and the tragedy of physical deterioration, death, and nothingness. Another fundamental ingredient in his works is humor, which ranges from gentle irony and parody to absurdity, biting satire, and grotesque tragicomedy. These elements are often rendered through the juxtaposition of sharply contrasting images, occasionally surrealistic, and frequent shifts in the narrative perspective. The psychological distance resulting from the informal tone of the speaker, usually Parra himself, and his haunting visions of doom provide an additional source of irony and tension.

Parra's characters, not surprisingly, are antiheroes such as those of the following poems in *Poemas y antipoemas*: "Autorretrato" ("Self-portrait"), which describes an aging, disillusioned, and overworked professor; "La víbora" ("The Viper"), about the love-hate relationship between the abused speaker and a vicious, domineering woman; "Mil novecientos treinta" ("Nineteen Thirty"), a listing of the injustices and horrors plaguing much of the world in a single year's time frame; and "Padre nuestro" ("Lord's Prayer"), in which the poet absolves God for the evil he has perpetrated.

As an enemy of tradition, Parra removes poetry from its conventional molds, making it a vehicle of protest against a corrupt, technological society that, in his view, has dehumanized his fellow men. At the same time his use of satire, anecdote, and direct, colloquial language appeals to large numbers of readers, perhaps because they can readily identify with the absurd, everyday situations he depicts. Parra's humor and irony, however, conceal deeply imbedded feelings of indignation and despair which occasionally surface in phrases such as "El mundo moderno es una gran cloaca" ("the modern world is a big sewer"), a conclusion he reaches in "Los vicios del mundo moderno" ("The Vices of the Modern World"), in *Poemas y antipoemas*. His works do not represent a search for truth, but rather an imaginative look at a hidden, but all too real, side of life as well as a radically different concept of the artistic endeavor.

AND MANY OTHERS

MEXICO

In Mexico the works of Enrique González Martínez (1871–1952) and Ramón López Velarde (1888–1921) best exemplify the wealth of fine poetry written during the *postmodernista* period. González Martínez's famous "Tuércele el cuello al cisne" ("Wring the Neck of the Swan," in G. Dundas Craig, ed., *The Modernist Trend in Spanish American Poetry*, 1971), published in *Los senderos ocultos* (1911; the hidden paths), expresses his desire to replace the superficial artistry of *modernismo* with a movement of deeper philosophical content symbolized by the meditative owl; "La suave patria" (gentle fatherland), in *El son del corazón* (1932; the sound of the heart), by López Velarde, represents a richly symbolic, impressionistic mural that not only captures the essence of Mexican life, but also marks a break with the preceding generation. Another poet of this same generation is José Juan Tablada (1871–1945), whose experimental verses in *El jarro de flores* (1922; the pitcher of flowers) were inspired by Japanese haiku (brief evocative poems).

The Mexican *vanguardistas* split into two groups: the *estridentistas* (the strident ones), who were influenced by Italian futurism and Spanish *ultraísmo*; and the *contemporáneos* (contemporaries), who tended to ignore social issues and concentrated on aesthetic questions such as the manipulation of free verse and the creation of fresh imagery. The most important of the *estridentistas* is Manuel Maples Arce (b. 1898), a man of vast culture and, as illustrated by his *Poemas interdictos* (1927; forbidden poems), an experimental poet intrigued with the marvels of modern technology. The influence of the *contemporáneos* was more far-reaching than that of the *estridentistas*. Inspired by González Martínez, López Velarde, and Tablada as well as by the French surrealists and other European movements, the *contemporáneos* sought to reveal the universal in the Mexican experience, their leading members being Carlos Pellicer (1899–1977), José Gorostiza (1901–1973), Jaime Torres Bodet (1902–1974), Xavier Villaurrutia (1903–1950), and Salvador Novo (1904–1974). Although they differ widely among themselves, the works of these writers have several characteristics in common: a modern urban vocabulary sprinkled with neologisms; the absence of rhyme and conventional poetic phrases; the use of images, not for decorative purposes, but as integral parts of the poem; and the rejection of anecdote and the first-person confessional tone.

Pellicer is known for his lyrical descriptions of nature and his religious fervor, both conspicuous elements in *Recinto, y otros imágenes* (1941; enclosure, and other images) and *Subordinaciones* (1949; subordinations). Gorostiza's *Muerte sin fin* (1939; *Death without End*, 1969), which conveys an existential fascination with nothingness, emerges as the most memorable work produced by the *contemporáneos*. Perhaps better known as a statesman than a poet, Torres Bodet articulated his meditations on time, death, and absurdity in numerous volumes, including *Cripta* (1937; crypt), *Sonetos* (1949; sonnets), and *Sin tregua* (1957; without truce). Villaurrutia's masterpiece is *Nostalgia de la muerte* (1938; nostalgia of death), which denies the objective world for a deeper, more intimate reality clouded by an obsession with the poet's approaching demise. In his *XX poemas* (1925; XX poems), Novo fuses youthful exuberance and irony, but *Nuevo amor* (1930; new love), a more mature work, exudes disillusion and somber premonitions of death.

The poetry of Efraín Huerta (1914–1982), unlike that of the *contemporáneos*, signals a shift of emphasis to social injustice, urban solitude, and the complexities of life in the modern world. He also reinstated anecdote and colloquial language as major elements in his works, which include *Poemas de guerra y esperanza* (1943; poems of war and hope) and *Los poemas de viaje, 1949–1953* (1956; travel poems, 1949–1953). Alí Chamucero (b. 1918) belongs to the same generation as Huerta, but in his *Páramo de sueños* (1944; barren plain of dreams) and *Palabras en reposo* (1956; words in repose) his world vision derives from existential and aesthetic impulses rather than from social conscience. Chamucero does, however, share Huerta's use of anecdote to concretize and objectify his concepts.

Three fine Mexican poets born in the mid-1920s are Jaime García Terrés (b. 1924), Rosario Castellanos (also discussed in the chapter on fiction), and Jaime Sabines (b. 1925). García Terrés impresses the reader with his ability to poeticize common occurrences in unadorned, everyday language and, at the same time, to convey his sentiments on philosophical subjects such as time and death. His most inspired volumes include *Las provincias del aire* (1956; provinces of the air) and *Todo lo más por decir* (1971; all the more to be said). Castellanos's books of verse include *Trayectoria del polvo* (1948; trajectory of dust), consisting of introspective reflections on metaphysical themes; and *Poemas 1953–1955* (1957; poems 1953–1955), which evokes the Indian civilizations she knew first-hand in her native state of Chiapas. In some of her poems, as, for example, in *Al pie de la letra* (1959; to the letter) and *Lívida luz* (1960; livid light), she makes effective use of dramatic monologue to express her feminist anger, pain, bitterness, and compassion. Perhaps her most famous poem is "Memorial de Tlatelolco" ("In Memory of Tlatelolco"), which was first published in *La noche de Tlatelolco* (1971; *Massacre in Mexico*, 1975), by Elena Poniatowska; the poem is a vehement denunciation of the Mexican government's role in the 1968 student massacre and a moving tribute to the victims. Also a native of Chiapas, Sabines writes in a more colloquial and direct style than Castellanos. His fear of death and his distaste for dehumanizing urban life emerge as major statements in *La señal* (1951; the signal) and *Diario semanario y poemas en prosa* (1961; weekly diary and poems in prose). In *Maltiempo* (1972; bad time), however, he satirizes the repressive Mexican government and parodies the hermeticism of the literary establishment.

Of the numerous gifted Mexican poets born in the early 1930s, the following rank among the most successful with the reading public: Marco Antonio Montes de Oca (b. 1932), Juan Bañuelos (b. 1932), Ulalume González de León (b. 1932), and Gabriel Zaid (b. 1934). Richly textured by a profusion of metaphors, Montes de Oca's verses stylize ordinary personal experiences with a lyric intensity transcending the limits of logic and approaching the surrealistic. Much of his best work appears in *Poesía reunida 1953–1970* (1971; collected poetry 1953–1970). Bañuelos is a revolutionary poet, who in *Espejo humeante* (1968; smoking mirror) and other volumes espouses the cause of the underdog and assails the United States for racial discrimination, the Vietnam war, and the suppression of liberation movements in Latin America.

A basic element in Zaid's work is the clash between the aesthetic, visionary ideal and the drab, prosaic reality of today's world. Also characteristic of his poems, many of which consist of only a few lines, is their tonal modulations, which range from the wryly humorous to the tragic and which depend on a frequently shifting point of view to create the desired effect. In his endeavor to expand poetic dimensions, Zaid embellishes the ordinary in precise, controlled language laced with visual motifs and mythical allusions. Among his best collections are *Seguimiento* (1964; pursuit) and *Campo nudista* (1969; nudist camp). González de León's *Plagios* (1973; plagiarisms) recycles fragments and verse forms from literary giants to forge new images and suggest subtle changes in meaning. The end result of these permutations is an ingenious sampling of metapoetry or poetry derived from the works of other practitioners of the genre.

Two of Mexico's most talented young poets are José Emilio Pacheco (b. 1939) and Homero Aridjis (b. 1940). Versatile and prolific, Pacheco is a competent novelist and critic, but above all, a first-rate poet. Perhaps his best and most typical collection is *No me preguntes cómo pasa el tiempo* (1969; don't ask me how the time passes), in which he presents contemporary man as both an agent of the historical process and a victim of temporal change and physical disintegration. *Irás y no volverás* (1973; you will go and not return) develops similar themes, but it is enriched by ironic overtones and evocative literary allusions. Aridjis reveals the influence of Octavio Paz, which is evident in one of his best collections, *Mirándola dormir* (1964; watching her sleep). Here the erotic experience emerges as central to the human experience and the sleeping lover as the point of departure for the surrealistic probing of the subconscious. Like Paz, Aridjis also uses poetry as a vehicle to transcend chronological time and transform reality into subjective images free of logical constraints.

THE CARIBBEAN

Cuba

Cuba, which has the largest population of any Caribbean nation, not surprisingly has the largest number of outstanding poets in the region. In addition to Nicolás Guillén (discussed above), Eugenio Florit (b. 1903), Emilio Ballagas (1908–1954), and the previously mentioned José Lezama Lima stand out as the finest representatives of the older generation. Born in Spain but a resident of Cuba from 1915 until 1940, Florit taught for many years at Columbia University. His work, much of which is written in classical meters, is a unique mixture of romantic melancholy and metaphysical anguish distilled into baroque lyricism. Despite his strong religious faith, Florit's overriding theme is man's solitude wherever he may be—on a crowded New York street, in a bookstore, standing before an unopened door, or contemplating a lush Cuban landscape. Much of his work has been collected in his *Antología penúltima* (1970; penultimate collection). Ballagas, like Guillén, was a practitioner of Afro-Cuban poetry, a genre that taps the sensual, musical tongue and primitive rhythms—expressed in onomatopoeia, alliteration, and anaphora—characteristic of black culture. Ballagas was less militant than Guillén, however, and occasionally escaped from reality into romantic reverie or philosophical reflection. *Obra poética de Emilio Ballagas* (1955; poetic work of Emilio Ballagas) contains his most significant works.

Probably better known for his novel *Paradiso* (discussed in the preceding chapter) than for his poetry, Lezama Lima is nevertheless considered by some critics as Cuba's premier modern poet. His verses baffle all but the most sophisticated readers because he seems deliberately to evade objective reality for a poetically conceived universe of his own invention, a characteristic that emerges as the theme of his poem "Ah, que tú escapes" (ah, may you escape), in *Enemigo rumor* (1941; enemy rumor). His poetry also represents an attempt to explore the latent possibilities of language, often conveyed in an abstruse, convoluted style perhaps best described as neobaroque. Two examples of these tendencies are his highly acclaimed volumes *Dador* (1960; giver) and *Órbita de Lezama Lima* (1966; orbit of Lezama Lima).

Among the many prominent Cubans of the younger generation are Roberto Fernández Retamar (b. 1930), Heberto Padilla (b. 1932), Rita Geada (b. 1937), and David Fernández Chericián (b. 1940). Critic, diplomat, and, more recently, editor of the prestigious literary journal *Casa de las Américas*, Fernández Retamar is one of the most important intellectuals in revolutionary Cuba. As a poet he celebrates the revolution, but he has also published exceptionally fine love poems, many of which appeared before he became involved in politics. His revolutionary poetry displays a unique combination of stylistic elegance and conversational intimacy, which enhances its accessibility to Cuba's large but relatively unsophisticated reading public. One of his most popular books touting his nation's recent progress is *A quien pueda interesar* (1970; to whom it may concern).

Heberto Padilla is known internationally as much for his bitter dispute with Fidel Castro as for his writings. In the late 1960s he came under attack because of his controversial prizewinning volume of poems *Fuera del juego* (1968; out of the game), in which he dared to imply criticism of Cuban society —the title poem describes the scornful treatment of poets in Cuba. He was imprisoned briefly in 1971 and released only after publishing a statement of self-criticism and recantation. He emigrated to the United States in 1980. Well versed in English and Russian literature, Padilla is a lyric poet who laments man's alienation and anguish in the face of overwhelming historical forces. The bitter irony in his work stems at least in part from his frustration as a writer in the suffocating atmosphere of a communist state.

Rita Geada's anguish is due not to political or historical forces, but to the dehumanization of contemporary life. A professor of literature in Connecticut, she has written several collections of poetry, her best being her introspective, prize-winning *Mascarada* (1969; masquerade), which exhibits her terse, elliptical style.

Fernández Chericián typifies the group of Cuban intellectuals who came to maturity with the revolution. His writing evolved from initial Marxist fervor to a more meditative and aesthetically exacting, but equally committed, phase. A major theme in one of his best-known works, *La honda de David* (1967; David's slingshot) is the war in Vietnam, which he sees as a prime example of U.S. imperialism. Fernández Chericián involves his readers by addressing them or his characters directly in tones ranging from intimate and conversational to humorous and ironic. The anti-imperialist stance of his poetry underscores his oft-expressed solidarity with all Third World nations.

Dominican Republic

Recent poetry in the Dominican Republic is best represented by the works of three older-generation poets: Manuel del Cabral (b. 1907), Héctor Incháustegui Cabral (b. 1912), and Pedro Mir (b. 1913). Del Cabral owes much of his reputation to his verses in the Afro-Caribbean tradition, in which he registers his protest against the social evils plaguing the black population of his nation. Typical of this segment of his work is his well-known *Compadre Mon* (1943; friend Mon), a lyrical epic depicting the exploits of a mythical hero. In addition, del Cabral has published numerous poems dealing with time, identity, and love in its multiple aspects. The most striking ingredient in these more universal works is the metaphor that in *Los anti-tiempos* (1967; the anti-times) is often intelligible only to the sophisticated reader.

Incháustegui Cabral's poems also fall into two fundamental divisions: those treating social problems and those with metaphysical themes. Typical of the former is *Poemas de una sola angustia* (1940; poems of a single anguish), a bitter lament over the backwardness and poverty of the Dominican Republic; representative of the latter is *Las islas extrañas* (1952; the strange islands), which views men's souls as entities (islands) isolated in time and place. This author's best-known work is *Diario de la guerra: Los dioses ametrallados* (1967; diary of war: the machine-gunned gods), a poetic evocation of war merging symbols and myths with poignant private reality.

A militant revolutionary and member of the Communist Party, Mir has gained international recognition for the intellectual power and technical brilliance he brings to his work. His themes include the injustices perpetrated by the regime (1952–60) of the Dominican dictator Héctor Trujillo, the imperialist role of the United States in the Caribbean, and the cry for solidarity among all Third World peoples. His optimism about Latin America emerges as the principal message of his highly acclaimed volume *Seis momentos de esperanza* (1953; six moments of hope).

Puerto Rico

Puerto Rico's poetic tradition may not be as rich as Cuba's, but it nevertheless is worthy of considerable attention. Some critics view Luis Palés Matos (1898–1959) as the Commonwealth's best twentieth-century practitioner of the genre. Although he developed a broad range of subjects, Palés Matos is best known for his treatment of Puerto Rico's black culture. He is also seen as a precursor of Guillén and Ballagas, but unlike his Cuban counterparts, he was not black, nor was he a social-protest writer. He resembles Guillén and Ballagas, however, in his ability to communicate the primitive sounds, rhythms, and rituals of the black people through phonetic verbalization—often in nonsense, onomatopoeic syllables—of music and dance. He also portrays the black as a vital force capable of regenerating the rationalistic white civilization. Thus, his work, fluctuating between reality and dream, is somewhat akin to the magical realism of contemporary fiction. His best poems have been published in his *Poesía, 1915–1956* (1957; poetry, 1915–1956).

Another of Puerto Rico's exceptional poets is Julia de Burgos (1914–1953), whose lyrical verses about love—often erotic—nature, solitude, and death ring true because of their fresh imagery and tonal sincerity. An innovator in neither form nor content, she evokes traces of romanticism in her frequent personification of nature and fascination with death. Her posthumous collection, *El mar y tú* (1954; the sea and you), illustrates the greater simplicity of her later style. Sixteen years younger than de Burgos, Jorge Luis Morales (b. 1930) emerged as the major poet on the Puerto Rican literary scene during the decade immediately following World War II. Although his poetry reflects the exuberant Puerto Rican landscape, Morales is a sophisticated, universal writer whose philosophical reflections on time and anguish link him with the existentialists of that period. Another of his more universal themes is the frustrating creative process, which he treats in evocative metaphors. As demonstrated by *La ventana y el yo* (1960; the window and the self), he is a technically versatile poet who writes in both free verse and traditional forms such as the sonnet and the ode.

Puerto Rico, like Cuba, has produced numerous revolutionary poets, perhaps because of the strong resentment among intellectuals of U.S. political, economic, and cultural domination of the island. The best of these writers include Iris M. Zavala (b. 1936), Pedro Pietri (b. 1944), and Iván Silén (b. 1944). Zavala's militant opposition to war, insensitive bureaucrats, and greedy conglomerates is vehemently articulated in *Barro doliente* (1964; aching mud) and *Poemas prescindibles* (1971; dispensable poems), often via poignant examples of personal testimony. Spare and polished, her verses also sparkle with surrealistic and, at times, grotesque images that serve to underscore her indignation.

Pietri was born in Puerto Rico but grew up in a poor section of New York City. In *Puerto Rican Obituary* (1973; title in English) he celebrates his Latin identity, which he feels is threatened by the Anglo-Saxon-dominated milieu. Like Zavala, he too poeticizes suffering, but his emphasis is on the Puerto Rican immigrant who dies longing for a winning lottery ticket, a retirement pension, a house in the suburbs, or a nostalgic journey to his birthplace. Even more militant than Zavala, Silén is an ex-seminarian who favors Puerto Rican independence and views poetry as a political commitment to this end. He also advocates what he calls "neosurrealism," a movement that attempts to reconcile anarchistic individualism with communism. His poems in *Después del suicidio* (1970; after the suicide) exalt revolution and guerrilla movements throughout the world in a medley of moods ranging from compassion for the dispossessed to irony about and belligerence toward the ruling classes.

CENTRAL AMERICA

Costa Rica

The most gifted Costa Rican poets include Alfredo Cordona Peña (b. 1917), Alfredo Sancho (b. 1924), and Jorge Debravo (1938–1967). Cordona Peña has lived in Mexico for many years, but his poetry reveals a yearning for the landscape and the people of his tropical homeland. His themes of love, nature, and the passing of time are elegantly stylized, conveying an inner serenity and an aesthetic appreciation of visible reality. A winner of several literary awards, he has also published insightful verses in praise of many Spanish American literary figures. His best work includes *La muerte cae en un vaso* (1962; death falls into a glass) and *Cosecha mayor* (1964; bigger harvest). Sancho is almost as prolific as Cordona Peña and shares not only his compatriot's nostalgia for a simple and happy past, but also his ability to poeticize the commonplace. A major aspect in Sancho's work is his view of poetry as something akin to religion, a humanizing influence on contemporary man who, he believes, has been debased by political corruption, technology, and greed. His goal, however, is to bring about a spiritual revival, not a revolution. Although he died in an accident at the age of twenty-nine, Jorge Debravo left a legacy of some eight volumes of poetry, among which *Cantera bruta* (1965; rough-hewn stone) remains one of the most inspiring. An idealistic humanist who sought a deeper comprehension of his fellow man, he recorded his anguish at the sight of suffering and his indignation over the silence it elicits from others. He also felt a strong sense of alienation in a cement-covered, urban environment where death looms as an ever-present reality. Nevertheless, he viewed life optimistically, sensing a collective realization of each individual's worth in today's world. Published posthumously, *Antología mayor* (1974; bigger collection) contains a broad selection of Debravo's oeuvre.

El Salvador

El Salvador's older generation is best represented by Claudia Lars (1899–1974), whose lyric poetry has been compared to that of Gabriela Mistral because of its simplicity, metaphysical dimensions, and sympathy for the humble. Her most successful verses appear in *Donde llegan los pasos* (1953; where the steps lead) and *Fábula de una verdad* (1959; fable of a truth). Claribel Alegría (b. 1924) also writes in a simple, direct style, but her imagery is more violent, more striking because of its powerful elements of social protest and its condemnation of Yankee imperialism. Her numerous collections of poetry include *Anillo de silencio* (1948; ring of silence), *Aprendizaje* (1970; apprenticeship), and *Suma y sigue* (1981; sum up and continue).

Three young Salvadoran poets of considerable talent are Roque Dalton (1933–1975), José Roberto Cea (b. 1939), and David Escobar Galindo (b. 1943). During the 1960s Dalton emerged as one of Central America's most widely read poets. A Marxist revolutionary, he lived in exile for several years in Mexico, Cuba, and Eastern Europe, and was eventually murdered for his political beliefs. In 1963 his collection *El turno del ofendido* (the turn of the offended one) was received favorably by the critics, and in 1969 *Taberna y otros lugares* (tavern and other places) was awarded the prestigious Casa de las Américas prize in Cuba. In addition to his revolutionary fervor, Dalton's anguish over suffering and injustice constitutes a major ingredient in virtually all his works. Like many Marxist poets, he frequently wrote in a direct, conversational style, creating a persona with whom his readers can readily identify. Typical of his works is "OEA" ("OAS," in Robert Márquez, ed., *Latin American Revolutionary Poetry*, 1974), published in *El turno del ofendido*, which attacks the Salvadoran leaders for their alignment with right-wing governments, especially that of the United States. In *Poemas clandestinos* (1981; *Clandestine Poems*, 1984) Dalton assumes the poetic personae of several individuals in order to comment on the convulsive events in his homeland the year before his death. *Poems* (1984) provides a wide selection of his poetry in English translation.

Very different from the politically committed Dalton, Cea typifies the folkloric poet who immerses his readers in the magical atmosphere of Indian culture through exotic vocabulary, exuberant images of the tropics, and repetitive rhythms usually set forth in free verse. His volume entitled *Códice liberado* (1968; liberated codex) also exudes a unique combination of poetic insight, primitive force, and sympathy for a way of life threatened by technology and war. Escobar Galindo speaks philosophically of time, change, and identity, but he also injects into his poetry personal experiences based on the recent tragic events in El Salvador. A statesman and editor in addition to being a prolific writer, Escobar Galindo assembled the best of his works up to the time in *Primera antología: Poemas* (1977; first collection: poems).

Guatemala

Guatemala's acute social problems and press censorship have induced many of this nation's intellectuals to turn to poetry as a vehicle of protest. Among these are Otto Raúl González (b. 1921), Otto René Castillo (1936–1967), and Marco Antonio Flores (b. 1937). As demonstrated by his *Cuchillo de caza* (1965; hunting knife), González is essentially a master of form who transforms the everyday into a steady flow of beautifully crafted metaphors, similes, and anaphoric phrases. Like the surrealists, he too juxtaposes contrasting images evoking life and death, pleasure and suffering, peace and violence, ancient myth and modern reality. His protest poems achieve universality through his skill in presenting abstract ideology and regional concerns via concrete, archetypal symbols appealing to, and understood by, all men.

Castillo and Flores are two of Guatemala's most militant revolutionary poets. During his short life, which ended when he was tortured and burned alive by government troops, Castillo published two books: *Tecún Uman* (1964; Tecún Uman) and *Vámonos patria a caminar* (1965; let's walk, fatherland). Often compared to Roque Dalton, Castillo reveals profound sensitivity to the plight of the oppressed and unbounded love for his homeland, from which he was forced into exile on several occasions. Although his style is direct and somber, his tone can turn bitterly satirical, above all when he describes suffering caused by the abuse of authority. He wrote almost exclusively in free verse, paying homage to the emotionally charged word "revolution" and condemning apolitical intellectuals for their indifference to social evils. His "Viudo del mundo" ("Widowed of the World," in Robert Márquez, ed., *Latin American Revolutionary Poetry*, 1974), which is included in *Vámonos patria a caminar*, portends his early death.

A journalist and film director as well as a poet, Flores

shares Castillo's direct conversational style, militant tone, and sensitivity to the suffering of his nation's lower classes. *La voz acumulada* (1964; the accumulated voice) and *Muros de luz* (1968; walls of light) celebrate the triumph of the Cuban revolution in a highly original, figurative idiom. In these collections Flores also expresses praise for his mother, whose love stands out in sharp contrast to his combativeness. Another tensive comparison is between the jail where he is confined, a symbol of corruption and brutality, and his infant daughter, who represents innocence and love.

Honduras

Of all the nations in Spanish America, Honduras has produced the fewest writers of international reputation. Thus, when Roberto Sosa (b. 1930) received the Casa de las Américas prize in 1971 for *Un mundo para todos dividido* (a world divided for all), he emerged as the nation's leading contemporary poet. In this and other volumes Sosa reveals an obsession with solitude, poverty, and death in the face of an indifferent world he believes headed for destruction. His overall tone, however, is sympathetic and tender rather than satirical or bitter.

Nicaragua

José Coronel Urtecho (b. 1906) was one of the first to rebel against the *modernismo* of his compatriot, Rubén Darío, and for many years stood out as his nation's leading *vanguardista*. Coronel Urtecho, whose works appeared principally in journals, writes in classical meters of commonplace things, but his irony and occasional flashes of surrealistic imagery appeal to many readers. A *vanguardista* poet of the same generation and a well-known journalist, Pablo Antonio Cuadra (b. 1912) describes nature and political injustice, the latter inspired by the famous Nicaraguan patriot Augusto César Sandino (1895–1934), whom Cuadra knew personally in his youth. As demonstrated in *La tierra prometida* (1952; the promised land) and *Poesía* (1964; poetry), Cuadra's treatment of everyday life, often in free verse, has made him, like Urtecho, a popular and accessible author.

The most outstanding Central American poet of the contemporary period is Nicaragua's Ernesto Cardenal (b. 1925), occasionally referred to as a revolutionary mystic. Cardenal was actively involved in the underground movement against the dictator Anastasio Somoza in the 1950s, but subsequently underwent a religious conversion, entering a monastery first in Kentucky and then in Mexico. He studied theology in Colombia and in 1965, ordained as a Roman Catholic priest and eager to reconcile Christianity and communism, founded a religious colony on an island in the Lake of Nicaragua. After the fall of the Somoza regime, he became the Sandinista government's minister of culture. In his role as a writer Cardenal combines religious and political fervor, his goal being to achieve justice through revolutionary poetry and faith. His first major work is *Hora zero* (1960; *Zero Hour*, 1974), which depicts in free verse the horrors of Central American history, with special emphasis on the Somoza dynasty in Nicaragua. Reminiscent of Neruda's *Canto general* and Ezra Pound's *Cantos*, this work also leans on hyperbole and the absurd to satirize the heavy atmosphere of misery and injustice perpetrated by tyrannical governments and, in Cardenal's view, gringo imperialism. In his *Salmos* (1964; *Psalms*, 1974), he undertakes the rewriting of the Psalms of David for modern man, again exposing present-day evils and sustaining a high degree of tension between his faith and his politicized sense of reality. Another of his well-known collections, *Oración por Marilyn Monroe, y otros poemas* (1965; prayer for Marilyn Monroe, and other poems), depicts the deceased actress as a victim of the corupt U.S. environment. Cardenal's increasing visibility among English-speaking readers is demonstrated by the publication of the bilingual collection of his works entitled *With Walker in Nicaragua, and Other Early Poems, 1949–1954* (1984).

Panama

Panama's first *vanguardista* poet was Rogelio Sinán (b. 1902), whose book *Onda* (1929; wave) brought home to his countrymen the reaction against *modernismo*. Other major practitioners of contemporary Panamanian poetry include Stella

Sierra (b. 1917) and José de Jesús Martínez (b. 1929). Generally considered one of Panama's leading poets, Sierra has declared her desire to write "pure poetry," that is, poetry inspired by the human spirit and detached from a specific time and place. In her most significant work, *Libre y cautiva* (1947; free and captive), she sings of the joy of living, of love, and of nature, all in flowing, impeccably honed verses rich in images inspired by her colorful native land. The sea emerges as the most striking leitmotif in her work, symbolizing life itself in its all-powerful, all-encompassing dimensions. More versatile than Sierra, Jesús Martínez has also excelled as a dramatist and essayist. In his poetry he develops a variety of themes ranging from ideal love to the basic absurdity in daily life. Thus, he obsessively repeats senseless conversational phrases and routine behavior to parody man's attempt to organize his chaotic, purposeless world. As illustrated by his *One Way* (1967; title in English), the medium of his message is characterized by wrenched syntax and rhythms, frequent changes in the author's persona, and a dynamic montage of clashing images.

COLOMBIA AND VENEZUELA

Colombia

Prior to 1965 Colombia was known as a land of poets, having produced few first-rate writers of prose fiction. The nation's two most important *postmodernistas* are Porfirio Barba Jacob (pseudonym of Miguel Ángel Osorio, 1883–1942), whose work fuses elements of romanticism and existentialism, and Luis Carlos López (1879–1950), who parodied the solemnity of *modernismo* with his vernacular style and irony. The internationally known León de Greiff (1895–1976) became Colombia's best-known *vanguardista*, although his poems retain occasional vestiges of *modernismo* such as romantic subjectivity, exoticism, and musical sonority. Aurelio Arturo (1906–1974) also belongs to the *vanguardista* group, but in addition he emphasizes the spectacular Colombian landscape, which he paints with both rustic vigor and poetic resonance.

During the late 1930s a movement led by Jorge Rojas

(b. 1911) and Eduardo Carranza (1913–1985) reacted against the excesses of the *vanguardistas* of the previous decade. Known as *piedra y cielo* (stone and sky), this movement felt the influence of Juan Ramón Jiménez, the Spanish poet who used traditional metrical forms with rigorous logic and lucidity. The mystic, metaphysician, and founder of the group, Rojas speaks of solitude, which he seems to enjoy, and of love, which for him is perhaps more anticipated than real. His "pure poetry" also displays an elusive, diaphanous quality, especially in his masterpiece, *Rosa de agua* (1941; rose of water). Carranza, who during his lifetime was called Colombia's best living poet, cultivated both classical and popular verse forms in a clear, transparent style rich in imagery and overtones of nostalgic melancholy. His collection *Los pasos cantados* (1970; the chanted steps) sets forth perennial poetic themes such as beauty in its multiple forms, a yearning for the unattainable, the ravages of time, and human and divine love.

One of the major voices in post-World War II Colombia is that of Álvaro Mutis (b. 1923), a long-time resident of Mexico. Mutis's tone is often satirical, probably because he considers the modern world to be in an advanced state of decay. He has published many prose poems, the best known narrated by one Maqroll el Gaviero (Maqroll the Mastman), whose bitter irony and grotesque humor reflect the author's pessimistic *Weltanschauung*. Mutis poeticizes the most banal aspects of everyday life: a homely woman getting off a train, snatches of conversations in a bar, sterile images of a city, and random examples of fear in a chaotic urban environment. *Los trabajos perdidos* (1965; the lost works) exemplifies his many successful publications.

Two important Colombian poets with much in common were Jorge Gaitán Durán (1924–1962) and Edgar Cote Lamus (1928–1964). Gaitán Durán, who died in an automobile accident before he could realize his full potential as a writer, dwelt on love and death, love being the only salvation for his anguish in the face of the existential void. However, even love—often erotic—emerges as a desperate attempt to forget the inexorable flow of time. In 1955 Gaitán Durán founded *Mito* (myth), a prestigious journal that treated the nation's problems with remarkable lucidity. His masterpiece is *Si mañana despierto* (1961; if I awaken tomorrow). Although Cote Lamus shared Caitán Durán's preoccupation with love and death, in his work love emerges as a form of destruction and death as an inevitable end rather than a constant menace. He also developed a wider range of themes, including strong religious faith, nostalgia for his childhood in Cúcuta (on the Venezuelan border), and *la violencia*, the civil war that raged in Colombia from 1948 until well into the 1960s.

Three of the younger Colombian poets worthy of note are X-504 (pseudonym of Jaime Jaramillo Escobar, b. 1933), Mario Rivero (b. 1935), and Eduardo Escobar (b. 1945). X-504 is considered by some critics as the most outstanding of Colombia's *nadaístas*, a group of young iconoclasts who appeared on the literary scene during the 1960s. His best work is *Los poemas de la ofensa* (1968; the poems of the offense). A narrative poet who speaks in conversational tones and in his own special vernacular, Rivero presents banal slices of life as metaphors of solitude, temporal anguish, purposelessness, and divine impotence in the face of human peril. His *Baladas* (1980; ballads) is a collection of his most highly acclaimed works. Eduardo Escobar, the youngest of the *nadaístas*, registers his denunciation of the bourgeois establishment, which he depicts as the embodiment of evil in *Invención de la uva* (1966; invention of the grape) and *Monólogos de Noé* (1967; monologues of Noah).

Although she is hardly a *nadaísta*, María Mercedes Carranza (b. 1945) seems to delight in demythicizing the past and draws inspiration from the ordinary, perhaps as an antidote to sentimentality and pomposity. Her verses in *Vainas y otros poemas* (1972; things and other poems) and *Tengo miedo, 1976–1982* (1982; I'm afraid, 1976–1982) inveigh against the hypocrisy and corruption of the past, which she believes has eroded present-day morality.

Venezuela

In Venezuela the most widely known and admired *modernista* is Rufino Blanco Fombona (1874–1944), also a competent novelist and critic. The so-called generation of 1918 reacted against the excessive ornamentation of *modernismo*, stressing content instead of form and describing Venezuela's colorful folklore and landscape. The best-known of this group is Andrés Eloy Blanco (1897–1955), who achieved fame throughout the Spanish-speaking world for his versatility and ability to excel in various schools of poetry. Romantic and *modernista* influences predominate in his early works, but *Barco de piedra* (1937; stone ship) and *Baedeker 2000* (1938; Baedeker 2000), both written in prison where Blanco was sent by the dictator Juan Vicente Gómez, protest against injustice and suffering. And in *Giraluna* (1955; moonspin) he universalizes the Venezuelan experience through his treatment of popular and folkloric themes.

Additional members of Blanco's generation are Luis Fernández Álvarez (1902—1952), Antonio Arraiz (1903–1963), and Miguel Otero Silva (also discussed in the chapter on fiction). Fernández Álvarez takes his readers into a lugubrious realm of mystery, nightmare, and death, evoking the subjective element of romanticism and, at the same time, suggesting a close kinship with the surreal. Typical of his many volumes is his *Soledad contigo* (1938; solitude with you). A journalist and novelist who, like Blanco, was imprisoned for political activities, Arraiz dominated the *vanguardista* movement in Venezuela and dedicated some of his early poems to the Indians of America, especially those of his volume *Áspero* (1924; harsh). He also registers his outrage over injustice, depicting the deprivations of the poor and dramatizing brutality and death in stark, shocking imagery. By contrast, as shown in *Cinco sinfonías* (1939; five symphonies), his poems occasionally exude tenderness and love for his native land and all humanity. Otero Silva's *Obra poética* (1976; poetic work) displays an array of themes by this well-known author. Like so many of his colleagues, he was jailed and exiled during the long regime of Juan Vicente Gómez. Although his poetry alludes occasionally to the adverse political ambience of his homeland, he writes primarily of love, nature, and death in a lucid, uncomplicated style accessible to most readers.

After Juan Vicente Gómez's death in 1935, a group of young

poets founded the journal *Viernes* (Friday) for the purpose of bringing their national literature into the mainstream of Spanish American letters. The outstanding member of the *Viernes* group is Vicente Gerbasi (b. 1913), a cosmopolitan writer generally linked to *vanguardismo*. Less an experimenter with new forms than an ingenious creator of mood, Gerbasi speaks of exotic nature, love, and death, but for him the true purpose of poetry is to immerse the reader in a world of mystery and ambiguity. He accomplishes this goal in *Los espacios cálidos* (1952; the warm spaces) by repeatedly suggesting states of temporary tranquillity subject to imminent change.

One of Venezuela's most distinguished literary figures today, Juan Liscano (b. 1915) is a major poet, critic, and journalist. His numerous collections of verse treat subjects ranging from man's place in the universe—*Humano destino* (1950; human destiny)—to Venezuelan folklore and history—*Nuevo mundo Orinoco* (1959; new world of the Orinoco). His collection *Nombrar contra el tiempo* (1968; name against time) also includes poems of love, death, and social protest, demonstrating both his ability as a lyricist and his sensitivity to suffering humanity. In his most subjective works Liscano uses expressionistic techniques to project his inner turbulence onto the tropical landscape of his homeland, transforming it into a vast montage of clashing, distorted images.

Several of Venezuela's best contemporary poets have been influenced by their compatriot José Antonio Ramos Sucre (1890–1930), a budding surrealist who committed suicide shortly after publishing his seminal volume, *Las formas del fuego* (1929; the forms of fire). Three of his ardent admirers are Juan Sánchez Peláez (b. 1922), Francisco Pérez Perdomo (b. 1929), and Juan Calzadilla (b. 1931). Sánchez Peláez's *Elena y los elementos* (1951; Elena and the elements) has been hailed as one of Venezuela's finest examples of surrealism. His more recent *Un día sea* (1969; let it be day), though not without remnants of the surreal, concentrates primarily on the frustrations of love and the creative process. Like Ramos Sucre, Pérez Perdomo emerges as a tormented writer with an affinity for surrealism, but he has assimilated innovative forms from a variety of sources. His *Fantasmas y enfermedades* (1961; phantoms and maladies) resembles a nightmare of thwarted desires, incoherent voices, and seemingly unrelated motifs. Calzadilla is one of the founders of *El techo de la ballena* (the roof of the whale), a journal designed to discredit the bourgeois establishment and effect radical literary and social change. Writing in both free verse and poetically inspired prose, Calzadilla imparts his feelings of imprisonment not only within his environment, but also within his own psyche, which he depicts as a spiritual abyss beyond his physical being. His *Dictado por la jauría* (1962; dictated by the pack) and *Malos modales* (1965; bad manners) poeticize his nonconformist torment along with his longing to escape into a poetic realm of imagination.

Two very different Venezuelan poets born in the mid-1930s are Ramón Palomares (b. 1935) and Edmundo Aray (b. 1936). Virtually all of Palomares's poems in *El reino* (1958; the kingdom) and *Paisano* (1964; compatriot), two highly touted collections, reflect his rural background; his symbolic treatment of a solitary bird, a meandering river, and a village threatened by the blackness of night also convey his metaphysical concerns and universalize his settings. Although, like Calzadilla, Aray helped to found *El techo de la ballena*, he is less introspective and more militant in his determination to change the world. His targets in *Nadie quiere descansar* (1961; nobody wants to rest) include the managers of the stock market and the ambitious "petit bourgeois" who, throughout his life, keeps "moving, moving, hitting, holding on, hitting, moving," only to receive "a fancy car, magnificent flowers, handsome wreaths, cards and more cards" for his funeral. Aray heaps praise, however, on Catholic priests committed to die in the anti-imperialist struggle, dedicating one of his poems to the Colombia priest Camilo Torres (1929–1966).

THE ANDEAN HIGHLANDS

Bolivia

Bolivia's most famous poet to date was the *modernista* Ricardo Jaimes Freyre (1868–1933), who wrote of a fantastic, mythological world more Nordic than Hellenic. Among contemporary Bolivian poets, four of the most outstanding are Oscar Cerruto (b. 1912), Yolanda Bedregal (b. 1918), Jaime Sáenz (b. 1921), and Pedro Shimose (b. 1940). Also a novelist who has written of his nation's role in the Chaco War with Paraguay (1932–35), Cerruto stands out for his adroit handling of classical meters and his rich imagery of the awesome Bolivian landscape. In *Patria de sal cautiva* (1958; fatherland of captive charm) he celebrates in particular the solitude of the vast *altiplano* (highland plain), where voices of the legendary past are still audible. Because of the lyrical strength and beauty of her verses, Yolanda Bedregal is often referred to as "Yolanda de Bolivia." Although her principal themes are love, social injustice, and revolution, her mass appeal stems from her gift for capturing the very soul of her native land via her poignant portraits of the humble. *Nadir* (1950; nadir), for example, pays tribute to a servant woman struck down by an automobile and a soldier killed in the Chaco War, both representative of Bolivia's long-suffering *raza de bronce* (bronze or Indian race).

Sáenz is probably the most unusual and misunderstood of all contemporary Bolivian poets. His anthology *Obra poética* (1975; poetic work) is written in free verse enlivened by a rhythmic, musical style likely to captivate the reader. His verses are also accented with obsessive repetitions and contradictions, generating the tension and ambiguity for which he is known. Sáenz writes principally of love, but in his world love is a fleeting, confrontational relationship vaguely reminiscent of the sado-masochistic dialectics described in existential psychology. Thus his readers, unlike Bedregal's, are thrust into a subjective, abstract realm more universal than Bolivian. Despite Shimose's Japanese descent, his poetry is firmly anchored in his native soil. A rebel by nature, he has been influenced by Vallejo, with whom he shares a deep sympathy for the poor, a colloquial idiom, and an intimate, conversational tone. Two of Shimose's principal themes are his sharp criticism of Bolivian society and his bitter resentment of tyranny wherever it may occur. *Poemas para un pueblo* (1968; poems for a people) alludes to Bolivia's tragic past, political instability, and social injustice, which the author blames primarily on the ruling classes. In 1971 Shimose won the Casa de las Américas prize for *Quiero escribir, pero me sale espuma* (I want to write but I can only foam at the mouth), a volume of poems written in free verse proclaiming his revolutionary ideas on a wide range of subjects.

Ecuador

Ecuador's most renowned twentieth-century poet, Jorge Carrera Andrade, is discussed earlier in this chapter. Two representatives of the succeeding generation are Alejandro Carrión (b. 1915) and César Dávila Andrade (1918–1967), both of whom belong to the so-called *Madrugada* (dawn) group. (*Madrugada* is the title of a journal founded in the mid-1940s.) Carrión evolved from lyrical neoromanticism in his early work to existentialism and vehement protest against injustice in more recent years. His *Poesía* (1961; poetry) provides the best of his poems in a single compact volume. Known for his melancholy, his solitude, and his esoteric interests in magic, the occult, and Zen Buddhism, Dávila Andrade lived for many years in Venezuela, where he died by his own hand. His poems abound in metaphors conveying metaphysical and social concerns as well as the torments of the creative endeavor. He also excels in depicting scenes of everyday life, which he enlivens with original, evocative imagery. *Conexiones de tierra* (1964; connections of earth) contains many of his most well-known poems.

Ecuador's most popular and influential living poet, Jorge Enrique Adoum (b. 1926), is also a member of the *Madrugada* group. He has traveled widely and won many literary prizes not only for his poetry, but also for his drama and fiction. His work reveals the influence of Neruda, perhaps because he served briefly as the Chilean poet's private secretary immediately after World War II. In more recent years he has lived in Paris, where he works for UNESCO. Adoum is known above all as a revolutionary writer who cries out against outmoded traditions, tyrannical governments, and U.S. imperialism, subjects treated in *Informe personal sobre la situación* (1973; personal report on the situation). He also describes the mestizo's lack of identity in Latin American society, and the communication breakdown in the modern world. Adoum's succinct style at times implies his affinity for the elegiac; he also demonstrates witty playfulness through the use of puns and neologisms.

Another prominent representative of Adoum's generation is Francisco Tobar García (b. 1928), a prolific playwright and short-story writer as well as a first-rate poet. As evidenced by his highly lauded *Naufragio* (1961; shipwreck), a major ingredient of his poetry is his sensitivity to undeserved human suffering. His resignation and religious faith are also expressed by a sprinkling of biblical motifs—Job, for example, representing an archetype of both victim and receiver of divine justice. Whereas Tobar García is generally seen as an intellectual practitioner of "pure poetry," Euler Granda (b. 1935) belongs to a group of rebels known as the *tzantzicos* (headhunters, roughly equivalent to the Colombian *nadaístas*), who were influenced by dadaism, surrealism, and the U.S. beatniks. Although much of his poetry denounces the poverty and exploitation of the Ecuadorian Indian, Granda's style differs from the direct conversational approach of the typical revolutionary poet. Rather, he invents sophisticated symbols and metaphors to suggest the abject poverty of peasants making their way to market, spending an entire life without hope, and searching in vain for identity in a world that has passed them by. Two of his most successful volumes are *La voz desbordada* (1962; the overflowing voice) and *El lado flaco* (1968; the weak side).

Peru

Peru's two best-known twentieth-century poets are José Santos Chocano (1875–1934), the flamboyant, bombastic *modernista*, and César Vallejo (discussed above), one of Spanish America's three or four most influential practitioners of the genre. During the 1930s and 1940s the two leading currents in Peruvian poetry were *indianismo* and surrealism. The former is represented by Alejandro Peralta (1896–1973), who painted in graphic detail the customs of the Peruvian Indians and the social injustice they suffer. César Moro (1903–1956) and Emilio Adolfo Westphalen (b. 1911) are generally recognized as the two leaders of the surrealist movement. Moro lived for several years in Mexico, where he declared his affinity for *estridentismo*, but a more significant source of inspiration is French surrealism, evidenced by the montage of evocative, incongruous images ("wheat growing on disused pianos, a gilded frying pan with my mother's portrait") in his posthumous volume *La tortuga ecuestre, y otros poemas* (1957; the equestrian turtle, and other poems). An eccentric, solitary figure of Peruvian letters, Westphalen writes what some critics have called amorphous verses with strong metaphysical and existential overtones. Above all, he dwells on the subject of death, which, as exemplified in *Abolición de la muerte* (1935; abolition of death), is lugubriously framed by shadows, twilight, night, or total blackness.

The winner of Peru's National Prize for Poetry in 1946 and 1961, Martín Adán (pseudonym of Rafael de la Fuente Benavides, 1908–1985) began his career in a baroque, hermetic vein; he gradually simplified his style, striving for greater lucidity and accessibility to his readers. He has developed his themes, which tend to be existential in nature, in traditional Spanish forms such as the sonnet and the *décima* (a stanza of ten octosyllabic lines), and he has also penned many of his poems in free verse. A basic concept emerging from Adán's work is that the compact art of poetry represents a unique source of meaning and order in a world characterized by steadily increasing chaos. The best of his oeuvre has been collected in his *Obra poética, 1928–1971* (1976; poetic work, 1928–1971).

Peruvian poets born during the 1920s include Xavier Sologuren (b. 1922), Alejandro Romualdo (b. 1926), Washington Delgado (b. 1927), Carlos Germán Belli (b. 1927), and Raquel Jodorowsky (b. 1927). A practitioner of "pure poetry" imbued with a lyrical melancholy, Sologuren writes conceptually obscure verses exuding an atmosphere of beauty and peace removed from any specific time or place. In the collection *Vida continua* (1971; continual life) he deals with solitude, nature, and love with occasional incursions into the metaphysical realm. His poetry has elicited praise for its lyrical inspiration and perfection of form. In sharp contrast to Sologuren, Romualdo calls to mind his bombastic compatriot Santos Chocano, al-

though, as one critic has pointed out, Romualdo resembles a
Santos Chocano *modernizado* and *humanizado*. Romualdo mil-
itantly defends freedom and justice for the common man, loudly
proclaiming his refusal to remain silent when protest is called
for and repeatedly alluding to life as a series of *luchas* (struggles). Typical of his many volumes of verse is *Edición extraor-
dinaria* (1958; extraordinary edition), which fuses poetic form
and journalistic content into a vehicle of political denunciation.
Delgado, like Romualdo, is basically a realist, but he is less
militant and more sensitive to tonal modulation than Romualdo. He protests against exploitation and laments the alienation of modern man, whom he considers a victim of antiquated
institutions. He nevertheless views the future with optimism
based on the solidarity and brotherhood of all human beings.
Two of his critically acclaimed volumes are *Para vivir mañana*
(1959; in order to live tomorrow) and *Parque* (1965; park).

Perhaps Peru's most original poetic voice since Vallejo,
Belli invents his own language—difficult at times for the foreign reader—based on Spanish Golden Age vocabulary and
verse forms as well as on the popular idiom of contemporary
Peru. Bitter, ironic, and satirical, he believes his fellow men
have become trapped in a Darwinian environment and dehumanized by their absurd condition. Some critics consider *El
pie sobre el cuello* (1964; the foot on the neck) as Belli's best
book, the title of which symbolizes the relationship between
the oppressor (the foot) and the poet (the neck). To portray
today's deteriorating world and express his personal anguish,
Belli often resorts to such literary weapons as parody, hyperbole, and black humor. Entire poems can often be read as metaphors of frustrated hopes, denied love, and rejected legacies
of history. *¡O hada cibernética!* (1971; O cybernetic fairy!) is a
collection of much of this prolific author's previous poetry.

Born in Chile the daughter of Jewish immigrants from
Poland, Raquel Jodorowsky is one of the best female poets of
Peru, where she has resided for many years. Her work reflects
various aspects of Eastern European culture, namely the legend of the Golem, the paintings of Chagall, the adverse life
of the ghetto, and a Kafkaesque world vision. Her major

themes in *El Ajy Tojen* (1964; the Ajy Tojen) include love (erotic and fraternal), the ravages of time, and the myriad conflicts that give tension and ultimate meaning to human existence. Sonorous, alliterative, and accented with anaphora, Jodorowsky's style blends readily with the urgent message her poetry conveys.

Peru's most prestigious revolutionary poets are Antonio Cisneros (b. 1942) and Javier Heraud (1942–1962). After receiving his doctorate in literature, Cisneros taught for a time at the University of San Marcos in Lima. His *Comentarios reales* (1965; royal commentaries) won the National Prize for Poetry in 1965, and three years later he was awarded the Casa de las Américas prize for *Canto ceremonial contra un oso hormiguero* (1968; ceremonial chant against an anteater). In the latter work he pays tribute to two of his heroes, Karl Marx and Fidel Castro, stressing their meaningful contributions to history. He also poeticizes the guerrilla wars that have raged off and on in Peru for the past two decades. Cisneros writes in free verse with studied precision and controlled passion, qualities that enhance the immediacy and revolutionary vitality of his work. He expands literary dimensions, moreover, by making frequent allusions to historical legends and classical myths. The precocious Heraud was born into a wealthy Peruvian family and entered Lima's Catholic University at the age of sixteen. After visiting the Soviet Union, he traveled to Cuba to study cinematography, and upon his return to Peru joined the revolutionary Peruvian Army of National Liberation. Soon thereafter he was killed by government troops in the northeastern part of the country. During his short life Heraud published two books of verse: *El río* (1960; the river) and *El viaje* (1961; the journey), the principal themes of which are social protest, solitude, death, and love of homeland. His transparent style and unique mélange of bitterness and compassion have attracted a large number of devotees in Peru, where he embodies the intellectual commitment to the revolution of the proletariat. A confirmed idealist, he viewed poetry not only as a weapon of liberation from political oppression, but also as a means of redemption for all mankind.

THE SOUTHERN CONE

Argentina

In Argentina the leading *modernista*, Leopoldo Lugones (1874–1938), wrote verses characterized by fresh imagery and an intensity of expression that revitalized the cliché-ridden language of his predecessors. Two *postmodernistas* worthy of note are Enrique Banchs (1888–1968), a disciplined, classical stylist, and Alfonsina Storni (1892–1938), a forerunner of feminism whose poems are molded by the themes of love, solitude, and resentment of male domination.

As mentioned above, Jorge Luis Borges, Argentina's most prestigious contemporary poet, brought *ultraísmo* from Spain in 1921, thus initiating the avant-garde reaction against *modernismo*. Though short-lived, *ultraísmo* served to unite an elitist group of poets who founded the literary journal *Martín Fierro* and sought to universalize Argentine letters. The 1930s saw a decline in the quality of Argentine poetry. Of vital importance during this decade, however, was the founding by Victoria Ocampo (1891–1979) of the literary journal *Sur*. The 1940s mark a subjective turn inward on the part of most Argentine poets, perhaps because of the sordid political environment. Occasionally referred to as neoromantic, the poetry of this period was dominated by two movements: *invencionismo* (inventionism), which advocated an antirhetorical style and rigorous linguistic discipline; and surrealism, dedicated to transforming the world through the fusion of subjective and objective realities.

Although Argentine poetry has evolved in various directions since midcentury, it nevertheless reveals some basic tendencies. The so-called "parricide generation" of the 1950s (which also includes prose writers) rejected the values of its predecessors, stressing individual freedom and a simplified idiom more accessible to the common man. During the 1960s poets assumed a militant posture against political and social injustice, but more recently a surrealistic subjectivity has once again prevailed.

Leading poets of the 1940s, all of whom continued to publish into the 1970s, are Ricardo E. Molinari (b. 1898), Enrique Molina (b. 1910), César Fernández Moreno (b. 1919), and Alberto Girri (b. 1919). Molinari, whose influence on the younger generation has been extensive, initiated his career as an *ultraista*, cultivating the twisted metaphor in *Imaginero* (1927; image maker). Subsequently, while continuing to write in free verse, he turned as well to classical forms such as the ode and the sonnet. In *El huésped de la melancolía* (1946; the guest of melancholy) his use of surrealistic imagery becomes increasingly evident as does his wistful introspection that, in reality, permeates much of his subsequent work. Existential solitude, a fundamental theme in *Un día, el tiempo, las nubes* (1964; a day, the weather, the clouds), is expressed by means of leitmotifs such as a bird silhouetted against the horizon and an all-enveloping night, agents of separation and death. Many of Molinari's poems have been collected in *Las sombras del pájaro tostado* (1975; the shadows of the roasted bird).

Even more representative of surrealism, Molina's poetry sings of the sea—Molina was a sailor in his youth—of far-off, imaginary islands, and of La Boca, a picturesque district of Buenos Aires. His images are sharp, dreamlike, and evanescent in their metaphoric juxtaposition of the concrete and the abstract ("the errant casket of memory," "the prison bars of your fear"). An inveterate traveler, he finds delight in the boundless, primitive beauties of nature but feels sadness at the sight of human corruption and decadence. Even a commonplace pair of shoes can become a source of inspiration, for they accompany him through life and somehow participate in his poetic impulses. During the 1960s Molina emerged from his comparative isolation and took up the cudgel of the *engagé* poet; his *Monzón napalm* (1968; napalm monsoon), for example, cries out in brilliant hallucinatory imagery against the slaughter in Vietnam.

Fernández Moreno's *Gallego ciego* (1940; blind rooster) associates him with the neoromanticism and *invencionismo* of the 1940s. During the following decade he felt the impact of surrealism, as illustrated by *Veinte años después* (1953; twenty years later). *Argentino hasta la muerte* (1963; Argentine until death) perhaps best typifies his social-protest verses of the

1960s, its colloquial idiom, bitter irony, and expressionistic techniques serving to assail the flaws in Argentine society.

Girri is probably Argentina's most widely known and respected living poet with the exception of Borges. His work resembles Borges's in its philosophical content, but he is more obscure, more hermetic than his renowned colleague. He is also more pessimistic than Borges, viewing the world as a labyrinth of fear and hatred, and Western culture as degenerate and gripped by endemic evil. His first book, *Playa sola* (1946; lonely beach), presents the irreconcilable opposites in human life, opposites the helpless individual finds himself obliged to accept. In *Línea de la vida* (1955; lifeline) Girri rails against the excess of materialism in contemporary society. An existential bent emerges from *Examen de nuestra causa* (1956; examination of our cause), which conveys man's fruitless attempt to conquer solitude through love. "Arte poética" (poetic art), in *La penitencia y el mérito* (1959; penitence and merit), describes the author's struggle with the creative process. And the poems in *El ojo* (1964; the eye) and *Envíos* (1966; dispatches) underscore his pessimistic world vision, the former relying on somber sexual connotations and the latter denouncing false appearances. Girri views poetry as the imperative to strip away the nonessential language of logic and convention that masks mysterious reality. Despite his concerns with form and philosophical content, order and coherence have eluded him, leaving him perpetually frustrated and dissatisfied.

Important Argentine poets born during the 1920s include Rubén Vela (b. 1923), Rafael Squirru (b. 1925), Raúl Gustavo Aguirre (b. 1927), and Ariel Canzani D. (b. 1928). Vela, who spent many years abroad in the diplomatic corps, celebrates Latin America's legendary past, its vast expanses, and its epic upheavals in a series of volumes best exemplified by his *Poemas americanos* (1963; American poems). Also a spokesman for his government abroad, Squirru depicts modern man struggling against the dehumanizing elements of civilization and technology. He is basically an optimist, however, finding consolation in religious faith and inspiration in the giants of government, philosophy, and the arts. Though not mentioned by name, the subject of his "La muerte se llevó al amigo" (death took away the friend), in *Poesía* (1966; poetry), is obviously John F. Kennedy. Aguirre's first book, *Tiempo de la rosa* (1945; time of the rose), reveals an optimist confident of man's steady march toward a better world. Two decades later, though, as seen in *Señales de vida* (1963; signs of life) and *La piedra novedosa* (1968; the novelty stone), he becomes more subjective and introspective, probing his own mysterious psyche and discovering an interiorized landscape of disillusion illumined by flashes of imagination. Today he stands out as one of Argentina's finest surrealists.

Canzani D., who has also spent much time abroad due to his position as an officer in the merchant marine, views poetry as a means of communication and understanding among all men. A constant in his work is the tension between good and evil, a tension sustained metaphorically by the dialectical interplay between beauty and ugliness, day and night, life and death. His poems have appeared in many literary journals, and the best of his works have been collected in *El sueño debe morir mañana* (1962; the dream must die tomorrow) and *El payaso del incendio* (1965; the clown of the fire).

Of the poets born during the 1930s, Juan Gelman (b. 1930), María Elena Walsh (b. 1930), Alejandra Pizarnik (1936–1972), and Luisa Futoransky (b. 1939) rank among the most talented. An inspired revolutionary, Gelman has been imprisoned for his political activities on more than one occasion. He admits to the influence of Vallejo, which perhaps explains his adroit manipulation of everyday language. Love and revolution emerge as his two most important themes, both conveyed with laconic understatement and subtle simplicity. In *Poemas* (1968; poems), his verbal criticism of bourgeois imperialism in Africa is reinforced formalistically by the absence of punctuation, a convention of the bourgeois establishment he abhors. Very different in tone and purpose, Walsh communicates her joie de vivre in verses rich in lyrical fantasy and spontaneous humor. In her work, life in all its dimensions is symbolized by the guitar, the medium par excellence of registering the Argentine heartbeat. Because she also writes for children, her language is often colloquial and, in *El reino del revés* (1964; the topsy-turvy kingdom), her absurd humor recalls *Alice's Adventures in Wonderland*.

Pizarnik, who took her own life at the age of thirty-six, is considered one of Argentina's most brilliant poetic voices. Her somber metaphors and brooding obsessions with night, disintegration, and death inform many of her poems, which tend to be short and surrealistically nightmarish. In the collections *Árbol de Diana* (1962; Diana's tree) and *Los trabajos de la noche* (1965; the work of the night) she exudes a kind of mystic yearning for the unattainable and an ingenious fusion of the real and the fantastic not unlike magical realism. The precision and clarity of her style lend greater intensity to her haunting imagery and intuitive world vision. Futoransky emerges as a kindred spirit of Pizarnik, sharing her pessimistic outlook on life and obsession with death. Her tone, however, suggests caustic dissatisfaction, disillusion, and terror in the face of a world devoid of hope. She envisions a city as a river, a metaphor of life in which, despite cherished moments of love, a stranger (man) is drawn inexorably toward a cemetery. One of her best volumes, *Babel Babel* (1968; Babel Babel), is sprinkled with symbolic motifs suggesting not only tragedy and hopelessness, but also an almost desperate faith in the occult.

Chile

Chile, of all the Spanish American nations, has produced the largest number of innovative, internationally known poets. Indeed, of the eight major figures discussed above, four are Chilean (Mistral, Huidobro, Neruda, and Parra). Another innovator of the older generation is Pablo de Rokha (pseudonym of Carlos Díaz Loyola, 1894–1968), who has been called an antipoet, a storm center in Chilean literature, and a *tremendista* (*tremendismo* is a tendency in modern literature to stress the basest human passions and the most unpleasant and violent aspects of life by means of exaggeration and distortion). Merchant, editor, and professor in addition to being a prolific and dedicated poet, de Rokha thrived on political and literary controversy throughout his turbulent life, which he ended by his own hand. His style is characterized by brilliant but undisciplined imagery, revealing his careful reading of Freud and the surrealists. An ardent Marxist, he attacked the reactionary elements of society and celebrated the potential power of the proletariat. He was also fascinated with the Spanish conquest because of its epic violence, and his heroic confrontation with death, which he apparently anticipated with relish, is the subject matter of his long prose poem *Canto del macho anciano* (1965; song of the old macho).

As illustrated in *Luz adjunta* (1950; attached light), Braulio Arenas's (b. 1913) early poetry typifies surrealism, with its dreamlike atmosphere and its juxtaposition of incongruent images. A competent painter as well as a poet, Arenas relies on visual metaphors to exteriorize a haunting inner landscape and develop the universal themes of love, time, and death. The sea stands out as a major leitmotif in much of his writing, which alternates between classical meters and free verse. More recently he has veered toward simplicity of form as a means of achieving greater profundity, a tendency perhaps most clearly exemplified by *Es el mejor de los mundos* (1970; it's the best of worlds).

Miguel Arteche (b. 1926) belongs to a group of poets who in the 1950s advocated a return to traditional poetic form and content. Thus, instead of free verse they emphasized classical meters, rhyme, and the suppression of all themes generally considered more appropriate for prose fiction. A devout Catholic, Arteche voices his concern with spiritual and metaphysical questions such as solitude and time. His tone, moreover, often turns nostalgic when he allows, for example, a bicycle, a dining room, or a castle to evoke memories from his personal unconscious. Many of his most anthologized poems are taken from his exceptionally fine collection *Destierro y tinieblas* (1963; exile and darkness).

Critics seem to concur that, with the exception of Nicanor Parra, Chile's three best living poets are Enrique Lihn (b. 1929), Efraín Barquero (b. 1930), and Jorge Teillier (b. 1930). The most widely read of these is undoubtedly Lihn, who writes antipoetry comparable to that of Parra. Like Parra, he often speaks directly to the reader, using an everyday vocabulary and a conversational tone to register his protest against injustice and lament his existential solitude. His antipoetry also aims at its own destruction, but he is less cynical, less imagistic than Parra. Many of Lihn's memorable poems appear in his *Algunos poemas* (1972; some poems). Another of his well-received collections is *Al bello aparecer de este lucero* (1983; on the beautiful appearance of this bright star), in which love is treated with contrasting moods ranging from profound sadness and sensitivity to passionate desire and disdain.

Barquero's poetry ranges from the political and satirical to the personal and amatory. In *Epifanías* (1970; epiphanies) he not only demonstrates his mastery of striking imagery and free-verse form, but also rails against the war in Vietnam and, by way of contrast, evokes memories of an idyllic past. Just as Lihn and Parra have much in common, Teillier's work approaches that of Barquero. His style relies on the tensive quality of the metaphor, but at the same time it is clear, intimate, and even colloquial. Like Barquero, Teillier writes principally in free verse, and a nostalgic quality permeates many of his poems. His themes of love, friendship, and time are given new poetic dimensions by his stylized visions of southern Chile, where he spent his youth. Thus, in *Poemas del país de nunca jamás* (1968; poems of the never-never land) he recalls a ticking clock in a tiny railway station, a quiet evening in a remote pueblo, a rain-soaked train headed north, and a marriage ceremony in a rustic chapel.

An outstanding representative of Chile's younger generation is Marjorie Agosín (b. 1955), a militant feminist and U.S. resident, who has strongly censured the military regime in her native land. The three collections of her poetry to date are *Chile: Gemidos y cantares* (1977; Chile: wails and songs), *Conchalí* (1980; Conchalí), and *Brujas y algo más* (1984; *Witches and Other Things,* 1985). In *Brujas y algo más*, probably her best volume, she sets forth a wide variety of themes including erotic love, political corruption, and the creative process.

Paraguay

Prior to 1940 Paraguayan literature was dominated by the historical essay. The 1940s, however, witnessed a literary revival with the appearance of two important poets: Hérib Campos Cervera (1908–1953) and Josefina Pla (b. 1909). Paraguay's first *vanguardista*, Campos Cervera published only one volume of poetry during his short life: *Ceniza redimida* (1950; redeemed ashes). *Palabras del hombre secreto* (1955; words of a secret man) appeared posthumously. As evidenced by the flow of nostalgic images evoking his youth in his native land (he lived for many years in Argentina), Campos Cervera was influenced by surrealism; his work also provides a vibrant testimony of the political realities of Paraguay. A dramatist, art historian, and ceramicist, Pla too wrote surrealistic poetry during the 1940s. She later veered toward classical simplicity, as seen in *Rostros en el agua* (1963; faces in the water), generally considered her best collection. Still, vestiges of the surreal remain in virtually all her poems, the principal theme of which is love. Pla was born in the Canary Islands (Spain) and uprooted to Paraguay after her marriage to a Paraguayan in 1927. She has contributed a great deal to the cultural life of one of Spanish America's most backward nations.

The leading member of the subsequent generation is Eliro Romero (b. 1926), a truculent poet who has traveled throughout much of the world denouncing the tyrannical government of Paraguay and, at the same time, nostalgically recording memories of his homeland, especially the desolate northern region known as the Chaco. Alternately lyrical and conversational, his tone can also be wistful or savagely satirical, depending on his subject matter and mood. Romero's poetry has appropriately been called a monument to his unhappy fatherland, a label particularly applicable to *Un relámpago herido* (1967; wounded lightning). Roque Vallejos (b. 1943) stands out among the Generation of 1960, a group of Paraguayan poets who see the contemporary world in shambles and endeavor to rescue it with their writings. Vallejos's utterances of despair, however, suggest that he may have abandoned this goal. Thus, in *Los arcángeles ebrios* (1963; the drunken archangels) he presents a series of images proclaiming the death of God—Nietzsche inevitably comes to mind—due to His horrendous errors and the threat of imminent disaster to the human race.

Uruguay

Uruguay's Julio Herrera y Reissig (1875–1910) remains to this day one of his nation's most renowned poets. The outstanding symbolist of the *modernistas*, he wrote verses ranging from simple lyricism to the extreme complexity of the subsequent *ultraísta* movement. Two of Uruguay's leading female poets are Juana de Ibarbourou (1895–1979) and Sara de Ibáñez (1910–1971). Known also as "Juana de América," de Ibarbourou achieved great prestige and popularity for her *Raíz salvaje* (1920; savage root) and *La rosa de los vientos* (1930; the rose of the winds). These early poems sing primarily of sensuous love—her entire oeuvre is intensely subjective, even narcissistic—and nature. In her later volumes, *Perdida* (1950; lost) and *Oro y tormenta* (1956; gold and torment), her pagan verses yield to a somber preoccupation with fleeting time and a horror of death and nothingness. The mother of the Mexican poet Ulalume González de León (discussed above), de Ibáñez is admired for her perfectly structured, rhythmically sonorous poems about love, nature, solitude, and death. She successfully revived the Spanish Golden Age *lira*, a stanza of five or six lines, each of seven or eleven syllables. Her volumes entitled *Hora ciega* (1943; blind hour) and *Apocalipsis XX* (1970; apocalypse XX) illustrate, respectively, her mastery of the hermetic symbol and her extraordinary ability to create an ambience of imminent disaster.

A contemporary of de Ibáñez, Juan Cunha (b. 1910) is a traditional poet who also speaks of love, nature, solitude, and death in classical meters and consistent rhyme patterns. His overriding theme, though, is nostalgia for a past that he would like to relive. Despite his prolific production, Cunha has not received the recognition he deserves. His *Sueño y un retorno de un campesino* (1951; dream and a return of a peasant) exhibits many of his most highly regarded poems.

Mario Benedetti, whose novels about the drab life of the Uruguayan capital are discussed in the preceding chapter, develops similar themes in his poetry, although the latter tends to be more revolutionary than his prose fiction. Critics generally consider his *Poemas de la oficina* (1958; poems of the office) as his best collection, its principal subject being the oppressive bureaucracy and dreary existence of office workers in a nation plagued by social and economic malaise. A strong supporter of Fidel Castro's Cuba, where he has lived for a number of years, Benedetti detests the rigid class structure of traditional Latin American societies and uses certain leitmotifs to represent the changes he hopes some day to see realized. Thus, a raised drawbridge that, in his view, should be permanently lowered symbolizes a means of isolating the masses and preserving the privileges of the rich. And the museum of the future in Benedetti's poetic imagination will serve only to house relics of an obsolete bourgeoisie.

Another revolutionary poet, journalist, and frequent visitor to Cuba is Carlos María Gutiérrez (b. 1926), whose *Diario del cuartel* (1970; barracks diary) was written while he was incarcerated during the regime of Uruguayan President Pacheco Areco. Gutiérrez was awarded the Casa de las Américas prize for this collection, which bitterly rejects the bourgeois establishment of the entire Western world. Thus, readers are urged to "vote anonymously" for the coming revolution by preparing Molotov cocktails and "casting their ballots" onto the streets. The author also describes his sudden awakening to the beauties of poetry and to the injustice around him upon reading for the first time the works of César Vallejo in a Montevideo bar. Other major influences on Gutiérrez's poetry are Neruda and Che Guevara.

A resident of Mexico in recent years, Saúl Ibargoyen Islas (b. 1930) is less vitriolic in his world outlook than Gutiérrez, but he nevertheless criticizes what displeases him in Uruguay and elsewhere. His "Arte poética" (poetic art) in *Pasión para una sombra* (1959; passion for a shadow) conveys both his aesthetic and social ideals, the emphasis being on the use of popular speech patterns, the revelation of injustice, and the invention of a poeticized, imaginary reality beyond the limits of the objective world. In this same collection Ibargoyen Islas astutely observes human behavior and expresses his disillusion and anguish over the *nada* (nothingness) of routine, everyday life.

Circe Maia (b. 1932) resembles Ibargoyen Islas in her ability to create a poeticized, imaginary reality, but she does not seem to share his concern for injustice or his anguish over the void in everyday life. As illustrated by *En el tiempo* (1958; in time), *El puente* (1970; the bridge), and *Dos voces* (1981; two voices), she paints images familiar to all her readers in a direct, conversational style, but through the magic of her pen, the daily world suddenly comes alive with mystery, full of potential for beauty and, on occasion, for terror. She also displays a philosophical bent and an exceptional capacity for illuminating her feelings via symbolic details of her immediate surroundings.

4 ▪ DRAMA

Until approximately the middle of the twentieth century the drama was seen as the stepchild of Spanish American letters, having emerged as a viable genre only after World War II. The nineteenth century, with its emphasis on romantic melodrama, social-protest realism, and the short comedy of Spanish origin known as the *sainete*, produced no playwrights of universal stature. Indeed, with the exception of the theater of the River Plate region (Argentina and Uruguay), the drama continued to stagnate in superficiality and naturalistic diatribe during the first two decades of the present century. The single major figure of this period is Florencio Sánchez (1875–1910), a Uruguayan who spent much of his short life in Buenos Aires. Influenced by Ibsen, Sánchez wrote prolifically (twenty plays between 1903 and 1909) about human conflicts stemming principally from the flood of immigrants entering the River Plate region and the resultant changes in both urban and rural life. Sánchez's theater is realistic, moralistic, and at times simplistically symbolic, but he initiated a more serious approach to the genre, probing contemporary issues with unprecedented depth and intensity and introducing modern techniques, all of which would leave a lasting impression on future Spanish American dramatists. Sánchez's two best-known works are *La gringa* (1904; *The Foreign Girl*, 1942; later tr., *The Immigrant Girl*, 1961), about a rural Argentine landowner's confrontation with a more progressive farmer of Italian origin, and *Barranca abajo* (1905; *Down the Gully*, 1961), which depicts the gradual decline of a gaucho family, culminating in the suicide of the father-protagonist, Don Zoilo.

The 1920s and 1930s represent a period of experimental ferment in the Spanish American theater, most of the new activity occurring in Mexico City and Buenos Aires. In Mexico the so-called Grupo de los Siete (founded 1923) reacted against the socialistic didacticism inspired by the revolution of 1910. More important on the Mexican scene, however, were the Teatro de Ulises (founded 1928) and the Teatro de Orientación (founded 1932), both of which sought to introduce universal themes, formal rigor, and more imaginative staging techniques. Somewhat less elitist but equally innovative, the Teatro del Pueblo (founded 1930) and La Máscara (founded 1937), both in Buenos Aires, also opened new vistas to the theatergoing public, elevating art and craftsmanship to the same level of importance as plot and thematic content. Additional groups with similar goals include La Cueva (founded 1936) of Cuba; Areyto (named after an indigenous dance-drama of the Caribbean and founded 1938) of Puerto Rico; and the Instituto de Teatro de la Universidad de Chile and the Academia de Artes Dramáticas of Cuba, both established during World War II.

The predominant influence of the 1920s and 1930s was Luigi Pirandello, whose *Six Characters in Search of an Author* (1922) demonstrated the relativism of reality and the tenuousness of the boundary between life and art. These concepts as well as the Italian playwright's belief in soliciting the spectator's participation in the drama were readily accepted by his Spanish American counterparts. Although the experimental groups of this period were mostly elitist, ephemeral, and, in the short term, ineffectual, they nevertheless laid the groundwork for a theater of broader universal perspectives, deeper psychological penetration, and expanded poetic dimensions.

The theater flourished during the 1950s despite increasing competition from television and repressive government censorship in large portions of the continent. The development of the genre was enhanced by foreign immigration, a growing, better-educated middle class, and a new generation of playwrights, many of whom received academic training in Europe and the United States. In the following decade the revolutionary Cuban government stimulated interest by sponsoring international theatrical festivals and awarding annual prizes for the most outstanding productions. Although the Spanish American theater has yet to attain the heights that prose fiction and poetry have reached, some critics have alluded to "the boom of the 1960s and 1970s," basing their judgment on the exceptionally fine dramatists who gained recognition during this period. Moreover, the list of major theatrical centers today includes not only Buenos Aires and Mexico City, but also Havana, Santiago, Montevideo, San Juan, Caracas, Lima, and Cali (Colombia). The major foreign influences on contemporary Spanish American dramatists—Bertolt Brecht, Eugene O'Neill, Jean-Paul Sartre, Albert Camus, Eugène Ionesco, Samuel Beckett, Antonin Artaud, Arthur Miller, and Peter Weiss—suggest that the theater of our southern neighbors has assimilated elements from a wide variety of sources. These elements, however, have been molded to fit the peculiar circumstances of developing societies struggling to determine their individual identities within the broad framework of Western culture. Thus, dramatists have increasingly articulated visions of reality that are both national and universal in scope.

Serious theater in Spanish America today can be divided into two broad categories: traditional realism and avant-gardism, the latter an outgrowth of the experimental works of the 1920s and 1930s. Realistic theater, which has been enriched by occasional injections of experimental elements, tends to be highly politicized, concentrating on the themes of injustice, revolution, and repression. Outright propaganda is rare because the new generation of dramatists prefers to express political commitment through action and representation of complex human relations. Additional realistic themes are urban violence, racial prejudice, the mounting frustrations of the middle class, and the erosion of the family, traditionally Spanish America's most revered institution. Since the mid-1960s the most pressing social issues have often been presented in what have become known as *creaciones colectivas*, that is, works written by several authors. These joint efforts have enjoyed particular success in Buenos Aires and Cali. Another form of realistic theater is the docudrama, which purports to deal objectively with well-known issues, usually political, of wide popular appeal.

Often characterized by the irrational, the fantastic, and the use of expressionistic techniques, avant-garde theater has been the forum not only for the presentation of existential and absurdist themes, but also for the treatment of cruelty and the grotesque. Dramatists often deliberately alienate the audience through the presentation of a strange, disjointed, or contrived reality instead of an imitation of everyday life. The avant-gardists also utilize masks, role-playing rituals, and abrupt temporal fragmentation in order to convey the instability of the individual identity in the technological world of today. Prominent among the more recent avant-garde groups are the Teatro Libre and the Teatro Abierto, of Argentina; the Teatro Experimental of Cali; the Teatro Rajatabla of Venezuela; and the Teatro Estudio of Cuba.

Despite the economic crisis of the 1980s, the future for the Spanish American theater remains promising. As a result of stimuli provided by governments, universities, and professional groups, most Spanish American countries have greatly improved the quality of theater created within their borders. While many of the playwrights who established their reputations during the 1950s and 1960s have continued to write prolifically, a new talented generation has emerged in the past decade. As in most parts of the Western world, the commercial theater still spawns plays devoid of intellectual and artistic merit, but the best of today's Spanish American dramatists are consummate craftsmen well versed in dramatic theory, alert to the latest trends, and committed to the improvement of both their art and their societies. Perhaps because of the grave problems plaguing the region, contemporary Spanish American theater can hardly be described as abstract or literary, but rather as a provocative, living art form designed to jolt audiences and effect changes. It is not surprising, then, that in recent years this rapidly evolving genre has become the focus of increasing critical attention. In addition to a steady flow of monographs and historical overviews, several periodicals devoted exclusively to the theater have been established. The best of these are *Conjunto*, published in Cuba, and the *Latin American Theatre Review*, published by the Center of Latin American Studies at the University of Kansas. If, as some critics believe, social ferment breeds superior art, the prospects for the Spanish American theater are better than ever.

MAJOR DRAMATISTS

Ten playwrights stand out for their extraordinary contributions to the contemporary Spanish American drama. Not only have they captured the immediate realities of their strife-torn lands, but they have also displayed a remarkable ability for assimilating foreign influences and evolving their own subjective visions of the world, which, coupled with the use of innovative strategies, have given universal appeal to their work. Their plays represent the most significant trends and thus constitute a kind of microcosm of the genre.

RODOLFO USIGLI

Born in Mexico City into a family of Italian and Polish origins, Rodolfo Usigli (1905–1979) dedicated most of his life to the theater. In 1935 he received a grant from the Rockefeller Foundation to study dramatic composition at Yale University, after which he returned to Mexico City and began the most productive period of his career. He taught theatrical history and technique at the University of Mexico and held diplomatic posts in France, Lebanon, and Norway.

The bulk of Usigli's theater can be divided into three broad categories, the first consisting of social or political satire, the second dealing with abnormal psychology, and the third depicting dramatic episodes of Mexican history. *El gesticulador* (1943; the imposter) and *Corona de sombra* (1943; *Crown of Shadows*, 1947) are generally considered his best works. The former, a deft portrayal of an impecunious history professor named César Rubio who assumes the identity of a deceased revolutionary hero to gain fortune and political power, rails against the betrayal of revolutionary ideals and the fraud prevalent at all levels of Mexican life. The cyclical recurrence of events in this drama underscores the archetypal struggle between good and evil as well as the author's belief in the unalterable essence of the human condition. César Rubio, moreover, represents Usigli's concept of the mythical hero, a charismatic leader who, at a crucial point in history, synthesizes conflicting currents and sets a new course for his nation. As the title suggests, a major theme of *El gesticulador* is the mask that, according to Usigli, the Mexican dons to protect himself from aggression and, at the same time, to compensate for his feelings of inferiority. Ironically, as seen in the case of César Rubio, the imposter is often capable of assimilating the characteristics of the mask and making them an integral part of himself.

One of a trilogy of historical dramas, *Corona de sombra* treats the attempt by Maximilian and Carlota to establish an empire in Mexico in the 1860s. An imaginative interpretation rather than a historical account, this play treats Maximilian as a sincere but weak leader who endeavors to help the Mexican people, and Carlota as an overly ambitious wife condemned to sixty years of madness. Both protagonists, however, emerge as victims sacrificed to the cause of Mexico's political unification and struggle against foreign intervention. The initial action takes place in 1927 in the demented Carlota's bedroom on the day of her death, but dimensions are expanded by skillfully manipulated flashbacks illuminating critical moments from the past.

Corona de fuego (1960; crown of fire) and *Corona de luz* (1963; crown of light) are the other titles of Usigli's historical trilogy. The former treats Cortés's execution of Cuauhtémoc after his conquest of New Spain and the Aztec leader's emergence as Mexico's national hero. Whereas *Corona de sombra* depicts the political unification of Mexico, *Corona de luz* dramatizes the nation's spiritual unification, a process brought to fruition by the sixteenth-century Virgin of Guadalupe legend, which, according to Usigli, the Spaniards fostered as a means of indoctrinating the Indians in the Christian faith. Usigli's intuitive dramatizations of the past not only reveal fundamental aspects of human behavior but also provide greater insight into present-day Mexican reality.

Two of Usigli's greatest box-office hits were *El niño y la niebla* (1950; the child and the fog), an emotion-packed naturalistic tragedy of congenital insanity, and *Jano es una muchacha* (1952; Jano is a girl), which caused a scandal because of its candid treatment of prostitution and sexual hypocrisy. The psychological themes of the double and the authenticity of the self dominate *Mientras amemos* (1956; while we love), in which the sterile protagonist hires a man to father his wife's child so that the latter can inherit her fortune. In a somewhat similar vein, *Los viejos* (1971; the old ones) dramatizes a series of meetings between a young and an old playwright, both of whom represent aspects of the author. An example of self-conscious metatheater, this play also deals with the complex creative process involving the development of characters, the reversal of roles, and the fusion of identities. *¡Buenos días, señor Presidente!* (1972; good morning, Mr. President!) represents a modern version of Calderón de la Barca's seventeenth-century masterpiece *La vida es sueño* (*Life Is a Dream*), but its real subject is the Mexican student revolt of 1968.

Usigli wrote extensively on the Mexican theater and dramatic theory, his most basic tenet being that Mexican playwrights should treat themes related to national realities; the theater should not mirror reality, however, but instead should strive for an artistic, fictionalized representation of its essential features. Although his plots are usually tightly structured, they are occasionally marred by contrived situations. In *El gesticulador*, for example, César Rubio has the same name and the same birthplace as the revolutionary hero he impersonates. As demonstrated by much of his oeuvre, Usigli is more concerned with the presentation of ideas than with the development of characters in real-life situations.

Despite his stress on national themes, Usigli has enjoyed greater success abroad than any other Mexican playwright with the possible exception of Emilio Carballido (discussed below). He has been influenced by numerous foreign authors including the ancient Greeks, Molière, John Galsworthy, the French playwright Henri-René Lenormand, and Bernard Shaw. In 1972, when he received the prestigious National Prize of Letters,

Usigli was recognized not only as the creator of the modern Mexican theater but also as one of Latin America's most distinguished dramatists.

RENÉ MARQUÉS

A native of Arecibo, Puerto Rico, René Marqués (mentioned earlier in the chapter on fiction) earned a degree in agronomy in 1942, after which he took courses in literature at the University of Madrid. In 1949 he received a Rockefeller grant to study theater arts at Columbia University, and upon returning to Puerto Rico he initiated a literary career that would make him the Commonwealth's best-known contemporary man of letters. He died in San Juan, having established a solid reputation not only as a dramatist, but also as a novelist and short-story writer.

Marqués's basic preoccupation as a writer was Puerto Rico's political future. An outspoken advocate of independence, he abhorred the domination of his homeland by the United States, which has led to the industrialization of the island's agricultural economy and to the contamination of its Hispanic culture. Marqués also sharply condemned his fellow countrymen who barter their national identity for economic gains.

Most critics agree that Marqués will be remembered primarily as a dramatist whose works revitalized the modern Puerto Rican theater. His most popular play, if not his best, is *La carreta* (1951; *The Oxcart*, 1960), depicting the plight of peasants who leave their farm in search of a better life, first in San Juan and then in New York. After suffering the dehumanizing misfortunes of slum life, they return to the land Marqués believes they should never have abandoned. A naturalistic drama replete with symbolism, *La carreta* attacks the technological progress so attractive to many Puerto Ricans and advocates a return to the traditional values of the past. Because of its basic theme and harsh view of life in the United States, this play has been called Puerto Rico's national drama and a theatrical cry for political independence.

Marqués's most highly acclaimed critical successes are *Un*

niño azul para esa sombra (1958; a blue child for that shadow)
and *Los soles truncos* (1958; *The Fanlights*, in George Woodyard, ed., *The Modern Stage in Latin America: Six Plays*, 1971).
The former is a poetic treatment of an idealistic boy, Michelín,
whose frustration and suicide result from the rift between his
Americanized mother and his revolutionary father. The color
blue of the title symbolizes idealism, and the shadow, Puerto
Rico's submission to American influence. Another major symbol
is a *quenepo* tree that Michelín identifies with both his father
and Puerto Rico's past. When his mother destroys the *quenepo*
by pouring poison into its roots and his father dies alone in
New York, Michelín ingests poison, emerging as a symbol of a
people victimized by an alien culture. *Un niño azul para esa
sombra* is a landmark in Marqués's oeuvre not only because of
its poetic treatment of the Puerto Rican political situation but
also because of its deftly organized flashbacks and its highly
effective use of lighting and auditory effects.

Similar devices characterize *Los soles truncos*, in which
three poverty-stricken, guilt-ridden sisters of a once wealthy
family are being evicted from their decaying mansion by creditors eager to convert it into a hotel for American tourists. Upon
the death of the eldest sister, Hortensia, the other two evoke
memories of the past explaining the reasons for their mental
torment. The theme of purification is conveyed when, in the
final scene, they bedeck themselves in the family jewelry—
symbolic of their glittering past—and set fire to the mansion.
Although the real villain is time, an irresistible force that destroys both the physical and the ideal, the drama can also be
read as an allegory of Puerto Rico's collective guilt and expia-
tion after centuries of domination by foreign powers.

Even more politically motivated are *La muerte no entrará
en palacio* (1956; death shall not enter the palace) and *La casa
sin reloj* (1960; the house without a clock). A thinly veiled portrait of Governor Luis Muñoz Marín, who held office from 1948
to 1964, *La muerte no entrará en palacio* satirizes a political
figure, Don José, who, in the course of the action, changes from
a sensitive, sympathetic opponent of colonialism to a petty tyrant and supporter of Puerto Rico's commonwealth status. The

tragic ending occurs when Don José's daughter Casandra murders her father in defense of the island's political freedom and Hispanic culture. The political overtones of *La casa sin reloj* are enriched with elements of the absurd and the search for authenticity in a rootless, atemporal world. At the beginning of this play the protagonist, Micaela, is presented as a confused woman whose bourgeois husband, Pedro, conforms to the status quo. His brother José, to whom Micaela is attracted, supports the Puerto Rican independence movement and is forced to hide from the police in his brother's home. Meanwhile Micaela becomes increasingly aware of the lack of purpose in her life—conveyed by verbal nonsense and disjointed conversations with her family—and determines to effect change through political action. Her climactic murder of José, a Christ figure as well as the embodiment of her ideals, signifies her assumption of the guilt Puerto Ricans bear for their submission to exploitation by the United States.

Marqués's most significant existential drama is *El apartamiento* (1964; the apartment), a vision of modern man's degradation resulting from technology and specialization. The setting is a windowless apartment occupied by an aging couple, Elpidio and Carola, whose sterile existence is controlled by two heartless inspectors. In contrast to their past, when Elpidio was a successful composer and Carola a talented poet, they now devote themselves to meaningless activities, Elpidio to assembling a puzzle in the form of a man and Carola to measuring segments of blue ribbon. Ordinary tasks such as cleaning and cooking have been eliminated from their lives because the air of the apartment is scientifically filtered and food delivered regularly by a dumbwaiter. The mechanical routine and resultant atmosphere of absurdity in *El apartamiento* bring to mind Sartre's *No Exit* and Beckett's *Waiting for Godot*. Marqués, however, introduces three symbolic characters designed to lend greater depth to his protagonists and enrich the play's thematic content. Lucio and Terra, the youthful doubles of Elpidio and Carola, evoke the idealistic spirit of the past until they are murdered by the inspectors, leaving the protagonists once again with nothing but their sterile routine to fill a timeless void. The dénouement is triggered by the sudden appearance of Tlo, an Indian in fetters, who embodies the cultural roots of the Spanish American man. Elpidio and Carola refuse to obey the inspectors' orders to kill Tlo but instead set him free, a metaphoric act suggesting that they too might eventually break out of their prison and recapture the creative spirit of their youth. *El apartamiento* is a work of universal dimensions; in addition, it contains elements of a reality peculiar to Spanish America.

Marqués also wrote three biblical/historical dramas, the best of which is *Sacrificio en el Monte Moriah* (1968; sacrifice on Mount Moriah). Based on the story of Abraham's willingness to sacrifice his son Isaac to prove his faith in God, this play deviates from the biblical myth, transforming Abraham into a morally corrupt individual who gives his wife Sarah to the pharaoh of Egypt for riches and political asylum. The author implies that Abraham's actions parallel those of Governor Muñoz Marín, who sold out his homeland to the United States for material benefits. The proposed sacrifice of Isaac, moreover, alludes to the loss of Puerto Rican youths in the Vietnam war. The other plays of this group are *David y Jonatán* (David and Jonathan) and *Tito y Berenice* (Titus and Berenice), which were published in *Dos dramas de amor, poder y desamor* (1970; two dramas of love, power, and hate).

René Marqués distinguished himself as a dramatist deeply concerned with both the fate of his homeland and the twentieth-century human condition. To convey his political and existential ideals he created works still acclaimed by critics and a broadly based public. Although he is known as a traditionalist opposed to industrialization and modern technology, he will also be remembered, paradoxically perhaps, for his imaginative experiments with avant-garde dramatic form and stage craftsmanship.

CARLOS SOLÓRZANO

Although a native of Guatemala, Carlos Solórzano (b. 1922) has resided in Mexico since 1939 and is often listed among

Mexico's leading playwrights. After completing his doctorate in literature from Mexico's National University, he studied dramatic art in France for two years (1948–50). During this time he was strongly influenced by Albert Camus and the Belgian dramatist Michel de Ghelderode, both of whom he came to know well. From 1952 until 1962 he was director of the University Theater in Mexico, and since 1962 he has lectured on drama and Latin American literature at his alma mater.

Solórzano began his career with the presentation of *Doña Beatriz* (1951; Doña Beatriz), the dramatization of an episode during the Spanish conquest of Guatemala. The proud, fanatically religious protagonist, wife of the conquistador Pedro de Alvarado, embodies long-standing European tradition, whereas her strong-willed husband symbolizes the dynamic vitality of the Renaissance transported to the New World. The future of Latin America is represented by Pedro's mestizo daughter Leonor, the only survivor of the climactic deluge that brings the play to its conclusion.

Also typical of Solórzano's theater is *El hechicero* (1955; the magician), a carefully structured tragedy that takes place in a starving medieval town. To save his beloved fellow citizens from their plight, the alchemist Merlín undertakes the search for the philosophers' stone, the hypothetical substance that would convert base metal into gold. Before he can complete his task, however, Merlín is murdered by his wife and her lover, who hope to steal the magic formula. The play ends with the revelation that Merlín's ashes, which have been scattered over the countryside, have fertilized the barren lands and made them bloom again. Thus, Merlín accomplishes what he set out to achieve, not through the discovery of the philosophers' stone, but through his selfless commitment to his fellow man. *El hechicero* presents a mélange of existentialist ideals and bold expressionistic symbols, but it is set in the classical mold, Merlín symbolizing generosity, his wife avarice, and her lover moral weakness. Moreover, the town citizens commenting on the action perform a function similar to that of the Greek chorus.

Solórzano's most widely acclaimed drama is *Las manos de Dios* (1957; *The Hands of God*, 1968), in which a peasant girl named Beatriz accepts the aid of the devil to free her unjustly incarcerated brother. Instead of the traditional embodiment of evil, however, the devil represents freedom, justice, and rebellion against the oppression of both the civil authorities and the Church. At the instigation of the priest, the citizens sacrifice Beatriz for her "crimes" against the Church, leaving the devil to carry on the struggle for individual freedom. *Las manos de Dios* emerges as a showcase of styles and influences. The archetypal struggle between good and evil is set forth in a biblical framework, but the inversion of roles played by the devil and the priest reflects the existentialists' rejection of timeworn tradition and hypocritical authoritarianism. The trappings of Greek tragedy include the chorus, which alternately affirms and denies the words of the antagonists, and the series of agons or conflicts giving structure to the plot. And the injections of song, dance, and pantomime suggest the possible influence of Brecht.

Solórzano has also written several one-act plays, the best of which is *Los fantoches* (1959; the puppets). An excellent example of the theater of the absurd, *Los fantoches* draws a gloomy portrait of the human condition based on the Mexican ritual known as the "Burning of Judas" the Saturday before Easter, when giant Judas figures made of papier-mâché are set ablaze with firecrackers to represent the punishment of mankind's most notorious traitor. The setting of the play is a storeroom where an old, blind, deaf-mute puppetmaker has imprisoned his creations: a young man, an old man, a woman, a thinker, an artist, and Judas. The puppets display explosive cartridges painted on their chests that destroy them when they are chosen, individually and at random, by the puppetmaker's daughter and led out of their "prison." Each of the puppets is dedicated to a worthless, repetitious activity conveying the absurdity of life without purpose in a world created by a silent, destructive god. To underscore the absurd, the young man beats a drum, the old man counts pieces of colored paper, the woman talks of love, the thinker seeks the reason for their confinement, the artist creates worthless works of art, Judas remains silent, and the old puppetmaker dozes. In the final scene the puppetmaker's daughter, dressed in the folkloric garb of Death, enters to choose her last victim; she spins about in the middle of the stage, stops suddenly, and, as the curtain falls, points with a menacing gesture in the direction of the audience.

Another of Solórzano's best one-acters is *El crucificado* (1957; *The Crucifixion*, in Gerardo Luzuriaga and Robert S. Rudder, eds., *The Orgy: Modern One-Act Plays from Latin America*, 1974). This play is a combination of biblical myth and Mexican folklore, expressing Solórzano's denunciation of Christianity, which he depicts as a bloody, sacrificial cult of fanatics. The action centers on a dramatization of the Passion of Christ in a Mexican village. Jesús, the protagonist, agrees unwillingly to play the role of the Savior, and during the presentation, having become thoroughly intoxicated, he imagines himself to be the true Jesus. The climax occurs when the play's protagonist, at his own urging, is actually crucified by the villagers. In the concluding lines the victim's sweetheart, Magdalena, weeps bitterly for having been abandoned by "the poor fool" who "thought that with his death we would gain something."

Solórzano's theatrical oeuvre also includes *Mea culpa* (1956; my fault), the confessions of an aging judge—in reality Pontius Pilate—who admits to having sentenced a man to die unjustly, and a mad, guilt-ridden priest seeking forgiveness for having tormented generations of sinners with threats of damnation; *Cruce de vías* (1959; railroad crossing), an absurdist, expressionistic representation of destroyed illusions experienced by two would-be lovers; and *El sueño del ángel* (1960; the angel's sleep), a dialogue between an aging, repentant woman and her cruel guardian angel, who will not permit her to forget a transgression in her past.

One of Latin America's foremost dramatists, Solórzano has been instrumental in the development of an avant-garde theater of ideas designed to replace realistic regionalism with a more poetically conceived, universal art form. An eclectic by nature, he has assimilated elements of classicism, expressionism, and psychoanalysis, but his primary preoccupations echo those of the French existentialists of the post-World War II era. Thus, in Solórzano's mythology individual freedom emerges as the equivalent of good, oppression as synonymous with evil, and religion as an escape from responsibility. His works universalize the Spanish American experience by dramatizing the intellectual and psychic currents undermining the established order of today's world.

EMILIO CARBALLIDO

Emilio Carballido (b. 1925) is a native of Córdoba, a provincial city in the state of Veracruz, Mexico, but he has spent many years of his life in Mexico City. After studying at the National University, he initiated his career as a dramatist in the late 1940s, a period of ferment and rapid development in the Spanish American theater. In 1950 he received a Rockefeller grant to study theater arts in New York, where he spent two profitable years. He has lectured at the National University, the University of Veracruz, and at several institutions in the United States. His reputation has been enhanced by the increasing number of translations of his works, which have also been presented in countries throughout Europe and the Western Hemisphere. He admits to having been strongly influenced by the classical Greek theater, Jean Giraudoux, Jean Anouilh, Tennessee Williams, and Arthur Miller.

Although Carballido is known for his felicitous fusion of realism and fantasy, his early works are entirely realistic, three examples being *Rosalba y los Lloveros* (1950; Rosalba and the Lloveros), *Felicidad* (1955; happiness), and *La danza que sueña la tortuga* (1956; the dance the turtle dreams). One of his most popular creations, *Rosalba y los Lloveros* is a satirical comedy of manners contrasting the social constrictions of life in the provinces with the more open, cosmopolitan life in the Mexican capital. Rosalba, a young *capitalina* with modern views on sex and Freudian psychology, arrives with her mother in a provincial town to visit her uncle's family. Among several problems she encounters in the old family home is that of her cousin Lázaro, whose withdrawal stems from the shame he has brought on himself and his family for fathering the illegitimate child of a servant. A major portion of the plot involves Rosalba's efforts, hilarious at times, to help Lázaro and the family overcome their stultifying inhibitions, but she too profits from the experience by becoming less the amateur psychologist and a wiser, more compassionate human being.

Whereas *Rosalba y los Lloveros* concentrates on comic situations and complexity of plot, *Felicidad* probes character in greater depth within a simplified framework of events occurring in Mexico City. The protagonist is a selfish, ill-tempered schoolteacher, Mario Ramírez Cuevas, whose mistreatment of his wife and children comes perilously close to causing their financial ruin and separation. Above all else, however, the characters represent penetrating studies of mediocrity, people incapable of achieving the happiness referred to ironically in the title. *La danza que sueña la tortuga*, perhaps the best of the three realistic comedies mentioned here, focuses once again on a provincial family and its complex interrelationships. Through a misunderstanding, one of the sons, Beto, is thought to be in love with his aunt Rocío and supposedly on the verge of proposing marriage. Beto's father, Victor, violently opposes the match, which leads to a series of tense but poignant episodes displaying Carballido's unerring sense of the comic and exceptional ability to delineate character.

Critics generally consider *La hebra de oro* (1956; *The Golden Thread*, in *The Golden Thread, and Other Plays*, 1970) as one of Carballido's most important works because it represents his first successful attempt to combine realism and fantasy. The action begins with the return of two elderly ladies, Leonor Luna and Adela Sidel, to the deteriorating estate of their grandson, Silvestre, who has been missing for several years. The appearance of a mysterious stranger named Man—actually Silvestre's spirit—signals the intrusion of the oneiric into the everyday world of the plot. Leonor, whose compassionate nature contrasts with that of the bitter, paranoiac Adela, serves as the medium or vehicle for resurrecting Silvestre. The latter eventually emerges as a metaphor of the vital, creative forces generating the action and, when Leonor assumes the task of raising a child abandoned on the decaying property, conveying the theme of cyclical regeneration.

El día que se soltaron los leones (1957; *The Day They Turned the Lions Loose*, in William I. Oliver, ed., *Voices of Change in the Spanish American Theater*, 1971) and *El relojero de Córdoba* (1960; *The Clockmaker from Córdoba*, in *The Golden Thread, and Other Plays*, 1970) also stand out among Carballido's many theatrical creations. The former is a modern morality play with political overtones and elements of the absurd. The protagonist, a sixty-year-old spinster named Ana, first appears in the everyday environment of the home she shares with her cantankerous aunt and her beloved cat. When the aunt chases the pet from the house, Ana looks for it in Chapultepec Park, which in her mind becomes an enchanted, dreamlike realm. Here she encounters a series of stereotyped individuals representing facets of life in the real world. One of these, a rebellious student being pursued by the police, frees several of the lions from the zoo to create confusion and cover his escape. The ensuing pandemonium is brought to an end when Ana leads the beasts back into their cage and elects to remain with them and "shout at the children so they'll learn." Her rejection of the status quo (more than likely the capitalistic system) is underscored by her subsequent statement, "The day will come when all of you will be in cages while we lions wander free, roaming through the streets."

Set in the seventeenth century in Carballido's native state of Veracruz, *El relojero de Córdoba* draws its plot from Mexican and Oriental legends, resulting in a comedy with a distinct folktale quality. The two protagonists are Martín Gama, an insignificant clockmaker, and a wise and witty magistrate, Don Leandro Penella de Hita. In an effort to emulate a successful friend he meets for the first time in many years, Gama fabricates a tale of wealth and adventure that leads to his arrest for murder. His problem is eventually solved by Don Leandro, who through devious cleverness discovers the culprit of the crime Gama allegedly committed. The remarkable structural unity of *El relojero de Córdoba* stems from two cleverly conceived "plays" integrated into the overall framework, the first consisting of Gama's fictitious tale to his friend, and the second based on the circumstantial evidence Don Leandro uncovers in the course of his elaborate investigation.

Carballido's two most highly acclaimed works are *Medusa* (1959; *Medusa*, in *An English Translation of Three Plays by Emilio Carballido*, 1974) and *Yo también hablo de la rosa* (1966; *I Too Speak of the Rose*, in George Woodyard, ed., *The Modern Stage in Latin America: Six Plays*, 1971). *Medusa* transforms the Greek tragedy into an ironic allegory with existential implications. Perseo, the protagonist, initially announces his determination to perform some heroic act, independent of the gods and free from all restrictions of fate. He sets out to kill Medusa but falls in love with her instead and, consequently, finds himself obliged to choose between not doing a deed he now considers morally reprehensible and doing it to realize his preconceived self-definition, even though the deed may compromise his freedom. With his murder of Medusa he becomes a dehumanized monster, imprisoned by his obsession with self-determination; he also emerges as a victim of irony because, for him at least, his fate is unwanted and unexpected. As seen by Carballido, Perseo's resultant alienation—and by implication, twentieth-century man's—stems from the clash between his role as a self-proclaimed deity and his role as a human being.

A fascinating one-act masterpiece, *Yo también hablo de la rosa* deals with the derailment of a train by two adolescents, Polo and Toña, but it focuses on the process of interpreting the event rather than on the event itself. The play consists of eighteen brief, rapidly paced scenes depicting human existence as a complex web of interrelationships presented through a fusion of realistic and poetic devices. Dramatic momentum is generated by the imaginative use of lighting and sound effects, especially those marking the abrupt transition between contrasting episodes. Reactions to the senseless derailment are set forth by a variety of characters: Maximino, a sympathetic older friend of the youngsters; their heartbroken mothers; a teacher; two professors, one a Marxist and the other a Freudian psychologist; and several journalists and newsboys. A character referred to as the Medium delivers a series of monologues conjuring up images seemingly unrelated to the train derailment. Each time she appears, her peasant costume becomes lighter in color until, in the final scene, it is a gleaming white. In a somewhat similar vein, a radio or television announcer describes a rose seen under a microscope as a maze of weblike fibers representing the primal energy of miraculous fiction. Ultimately the rose of the title comes to symbolize art, the purpose of which is to preserve for posterity a unique reality envisioned by its creator. The entire work, then, emerges as an artistic interpretation, reinforced by social commentary, of a banal occurrence that, like the Medium's costume, is transformed from a shadowy blur into a purified, aesthetic whole.

More than any other Mexican dramatist since World War II, Carballido has been instrumental in changing the course of the Mexican theater. Although his principal hallmark is his ingenious ability to combine reality and fantasy, he has also utilized folklore, classical myths, and existential concepts to create a wide variety of works both national and universal in scope. His broadly based satire and experiments with avant-garde technique have also contributed much to the contemporary literary scene. In its entirety his theater has made him Mexico's most outstanding living dramatist and one of Spanish America's leading men of letters.

EGON WOLFF

A native of Chile and the son of German immigrants, Egon Wolff (b. 1926) graduated from the Catholic University of Santiago with a degree in chemical engineering. After winning several prizes for theater in the late 1950s, he was awarded a scholarship to study in the United States, and since the mid-1960s he has been recognized as one of Spanish America's most sophisticated realists. In his dramas he severely criticizes social conditions in his part of the world, excelling in the delineation of conflicts between classes and in the exploration of complex human relationships.

Wolff's theater often dramatizes the disruption of a state of tranquillity or artificial equilibrium, usually by some political, social, or psychological force originating from without. His first play, *Mansión de lechuzas* (1957; mansion of owls), focuses on an upper-class woman who attempts to shut her two teenage sons up in the family's decaying mansion to protect them from the evils of the present symbolized by a modern housing development encroaching on their domain. The situation is reversed in *El signo de Caín* (1971; the mark of Cain), which portrays two couples of conflicting ideologies. Portus has abandoned his upper-middle-class home to live in poverty with Charito, an uneducated woman of the proletariat. Their contentment is disturbed by the unexpected arrival of Portus's friend Joaquín and his wealthy wife, Leonor, who plan to lure Portus, without Charito, back to his bourgeois milieu. In the ensuing verbal melee, the four strip themselves of all pretenses, exposing weaknesses and destroying friendships, probably forever.

Wolff's most memorable work to date is *Los invasores* (1970; *The Invaders*, in *Modern International Drama*, Spring 1975), which was inspired by the Chinese and Cuban revolutions. Lucas Meyer, the protagonist, is a wealthy industrialist who murdered his partner years ago and made the crime appear to be suicide. In the opening scene Meyer and his wife, Pietá, return to their luxurious home from an evening party. That night Meyer is awakened by a prowler whose hand is seen breaking a window and opening the latch. China, the prowler, turns out to be the first of a number of revolutionary slum dwellers invading not only the Meyer residence, but the entire city as well. Throughout much of the play the spectator/reader is puzzled by a series of inexplicable images and occurrences. China, for example, is dressed in rags, but in sharp contrast he wears a stiff, white collar and a carnation. Grotesque, shadowy figures seem to glide through the walls; nuns and beggars appear asking for money; haunting music and a chorus accompany parts of the action; and occasionally the dialogue reflects stereotyped rather than subtle human behavior, as, for example, when Meyer, increasingly fearful that China is wreaking vengeance for the death of his partner, suddenly blurts out, "I killed him! I killed him!" In the final scene Pietá awakens Meyer from his nightmare, thus explaining the surrealistic atmosphere of the play. The real climax, however, occurs moments later when, to Meyer's horror, a hand breaks the windowpane and reaches in to unlock the latch. His nightmare has become reality.

Los invasores emerges as a warning to upper-class citizens who continue to ignore the plight of the poor. The two principal themes, guilt and fear, are expressed through Meyer, but the murder of his partner and the threat of retribution are symbolic of the "crimes" committed by the rich for many generations and their subconscious dread of the consequences. The play can also be read as Meyer's confrontation with this shadow, the repressed part of his psyche represented by China. However it is interpreted, *Los invasores* looms as a masterwork depicting the intrusion of dream into the everyday world of reality. Impressive also is its foreshadowing of the radical changes that occurred in Chile a decade after its first presentation.

Flores de papel (1970; *Paper Flowers*, 1971), another of Wolff's major works, conveys a message similar to that of *Los invasores*, namely, the threatened destruction of the status quo. Here a vagrant named Merluza helps a middle-class widow, Eva, carry her groceries to her apartment. When she offers to pay him for his assistance, he asks for a cup of tea, spends the night with her, and then moves in permanently. In a classic case of role reversal, guest soon becomes master of the household and Eva, his subjugated slave. However, instead of raising himself to Eva's level, Merluza little by little destroys her fine furnishings, converting the entire dwelling into a shambles. In the last scene they leave to take up residence in a shantytown far removed from the comfortable middle-class section of the city.

Like Meyer and China in *Los invasores*, Eva and Merluza symbolize their respective classes, and just as China triumphs over Meyer, Merluza dominates Eva. The play's title refers to the paper flowers Merluza makes with newspapers to decorate the walls and every available space in the apartment. These creations acquire symbolic value when, just before their departure for the shantytown, Merluza thrusts one of them into the neck of Eva's dress, completely covering her face. Eva's identity and that of her class have been obliterated.

Two additional works worthy of note are *Kindergarten* (1978;

kindergarten) and *José* (1981; José). The protagonists of *Kindergarten* are two elderly brothers of proud lineage who share their musty old family home. From the opening scene it becomes evident that Miguel and Antonio (Mico and Toño) have, in a sense, returned to their childhood—thus the title—bickering over trivial matters and playing games of domination and submission or of outright war and uneasy truce. This false stability, which one presumes has lasted for years, is interrupted by two events: a telephone call communicating an attempt to blackmail Toño for not paying a gambling debt; and the arrival of the protagonists' sister, Mercedes (Meche), who, after many years of absence, has returned to the city in search of her daughter. Toño's gambling debt is eventually paid to salvage the family's reputation, but Meche's declared intention to remain in her brothers' home suggests, ominously, that the precarious equilibrium established by the two original game players will now be shattered by the weight of a third.

In *José*, Wolff renews his attacks on the complacent bourgeoisie, but his emphasis here is more idealistic than political. José is a young man recently returned to Chile after having lived in the United States. Tired of the crass materialism he encountered there, he longs for a simpler life amid the love and affection of his family. Upon his arrival, however, he finds his mother and sister residing in the luxurious home of his uncle, a powerful industrialist who controls their every move, and his grandfather relegated to a church-operated institution for the aged. Although José's idealism turns out to be no match for the prevailing mores of a success-oriented environment, he does succeed in dissuading his sister from entering into a marriage of convenience.

As illustrated by *José*, Egon Wolff emerges as an idealistic critic of Chilean society, but he is also a universal dramatist who views art as an antidote to alienation and a means of nurturing human rather than material values. His dramatic structures are usually based on the tension between static, internal situations and external forces bent on destruction. A penetrating observer of human nature, Wolff deftly depicts the disastrous effects of domination and submission on human relationships. But the salient feature of his theater is its disturbingly intuitive vision of a world teetering on the brink of upheaval and chaos.

GRISELDA GAMBARO

A novelist and short-story writer as well as one of Spanish America's finest dramatists, Griselda Gambara (b. 1928) was born in Buenos Aires and has lived in the Argentine capital most of her life. Her name is usually linked to the theater of the absurd and the theater of cruelty, a major influence on her works being the French dramatic theorist Antonin Artaud. Like Artaud, she stresses nonrhetorical, nonliterary language as well as gestures, sounds, black humor, and violence to convey the anguish and tragic futility of human existence. She does not develop characters by traditional means but rather thrusts her protagonists into inexplicable, frightening situations in which they are victimized or destroyed, usually by formidable adversaries.

Of the list of approximately a dozen plays Gambaro has written, the following four stand out for their excellence and the wide critical acclaim they have received: *Las paredes* (1979; the walls), *El desatino* (1965; the blunder), *El campo* (1967; *The Camp*, in William I. Oliver, ed., *Voices of Change in the Spanish American Theater*, 1971), and *Los siameses* (1967; the Siamese twins). First presented in 1963, *Las paredes* portrays three characters, the Youth, the Custodian, and the Official, in a room that becomes smaller as the action progresses. The Youth, who has been arrested for some unknown reason, is manipulated psychologically, insulted, and beaten by his two captors until he is transformed into a mindless, desensitized automaton. Although the door of the interrogation room is left open at the end of the play, he does not even attempt to escape. *Las paredes* is replete with symbolic elements. The Custodian and the Official represent military or dictatorial authority and the room the totalitarian state; the shrinking spatial dimensions suggest the individual's (the Youth's) gradual realization of his metaphysical limitations in a world where freedom is illusory, degradation normal, and fear of death omnipresent. A more enigmatic motif is a statue the Custodian and the Official first praise for its aesthetic value and then encourage the Youth to smash. His inability to perform this decisive act reflects not only his physical and mental paralysis, but also his subconscious identification with the lifeless object, possibly a symbol of his imminent death.

In some respects *El desatino* repeats the pattern of events seen in *Las paredes*. Here a young man named Alfonso awakens one morning to find himself immobilized by a bulky iron object firmly attached to his foot. Although he begs for help from his mother Viola and his friend Luis, his pleas go unanswered. His mother asserts her domination over him by withholding his food and attempting to usurp his wife's role as an alluring mate, while Luis sadistically singes his eyelashes with a cigarette and almost strangles him with a scarf. Alfonso's wife Lily is frequently mentioned but never actually appears except in a dream sequence in the form of an oversized mannequin. The news that Alfonso has fathered a child is celebrated just prior to the arrival of the Boy, a strapping young construction worker who manages to free Alfonso's foot, now rotting from lack of circulation. Like the Youth in *Las paredes*, however, Alfonso has lost all desire to survive and falls back limply on the bed, thus becoming the child he supposedly fathered. The themes of victimization and submission are reinforced by numerous symbols. For example, Lily embodies Alfonso's sexual fantasies; the iron object attached to his foot stands for his dependence on others; Viola evokes the Freudian principle of maternal castration; and Luis and the Boy lend social significance to the play, the former representing the egotistical bourgeoisie and the latter the more compassionate working class. The reversal of traditional roles such as the selfish, rather than nurturing, mother and the cruel, rather than benevolent, friend are absurd elements also contributing to the thematic development. An additional interpretation worthy of mention is that *El desatino* can be read as an allegory of the Spanish American middle-class male fettered by sexual fantasies, a matriarchal family structure, and a callous, rigidly structured society.

El campo is Gambaro's most political work with the possible exception of *Las paredes*. The unidentified setting resembles a Nazi concentration camp, but it is also a metaphor of Argentina or any other nation suffering under an oppressive dictatorial regime. In the initial scene Martín enters the establishment to begin his duties as a bookkeeper. His supervisor, Franco, dressed in a Gestapo officer's uniform, greets him in a friendly manner but soon reveals the cruel side of his personality. The third and most enigmatic character is Emma, a worldly, slightly mad pianist with a shaved head, an ugly gash on her right hand, and a persistent itch that causes her to scratch constantly. Although she talks with assurance and often refers to Franco as her friend and guardian, she flinches and cowers when Franco cracks the whip he is carrying. The most grotesque scene involves Emma's concert for the prisoners and the Gestapo officers. Moments before the performance her scratching induces Franco to daub a liquid substance on her skin, which only increases her discomfort; then the inmates insult her; and finally, when she attempts to play, the piano keys are dead. In the last act, after having been granted permission to leave the camp, Martín and Emma appear in Martín's home. Their freedom is cut short by the arrival from the camp of three male nurses who subdue Martín and "immunize" him. Now in a state of lethargy, he is about to be tortured with a branding iron when the curtain falls. *El campo* utilizes cruelty and absurdist techniques to dramatize political oppression. Emma, however, introduces another dimension, namely, the adversarial relationship between the state and the artist, whose freedom to create is perpetually under siege.

Critics generally consider *Los siameses* as Gambaro's most powerful creation. A modern portrayal of the Cain and Abel motif, this play's two protagonists are neither Siamese twins nor blood brothers, but two fellow beings bound together by a common destiny. They are also opposites, Lorenzo astute, domineering, and envious and Ignacio docile, compassionate, and handsome. Together they represent man's dualism or two complementary halves incapable of existing harmoniously, either with one another or apart. The plot involves Lorenzo's treacherous maneuvers to rid himself of his "brother," first by having him beaten by the police and finally by causing his arrest and imprisonment for bank robbery. After Ignacio's death, Lorenzo appears alone on the stage, devastated by the realization that his own well-being is bound to that of his "brother." And, upon imitating the latter's demeanor, the victimizer assumes the role of victim as well.

The overriding theme giving unity to Gambaro's theater is the victimization of man in today's dehumanized world. Additional themes include the loneliness, isolation, and lack of communication caused not only by social and political pressures, but also by the limitations of language. The power and intensity of Gambaro's theater are enhanced by her expressionistic staging techniques and occasional flashes of black humor, all of which elicit a visceral rather than an intellectual response from her audiences. Although her plays exude disillusion and skepticism, they are obviously designed to create an awareness of the absurd human condition, often viewed by the existentialists as the first step toward man's liberation.

OSVALDO DRAGÚN

Generally considered the best Argentine playwright of his generation, Osvaldo Dragún (b. 1929) was born in the province of Entre Ríos, north of Buenos Aires. He abandoned the study of law during the 1950s to join the Teatro Independiente Popular Fray Mocho, an experimental group that produced several of his early plays. The most important single influence on his work is Brecht, whose techniques he utilizes to denounce social injustice and assail the dehumanizing influence of hypocrisy and materialism in the present-day world.

Dragún's first play was *La peste viene de Melos* (1956; the plague comes from Melos), which utilizes an ancient Greek setting to pit economic greed against national honor and love of liberty. Inspired by the United States involvement in the 1954 overthrow of Guatemalan President Jacobo Árbenz, *La peste viene de Melos* draws obvious parallels between the Athenians' intervention, principally for economic gain, in the internal affairs of Melos and the tragic events occurring in the Central American country during the 1950s. Also set in the remote past is *Tupac Amarú* (1957; Tupac Amarú), considered by some critics as Dragún's best creative endeavor to date. The title refers to the Peruvian Indian rebel who was tortured and put to death by Spanish colonial officials after an uprising in 1781. The principal source of dramatic tension stems from the conflict between Tupac Amarú and Areche, the Spanish king's representative bearing the title Visitador General (Visitor General). A symbol of absolute power, Areche finds himself caught between enforcing his king's authority and respecting the legitimate rights of the Indian. His moral dilemma, together with Tupac Amarú's existential self-realization through choice of action, transcends the temporal and geographical limitations of the plot, universalizing the conflict between the two antagonists. In the final act both are depicted near death on a divided stage, one section representing Tupac Amarú's cell and the other, Areche's office. The former's demise from torture and the latter's from a crisis of conscience bring the play to its climax. In the concluding lines Tupac Amarú's moral victory becomes evident when a storm symbolic of Areche's inner torment scatters the Indian's ashes over the land, raising him to the status of a mythical hero.

The most celebrated of Dragún's works is a trilogy of one-act tragicomedies entitled *Historias para ser contadas* (1957; stories to be told). Characterized by strong doses of the absurd and the grotesque, these masterfully drawn vignettes are narrated and enacted by a cast of four who alternate between raconteurs and fictional characters, usually on a stylized or empty stage. This Brechtian technique serves to distance the actors from both the dramatic material and the audience, obliging the latter to concentrate on themes or ideas rather than on the story itself. Moreover, because each member of the cast portrays several roles, the spectators are never allowed to forget that they are viewing theater, not real life. The use of colloquial language, poems, songs, and dances—additional Brechtian devices—has increased the popularity of these plays, especially among Argentine audiences.

Historia de un flemón, una mujer y dos hombres (1957; story of an abscess, a woman, and two men), the first of the three *Historias*, portrays a street vendor whose abscessed tooth prevents him from earning a living. In desperation he finally visits a dentist who charges him an exorbitant fee and gives him no relief. Eventually the unfortunate man dies in solitude, ignored by his wife, his friends, and the multitude of indifferent passersby in the bustling metropolis. The second of these pieces, *Historia de cómo nuestro amigo Panchito González se sintió responsable de la epidemia de peste en Africa del Sur* (1957; *Story of How Our Friend Panchito González Felt Responsible for the Plague Epidemic in South Africa*, in Gerardo Luzuriaga and Robert S. Rudder, eds., *The Orgy: Modern One-Act Plays from Latin America*, 1974), describes the absurd predicament of a man who, in order to support his large family, accepts a well-paying job in a packing plant that cans rat meat for blacks in South Africa. The government eventually rewards Panchito González for his contribution to the city's anti-rat campaign, but his sense of satisfaction ends with the news of an outbreak of bubonic plague in South Africa. Because of Panchito's great sense of guilt over his role in the tragedy, his Italian and English bosses consider him unfit to work in their firm and fire him from his lucrative position. The most grotesque of the trilogy, *Historia del hombre que se convirtió en perro* (1957; *The Story of a Man Who Turned into a Dog*, in Luzuriaga and Rudder, eds., *The Orgy: Modern One-Act Plays from Latin America*, 1974), concerns another human failure, a worker obliged to accept a job as a watchdog for a factory. The dehumanizing influence of his social milieu becomes apparent when, accustomed to his new role, he begins to speak in a garble of words and barking.

Another of Dragún's master achievements, *Y nos dijeron que éramos inmortales* (1962; *And They Told Us We Were Immortal*, in George Woodyard, ed., *The Modern Stage in Latin America*, 1971), attacks the false values the middle class attempts to instill in its youth. The protagonist is a young man named George who has just returned home after having served in the army where he, Berto, and Arón became close friends.

During an unspecified military action George suffered superficial wounds, Berto was permanently disabled, and Arón was
killed. George attempts to resume his former way of life and
makes plans to marry his fiancée Ada, but he is troubled by
the adverse fate of his two army friends and realizes that the
life he has known at home is illusory. His feelings are reinforced
by a poster hanging on the wall with the motto, "This home is
the whole world." A metaphor of middle-class complacency, this
motto represents an attempt to preserve the status quo and
shield middle-class youths from the more vital, rapidly evolving
reality around them. During Ada's birthday party George receives a telephone call from Berto, who has been arrested for
robbery and needs George's help. Urged by his family to ignore
the call, George launches into a long monologue parodying not
only the social customs his family holds dear, but also the
military code he was taught as an army recruit. The only person
who understands him is his older brother Stephen, whose final
words convey the drama's existentialist message and its only
optimistic note: "Georgie, listen to me! Georgie! Death exists,
and it is waiting, but it's not a problem. Our only problem is
how to live." The two brothers' rejection of time-worn tradition
is also suggested by songs, dances, and poetry that are skillfully
integrated into the plot. In addition, the play's title reinforces
its attack on the bourgeois establishment.

Although *Heroica de Buenos Aires* (1966; epic of Buenos
Aires) won the coveted Casa de las Américas prize for its author, it has been sharply criticized for its obvious left-wing
ideology, the peripheral elements of its plot, and its excessive
length. The central figure is an impoverished widow, María,
who dreams of wealth and security for her two children. The
latters' financial success, however, destroys their capacity for
love, and María ultimately returns to her life of poverty. *Heroica
de Buenos Aires* inveighs against the materialism of the rich,
the ignorance of the military, and the hypocrisy of the church,
but its heavy-handed political message is at least partially overshadowed by the insightful development of its characters.

In *El amasijo* (1968; the hodgepodge) Dragún continues
the experimental techniques he so successfully displayed in
Historias para ser contadas. The plot sketches the relations

between José and María, bored office workers whose meaningless, fragmented dialogues reveal the frustrations and
repressed anxieties they have concealed behind masks of
machismo and maidenly propriety. The stage is divided into
three sections, the opposite sides representing the protagonists' bedrooms—symbolic of their loneliness—and the
sparsely furnished center, an office, a street, a café, and an
amusement park signifying bridges of communication with
the outside world. Although the foreground action occurs in
approximately a week, flashbacks and projections into the
future provide the means through which the characters define their complex personalities. The ending remains ambiguous, the only certainties being that José and María need to
break out of their loneliness and that their relationship may
enable them to fulfill this need. Fortunately *El amasijo* contains none of the political ideology that detracts from *Heroica
de Buenos Aires*. Its convincing dramatization of solitude and
ingenious manipulation of technical innovations make it one
of the author's most successful and universal works.

   Osvaldo Dragún's oeuvre ranges in scope from modern interpretations of ancient Greek and colonial Spanish American
history to deftly drawn social and political portraits of present-
day Buenos Aires. He is perhaps most admired for his mastery
of experimental forms such as those exhibited in his fresh,
provocative one-act tragicomedies. His existential insights into
the problems of isolated, desensitized individuals struggling to
attain freedom and dignity in contemporary society also demonstrate his command of the dramatic medium.

JORGE DÍAZ

Jorge Díaz (b. 1930) was born in Argentina, but in 1934 his
family moved to Chile, where he spent his formative years. He
graduated with a degree in architecture from the Catholic University in Santiago in 1955 and since 1960 has dedicated himself exclusively to the theater. Considered Spanish America's
leading playwright of the absurdist tradition, he utilizes irony,
black humor, and physical violence to create a grotesque, nonrealistic world vision reminiscent of Ionesco, Beckett, and Har-

old Pinter. Although his dramas develop the themes of failure of communication, alienation, and lack of purpose in human existence, they tend to concentrate more heavily on political and social issues than does the French theater of the absurd. Díaz has resided in Spain since 1965.

One of Díaz's first plays, *El cepillo de dientes* (1961; the toothbrush) remains his most widely performed and perhaps his best to date. The overriding theme of lack of communication evolves through a series of ritualistic games enacted by a couple, He and She, who invent preposterous situations usually leading to a violent climax. In the first act He discovers that She has used His toothbrush, a symbol of His individuality, to whiten Her shoes; infuriated by Her behavior, He "kills" Her. In the second act She returns disguised as the cleaning woman, initiating a lively exchange that culminates in a passionate sexual encounter and Her "killing" Him. The play ends with the survival of both protagonists and the impression that their absurd games will begin anew.

Dramatic tension and theme are conveyed in *El cepillo de dientes* by a series of sharply contrasting elements. The incongruous furniture styles of the stage set establish an atmosphere of contradiction even before the action begins, and in the second act, after Her "death," the inversion of the set—the furniture on the right side has been moved to the left and vice versa—foreshadows the reversal of roles that will lead to His "death." The ultimate destruction of the set exteriorizes the protagonists' emotions, signaling an abrupt end to their conflict. Additional contrasts include the alternating sounds of jazz and harp music heard repeatedly on a transistor radio; the montage of unrelated monologues highlighting the couple's failure to communicate with one another; and the ironic use of coined phrases and clichés to depict a highly complex reality. In the final lines He searches for "a simple word to explain it all" and comes up with "shit." Somewhat more subtle is the irony conveyed by the various names He calls Her (her real name escapes Him) including Consuelo, Mercedes, and Amelia, all denoting a tenderness that belies Her belligerent nature. *El cepillo de dientes* emerges as a very amusing work, but its humor is not frivolous; rather, it provides insight into the dialectics of alienation and hostility in today's world.

Death becomes a major ingredient in Díaz's next two works: *Réquiem por un girasol* (1962; requiem for a sunflower) and *El velero en la botella* (1962; the sailing ship in the bottle). The setting of the former is a funeral home for animals, whose ghoulish proprietor, Mr. Linfa, thrives on the misfortunes of others. By way of contrast, his assistant, Manuel, appreciates the beauties of nature, and, although he dies in the first act, he emerges in the second as a symbol of regeneration through the birth of his son, Girasol (Sunflower). The scene describing Manuel's funeral exemplifies the play's black humor: his body is placed in a coffin made for a giraffe. Whereas *Réquiem por un girasol* optimistically dramatizes the recurring cycle of life and death, *El velero en la botella* demonstrates how lack of communication can lead to tragedy. The protagonist is a young mute, David, living with his father and two aunts, none of whom gives him the love and understanding he needs. A marriage of convenience is arranged between David and Emiliana, a wealthy couple's daughter grotesquely described as a Tudor-style commode, but his only meaningful relationship is with the maid, Rocío, who helps him to recover his speech. Soon thereafter, when all attempts to communicate with his father and aunts fail, David is driven to suicide. Like many of Díaz's plays, *El velero en la botella* illustrates the limits of language as an antidote to solitude. Thus, the inane prattle of David's aunts consists of trite phrases repeated ad nauseam, while his father shows more interest in the beeps of his ham radio than in the pathetic verbal messages of his son.

El lugar donde mueren los mamíferos (1963; *The Place Where the Mammals Die*, in George Woodyard, ed., *The Modern Stage in Latin America: Six Plays*, 1971) continues the absurd tone of Díaz's previous works. Here a charitable organization (the Ecumenical Institute of Total Assistance) is in danger of disappearing for lack of welfare recipients. The disaster is prevented by the discovery of Rusty, a starving slum dweller who arrives at the organization headquarters in a crate. After being offered everything except the food he so desperately needs to stay alive, Rusty hangs himself, but to save the Institute, the directors preserve his body for weekly burials as a means of demonstrating the fine services they are performing for the underprivileged. In the final scene, having ignored the hordes of beggars who have suddenly appeared in search of assistance, the director of the Institute delivers his report to the World Congress on Poverty. Obviously a satire on false charity and its selfish motives, this play can also be read as a political allegory about the exploitation of the Third World by developed nations whose "generosity" conceals their own self-interest. The symbolism, psychological subtleties, and grotesque irony of this work make it one of Díaz's most successful.

Another of the Chilean's highly praised dramas, *Topografía de un desnudo* (1967; topography of a nude), marks a turn toward a more realistic form. Based on an actual massacre of slum dwellers in Brazil, it has a documentary slant in its investigation of the drowning of a misfit named Rufo, who, it turns out, was killed by the police for refusing to cooperate with them to expel a group of squatters. The investigation into Rufo's death triggers a series of skillfully arranged flashbacks, revealing his past along with the machinations of Don Clemente, a powerful and ruthless newspaper editor who plans to develop the property in question. The subsequent murder of a police corporal is believed to have been perpetrated by the irate squatters in retaliation for Rufo's death, but in reality Don Clemente ordered the crime to incite the police to carry out his nefarious scheme. Although *Topografía de un desnudo* is less sophisticated in its thematic content than its predecessors, its deft handling of time sequences, which serve to highlight tension and reveal hidden motives, results in a masterfully structured work of art rather than in what might have been a run-of-the-mill social-protest drama.

Additional works representative of Díaz's talent include *La víspera del degüello; o, El génesis fue mañana* (1965; *The Eve of the Execution, or Genesis Was Tomorrow*, in Gerardo Luzuriaga and Robert S. Rudder, eds., *The Orgy: Modern One-Act Plays from Latin America*, 1974), a surrealistic vision of a world devastated by nuclear war; *Introducción al elefante y otras zoologías* (1969; introduction to the elephant and other zoologies), a montage of realistic episodes about Latin American revolutionaries, corrupt government officials, and U.S. imperialists; *La pancarta* (1970; the poster), in which a household of exploiting masters and exploited servants becomes a microcosm of a world fraught with tension; and *El locutorio* (1976; the parlor), an absurd representation of a couple wrestling with the existential issues of life, love, and elusive truth.

Jorge Díaz's theater of the absurd covers a wide range of themes. Like his French counterparts he is concerned with lack of communication, solitude, and metaphysical questions. However, he utilizes absurdity above all to expose injustice and exploitation, which, as he demonstrates, often lead to despair, dehumanization, and violence. Díaz is vitally interested in the problems plaguing Spanish America today, but as a penetrating observer of human behavior, he has created a theater that transcends national and continental boundaries. Indeed, his protagonists' basic responses to adverse conditions suggest an archetypal quality characteristic of universal myth. An inveterate experimenter, Díaz admittedly strives to shock his audiences into new areas of awareness. His success in attaining his goal is admirable.

JOSÉ TRIANA

José Triana (b. 1932) is the most prominent of a group of Cuban playwrights who revitalized their nation's theater during the 1960s. He was born in the provincial town of Bayamo, studied in Santiago de Cuba, and lived for several years in Spain prior to the revolution. Like Jorge Díaz, he has mastered the conventions of the European theater of the absurd and utilizes absurdist techniques to expose social and political evils. His dramas depict lower-class Cubans living precariously in a hostile urban milieu. Although his settings are contemporary, his plots often reinterpret classical or religious myths, his purpose being to explain the violence, irrationality, and moral decay in his midst through an examination of archetypal behavioral patterns.

Triana's first play, *El Mayor General hablará de teogonía* (1957; the Major General will speak of theogony), portrays four

characters: Petronila, her husband Higinio, her sister Elisiria,
and the Major General. The latter is the owner of a boardinghouse where the other three have lived for many years. Against
the wishes of her sister, who detests the Major General, Petronila
has invited him to her twenty-seventh wedding anniversary,
to be celebrated the evening of the day the action begins. She
reminds Elisiria that she lost her unborn child in an accident,
for which she blames herself, twenty-five years ago, and that
immediately thereafter the Major General received all three of
them into his home out of the goodness of his heart. When
Higinio returns from his office, he and Elisiria divulge their
diabolical plan to murder the Major General so that they can
be "free." They also reveal that they were lovers at the time of
Petronila's accident and that they had tried to kill her. When
the Major General finally appears, the murder plot dissolves
as Higinio, Elisiria, and Petronila respectfully request comments on theogony (the origin of the gods). He declines to speak
on the subject, however, and a short while later disdainfully
retires.

   El Mayor General hablará de teogonía is a parody on religion with strong existentialist overtones. The Major General represents a negative god figure and his three "guests,"
guilt-ridden beings seeking freedom from his domination. The
anniversary celebration suggests the Mass, but it is a Black
Mass, the purpose of which is the death of God rather than
the celebration of His miracles. The Major General, who is
about to be sacrificed, recalls Christ's passion, and Higinio,
the betrayal of Judas. And the wine and snacks Petronila
prepares evoke the Holy Communion. Triana implies, it would
seem, that human existence depends on an indifferent god
whose human creatures are too weak to exercise their free
will. The sense of absurdity stems from the banal dialogues
reminiscent of Beckett, as well as from the character of the
Major General, who emerges as a Godot hardly worth waiting
for.

   In *Medea en el espejo* (1960; Medea in the mirror) Triana
transposes the myth of Jason and Medea to a Cuban slum
setting not only to parody Euripides' classical tragedy, but also
to reveal the archetypal structures and universal human traits

inherent in even the lowest, most abandoned levels of society. The protagonists are a passionate mulatto woman named María; her white lover Julián, an unsavory underworld figure; and Perico Piedra Fina, a corrupt politician and slumlord. When María learns that Julián has abandoned her for Perico's daughter, she vows revenge, which she carries out by killing Perico, his daughter, and her own (and Julián's) two children. Thus, she hopes, the grief-stricken Julián will be condemned to a life of loneliness. *Medea en el espejo* closely follows the ancient Greek model; María plays the role of the sorceress Medea, Julián that of Medea's lover Jason, and Perico Piedra Fina that of King Creon. Like her legendary counterpart, María is the most memorable character and, in Triana's play, the only one who achieves tragic dimensions. The title alludes to her obsession with mirrors, in which she finds the affirmation of her true self, beyond moral codes, and thus the will to perform her frightful deeds.

La muerte del Ñeque (1964; the death of the Villain) also draws from tragic form to dramatize events in a violent, criminal-fringe society. The Ñeque or Villain is Hilario García, a mulatto who has risen through chicanery and crime to a high position in the police administration. Other major characters include Blanca Estela, his white mistress; his son Pablo; and Juvencio, the son of one of Hilario's victims. Juvencio plots the murder of Hilario, which is eventually carried out by a trio of thugs: Pepe, Ñico, and Juan el Cojo (John the Cripple). Hilario's rise and fall stem from, respectively, his hubris or supreme confidence in his own strength and the role of chance, which replaces the vengeance of the gods, a common element in Greek tragedy. The three thugs in control of Hilario's destiny represent not only the mythological Fates, but also the racial composition of the Cuban community, Ñico being white, Juan el Cojo black, and Pepe a mulatto. Their dice games symbolize the hazards of life in an irrational world abandoned by a just deity.

Triana's renown derives primarily from his masterpiece, *La noche de los asesinos* (1965; *The Criminals*, in George Woodyard, ed., *The Modern Stage in Latin America: Six Plays*, 1971). An account of three adolescents who enact the symbolic murder of their parents, this play has been performed throughout Spanish America, Europe, and the United States. The protagonists are Cuca, her sister Beba, and their brother Lalo, but like the four actors in Dragún's *Historias para ser contadas*, they assume additional roles, including those of their parents, their neighbors, the police, the newsboy, the judge, and the prosecuting attorney. The constant shifts between reality (the immediate world of the resentful siblings) and illusion (the imaginary world of the murders) forge a play-within-a-play structure, causing the audience to question whether they are witnessing an absurd game of role-playing or some sort of bloody dress rehearsal. Act I ends when Lalo simulates his parents' murder by thrusting the knife he has been sharpening into a table.

The second act dramatizes the police investigation and the trial, during which the "victims" air their versions of their shattered relations with their children and each other. The play-within-a-play ends abruptly with Beba running about the stage shouting, "The living room is not the living room. The living room is the kitchen. The bedroom is not the bedroom. The bedroom is the lavatory" and her ensuing statement, "I see my mother dead. I see my father beheaded. We've got to tear this house down." The final dialogue makes it clear that the imaginary murder has not been enacted for the first time, nor will it be the last.

> *Beba:* How do you feel?
> *Cuca:* Stronger.
> *Beba:* Satisfied?
> *Cuca:* Yes.
>   . . .
> *Beba:* Ready to do it again?
> *Cuca:* You don't have to ask.
> *Beba:* One day we'll do it properly . . .
> *Cuca:* Without anything going wrong.

La noche de los asesinos concentrates on games and rituals to capture the tensions within a family, all of whom are both guilty and innocent of wrongdoing. The children emerge as

brats unwilling to accept the authority they consider dictatorial, but they understandably resent their parents' mediocrity
and insensitivity, which provokes their savage parody of the
adult world. Beba's cry that the living room is not the living
room but the kitchen articulates their desire to structure their
own world without regard for prefabricated regulations or antiquated traditions. The parents' testimony at the trial invests
them with more human proportions; the mother recalls having
been forced by pregnancy into a marriage she did not want and,
subsequently, into a life of poverty and loneliness; the father
expresses his disillusion with marriage and desire to escape
from his wife's constant nagging. In reality they are middle-
aged nobodies who have spent their entire married life bickering over the pettiest of matters.

The play is far more than a domestic tragedy, however; it
is also a dramatic metaphor of a decaying institution—the
family—usually venerated as the foundation of society. The
protagonists' game of murder allows them to give vent to their
hatred of the tawdry lower middle class through mockery and
feigned violence. And as a ritual that will undoubtedly be repeated, it could lead, as suggested above, to the grimmest of
consequences.

José Triana is clearly a social-protest writer, but not in the
orthodox, timeworn sense of the term. He appears to be obsessed with the violence and irrationality he observes in Cuban
life and seeks an understanding of these phenomena by under-
pinning some of his works with mythical structures. He is also
sharply critical of stagnant and decayed institutions such as
the church and the family, which in his view have created the
need for existential revolt in the form of absurd games or bloody
rituals. His bold experiments and keen perceptions of universal
issues have made him one of Spanish America's most widely
acclaimed playwrights.

VICENTE LEÑERO

Although he was born in Guadalajara, Mexico, Vicente Leñero
(also discussed in the chapter on fiction) has lived most of his

life in Mexico City. Soon after graduating from the National
University with a degree in civil engineering he turned to journalism and literature for his livelihood. Modest, unassuming,
and deeply religious, he is equally well known for his prose
fiction and his dramas. His theater can be divided into two
basic categories: docudramas and psychological works with social and/or philosophical overtones.

Pueblo rechazado (1969; rejected community), Leñero's first
play, marks the beginning of Spanish America's documentary
theater, a genre whose fundamental purpose is to enhance the
public's perception of well-known current or historical events,
usually via precise, unequivocal modes of expression. The central figure is Gregorio Lemercier, the founder and prior of a
Benedictine monastery, located near Cuernavaca, where he introduced the practice of psychoanalysis in order to determine
the suitability of its members for the priesthood. Lemercier
had begun his experimental activities in 1961 with the approval
of the liberal Bishop Méndez Arceo, but in 1965 the Vatican
condemned them and in 1967, after a trial lasting eight months,
ordered Lemercier to discontinue the use of psychoanalysis in
the monastery. Soon thereafter Lemercier announced his break
with the Church and his decision to found a new order independent of Rome.

Described in great detail by the Mexican press, the case
captured the interest of the intellectual community, perhaps
because it exemplified the assault on institutionalized authority during the 1960s and raised the question of the need to
modernize the Catholic Church. Leñero visited the Benedictine
monastery on several occasions and, like most documentary
dramatists, relied on journalistic reports, taped interviews, and
official records to make his finished product as objective and
informative as possible. The first of the two acts of *Pueblo
rechazado* focuses on the need for psychoanalysis in the monastery, and the second on the central issue of science versus
religion. Through his necessarily subjective selection of materials, Leñero appears to sympathize with Lemercier, imply-
ing criticism of the Church authorities for their refusal to
recognize the legitimate role of science in the present-day world.

The author nevertheless underscores the enduring qualities of the Church by extolling, through choruses of monks and Catholic laymen, the beauty of its rituals and the spiritual joys of monastic life. The play's aesthetic qualities include its poetic language, dramatic stage sets, and Brechtian techniques such as the rapid succession of scenes and the deliberate negation of illusion.

El juicio (1972; the trial) synthesizes with scrupulous objectivity the court proceedings of the trial of José de León Toral and Concepción Acevedo de la Llata (Madre Conchita), who were accused of assassinating President-elect Álvaro Obregón in 1928. The drama begins with a short film narration of the clash between the Catholic Church and Plutarco Elías Calles's regime (1924–28), which led to the *cristero* rebellion and Obregón's death, and ends with a statement on the fate of the two defendants (Toral received the death penalty and his accomplice a twenty-year prison sentence). Seven court sessions are depicted in linear form with brief flashbacks interjected into the text to reenact conversations between the leading figures of the case, thus heightening the dramatic effect. While there is no question about Toral's guilt, the "proof" of Madre Conchita's alleged role as the "intellectual author" of the crime remains less than convincing. What does stand out clearly is the bitter antagonism between religious fanaticism and inflexible partisan politics, the repercussions of which are still felt today. Indeed, government censors attempted to prohibit the play's performance for political reasons, but their original decision provoked such a torrent of indignation from intellectuals that it was reversed. Additional examples of Leñero's documentary theater include *Compañero* (1970; comrade), based on Che Guevara's diary; and *Martirio de Morelos* (1981; martyrdom of Morelos), which chronicles the last days in the life of Father José María Morelos, a hero of the Mexican War of Independence who was captured, tried, and shot by the Spanish forces in 1815.

An adaptation of his prize-winning novel of the same title, *Los albañiles* (1970; the bricklayers) is Leñero's best play to date and one of the most successful ever by a Mexican dramatist. Although the theatrical version generally remains faithful to the novel, in his introduction to the drama the author indicated that it places greater emphasis on religious symbolism than does the novel. Moreover, the epigraph to the theatrical version, "For he hath made him to be sin for us, who knew no sin, that we might be made the righteousness of God in him" (II Corinthians 5:21), provides a clue to the meaning of the drama whose protagonist emerges as a Christ figure, or perhaps as an anti-Christ figure. Don Jesús, an old, half-crazed night watchman on an apartment-house construction site, is found murdered in the opening scene. The interrogation conducted by the detective Munguía unleashes a series of flashbacks in which the evil, perverted character of the victim gradually comes to light along with the entirely plausible motives of each of the bricklayers for killing him. The plot comes full circle when the terrified Don Jesús is pursued by an invisible enemy along the scaffold (symbolic of the crucifix) and slain on the spot where he lay dead at the beginning. In a kind of epilogue Munguía, who has just been taken off the case because of his failure to find the culprit, returns to the construction site, where he greets another watchman very similar in appearance to Don Jesús.

The theme of degenerate mankind cleansed by an ironic Christ figure is suggested by Don Jesús, who commits virtually every sin, dies at the hands of his fellow man, and perhaps rises again. Mexico's corrupt social structure, another major ingredient, is evidenced by crimes ranging from the purchase of an engineering degree to theft, prostitution, blackmail, and murder. And Munguía's frustrating search for the elusive truth emerges as a philosophical theme distinguishing *Los albañiles* from the run-of-the-mill murder mystery. Of major interest also is the play's complex structure, which Leñero organizes by dividing the stage into two separate areas: Munguía's office, where the interrogations take place in the present tense, and the construction site, where events leading up to the murder occur. The abrupt shifts between the two temporal and spatial settings not only accelerate dramatic momentum, but also generate tension, as does the bricklayers' vernacular idiom, which alternates between hilarious humor and jolting vulgarity rarely heard before on the Mexican stage.

Other fine examples of Leñero's theater are *La mudanza* (1980; the move), a chilling, prize-winning account of a couple's move to an old colonial home and their sudden, life-threatening confrontation with a group of squatters from a nearby slum; *La carpa* (1985; the tent), a sophisticated satire on television soap operas reminiscent of Leñero's novel, *Estudio Q*; *La visita del ángel* (1985; the angel's visit), the rambling monologue of a scatterbrained student who drops in on her aging grandparents for lunch; and *Alicia, tal vez* (1985; Alice, perhaps), an ironic, but scathing feminist attack on the exploitation of women both in the home and in the workplace.

As a playwright Leñero is best known for his creations in the area of documentary drama, a genre he initiated in Spanish America. His remarkable versatility, however, is demonstrated by his additional theatrical works, which range in content from contemporary religious and philosophical concepts to deftly drawn psychological portraits and vehement protests against injustice. Although he has remained aloof from the literary coteries of the Mexican capital, he stands out as one of his nation's most prestigious writers.

AND MANY OTHERS

MEXICO

As mentioned previously, Mexico is one of the major theatrical centers in Spanish America. Two of that nation's most important innovative groups were Teatro Ulises and Teatro de Orientación. Other groups contributing to the renovation and universalization of the Mexican stage have been the Teatro de Ahora (founded 1942) and Proa (founded 1947), both of which presented pressing social and political issues. The most significant event of the 1940s was the foundation of the government-sponsored Instituto Nacional de Bellas Artes (INBA) and its subdivision, the Escuela de Arte Dramático in 1947. INBA fosters the development of the theater, providing financial support as well as professional stimulation for dramatists, actors, and directors.

The three leading playwrights prior to World War II were Rodolfo Usigli (discussed above), Xavier Villaurrutia (also discussed in the chapter on poetry), and Celestino Gorostiza (1904–1967). During the 1930s Villaurrutia produced five experimental one-act plays, which, published under the title *Autos profanos* (1941; worldly mysteries), constitute the most significant portion of his theater. (The title is a play on words on *autos sacramentales*, the Spanish religious plays, or "mysteries," popular during the sixteenth and seventeenth centuries.) Ironic in tone, they embody the human condition in weak, puppetlike characters torn by indecision, frustrated by their inability to communicate, and ultimately condemned to loneliness. The poetic style and subtle, philosophical nature of these works create a timeless, ivory-tower atmosphere. A fine example of the *Autos profanos* is *¿En qué piensas?* (what are you thinking about?), in which a young woman flirts with three men, each of whom would like to get rid of the others. The rapid-fire dialogue and swiftly changing scenes generate fresh humor, but the piece's salient characteristic is its sophisticated ambiguity.

In the final decade of his life Villaurrutia wrote and successfully staged a number of three-act plays that have wider popular appeal because of their well-constructed plots and situations bordering on the melodramatic. Generally speaking, however, they lack the artistic merit of the *Autos profanos*, the only exception being *Invitación a la muerte* (1944; invitation to death). A provocative adaptation of *Hamlet*, this play portrays a sensitive, tormented youth attempting to determine his role in modern Mexican society while facing a dilemma similar to that of Shakespeare's hero. Other works of this period include *La hiedra* (1942; the ivy), in which a widow falls in love with her stepson, and *El pobre Barba Azul* (1947; poor Bluebeard), an amusing farce about a man's frustrating quest for truth. Although Villaurrutia is generally regarded as an innovative, cosmopolitan writer, his work is firmly rooted in the realities of Mexico. He will be remembered above all for his literary craftsmanship and his original treatment of existential themes.

Like Villaurrutia, Celestino Gorostiza began his career as an avant-garde innovator, probing the dreamlike subconscious states of his protagonists as well as their conflicts of conscience and complex psychic reactions to the flux of time. Examples of these early works are *Ser o no ser* (1934; to be or not to be), *La escuela de amor* (1935; the school of love), and *Escombros del sueño* (1938; ruins of the dream). Again, like Villaurrutia, he then turned to realism, producing his biggest box-office success, *El color de nuestra piel* (1952; the color of our skin), which represents a strong attack on racial prejudice. Most of the characters of *El color de nuestra piel* are members of an upper-class mestizo family, one of whose sons happens to be fair-skinned. The father's preference for this child, Héctor, causes tensions that almost destroy the family unity and ultimately lead to Héctor's suicide. In this play Gorostiza not only censures Mexicans who view light skins as a mark of superiority, but also denounces *malinchismo*, the belief on the part of some Mexicans that the foreigner is automatically better than their compatriots. Other realistic works by Gorostiza are *La columna social* (1955; the social column), a farce satirizing the pretensions of the nouveaux riches, and *Malinche* (1958; Malinche), a reinterpretation of the story of Cortés and his Indian mistress.

Although by age Salvador Novo (also discussed in the chapter on poetry) belongs to the same generation as Usigli, Villaurrutia, and Gorostiza, and although he collaborated with them in the major theatrical groups of the 1930s and early 1940s, he wrote most of his works after World War II. The broad variety of his themes, as seen below, derives from his deep interest in literature, social issues, psychology, history, and myth. *Don Quijote* (1947; Don Quixote) stands out as a poetic adaptation of Cervantes's classic; in *La culta dama* (1951; the cultured lady) Mexican high society becomes the butt of the author's satire; *A ocho columnas* (1956; with eight columns) takes the press to task for its rampant corruption; the psychic disintegration of an actor unable to distinguish between reality and fiction is depicted in *Yocasta; o, Casi* (1961; Yocasta; or, almost); *Cuauhtémoc* (1962; Cuauhtémoc) reexamines the life of the sixteenth-century Aztec hero; and in *Ha vuelto Ulises* (1962; Ulysses has returned) a bored Ulysses, having returned to Ithaca, yearns to repeat his recent triumphs, and an equally bored Penelope would now welcome the presence of the suitors she rejected.

Luis G. Basurto (b. 1920) and Elena Garro (also discussed in the chapter on fiction) differ widely in their artistic approaches to theater. Basurto merits mention primarily because of his outstanding box-office successes, occasionally denounced by the League of Decency, such as *Miércoles de ceniza* (1956; Ash Wednesday), about the regeneration of a prostitute through love; *Cada quien su vida* (1958; to each his own life), which describes the New Year's Eve capers in a slum nightclub; *La locura de los ángeles* (1959; the madness of the angels), the account of an idealistic woman's struggle against usurers who exploit residents of a tenement; and *Frente a la muerte* (1961; in the face of death), in which a desperate wife shoots her husband's mistress when the two lovers attempt to cross the U.S. border with a cargo of dope.

In contrast to Basurto's sensational treatment of sordid reality, Garro's theater is poetic, artistically innovative, and often leavened with fantasy and myth. Two of her most highly acclaimed pieces, both one-acters, are *El hogar sólido* (1958; the stable home) and *La señora en su balcón* (1967; the woman on her balcony). The setting of the former is a tomb where the ghosts of nine family members recall events that occurred during their lives and express their present desires, fears, and disillusionment as if they were still mortal beings. Ranging in age from five to eighty, they all long for permanence and stability—thus the title—but ironically they discover death to be as ephemeral and unsatisfying as the lives they knew. The play's single-night time frame constitutes an absolute moment of eternity in which the ghosts are able to materialize and come together, but at dawn the magic spell is broken and they resume their phantom characteristics. Garro's portrait of death is a fine example of the macabre poeticized by elements of Mexican folklore and her own imagination. *La señora en su balcón* also suggests the author's disenchantment with human existence. The protagonist is an aging woman who from her balcony views reenacted scenes of her life at the ages of eight, twenty, and forty. Each episode dramatizes the destruction of her dreams, gradually bringing her to the realization that escape from humdrum everyday existence is impossible. The theme of poetry versus reality becomes even more apparent when, in the final lines, the protagonist leaps to her death, and a milkman arriving on the scene identifies her as "the old lady of apartment 17."

One of Garro's best surrealistic fantasies is *Los pilares de doña Blanca* (1958; the pillars of doña Blanca). In this highly symbolic playlet Doña Blanca lives in a tower with thick walls and pillars. After four knights surrender their hearts to her with romantic phrases, a fifth knight, Alazán, appears and proceeds to knock down the walls of the tower with his lance. When the tower falls, Doña Blanca disappears, and Alazán finds in the ruins a dove, which he hides under his shirt. Analyzed according to Jung's psychology of the hero myth, *Los pilares de doña Blanca* dramatizes the young knight's (Alazán's) liberation of the captive or anima (doña Blanca or the dove) from his own subconscious (symbolized by the walls of the tower), the integration of the anima into his psyche (he hides the dove under his shirt), and the resultant development of his ego-consciousness or rebirth in the form of the mythical hero.

Two of Garro's more realistic one-act plays are *Los perros* (1965; the dogs), which depicts the rape of a twelve-year-old girl in a poverty-ridden village where her mother suffered the same fate years before; and *La mudanza* (1959; the move), about an aging, financially strapped spinster who is obliged by her embittered sister-in-law to leave her lifetime family home.

Wilberto Cantón (1923–1979), another prominent member of Garro's generation, is essentially a realistic delineator of social and political issues. *La escuela de cortesanos* (1954; the school of courtesans) satirizes a viceroy's venality during Mex-

ico's colonial period, but in reality it alludes to the contemporary political situation. One of this author's most popular
creations is *Nocturno a Rosario* (1957; nocturne to Rosario), a
romantic tragedy based on the love affair and suicide of the
famous nineteenth-century Mexican poet Manuel Acuña. *Mal-
ditos* (1958; cursed ones) was banned for a time from the Mexican stage because of its graphic treatment of juvenile
delinquency. In *El juego sagrado* (1960; the sacred game) an
aging couple's sordid past gradually comes to light when a
census taker is mistaken by the mad wife for the lover who
rejected her years before. Perhaps Cantón's best-known work
is *Nosotros somos Dios* (1962; we are God), a critical look at
President Victoriano Huerta's corrupt regime (1913–14) during
the revolution. The protagonists of this political tragedy are
members of a family whose ideological differences ultimately
lead to the father's suicide.

   One of several fine playwrights trained by Usigli, Sergio
Magaña (b. 1924) consistently displays his keen psychological
insight and acute sense of the dramatic. His first important
play, *Los signos del zodiaco* (1953; the signs of the zodiac), is
a bitter, depressing story reminiscent of Sartre about a communist student, a prostitute, and other outcasts living in a
boardinghouse during the 1940s. The author's ability to ma-
nipulate structural techniques for dramatic impact is demonstrated by the rapidly moving scenes within this setting as well
as by the carefully organized events preparing the climactic
murder and solution of the crime. *Los signos del zodiaco* is
generally considered one of the finest Mexican plays of its decade. Another of Magaña's successes, *Moctezuma II* (1954; Moctezuma II), depicts the Aztec chief's last day in power, November
7, 1519. Imagining himself to be a figure of destiny, Moctezuma
decides to bring about the defeat of the white man's god through
passive resistance, but as the curtain falls on the eve of Cortés's
arrival, a chorus of old women chants the end of a race of people.
El pequeño caso de Jorge Lívido (1958; the little case of Jorge
Lívido) utilizes the framework of a well-made detective play to
speculate about good and evil, a question made more dramatic
by a villain-protagonist masquerading as a just man. A family

voluntarily isolates itself from the outside world in *Los motivos del lobo* (1963; the motives of the wolf), but when social contact is finally reestablished, they find themselves so out of touch with everyday matters that they are unable to function normally.

El suplicante (1971; the supplicant) marks Magaña's venture into antitheater, a genre that attempts to create a less contrived, more lifelike experience by making the audience believe that the action presented on the stage is spontaneous, not controlled by a script. In *El suplicante*, techniques developed by Pirandello serve to blur the boundaries between fiction and reality. Thus, a sordid tale of incest the director refuses to include on the program is ingeniously fused with two *sainetes* (short comedies) written by Sor Juana Inés de la Cruz (the eighteenth-century Mexican poetess), which at the last moment are substituted for *El suplicante*. The onstage bickering over the altered program results in chaos deliberately planned to render the illusion of an immediate, ongoing reality instead of a carefully rehearsed series of events.

Mexico's most important living dramatist after Emilio Carballido and Vicente Leñero is Luisa Josefina Hernández (b. 1928). A former student, like Magaña, of Usigli, Hernández studied dramatic art at Columbia University, where she became interested in O'Neill, Williams, and Brecht. The trajectory of her career follows that of Carballido (a close friend), her early works representing realistic psychological portraits of stifling provincial life and her later creations evolving innovative, experimental forms appropriate for a broader range of subjects. Though not one of her best, Hernández's first play, *Agonía* (1951; agony), contains ingredients typical of her early years. The story of a dying middle-aged woman, this play dramatizes the rising tensions within her provincial family and her increasing isolation prior to her demise.

Los frutos caídos (1955; the fallen fruit) and *Los huéspedes reales* (1958; the royal guests) are generally considered Hernández's best works written in the realistic mode. The former, a balanced, tightly structured drama the author wrote as her thesis under Usigli's direction, leans heavily on Freudian psychology to capture the conflict between the life styles of a twenty-six-year-old divorcée, Celia, and that of the provincial town of her birth to which she returns from the Mexican capital. The principal antagonist is her uncle Fernando, a symbol of the decaying provincial order whose conservative views ultimately prevail, locking Celia into the patterns of her former life. Seething with anger and bitterness, she exacts her revenge by destroying the illusions of an innocent teenager, Dora, making her aware that, like Celia's, her desires for a freer life will never be fulfilled. The play's title refers to the rotting fruit that falls from the same tree year after year, a metaphor of circular time stifling Celia and others of her generation. The Freudian influence on Hernández is particularly evident in *Los huéspedes reales*, a depressing tragedy of the unhealthy relationships between an ineffectual, emotionally impotent father, his jealous, domineering wife, and their daughter. The latter overcomes her initial weakness and eventually emerges as an Electra who challenges her mother and almost seduces her father. Realizing too late the disastrous results of his weakness, the latter is driven to suicide, his only solution.

In her more subjective, avant-garde dramas Hernández takes an equally critical stance, but her ire is broader in scope and often designed to explode the political and social myths perpetrated by the revolution. These dramas are also characterized by a greater emphasis on symbols, increasingly complex structures, and more imaginative use of stage settings and lighting effects. The three most significant works of this period are *La paz ficticia* (1960; the fictitious peace), *La historia de un anillo* (1961; the story of a ring), and *La fiesta del mulato* (1966; *The Mulatto's Orgy*, in William I. Oliver, ed., *Voices of Change in the Spanish American Theater*, 1971).

In *La paz ficticia* Hernández evokes a disgraceful episode in Mexican history, namely, the Mexican army's brutal campaign in the 1880s against the Yaqui Indians for the purpose of seizing their land and selling it to foreign mining companies. After suffering the inevitable defeat, the Yaquis were ruthlessly dispersed throughout the country. Outraged, the author dramatizes the incident, hoping that such a terrible injustice will never be allowed to recur. Despite its rather banal, melo-dramatic plot, *La historia de un anillo* produces an impact on the reader through its rapidly shifting scenes and abrupt jux-tapositions. The setting is an isolated village where the mayor and the priest conspire to prevent the townspeople from learn-ing of their rights provided by the Constitution. An ugly con-frontation ensues, culminating with the mayor's appeal to the central government for help and the climactic massacre of protesters.

Some critics consider *La fiesta del mulato* as Hernández's masterpiece. Set in colonial Mexico in 1799, the plot involves the trial of a mulatto, part owner of a gold mine, who spends his profits on a three-week-long fiesta instead of paying the heavy mining tax levied by the authorities. Suspected of in-stigating revolutionary activities and accused of heresy by the Inquisition, the mulatto, in part because of his race, is por-trayed as an outcast caught between the corrupt officials of a disintegrating social order and the Indian masses who would like to be rid of them. The final scene nevertheless strikes a harmonious chord with the acquittal of the mulatto and the anticipation of racial unity, peace, and justice. *La fiesta del mulato* stands out as a colorful spectacle of music, dance, and elegant costumes, but these trappings of Spanish culture con-stitute an ironic contrast with the revolutionary ideology con-veyed by the plot. The dynamic montage of spectacle, dialogue, and narration (the narrative voice is that of the mulatto's ser-vant) also serves to heighten the overall dramatic impact.

Luisa Josefina Hernández emerges as a pessimistic ob-server of the Mexican experience. She not only depicts the bank-ruptcy of the conservative middle-class establishment, but also lashes out at injustice in many of its forms. Indeed, her moral indignation and harsh treatment of her characters represent unifying elements of her oeuvre. Her deep understanding of human nature and her ventures into innovative technique give universal significance to her dramaturgy.

Jorge Ibargüengoitia and Carlos Fuentes (both also dis-cussed in the chapter on fiction) were born in the same year, and both have achieved greater recognition for their novels than for their plays, but they have little else in common. An ironic, tongue-in-cheek satirist, Ibargüengoitia earned a solid literary reputation in Mexico; Fuentes is known to a worldwide audience as a sophisticated intellectual interested in avant-garde forms and a broad range of ideas. Ibargüengoitia excelled in the dramatization of family conflicts seething beneath a calm surface of middle-class stability. *Susana y los jóvenes* (1952; Susana and the youths), for example, depicts a respectable young woman's vain pursuit of an opportunistic male, and *Clotilde en su casa* (1955; Clotilde in her home) treats the protagonist's clandestine affair with a friend of her husband. The author's successful incursion into the theater of the absurd characterizes his prize-winning farce *El atentado* (1963; the assassination attempt), which pillories both the enemies and the supporters of President-elect Álvaro Obregón, assassinated in 1928 by a religious fanatic. This play also represents an assault on the mythologizing rhetoric of the revolution through its comic visual effects and its Brechtian technique of distancing the audience from the action and forcing a reevaluation of the entire historical episode. And sardonic commentary on immorality informs *Pájaro en mano* (1964; bird in hand), about a rogue who succeeds because he has mastered all the tricks of his trade.

Carlos Fuentes has published three plays: *El tuerto es rey* (1970; the one-eyed man is king), *Todos los gatos son pardos* (1970; all the cats are gray), and *Orquídeas a la luz de la luna* (1982; orchids in the moonlight). An existential statement on man's relations with God, *El tuerto es rey* takes place in an old mansion where Donata and her servant Duque await the return of her husband (el rey) from a trip to a casino in Deauville. Meanwhile the two protagonists, the only characters, argue, cajole, and play verbal games, the last of which is Duque's imitation of the returning master and his (Duque's and by implication the master's) subsequent death at the hands of a guerrilla band because he cannot prove the house belongs to him. Though ambiguous, the action appears to dramatize the absence of God (el rey) and the fictions man (Duque) creates to fill this vacuum. Thus, Duque believes in the existential tenet of total responsibility, his way of replacing the missing God, but in the end he himself is ironically abandoned by an uncaring deity of less than perfect vision.

Todos los gatos son pardos is a historical drama whose vast time frame contrasts sharply with the temporal and spatial concentration of *El tuerto es rey*. Set in Mexico City during the Spanish conquest, this play explodes the myth of Moctezuma's heroic defeat by circumstances of history, portraying him as a tormented, vacillating soul terrified of responsibility and consumed by a war he is incapable of fighting. Fuentes inverts the mythical role of Malinche, the Indian princess who became Cortés's mistress and interpreter, transforming her from a long-maligned symbol of betrayal to a positive, creative force favoring the establishment of a multicultural society over which a benevolent conqueror should reign. Cortés, however, rejects her request not to violate her native land, adhering instead to the medieval principles of faith, honor, courage, and violence in order to achieve his goal. The play ends with the death of a student during the 1968 Tlatelolco massacre, the same youth who was sacrificed previously by the ancient Aztec rulers, and the appearance of Cortés dressed as a U.S. general and Malinche as a call girl. Thus, Fuentes discovers in Mexico's tragic past the patterns of tyranny, blood sacrifice, and foreign intervention that continue into the twentieth century.

In *Orquídeas a la luz de la luna* two aging ex-actresses living in a shabby apartment evoke the legendary fame of Dolores Del Río and María Felix as they desperately seek to convince both themselves and the audience that they are the two cinema stars of several decades ago. The art of role reversals becomes apparent when María and Dolores imitate their two film heroines—Felix was the domineering woman and Del Río the submissive one—and then exchange identities, suggesting that together they constitute opposite sides of a single personality. Fuentes undermines the myth of the superstar, who has been magnified by larger-than-life celluloid illusions, corroded by time, and dehumanized by the need to project the hollow goddess image. But at the same time he portrays his two protagonists as vibrant examples of emancipated Mexican women, both having escaped from the oppressive familial structure of their culture.

Maruja Vilalta (b. 1931) was born in Spain, but she has lived most of her life in Mexico, where she enjoys a reputation as one of her adopted nation's best dramatists writing in the absurdist mode. The typical absurdist characteristics of her theater include its devaluation of orderly plot and character development; its use of the grotesque, violence, and game playing; and above all, its presentation of a disjointed, "Kafka-esque," and often allegorical world vision that obliges the reader/spectator to view reality in a radically different manner. Vilalta and most Latin American absurdists differ from their European and U.S. counterparts, however, in their strong denunciation of political and social injustice.

Vilalta's first important play, *El 9* (1965; Number 9), is a symbolic depiction, with absurd overtones, of the mechaniza-tion and dehumanization of the modern-day worker. The set-ting is a patio next to the gray walls of a canning factory where Number 9 and Number 7 are employed. The third and only other character is a child (el Niño) who at some future date will join the work force behind the gray walls. Throughout the play a voice is heard over a loudspeaker giving orders, and despite its amiable tone, it eventually comes to signify man-agement's domination of labor. Indeed, the action, like that of other dramas by Vilalta, becomes a kind of power game, in this case a game in which the workers remain passive pawns of omnipotent, anonymous players. In the final lines Number 9 is driven to suicide, his only means of expressing his free will, but the child will replace him, thus assuring that the action metaphor (the game) of oppression and alienation will continue.

Cuestión de narices (1966; question of noses), Vilalta's most absurd work, is an allegorical farce based on a quarrel between two bank clerks, previously close friends, over the size of their noses. Eventually the entire community becomes involved, donning short or long false noses in order to designate which party they are supporting. The situation gets completely out of hand when a bride and groom are forced onto opposite sides, and the groom is killed. After a brief reconciliation another feud erupts between the tall and the short citizens of the town. Meanwhile a radio announcer reports the outbreak of two wars, the first between Galgolandia (Greyhoundland) and Sabuesolandia (Bloodhoundland), and the second between Pericolandia (Parakeetland) and Urracolandia (Magpieland). Through its nonsensical humor, grotesque imagery, and rapid movement, *Cuestión de narices* lampoons a multitude of human vices, but its most obvious emphasis falls on man's inability to live in peace with his fellow man.

Esta noche juntos, amándonos tanto (1970; together tonight, loving each other so much) portrays an aging couple, Casimiro and Rosalía (also referred to as Él and Ella) isolated from the outside world. Trapped in a pattern of absurd daily routine, they embody egotism, caring nothing about others and even denying aid to a dying neighbor. Their checker games, moreover, become a battleground or action metaphor of their hatred for one another, Rosalía constantly reminding her husband of their inadequate pension because he was never promoted to the position of department head in the government office where he was employed. An ironic parallel to their domestic battles appears in the form of newspaper articles describing the institutionalized violence outside their dwelling. Read aloud with total indifference by the two protagonists, these articles are graphically illustrated by slides projected onto a screen to be viewed by the audience. Through its meaning-charged language and symbolic action, the play condemns individual egotism and social injustice as opposite sides of the same coin.

Vilalta's most highly praised work is *Nada como el piso 16* (1975; nothing like apartment 16), which also utilizes the absurdist technique of game playing as an action metaphor of the struggle for power and domination. The setting is an elegant Manhattan apartment shared by Max, a corporate executive, and his prostitute mistress, Stella. The arrival of Jerome, an electrician making a house call, initiates the game that lasts throughout the play. In the first act Jerome is persuaded to stay with Max, seduced by the latter's luxurious life style; act two reveals Max's increasing domination of Jerome; and in the third act Jerome, having mastered the game, dominates Max until Stella becomes an active participant, introducing a final note of ambiguity. Unlike *El 9*, *Nada como el piso 16* is concerned with the power struggle between individuals and thus remains further removed from the social context. In its entirety, however, Vilalta's theater is an ingenious representation of the absurd human condition anchored to reality by elements of protest.

Although José Agustín (also discussed in the chapter on fiction), like Fuentes and Ibargüengoitia, is better known for his fiction than for his theater, he has written two plays worthy of note: *Abolición de la propiedad* (1969; abolition of property) and *Círculo vicioso* (1974; vicious circle). The former is an experimental work, consisting of a long dialogue between two young people, Norma and Everio; Norma, however, also alternates as a first-person narrator. Set in a basement room filled with old furniture and audiovisual devices typical of a recording studio, the play involves the confrontation between two opposite types, Norma emerging as a liberal advocate of individual freedom and social justice, and Everio as a conservative exponent of the bourgeois establishment. What makes *Abolición de la propiedad* an experimental drama is its use of the mass media—recordings, films, and live rock music—to pace the action and highlight the protagonists' light repartee and word games, which at times deteriorate into violent arguments. The audiovisual devices also repeat and foreshadow some of the episodes, a case in point being Everio's attempt to strangle Norma. Although he desists before killing her, the play ends with the ominous suggestion that the incident will recur. Agustín's dramatization of issues usually rooted in the generation gap is original because his two characters are both young. One might speculate, then, that their contradictory attitudes toward life represent universal archetypes rather than a Mexican phenomenon of the 1960s.

Círculo vicioso is a shocking exposé of conditions in Mexico's infamous Lucumberri prison, now closed. The plot involves the traumas of several inmates all victimized by a thoroughly corrupt penal system, which, the author strongly suggests, constitutes a microcosm of Mexican society. Just as important as the message is the medium, a prison vernacular at times barely intelligible to the outsider. Although undoubtedly authentic (Agustín spent several months in Lucumberri after being arrested on charges of drug possession), the language was judged obscene by government censors, who withheld authorization to present the play for more than a year.

THE CARIBBEAN

Cuba

Marxist critics would have their readers believe that Cuban playwrights produced little of value before the revolution, and it is true that the quality of the nation's theater has vastly improved since 1959. Nevertheless, for more than two decades prior to Castro's victory the genre showed more signs of life in Cuba than in many other Spanish American countries. Early theatrical organizations that stimulated artists and attracted audiences include the previously mentioned La Cueva, which presented some of the finest works from abroad; the Academia de Artes Dramáticas (ADAD, founded 1941); the Teatro Popular (founded 1943); the Teatro Prometeo (founded 1947); and the Teatro Experimental de la Universidad (founded 1949). A direct result of the revolution and a determining factor in the development of Cuba's contemporary theater is the official support provided by the Consejo Nacional de Cultura (National Council of Culture), which, through its professional direction and financial subsidies, engendered a cultural atmosphere conducive to artistic creativity. Prior to 1968, when government censorship became increasingly heavy-handed, Cuban theater could be divided into two segments: realistic works justifying the revolution, and nonrealistic works, often absurd or allegorical, conveying a more universal experience. Since the late 1960s playwrights have prudently kept in mind the needs and the future goals of their socialist state. Another important development has been the establishment of provincial theaters throughout the island to dramatize local problems and educate local audiences.

The two dramatists whose works best typify the Cuban

theater prior to the revolution are Carlos Felipe (pseudonym of Carlos Fernández, b. 1914) and Fermín Borges (b. 1931). Felipe, a self-taught man of letters, wrote numerous plays for the commercial theater, the best of which is *El travieso Jimmy* (1947; mischievous Jimmy). The plot evolves through the memories of an old man, Leonelo, who recalls his youth on the Isle of Pines, off the coast of Cuba, in the early twentieth century. An orphan raised in the home of a pharmacist, Don Sixto, Leonelo meets a foreign drifter named Jimmy who gains his confidence by promising to take him to his mother. Jimmy also convinces Raimundo, the timid boyfriend of Don Sixto's daughter Lila, that the only way to win Lila's love is to become a sailor. Raimundo's disappearance in a shipwreck, Lila's death, and Jimmy's revelation to Leonelo that his mother was a prostitute, a fact known to all except him, precipitate the boy's departure for Havana. A psychological study of complex human relations, *El travieso Jimmy* depicts the impact of an outsider on the lives of individuals shielded from, or unwilling to face, reality.

Fermín Borges is also a realist, but he concentrates more heavily on the everyday frustrations of the lower classes. His best works include *Gente desconocida* (1953; unknown people), about the struggles of impoverished slum dwellers; *Pan viejo* (1954; old bread), the depressing portrait of a poor couple whose only hope after the death of their son is a lottery ticket; and *Doble juego* (1954; double game), which details the crimes of depraved juvenile delinquents.

The most influential Cuban playwright of the older generation is Virgilio Piñera (also discussed in the chapter on fiction), whose career spans both the prerevolutionary and contemporary periods. A poet, short-story writer, and novelist, Piñera presented an anguished, existential view of the world reminiscent of Sartre, but he is also known for his biting irony and grotesque humor. The decade he spent in Buenos Aires in the 1940s and 1950s undoubtedly had an impact on his theater. *Electra Garrigó* (1945; Electra Garrigó) is based on Sophocles' play, which narrates Orestes' murder of his mother, Clytemnestra, and her lover, Aegisthus, for killing his father, Agamemnon. The real instigator of Orestes' crime, however, is

Electra, who in Piñera's work looms as physically passive, but domineering, cold, and selfish. Piñera's Orestes, on the other hand, defines himself through his Sartrean commitment to both existential and political freedom.

Falsa alarma (1949; false alarm), a satire of the corrupt legal system, is considered the first example of absurd theater in Cuba. Additional examples of the absurd by Piñera are *Dos viejos pánicos* (1968; two old provokers of panic), about an aging couple whose violent word games all but destroy their marital relations; and *Estudio en blanco y negro* (1969; study in black and white), in which a young man and woman making love on a park bench suddenly find themselves on opposite sides in a preposterous argument between two enraged passersby.

Abelardo Estorino (b. 1925) is one of several outstanding realists to emerge since the revolution. His best-known play, *El robo del cochino* (1964; the theft of the pig), delineates the conflict between the status quo and revolutionary ideals on the eve of Castro's rise to power. Cristóbal, a wealthy self-made businessman, and his left-wing son Juanelo strongly disagree when Tavito, Juanelo's friend and the son of a longtime employee of Cristóbal, is detained by the police for stealing a pig. The real reason for his arrest is that he gave aid to a wounded escapee. When Cristóbal refuses to intervene with the authorities on Tavito's behalf and the latter is murdered by the police, Juanelo heads for the Sierra Maestra to join the guerrillas in their fight against tyranny. A graphic depiction of the dichotomy between the wealthy and the oppressed, *El robo del cochino* captures the stifling atmosphere of a provincial town, a microcosm of prerevolutionary Cuba.

Two realistic contemporaries of Estorino are José Brene (b. 1927) and Manuel Reguera Saumell (b. 1928). Popular and prolific, Brene is a masterful creator of colloquial dialogue, which serves to dramatize political and social corruption in works such as *Santa Camila de la Habana vieja* (1962; Santa Camila of old Havana) and *El gallo de San Isidro* (1964; the rooster of San Isidro). His most successful creation is *Fray Sabino* (1971; Fray Sabino), a hard-hitting attack on capitalistic exploitation and religious hypocrisy in his native land. Reguera Saumell sketches a satirical political portrait in *El general Antonio estuvo aquí* (1961; General Antonio was here), while *Sara en el traspatio* (1950; Sarah in the backyard) describes the frustrations of provincial life via the disintegration of a financially strapped and emotionally shattered family. Most memorable is his *Recuerdos de Tulipa* (1962; memories of Tulipa), about an aging dancer in a second-rate carnival, the symbol of a depraved society.

Matías Montes Huidobro (b. 1931) left Cuba in 1961 and has taught Spanish American literature for many years at the University of Hawaii. He belongs to a group of dramatists who, while firmly anchoring their works in the recent Cuban experience, also stress nonrealistic devices to expand aesthetic dimensions. *Los acosados* (1959; the pursued) combines reality and dream to portray a young married couple struggling to overcome personal and economic adversity; *La botija* (1959; the milk jug) and *Las vacas* (1959; the cows) focus on the problems Cuban peasants faced immediately after the revolution; and *El tiro por la culata* (1961; the backfire) is a farce about a lecherous landowner who is foiled in his attempt to seduce a nubile peasant girl. One of Montes Huidobro's most successful works is *La sal de los muertos* (1971; the salt of the dead), which describes the moral disintegration of a family and, by implication, all of Cuban society. Tigre, the wealthy, venal patriarch, and his second wife, Cuca, a former prostitute, represent the decadent past; Tigre's son Lobo and his wife Aura, both eagerly awaiting Tigre's death in order to lay claim to his fortune, stand for the present; and Lobito, Lobo's dishonest son, adumbrates the disastrous future engendered by the preceding generations. The only sympathetic character is the family's long-time maid, Caridad, whose suffering mirrors that of Cuba's lower classes. The climactic deaths of Tigre and Lobito create a crazed, chaotic ambience in which Lobo and Aura search desperately, and probably in vain, for Tigre's hidden wealth.

Cuba's most outstanding contemporary playwright with the exception of José Triana (discussed above) is Antón Arrufat (b. 1935). After two years of exile in New York, Arrufat returned to his homeland in 1959 to participate in the cultural programs sponsored by the revolutionary regime. A major influence on his writings is the old *teatro bufo*, a combination of musical comedy and vaudeville, which he uses to discover essential aspects of the Cuban past and to delineate present-day issues. His first creative effort was *El caso se investiga* (1957; the case is investigated), a venture into the absurd that had a six-year run in Havana. The plot involves the investigation of a murder, suspects in which are the victim's widow, her sister, and the maid. However, the rigid logic of the detective story is undermined by the contradictions and non sequiturs of the dialogue and the infusion of grotesque humor, music, and dance. In *El último tren* (1957; the last train) Arrufat develops one of his major themes, namely, man's immersion in time through obsessive routine. Here an aging bachelor and his fiancée, bored with each other after a long engagement, confront the truth of their failed relationship and bid each other a final farewell. But when Martel returns to Alicia's home for his cane, their semiweekly evenings of dinner and cards begin anew. Victimized by habit and frightened by a glimpse of freedom, they have, in a sense, missed "the last train."

Arrufat irreverently mocks death in another of his successful comedies, *El vivo al pollo* (1961; long live life), whose title is taken from a proverb, "El vivo al pollo y el muerto al hoyo" ("Long live life and to the grave with the dead"). Unable to accept her husband's death, Matilde has him embalmed, makes a permanent place for him in her living room, and treats him as if he were alive. The macabre humor reaches its peak when she becomes the undertaker's business partner, and her husband's body, their prize advertising display. In *La repetición* (1963; the repetition) the author again turns his attention to the subject of time, the characters here being an impoverished married couple (the Neighbor and the Husband), the Girl, and the Salesman. The Girl, who occupies an upstairs apartment, is visited first by the embittered occupant (the Neighbor) of the downstairs apartment, and then by the Salesman, a young man who attempts to sell her an electric iron she can ill afford. The Girl and the Salesman are strongly attracted to each other, but their future becomes clouded when, upon descending the stairs on their way to a dance, they stop at the Neighbor's apartment and exchange masks with her and her husband. Like the older couple on the lower level, they are destined to see their hopes dashed and their youth destroyed by the inexorable flow of time.

Some critics consider *Todos los domingos* (1965; every Sunday) as Arrufat's best work to date. The protagonist is a crippled woman, Elvira, whose fiancé abandoned her some twenty years ago. With the assistance of her domineering servant, Alejandrina, she hires a young man every Sunday to play the role of her fiancé, repeating the exact scene of their last meeting. Although she has never engaged the same person more than once, the last "fiancé" is permitted to return for a second visit. When he declares his love for her, Alejandrina kills him with a pair of scissors while Elvira cackles madly in her wheelchair. *Todos los domingos* dramatizes the repetitive, ritualistic aspect of human behavior and, in addition, introduces the themes of domination and exploitation. Thus, not only does Alejandrina appear to control Elvira, but there is also evidence that the latter's Sunday rituals are mere dress rehearsals for her final act of vengeance.

Los siete contra Tebas (1968; the seven against Thebes) won a literary prize for its author, but it has never been performed in Cuba because of the political controversy it aroused. Following Aeschylus' model, this play focuses on the conflict between the two brothers, Etéocles and Polinice, who ultimately slay one another in the battle for the city they both seek to govern. Etéocles could be construed as a fictional portrait of Castro because when Polinice accuses him of seizing absolute power, he defends himself by stating that he was obliged to act accordingly in order to protect and provide for the poor. Whereas the Greek play ends pessimistically with the city of Thebes divided and prepared to renew the struggle, in the Cuban version the two opposing factions unite, burying the past and laying the groundwork for future progress. Despite its optimistic ending, Arrufat's work has received wide critical acclaim as a first-rate example of tragedy.

Dominican Republic

Modern Dominican theater began in the late 1950s with the almost simultaneous appearance of two talented innovators: Máximo Avilés Blonda (b. 1931) and Franklin Domínguez (b. 1931). Avilés Blonda's existential drama *Las manos vacías* (1959; the empty hands) portrays two anguished victims of World War II: an amnesiac ex-priest who recovers his memory after marrying and fathering a child; and a former Nazi haunted by the crimes he committed as commandant of a concentration camp.

Domínguez began his career as a playwright after studying dramatic art at the University of Texas. His best works include *La broma del senador* (1958; the senator's joke) and *El último instante* (1958; the last instant). The former is a fast-moving farce in which a senator stipulates in his will that to inherit his fortune his widow must marry a former suitor and, in addition, leave the senator's portrait hanging in her living room. The widow outwits the deceased by devising a solution that delights both her new spouse and the audience: she leaves the portrait on the wall but covers it up. Very different in tone, *El último instante* presents an aging prostitute whose rambling monologue exteriorizes her remorse as she evokes obsessive memories of her past. These include the loss of her sweetheart; her break with her parents; and the birth of her son, whom she has not seen for many years. Her overwhelming solitude emerges as the principal theme when, in the final lines of her monologue, she slits her wrists and listlessly awaits death.

The most talented of the younger generation of Dominican playwrights is Iván García (b. 1938), whose somber, nihilistic world vision masks a strong commitment to social reform. *Un héroe más para la mitología* (1963; one more hero for mythology) is a satire about a political coup with many of the stock characters: the corrupt dictator, his military strongman, a group of young, idealistic rebels, and an obscure politician (Manuel Pérez) who orchestrates the revolt for his own personal gain. The title refers to an unknown youth, David Morales, whom Pérez proclaims as a national hero—actually he is a sacrificial victim—in order to divert public attention from the bloody crimes at the center of power and create a myth to inspire future generations. An allegory of the absurd human condition, *Fábula de los cinco caminantes* (1969; fable about five travelers) sketches a desert landscape across which five men are slowly making their way. Representatives of easily recognizable human types, they symbolize the brutal, the religious, the rich, the oppressed, and the rebellious elements of society. The theme is conveyed by the travelers' barely perceptible movement as well as by their fruitless discussions and bitter arguments, all metaphors of man's faltering progress through the ages.

García's most entertaining creation is *Don Quijote de todo el mundo* (1971; everybody's Don Quixote), a modern version of Cervantes's classic. After devouring the "subversive" volumes in his library, the half-crazed, idealistic Don Alonso Quezada (Don Quixote's real name was Alonso Quijano) and his friend Juan Sánchez (Cervantes's Sancho Panza) set out in a rickety auto to right the wrongs of the world. The most amusing of their adventures involves Don Alonso's attempt to settle a dispute between a waiter and a restaurateur, each of whom has swindled the other. After witnessing the incident, three conspirators in need of transportation convince Don Alonso to lend his support to a band of guerrillas based in the mountains. While the protagonist is searching for the guerrillas to persuade them to negotiate their demands, he is stabbed by a peasant woman who mistakes him for a dangerous revolutionary. *Don Quijote de todo el mundo* exudes much of Cervantes's mirth, but like García's previous works, it conveys a pessimistic message, namely, that the lessons of history notwithstanding, man's essential nature remains unchanged.

Puerto Rico

The modernization of Puerto Rican theater began in 1938 with the founding of the above-mentioned Areyto group, which presented dramas dealing not only with the island's cultural past, but also with present-day problems. The founder of Areyto, Emilio S. Belaval (b. 1903), also wrote several of the early plays performed by this group, one of his best being *La hacienda de los cuatro vientos* (1940; the hacienda of the four winds), about the struggle to end slavery. Another prominent figure who wrote for Areyto is Manuel Méndez Ballester (b. 1909), whose works depict the lives of the Puerto Rican *jíbaro* (peasant). Typical of his theater is *Tiempo muerto* (1940; dead time), the depressing story of an impoverished family who leave the farm only to encounter more misery laboring in a sugar mill. This same author's *Encrucijada* (1956; crossroads) dramatizes the tragic fate of a Puerto Rican family who move to New York, where all the members succumb to the shock of an alien culture.

With the exception of René Marqués (discussed above), Puerto Rico's most influential contemporary dramatist is Francisco Arriví (b. 1915). The founder in 1944 of the experimental theater known as Tinglado Puertorriqueño, Arriví also served for many years as director of the theater section of the Institute of Puerto Rican Culture. His dramas are usually divided into two groups: those dealing with dreams or fantasies and those more firmly anchored in Puerto Rican reality. One of his early efforts, *María Soledad* (1947; María Soledad), portrays a highly sensitive woman who, despite her obsession with chastity, has an adulterous affair with a poet, resulting in the latter's murder by the woman's husband and the husband's suicide. In sharp contrast to this tense psychological drama, *Club de solteros* (1953; bachelors' club) approaches the theater of the absurd with its farcical description of the eternal battle of the sexes, a battle from which men emerge a poor and ludicrous second.

Between 1956 and 1958 Arriví treated Puerto Rico's pronounced African heritage in his trilogy *Máscara puertorriqueña* (Puerto Rican masquerade), consisting of *El murciélago* (1956; the bat), *Medusas en la bahía* (1956; medusas in the bay), and *Vejigantes* (1958; vejigantes). The best of the three and Arriví's most highly acclaimed work is *Vejigantes*, whose title signifies not only a Puerto Rican folk festival of African origin (the *vejigante*), but also the masked individuals (*vejigantes*) who participate in the festival. The first act, which takes place in 1910, combines the exotic music and dance of the festival with dramatic action to show the seduction of Toña, a sensuous mulatto woman, by Benedicto, a young Spanish immigrant. The second and third acts occur in 1958, almost fifty years later, in the upper-middle-class home of the now deceased Benedicto. His survivors are his lifelong mistress, Mamá Toña; her daughter Marta, the widow of a Spaniard; and their daughter Clarita who, as her name suggests, is white. The tense racial issue comes into focus when Bill, a young American businessman from Alabama, falls in love with Clarita without realizing that her grandmother, whom Marta relegates to the back room of the house, is part black. Although Marta encourages her daughter to marry Bill and escape the stigma of her African blood, Clarita rejects Bill's proposal upon learning of his strong racial prejudice. In the final scene the music of the *vejigante* heard in the first act is repeated, this time on a record Clarita has given to Mamá Toña, and Marta removes the makeup and turban she has worn throughout the play to conceal her African ancestry. *Vejigantes* is not just an assault on racial prejudice; it also represents a serious study of the psychological complexes and social alienation among Puerto Ricans unable to accept themselves as they are. Because of its deft integration of theme, action, and form, it is considered one of Spanish America's finest examples of modern theater.

One of Arriví's most intriguing poetic fantasies is *Un cuento de hadas* (1967; a fairy tale), which dramatizes the psychological theme of the double. Rafael, a young journalist miserable with his arrogant wife Carola, returns home very late on several occasions without knowing where he has spent the evening. Through a conversation with his friend Miguel, it is revealed that he has been meeting a beautiful woman in a restaurant where, under the name of Leonardo, he appears to be carefree and happy. As the action progresses, Rafael loses his identity to "the other" more and more frequently until, in the final scene, he breaks with his past, sheds his former self, and begins life anew as Leonardo.

Puerto Rico's leading dramatist of the younger generation is Luis Rafael Sánchez (previously discussed in the chapter on fiction), also a well-known novelist, short-story writer, and essayist. Sánchez's most significant play is *La pasión según Antígona Pérez: Radiografía de la dictadura* (1970; the passion according to Antígona Pérez: X-ray of the dictatorship), a modern adaptation of Sophocles' *Antigone*. The setting is a Spanish American nation governed by a dictator, Generalísimo Creón Molina, who decrees that the bodies of two executed conspirators, the

Tavárez brothers, shall remain uninterred, food for the vultures. In defiance of this decree, Antígona buries the dead brothers, and when she refuses to reveal the location of their graves, she is condemned to death and, ultimately, executed. Her actions are all the more heroic because she stands alone and condemned by all those around her. Molina, an archetypal Spanish American despot, perpetuates his reign of terror through his brutality and his vast network of spies, generating a climate of adulation, subservience, and betrayal. The highest ecclesiastical official in the land, Monseñor Bernardo Escudero, strongly supports the regime, as does Antígona's mother, a fanatical reactionary. Even Antígona's friend Irene betrays her by taking up with her sweetheart, a rising lieutenant colonel in the palace guard and a favorite of the dictator. Only the women's chorus champions Antígona's cause, conveying, in addition, the principal theme, namely, that the sacrifice of one heroic life may assure the liberation from oppression of an entire people.

The play's Brechtian technique is another of its major aspects, Antígona's dual role as both protagonist and narrator serving as a distancing device to oblige the audience to focus on Sánchez's attack on tyranny rather than to identify emotionally with the protagonist's plight. Brecht's didactic theater is also reflected by the stage setting, which, instead of attempting to create an illusion of reality, displays a vast collage of newspaper headlines announcing tragic news items of the day such as the assassinations of Martin Luther King, John F. Kennedy, and Che Guevara. Like Brecht, Sánchez aspires to entertain and educate his audience simultaneously.

CENTRAL AMERICA

Costa Rica

Although Costa Rican dramatists have recently begun to emerge in greater numbers, they have yet to establish what might be deemed a national drama. During the years immediately following World War II foreign imports were the principal fare. The 1950s witnessed the formation of several theatrical groups, the best of which was El Arlequín. It was not until the 1960s, however, that local dramatists began to produce works of high quality, and soon thereafter, in 1970, they were stimulated by the foundation of the Ministry of Culture, the equivalent of Mexico's INBA.

Three of Costa Rica's best contemporary playwrights are Alberto Cañas (b. 1920), Daniel Gallegos (b. 1930), and Samuel Rovinski (b. 1932). A diplomat and poet, Cañas was also named the first Minister of Culture. Among his dramas, many of which have been successfully staged but never published, is *Algo más que dos sueños* (1969; something more than two dreams). Set on a bare stage in a timeless, dreamlike atmosphere reminiscent of Pirandello's plays, it consists of a dialogue between two former lovers, Isabel and Antonio, who, on the day of Antonio's marriage to another, evoke both a real and an imaginary past.

Daniel Gallegos has taught dramatic arts at the University of Costa Rica and is one of the nation's finest directors. *Los profanos* (1959; the irreverent ones) focuses on the evils of technology and the lack of communication in the modern world through its portrait of a bourgeois woman, Patricia Andre, who abandons her hypocritical milieu for a bohemian life with four artists. Though happy with her new companions, she ultimately returns to her previous home, convinced that she has not solved, but only avoided, her existential problems. Unlike *Los profanos*, which at times tends to be excessively discursive, *Ese algo de Dávalos* (1960; that something of Dávalos) is a witty, fast-paced story of two artists, Ricardo Dávalos and Casandra Martín, who exploit friends and reject family responsibilities to achieve professional renown.

La colina (1968; the hill) is not only one of Gallegos's most ambitious and complex plays, but also his most controversial. A frontal attack on orthodox religion, it proposes an alternative to a dehumanized, godless world. The setting is an inn where a group of individuals react to the news that the United Nations has declared the death of God. Although at first they are all devastated, they gradually discover new, more positive values by which to live. Tomás Ávila, an atheistic artist with a fatal ailment, renews his faith in God through his platonic relations with Marta, a novice for whom institutionalized religion is replaced by a more humanized version. Gregorio Fernández and his wife Mercedes commit themselves to the revitalization of their shattered marriage. In contrast to the others, Padre José and the Mother Superior, freed from the feelings of repression imposed on them by their ecclesiastical vows, devote themselves to the pursuit of pleasure.

Although the initial proclamation of God's death strikes an absurd note, Gallegos's drama does not present life devoid of purpose; it musters a positive *Weltanschauung* as its characters give meaning to their lives through their commitment to love, compassion, and communication. By the final act, then, they are no longer concerned with God, but instead with the unity and well-being of all men. *La colina* shocked traditional Costa Ricans (the Mother Superior cavorts in a filmy negligee and Padre José smashes a crucifix), but it offers a universal message for those in search of guiding principles to structure their lives.

A civil engineer as well as a man of letters, Samuel Rovinski combines science fiction and social protest in his dramatic works. *El laberinto* (1969; the labyrinth) portrays a paranoiac scientist haunted by the notion that technology will eventually destroy mankind. A similar theme emerges from *La Atlántida* (1970; Atlantis), whose protagonist dreams of a future "brave new world" in which society controls not only its citizens' every action, but even their emotions. A political farce based on conditions all too real in Spanish America, *Gobierno de alcoba* (1971; bedroom government) presents a dictator (Leoncio) and his mistress (María) whose love has turned sour because of Leoncio's cruelty and violence. The arrival of Martínez, an articulate, idealistic revolutionary who breaks into María's apartment in order to kill Leoncio, renews María's hopes for peace and justice. After Leoncio's death, however, Martínez's character undergoes an abrupt metamorphosis, indicating that the cycle of revolution and oppression has begun anew.

El Salvador

The development of El Salvador's contemporary theater began in 1952 with the establishment of the government-sponsored Dirección General de Bellas Artes (General Direction of Fine Arts) and its subdivision, the Departamento de Teatro (Department of Theater). Three of El Salvador's leading playwrights are Walter Béneke (b. 1928), Roberto Arturo Menéndez (b. 1931), and Álvaro Menéndez Leal (also discussed in the chapter on fiction), all of whom prefer universal to regional themes. Béneke is primarily preoccupied with the moral bankruptcy of the twentieth century, focusing on existential freedom, solitude, and the emptiness of human relations. His first play, *El paraíso de los imprudentes* (1956; the paradise of the imprudent), is set in the Latin Quarter of Paris during the 1950s where a Central American student, Carlos, and his French counterparts confront the political and moral crises typical of the day. Of central importance is Carlos's relations with his girlfriend Christiane, an intellectual who has rejected her bourgeois background through her relations with Carlos but gradually returns to the traditional values of love and marriage. Carlos, on the other hand, when faced with the choice of living with Christiane in the conservative environment of Central America or remaining free from familial obligations, chooses the latter.

Béneke's second and most widely acclaimed work is *Funeral Home* (1959; title in English), whose setting is a funeral parlor in New York. It is Christmas Eve, and a young widow, María, is watching over the body of her husband, when Bernardo, a doctor from Latin America, enters the establishment to escape from the cold. Although out of loneliness they feel a strong attraction to one another, they are kept apart by María's desire for a lasting relationship and an unspecified tragedy in Bernardo's past that prevents him from making such a commitment. After Bernardo's departure, María learns that he has just been released from a five-year term in prison for murdering his wife. In her eyes, his motive justifies the crime, and she vows to find him the next day. Minutes later a telephone call reveals that Bernardo has committed suicide in his hotel room. Tightly structured and fraught with emotion, *Funeral Home* has been praised as one of the most artistically conceived Spanish American dramas of its decade. Its existential assault on time-worn patterns of behavior finds expression through María's desire to determine her own values, but she is thwarted by Nancy, the conformist wife of the owner of the funeral parlor. Also in a negative vein, Bernardo loses his chance for happiness because of a deep-seated guilt that prevents him from burying the past and living in the Christmas spirit of rebirth.

Roberto Arturo Menéndez has written several plays, the best of which is *La ira del cordero* (1958; the ire of the lamb), based on the biblical story of Cain and Abel. In the opening scene Andrés learns that his son Adán has just murdered his other son, Saúl. Shocked and grieved, Andrés dies of a heart attack, whereupon Adán commits suicide. In the rest of the play María, Andrés's widow, relives scenes from the past that alter the biblical version of the tragedy, blaming the parents and the victim for the crime instead of the "guilty" son. Thus, it becomes clear that Andrés and María viewed Saúl as a saint, praising his every action and remark, while Adán, despite his sincere efforts to please, could do nothing right. Saúl, moreover, treated his brother with scorn and ultimately incurred his murderous wrath by killing one of Adán's favorite lambs. Menéndez's reworking of the well-known story is modern not only in its psychological twist, but also in its dynamic structure, which creates movement by linking present and past as well as objective and subjective realities.

A well-known poet and writer of fiction, Álvaro Menéndez Leal has lived for more than a decade exiled from El Salvador. His highly successful, oft-translated play, *Luz negra* (1966; *Black Light*, in *Drama and Theater*, Winter 1971–72), consists of a dialogue between the severed heads of two recently executed men. Moter and Goter are, respectively, a swindler and an idealistic revolutionary whose absurd, disjointed conversation alludes to the world's horrifying conflicts and paradoxical contradictions reflected in the oxymoron of the play's title. A third character, a blind passerby, participates briefly in the exchange, stating that the saint and the hoodlum are indistinguishable. The protagonists' final words, shouted at a deaf street sweeper cleaning up the debris from the execution, underscore the contrasts characterizing the grotesque human experience: "Spirit of God! Spirit of God! . . . Love! Love! Love! Love! . . ."

Guatemala

Guatemala's modern theater began in 1944 after the fall of the dictator Jorge Ubico. Nevertheless, since that date other right-wing military regimes have on occasion strangled the development of all art forms. The nation's three leading playwrights since World War II are Carlos Solórzano (discussed above), Miguel Ángel Asturias (also discussed in the chapter on fiction), and Manuel Galich (1913–1984).

Asturias's *Soluna* (1955; sunmoon) has been called a modern miracle play; like this author's well-known novels, it blends ancient myths and modern everyday life into a dreamlike magical realism. The protagonist is Mauro, a prosperous landowner who marries Ninica with the understanding that if she is unhappy with life in the country, she can go back to the city. At the beginning of the play, Ninica is preparing to leave her husband. Hoping to prevent her departure, Mauro consults a sorcerer, Soluna, who gives him a medicine mask that will make time pass more rapidly and thus enable him to wait for Ninica or forget her. After a long dream sequence in which he envisions a battle between the sun and the moon, Mauro learns that Ninica has been injured in a train wreck; as a result she has decided to return to him. *Soluna* dramatizes the Jungian conflict between the rational consciousness (the sun) and irrational unconscious (the moon), a conflict that ends in destruction (the train wreck) and renewed psychic energy (Mauro's and Ninica's revitalized marriage). As suggested by the title, Asturias's theme is that man cannot live by reason alone, but that in order to attain psychic wholeness he must retain contact with the myths of his ancestral and telluric origins.

Set in the sixteenth century, *La audiencia de los confines* (1957; the tribunal of the frontier) dramatizes the struggles of Bishop Bartolomé de Las Casas to prohibit slavery among the Indians. Las Casas deals effectively with his antagonists, the corrupt governor and the avaricious colonists, but, as Asturias implies, the exploitation of the Guatemalan Indian continues unabated into the twentieth century.

In contrast to his Nobel Prize-winning colleague, Manuel Galich is a vigorous realist who satirizes political and social conditions in his native land. A left-wing professor, statesman, and diplomat as well as a prolific playwright, Galich spent many years of his life in exile, principally in Argentina and in Cuba, where he died. His early works include *M'hijo el bachiller* (1939; my son the graduate), a violent denunciation of the education system in Guatemala; *De lo vivo a lo pintado* (1947; from the living to the painted), which inveighs against the corrupt legal profession and injustices to women; and *El tren amarillo* (1954; the yellow train), a somewhat sensational and hard-hitting attack on the foreign banana companies operating in Guatemala.

Two of Galich's most typical plays are *Entre cuatro Paredes* (1964; among four Paredes) and *El último cargo* (1974; the last charge). The former is a comedy of manners satirizing upper-middle-class hypocrisy. Señora Paredes, an active member of the society to protect illegitimate children, fires her pregnant maid Felipa and orders her daughter to break her engagement to Antonio because he has fathered an illegitimate child. The situation is saved by Señor Paredes who, upon discovering that his son is the father of Felipa's unborn child, obliges him to marry her. Antonio's name is cleared when it becomes known that he has recognized his son and is providing for his support. The pun of the title, which also means "within four walls," is indicative of the author's lively style.

El último cargo exemplifies what is known as *la pieza de guerrilla* (the guerrilla drama), a political work based on the confrontation between the conservative establishment and revolutionaries attempting to seize power and institute social justice for the common people. The *pieza de guerrilla* is usually presented in simple, direct language and tightly structured plots to convey an unequivocal message. In *El último cargo* an army colonel is led to believe that his troops have killed his rebel son Quique who, along with a hundred other guerrillas, has been betrayed by the colonel's brother-in-law. The play ends with the execution of the traitor after his trial before a "court of the people" and the revelation that Quique has managed to escape unharmed.

Honduras

The Honduran theater is surely one of the least developed in Spanish America. The nation's leading dramatist, Andrés Morris (b. 1928), immigrated to Honduras from Spain in 1961 and immediately began to play an active role in the cultural life of his adopted land. In 1965 he helped to found and became the director of the Teatro Nacional in the capital city of Tegucigalpa. Virtually all of his plays written in Honduras, the best example of which is *Oficio de hombres* (1970; a man's job), satirize the problems of underdevelopment plaguing Central America's poorest and most backward country. In *Oficio de hombres*, an absurd tragicomedy, a group of professionals who have been trained abroad on scholarships return home hoping to contribute their knowledge to badly needed programs of technological development. In addition to learning to dodge bullets at every turn, a leitmotif signifying political instability, they find themselves obliged to deal with incompetent officials who pocket tax revenues or send folkloric groups abroad instead of establishing irrigation projects or building nuclear power plants.

The leading characters are Lidgardo, an agricultural engineer; his wife Orquídea, an expert in linguistics and pedagogy; and Chema, a senator they hope will persuade congress to provide funds for educational and agricultural programs. Confronted with a lack of income and Chema's inability (or unwillingness) to help them, Lidgardo and Orquídea decide that their only means of survival is to transform Lidgardo into an ignorant macho slob like Chema, thus qualifying him for a lucrative government sinecure. Lidgardo's training, directed by Orquídea with the help of tape recorders and slide projectors, is arduous, but he finally becomes illiterate in Spanish and utterly uncouth in manner. In the final scene, though, just before leaving for a job interview with Chema, he begins to quote passages from *Hamlet*, an indication that Orquídea must now render him illiterate in English. The farce ends tragically when Lidgardo leaves for his appointment and is shot dead on the street.

Nicaragua

Although Nicaragua's modern theater did not begin until the mid-1950s, critics still admire its precursor, Pablo Antonio Cuadra (b. 1912), whose most famous work is *Por los caminos van los campesinos* (1937; along the roads go the peasants). Still applicable in some respects to the present-day situation, this moving drama depicts a peasant family's tragic plight during the U.S. military intervention of the 1920s. The daughter is raped by a gringo officer; the two sons are drafted into the army and disappear; and the parents flee to the mountains after the father kills a lawyer who, through chicanery, has gained possession of their land.

Nicaragua's best contemporary playwright is Roland Steiner (b. 1936), whose dramas often combine reality and dream to depict the erosion of love and the lack of communication between the sexes. In *Judit* (1957; Judith) a man bored with his wife dreams of a blissful affair with a young art student, but when the latter becomes pregnant, their love turns to hatred and, in the final scene, he strangles his wife, confusing her with his imaginary mistress. Marital friction also emerges as a major element in *Un drama corriente* (1963; an ordinary drama), about a wealthy industrialist whose wife seeks to revive their past love by conjuring up his youthful double. When her insensitive husband has the youth committed to an insane asylum, she disappears, leaving him prey to overwhelming guilt and remorse. The communication barrier is perhaps most graphically portrayed in *La puerta* (1966; the door), in which a man returns home from work to find his key will not unlock his door, nor can his wife open it from the inside. The ensuing dialogue, increasingly strident and acrimonious, comes to an end when he breaks down the door and finds himself in an empty dwelling symbolic of the couple's failed relationship.

Since the overthrow of the Somoza dictatorship in 1979, the Nicaraguan theater has become highly politicized; plays are often performed by inspired amateurs who convey their ideas in a direct, unadorned idiom on crude stages set up in city streets or villages. Approved by the Sandinista regime, this popular theater exalts the virtues of the revolution and exhorts Nicaraguans to overcome its opposition.

Panama

Although Panamanian dramatists produced a number of fine children's plays during the 1930s and 1940s, the nation's modern theater did not begin until the early 1950s. The older generation of playwrights is best represented by Renato Ozores (b. 1910), who was born in Spain but has lived most of his life in Panama. His most memorable work is *La fuga* (1959; the flight), a penetrating psychological drama about a young woman, Daniela, whose husband dies in an accident. After being confined in a mental hospital, the bereaved widow is taken to the home of her aunt, but the subsequent revelations about Daniela's husband and late father (the former was unfaithful and the latter dishonest) cause mounting tensions, culminating in the protagonist's "flight" into madness.

Panama's leading dramatist and one of the most admired in Spanish America today is José de Jesús Martínez (also discussed in the chapter on poetry). A professor of philosophy at the University of Panama, Martínez has obviously been influenced by the French existentialists, his principal themes being metaphysical and psychological rather than regional or political. His two most widely acclaimed dramas are *Juicio final* (1962; final judgment) and *Enemigos* (1963; enemies), both of which focus on man's loneliness and inability to find a purpose in life. The protagonist of *Juicio final* is a recently deceased bourgeois, referred to as "The Man," who presents himself before a judge to receive the verdict regarding his final destiny. Assuming that he must give an account of his respectability and many accomplishments, he is shocked to discover that none of this matters after death; rather, the judge wants to know how his good deeds have affected *him* and if he is truly the product of his actions. Thus, the central question asked by the play is where man's true identity lies, and the answer would seem to be, not in what he has done, but in what he is. An important leitmotif is the haunting sound of a flute, which symbolizes feeling, or the flow of psychic energy that animates the individual and draws him into the vital rhythm of life. It also reminds the protagonist of his youthful desire to become a musician, a desire that remained unfulfilled like the love he felt for a woman he never married. In a sense, then, he is an egocentric outsider, never having participated in the joys, sorrows, or mysteries of human existence. And because his essence remains a hollow shell without a soul, his *juicio final* is his condemnation to an eternity of absolute nothingness, the ultimate of isolation and solitude.

The action of *Enemigos* takes place during the Mexican revolution in an enclosed area where three combatants (First, Second, and Third) spend a night. Refusing to reveal their identities or the parties (Federalists or Revolutionaries) for which they are fighting, they converse while keeping their guns aimed at each other and threatening to shoot at any moment. First, who is a schoolteacher, gradually emerges as an idealist who cries out in vain for divine justice. Third, an older man and a kind of father figure, insists that he is God, bringing to mind existential man's attempt to replace the missing deity. And Second, the villain, mocks the other two and finally kills them both moments before he is surrounded and shot by a detachment of soldiers. The Mexican revolution and the enclosed area represented by the setting serve as metaphors of the violence-ridden, existential "prison"—Sartre's *No Exit* comes to mind—in which modern man finds himself trapped and from which death is the only escape. The identification of the three combatants by numbers underscores their dehumanization, as do their irrational hatred and fear of one another. Like "The Man" of *Juicio final*, the protagonists of *Enemigos* stand out as alienated, soulless individuals devoid of humanity and incapable of forging meaningful human relationships. Martínez utilizes his art not only to mirror man's flaws, but also to attempt a definition of human existence.

COLOMBIA AND VENEZUELA

Colombia

The two most important initiators of Colombia's modern theater are Antonio Álvarez Lleras (1892–1956) and Luis Enrique Osorio (1896–1966). Influenced by Ibsen and the Spanish playwright Jacinto Benavente, Álvarez Lleras wrote realistic thesis dramas aimed at social reform. Among his most popular works are *Almas de ahora* (1944; present-day souls), which concerns the tragic fate of a young woman at a time of rapidly changing mores; and *El virrey Solís* (1948; the viceroy Solís), a finely honed portrait of a rakish eighteenth-century viceroy who abandons his mistress to become a monk. Osorio is also known as a social-protest writer, but the influence of Shaw, Pirandello, and O'Neill make him somewhat more innovative than Álvarez Lleras. *El doctor Manzanillo* (1943; Doctor Manzanillo) and its sequel, *Manzanillo en el poder* (1944; Manzanillo in power), both of which satirize the corrupt politics practiced by the upper classes, demonstrate Osorio's exceptional ability to delineate believable characters and well-structured plots.

Another successful figure of the 1940s is Oswaldo Díaz Díaz (b. 1910), whose work emphasizes irony and poetic symbolism rather than political or social ills. In *La comedia famosa de Antonia Quijana* (1947; Antonia Quijana's famous comedy), for example, he portrays Don Quixote's niece, a headstrong young woman obsessed by the desire to marry a man who knows nothing about novels of chivalry. In the end, however, she leaves for America with a *caballero de aventuras* (a gentleman fond of adventure). Idealistic but less ironic in tone, *Mydas* (1948; Mydas) depicts a man who renounces the savage world of business for the freedom of artistic creation.

The civil war known as *la violencia* that racked Colombia from 1948 until well into the 1960s has inspired numerous dramatists, two of whom are Manuel Zapata Olivella (also discussed in the chapter on fiction) and Gustavo Andrade Rivera (b. 1921). Better known for his novels than for his plays, Zapata Olivella reinterprets biblical myth in *El retorno de Caín* (1962; the return of Cain), which pits the powerful aggressor Cain against Abel, the underdog ultimately compelled to slay his brother. Andrade Rivera's plays based on *la violencia* include *Historias para quitar el miedo* (1960; stories to take away fear), about a grandfather who stubbornly refuses to leave his ranch when he is threatened by bandits; *Remington 22* (1961; Remington 22), an attack on sensational journalism portraying two brothers killed by Remington 22 rifles after writing newspaper articles on their 1922 Remington typewriter; and *El camino* (1962; the road), which portrays a youth determined to avenge the murder of his parents, grandparents, and sisters.

Colombia's leading contemporary playwright, Enrique Buenaventura (b. 1925), is also one of Spanish America's best directors and drama theoreticians. After leading a bohemian existence throughout much of Latin America, Buenaventura returned to his native Cali, where in 1955 he founded the now famous Teatro Experimental de Cali (TEC). Subsidized by government funds until 1967, when one of its productions incurred the wrath of public officials, the TEC has prospered independently since that time, presenting some of the nation's best drama and offering serious training for actors. Buenaventura's strong commitment to airing political and social issues has become increasingly evident with the evolution of his drama. His first major work, *En la diestra del Dios Padre* (1960; *In the Right Hand of God the Father*, in William I. Oliver, ed., *Voices of Change in the Spanish American Theater,* 1971), is a kind of *auto sacramental* (religious mystery play) enlivened by humor and folkloric elements. Peralta, the protagonist, is a virtuous soul to whom God grants five wishes so that he might improve the lot of his fellow man. Although he gives large sums of money to the poor and keeps death at bay for millions, his newly acquired powers undermine the social order, infuriating relatives of the ill, the devil, priests, and even Saint Peter, who is no longer needed to judge the dead. Finally Peralta is persuaded to unfetter death, and he himself ascends to heaven, where he sits on the right hand of God (one of his wishes was to be able to make himself as small as he desired). The irony stems from the inability of God, who naïvely allied himself with the all-too-human Peralta, to perfect his flawed universe.

Two of Buenaventura's historical dramas, *La tragedia del*

rey Christophe (1963; the tragedy of King Christophe) and *Requiem por el padre Las Casas* (1963; requiem for Father Las Casas), were written to denounce colonialism and to fortify the cultural identity of Spanish Americans. The former deals with the brutal reign (1811–20) in Haiti of Henri Christophe, whose officials attempt a grotesque imitation of French nobility, while the latter depicts the vain efforts of Father Bartolomé de Las Casas to bridge the gap between the sixteenth-century Spanish colonists and the Indian culture they set out to destroy.

More modern settings frame *La trampa* (1966; the trap) and *Tirano Banderas* (1968; tyrant Banderas), both of which also treat exploitation and injustice. A satire of political corruption in Guatemala under the regime (1931–44) of Jorge Ubico, *La trampa* alludes also to conditions in Colombia; as a result of this play, government subsidies for Buenaventura's theater were withdrawn. *Tirano Banderas* is based on the novel of the same title by the Spanish writer Ramón del Valle-Inclán, its subject matter being an aborted revolution of peasants in an unnamed Spanish American nation. Like Valle-Inclán, Buenaventura believes that since independence, the tyranny of Spanish colonialism has merely been replaced by that of brutal military dictators of local origin.

Buenaventura is perhaps best known for his *Papeles del infierno* (1968; documents from hell), a group of one-act plays depicting *la violencia* and generally falling within the theater of cruelty. In *La maestra* (*The School Teacher*, in Gerardo Luzuriaga and Robert S. Rudder, eds., *The Orgy: Modern One-Act Plays from Latin America*, 1974) the spirit of the dead protagonist evokes her father's murder by soldiers who then raped her, depriving her of all will to live. The road of red clay along which the soldiers enter and leave the village emerges not only as a unifying image in this drama but also as a symbol of the overriding theme of violence. *La orgía* (*The Orgy*, in Gerardo Luzuriaga and Robert S. Rudder, eds., *The Orgy: Modern One-Act Plays from Latin America*, 1974) presents an aging prostitute visited by four beggars, each of whom must play the role of a former suitor. The first beggar portrays a wealthy aristocrat, the second a corrupt politician, the third a one-legged

colonel, and the fourth a grotesque clergyman. The play ends
with the murder of the prostitute, a symbol of Colombia, by
the greedy representatives of the four oligarchies, and the appearance of the prostitute's mute son, Colombia's exploited "silent majority," asking why all this has happened. The protagonist
of *La tortura* (torture) is an official charged with the task of
interrogating prisoners. When on one occasion torture fails to
produce the desired results, he takes out his rage on his wife,
accusing her of infidelity and ultimately killing her. The plot
of this piece implies that the brutality perpetrated by government eventually permeates all levels of society. A moral dilemma informs *La autopsia* (the autopsy), in which a doctor is
under strict orders to confirm the "official" reason for death
whenever he performs an autopsy on a victim of *la violencia*.
However, when the body of his murdered son, a left-wing activist, appears in his office, he finds himself torn between his
duty to the deceased and his fear of the authorities. In their
entirety, the playlets of *Papeles del infierno* paint a bleak picture of a nation in desperate need of political and moral reform.

Colombia's best dramatist of the younger generation, Carlos José Reyes (b. 1941), is also concerned with his homeland's
tragic civil war. *Bandidos; o, Farsa de una guerra de nunca
acabar* (1962; bandits; or, farce about a neverending war) dramatizes the effects of *la violencia* on a pueblo, whose harassed
citizens ultimately take to the hills to join the guerrillas; *Soldados* (1967; soldiers) sketches episodes of brutality within the
armed forces; and the efforts of family members to conceal a
young man's death from his grandmother constitute the warp
and woof of *Los viejos baúles empolvados que nuestros padres
nos prohibieron abrir* (1968; the old dusty trunks our parents
forbade us to open). Very different in subject matter and tone,
Variaciones sobre "La metamorfosis" (1970; variations on "The
Metamorphosis") emerges as an intriguing version of Kafka's
masterful tale. In this drama Reyes makes effective use of stage
settings, lighting, and music to capture the devastating alienation, both psychological and economic, that destroys a middle-
class family of parasites after the son Gregorio contracts his
mysterious "illness."

The importance of collective creation in Colombian theater cannot be overlooked. Although it was initiated by Buenaventura's Teatro Experimental de Cali during the 1950s, its concept has been more fully developed by La Candelaria, a group formed in 1966 by Santiago García. Thus, whereas the TEC is principally a product of Buenaventura's efforts, the presentations by La Candelaria involve its entire membership in the creative process, from the preliminary research into the subject matter through the final staging of the play. Like the TEC, La Candelaria projects a commitment to basic structural changes in Colombia's strife-torn society. Experimental theater in Colombia has also been stimulated by university groups and theater festivals, the most famous of which is held annually in Manizales.

Venezuela

Venezuela's modern drama dates back to the early 1950s, when César Rengifo (b. 1915) gained recognition as the nation's leading young playwright. In 1954 the Federación Venezolana de Teatro was founded, giving rise to affiliated groups including El Ateneo de Caracas, Las Máscaras, El Teatro Universitario, and El Teatro Popular. The annual Venezuelan theater festival began in 1959, and two decades later, in 1979, the Latin American Center for Theater Creation and Research held its first meeting in Caracas. Major projects of this international organization, which is subsidized by the Venezuelan Ministry of Education, include the publication of an encyclopedia of Latin American theater and a dictionary of Latin American playwrights.

Some critics still consider César Rengifo as Venezuela's most significant contemporary dramatist. Born in Caracas of working-class parents, he became a respected painter and journalist before he began to write seriously for the theater. Although he deals primarily with his homeland's historical and present-day realities, his occasional use of Brechtian techniques has expanded the aesthetic dimensions of his works and given them more universal appeal. Rengifo's historical dramas include *Manuelote* (1950; Manuelote), a character sketch of a slave who murders his wife and then atones for his crime by fighting for the cause of freedom; *Soga de niebla* (1954; rope of mist), the late-eighteenth-century story of a murderer-executioner symbolizing the colonial regime's moral decay; and *Obscénaba* (1959; "love" in a native Caribbean tongue), which focuses on the exploitation of Indian pearl divers during the early Spanish conquest.

Another venture into history and one of Rengifo's most highly regarded works is *Lo que dejó la tempestad* (1957; what the tempest left behind). Set in a Venezuelan village in 1865 at the end of a civil war, the plot dramatizes the aftermath of the liberal leader Ezequiel Zamora's defeat by the conservatives. Although the memory of the slain Zamora dominates the course of events, the leading character is a madwoman, Brusca, who proclaims the live presence of Zamora and encourages his followers to continue the struggle of their leader—already more mythical than human—for justice. As suggested by its title and demonstrated by its plot, Rengifo's drama limns the impact of war on the popular imagination.

Two of this author's best-known plays depict what he views as the disastrous results of Venezuela's oil boom. *El vendaval amarillo* (1954; the yellow gale) reveals the effects, in about 1920, of the "bonanza" on a community whose agricultural economy is destroyed and whose young people are corrupted. Also condemned is the unequal distribution of the suddenly acquired wealth, resulting in a dichotomy between rich and poor. Rengifo's artistic maturation is demonstrated by the sharp differences between this traditional example of social-protest realism and *Las torres del viento* (1970; the towers of the wind), a sophisticated presentation of essentially the same theme. The protagonist of the latter is a young geologist mortally injured in an accident in a remote area where, many years before, a boom town mushroomed and disappeared. Having stumbled upon the dilapidated inn of the ghost town, he envisions in his dying moments episodes of the past involving moral degradation and bitter property disputes. The play's circular structure is suggested by the revelation that an idealistic young geologist, played by the same actor as the protagonist, was killed during the initial boom because he sided with the Indians against those attempting to seize their lands. The ghost town, moreover, stands for modern Venezuela, a nation stricken with spiritual and ethical decay. *Las torres del viento* has been likened to Brechtian epic theater at its best, its temporal disruptions artfully probing the historical past and, at the same time, causing the audience to identify intellectually rather than emotionally with the characters. Equally universal in its aesthetic appeal is *La esquina del miedo* (1970; the corner of fear), which describes the dehumanization of a community that refuses help to a dying man out of fear of his enemies.

The next generation of dramatists is best represented by Román Chalbaud (b. 1931) and Isaac Chocrón (b. 1933), both of whom seek to universalize the Venezuelan experience. In *Caín adolescente* (1955; adolescent Cain) Chalbaud, the more intellectually sophisticated and controversial of the two, captures the alienation of peasants unable to adapt to life in an urban metropolis. This same author's *Requiem para el eclipse* (1957; requiem for the eclipse), which has been compared to Sophocles' *Oedipus the King*, probes the problems of social rejection and solitude caused by homosexuality. The vehement denunciation of political corruption set forth in *Sagrado y obsceno* (1961; sacred and obscene) led to its closing by government censors, and *La quema de Judas* (1964; the burning of Judas) has been interpreted as a metaphor of the sharp contradictions and shocking brutalities in Venezuelan life, its subject matter being the murder of two brothers, one a soldier and the other a criminal.

Some critics consider *Los ángeles terribles* (1967; the terrible angels) as Chalbaud's best work. An absurd representation of existential psychology, it presents four characters: Zacarías, an old dollmaker; Sagrario, a pregnant prostitute he has adopted; and two youths, Ángel and Gabriel, also adopted by Zacarías. All four take part in the fabrication of a doll, an action metaphor of the ambiguous engendering of Sagrario's unborn child. The characters' verbal sparring captures the dynamics of domination and submission, not only between human beings, but also between human beings and God—Zacarías emerges as an ironic deity. In the final lines the defeat of Zacarías in the word game, "From Havana comes a boat loaded with . . ." leaves his three "children" free to continue their intense, belligerent dialogue suggesting, like Sartre's *No Exit*, that hell is indeed other people.

Like his contemporary Chalbaud, Isaac Chocrón reveals an overriding preoccupation with frustrated human relationships. A founder of the experimental Nuevo Grupo in 1967, he initiated his career with *Mónica y el florentino* (1959; Mónica and the Florentine), a psychological study of failure of communication and loneliness set in a boardinghouse. *El quinto infierno* (1961; the fifth hell) also depicts an alienated female protagonist, in this case a woman from New Jersey who prolongs her unhappy existence for ten years in Venezuela. The title, however, does not refer to her adopted homeland, but to the hell she has created in her own psyche. A powerful example of the theater of cruelty, *Animales feroces* (1963; ferocious animals) describes the friction and bitterness among members of a volatile Jewish family, and *O.K.* (1969; O.K.) emerges as a provocative portrait of a ménage à trois replete with erotic allusions.

Chocrón's *Tric trac* (1971; tric trac), whose title represents an absurd leitmotif, consists of a fast-paced dialogue of characters identified only as numbers one through ten. An expression of the multiple aspects of human nature and a satire of man-made institutions, this experiment in theater technique in reality limns ten facets of a single personality unable to live in harmony with the everyday world. In its timeless setting and total lack of stage scenery *Tric trac* differs sharply from *La revolución* (1971; the revolution), a bitterly aggressive portrait of homosexuality. But instead of dwelling on his protagonist's psychological aberrations, the author depicts him as a prototype of the misfit whose only vehicle to social justice is revolution. Twelve years later Chocrón focused on a different kind of revolution in *Simón* (1983; Simón), a re-creation of Simón Bolívar's historic meeting in 1804 with his tutor, Simón Rodríguez, who inspired Bolívar's commitment to the liberation of Latin America from Spain.

Venezuela's best-known and most prolific playwright of the

younger generation is Rodolfo Santana (b. 1944), initially a writer of science fiction dramas and subsequently a practitioner of the theater of the absurd and the theater of cruelty. *Algunos en el islote* (1967; some on the islet), which recalls *Waiting for Godot*, presents three irrational adversaries in a trash heap, a metaphor of contemporary society. *Elogio a la tortura* (1967; praise of torture) extols torture not as a means to an end but as an end in itself. Perhaps Santana's most successful work, *La muerte de Alfredo Gris* (1968; the death of Alfredo Gris) is set in a jail cell shared by Prisoner I and Prisoner II. At first a sadist, Prisoner I becomes the ardent admirer of Prisoner II when the latter is condemned to death. And Prisoner II, who initially behaves like a coward, ultimately emerges as a hero, facing death calmly despite the lack of charges against him. The personae engendered by this absurd chain of events disprove the unity of the personality and debunk the sham pretensions of efforts to understand complex human relationships.

Violence combines with pornography in Santana's *Las camas* (1969; the beds), which delineates three crucial moments in the protagonist's political evolution. Political events also inform *El sitio* (1969; the place), an examination of the conscience of a revolutionary who leads a coup d'état only to become more dictatorial than his predecessor. And *Los criminales* (1970; the criminals), another example of the theater of cruelty, represents the satanic rituals of a wealthy man's guests when they cajole a would-be robber into surrendering his pistol and then murder him in cold blood.

THE ANDEAN HIGHLANDS

Bolivia

Bolivia's modern theater is one of the least developed on the continent, consisting of isolated works by dramatists who, in most cases, have only a few titles to their credit. Mario Flores (b. 1901) emigrated in the 1920s to Argentina, where he achieved considerable success with his comedies of manners. His political satire *Veneno de ratones* (1950; mouse poison), still considered one of the best Bolivian dramas, has been called an adroitly structured X-ray of the human soul revealing the influences of O'Neill and Sartre. In another of his successes, *La casa sobre la roca* (1961; the house on the rock), a mother who has convinced her children that their father is dead faces the problem of his unexpected release from prison.

Raúl Salmón (b. 1925), Bolivia's leading historical dramatist, has based three of his works on nineteenth-century presidents. *Viva Belzu* (1952; long live Belzu) portrays Manuel Isidoro Belzu (1808–1865) as a mestizo populist who once proclaimed that the color of a man's skin does not determine his worth as a human being. In *Juana Sánchez* (1966; Juana Sánchez) Mariano Melgarejo (1820–1871) is depicted as a brutal dictator who tests a new weapon by firing it at the first person to appear in the plaza, but he satisfies every whim of his domineering mistress. And Belzu, Melgarejo, and Andrés de Santa Cruz (1792–1865), the last the most honest of the three, are all described in *Tres generales* (1969; three generals), which captures crucial moments of Bolivia's tormented past. Disturbed by his nation's chronic instability, Salmón issues a plea to his fellow citizens for unity and exhorts them to benefit from the lessons of history.

Another reasonably successful playwright on the Bolivian scene is Jorge Rozsa (b. 1923) who, though Hungarian by birth, has lived in his adopted homeland for many years. His symbolic drama *Hambre* (1971; hunger) describes the impact of nuclear war on a group of mourners attending a burial. As they are about to leave the cemetery, a nuclear blast destroys the city around them but for some unexplained reason leaves them and the cemetery unscarred. After several days without food two of the group die of severe burns when they attempt to leave their oasis of safety, while others perish as a result of disputes over petty matters. In the final lines only the debilitated and perhaps delirious priest remains to witness a parade of dead souls, the only winners in the battle against hunger. The title refers not only to the craving for food of millions in Bolivia and elsewhere, but also to man's innate animal instincts that impel him to savagery in the universal contest for possession, domination, and survival.

Ecuador

Modern Ecuadorian theater traces its origin to the early 1950s when a talented young playwright, Francisco Tobar García (discussed below and also in the chapter on poetry) launched his career. During the 1960s and 1970s several experimental groups were formed, the most significant being Teatro Ensayo, Taller de Teatro, Teatro de la Calle, Teatro Experimental Ecuatoriano, Teatro Universitario, and Tobar García's Teatro Independiente. In addition, the Casa de la Cultura Ecuatoriana, a governmental agency for the arts, has sponsored its own theatrical productions for well over a decade.

Ecuador's leading dramatist of the older generation, Demetrio Aguilera Malta (also discussed in the chapter on fiction), is one of the nation's best novelists as well. His theater, which fuses myth, folklore, and social protest, can be divided into three stages: realism, a transitional period, and expressionism. Typical of his realistic works are *España leal* (1938; loyal Spain), the portrait of a youthful martyr to the Republican cause in the Spanish Civil War, and *Lázaro* (1941; Lazarus), a popular tragicomedy about an impecunious high school teacher's triumph over powerful adversaries. In its transitional phase Aguilera Malta's drama becomes less mimetic and more subjective and symbolic, as exemplified by *Dientes blancos* (1955; white teeth) and *El tigre* (1955; the tiger). The setting of the former is a nightclub where three black musicians are entertaining a white clientele. Suddenly a quarrel breaks out between William, the saxophonist hired to enliven the atmosphere with his infectious laugh, and Peter, the pianist, who sees himself and his fellow entertainers as victims of exploitation. The play ends with Peter's dismissal and William's forced guffaws, the image of his *dientes blancos* reinforcing the theme of racial discrimination.

One of Aguilera Malta's masterworks, *El tigre* depicts a small group of plantation workers in a tropical region near the Ecuadorian coast. Aguayo is obsessed by fear of *el tigre*, which follows him everywhere and which, he is convinced, will someday kill him. Don Guayamabe, the foreman, represents the aggressive macho who refuses to be intimidated by the beast and ridicules Aguayo for showing his fright. Eventually Aguayo decides to seek safety elsewhere, but as he paddles his canoe toward a nearby town, he sees the eyes of *el tigre* following him in the water and returns to the plantation, resigned to his fate. In the final scene his cries for help are answered by Don Guayamabe, but although the latter slays the tiger, he arrives too late to save Aguayo. The theme of fear is conveyed not only by the imaginary, as opposed to the real, tiger, but also by the artfully designed stage setting, the bonfire around which the action evolves symbolizing safety, and the shadows of the surrounding thicket, the ever-present threat of evil and death.

Characterized by violent distortions and fantasy, Aguilera Malta's expressionist works include *Infierno negro* (1967; black hell) and *Muerte, S.A.* (1970; Death, Inc.). The former delineates two antithetical worlds: Nylónpolis, an affluent urban community of whites; and Necrópolis, a kind of purgatory inhabited by dead blacks. The action begins with the funeral of Horridus Nabus, a wealthy white inventor-capitalist who died of a heart attack upon learning that he would not get a share of the profits of his *aerómetro*, a machine to be used for apportioning air to people according to their social status. After his funeral in Nylónpolis, Horridus Nabus is tried in Necrópolis for various crimes, one of which is his invention of a sausage machine that uses black flesh as raw material for its products. At the conclusion of the trial the defendant is condemned to the *infierno negro*, that is, he must return to earth and lead the life of a black. *Muerte, S.A.* is equally fantastic, but its plot is rooted in the folkloric traditions of the Colorado Indians of tropical Ecuador. One of the protagonists, the idealistic Reinaldo Fuentes, acquires from a *curandero* (witch doctor) a secret substance extracted from an orchid that restores life to the dead. Fuentes, who intends to use the magic formula only for the benefit of his fellow man, makes the mistake of giving it to Patricio Contreras, an opportunist who builds a *resurrectorio* (resurrection parlor) for the wealthy. However, Contreras receives an even higher fee from one Jesús Icaza for withholding the substance from Icaza's deceased father-in-law, a man of considerable means. And soon thereafter Icaza proposes that Contreras join him in a business venture that would *"cobrar por no resucitar"* (charge for not restoring life). The farce ends with the murder of Contreras shortly after Fuentes administered the last dose of the formula to a schoolteacher he held in high esteem.

In contrast to Aguilera Malta, Francisco Tobar García is an intellectual interested in philosophy, psychology, and avant-garde techniques. A professor of literature at the Catholic University in Quito, he has studied dramatic art in Europe and traveled widely. Although he has written a variety of plays in both prose and verse, the basic characteristics of his theater are its revelation of the poetic and the mysterious in the everyday world, its subtle social satire, and its presentation of ideas in the vein of Brecht and Sartre. It is not surprising, then, that he has been referred to on occasion as the creator of *un teatro de élite* (an elitist theater). Tobar García's most successful creative efforts include *La res* (1956; the beast), a one-act thriller set in a jungle community where an escaped convict plots the murder of a shopkeeper; *Los dioses y el caballo* (1956; the gods and the horse), which contrasts Indian and white cultures; *La llave del abismo* (1961; the key to the abyss), a tragedy inspired by Sophocles; and *En alguien muere la víspera* (1962; the eve dies in someone), a detective play in verse freighted with philosophical overtones.

Typical of Tobar García's dramaturgy is *Las sobras para el gusano* (1969; the leftovers for the worm), which depicts the life of a demented old woman (Nelly) living in a dilapidated house near the ocean. Generated by her unstable psyche, the nightmarish plot is characterized by temporal dislocations, fusions of identities, and fluctuations between objective reality and fevered imagination. Thus the spectator/reader is obliged to put in chronological order events that include the mysterious death of Nelly's mother Carolina, whose madness perhaps resulted from an incestuous relationship with her father; the beatings Nelly received from Gilberto (her father), who hated his wife and sees her face reflected in that of his daughter; the doctor's warning to Gilberto of Nelly's incipient madness provoked by fear; Nelly's love for a tender, idealistic youth named Ramiro, probably a figment of her imagination; and her marriage to a man who remains a mere phantom in her subconscious. In the final scene of the play Nelly's son Eduardo, whom she has not seen for many years, arrives with his young wife Mariana, a reincarnation of Gilberto's mistress of over fifty years before. Tobar García's portrait of madness, lack of communication, and solitude is enhanced aesthetically by echoes of Freud and the ingenious elimination of temporal barriers. The end result is a sophisticated, ambiguous, and original work of art.

José Martínez Queirolo (b. 1931), Ecuador's other major contemporary dramatist, is best described as a nonconventional, experimental realist whose hallmarks include irony, satire, and black humor. In addition, his concern for Spanish America's political and social problems also underlies many of his works. *La casa del qué dirán* (1962; the house of "what will they say?") is a jocund farce assailing prejudice and religious hypocrisy. *Requiem por la lluvia* (1963: requiem for the rain) consists of a soliloquy in verse by the husband of a laundress, Jesusa, who died of a heart attack while washing clothes for her rich employers. Besides blaming an indifferent society for the circumstances leading to his wife's death, the grief-stricken husband praises her diligence, recalls her debilitating illness, and condemns himself for his shabby treatment of her. The authentic language and poignancy of this one-act drama make it one of the author's most admired creations.

Irony and the absurd are the major ingredients of *Montesco y su señora* (1965; Montague and his wife), which describes the hypothetical marriage—boring and acrimonious—of Romeo and Juliet if they had lived together for thirty years. Somewhat similar in tone, *R.I.P.* (1969; R.I.P.) presents a dead middle-aged couple, Enrieta and Simón, who, witnessing their own funeral, recall the shallow life they ended in an automobile accident while drunk. This moral autopsy of the degenerate upper class concludes with the two protagonists giggling hysterically in their graves because worms are beginning to "tickle" them. *Los unos vrs. los otros* (1970; the ones versus the others) is not only Martínez Queirolo's funniest play, but also the most critical of his nation's social structure. The plot takes the form of an absurd boxing match between Don Dinero (Don Money), a member of the decadent oligarchy, and Don Fulano (Don So-And-So), the unemployed father of a starving brood. The referee, an obvious symbol of "justice," kowtows to Don Dinero's family, while treating Don Fulano and his kin with the utmost scorn. At first the priest seems to favor Don Dinero, but when the latter attempts to determine the outcome of the match by offering money to, or withholding it from, the Church, the priest tips the balance in favor of Don Fulano, who manages to score the knockout blow. *Los unos vrs. los otros* stands out as a hilarious farce delineating the shocking social dichotomy and the changing role of the clergy in Spanish America today.

Peru

Modern Peruvian theater began to develop soon after World War II when cultural contacts were reestablished with Europe and the United States, and Peruvian playwrights had more opportunities to study abroad. In 1953 Sebastián Salazar Bondy (discussed below and in the chapter on fiction) founded the now well-known Club de Teatro, which has presented many of the best national and foreign dramas. Further development of the genre ensued with the organization, at approximately this same time, of the Escuela Nacional de Arte Escénico and the Compañía Nacional de Comedias. In 1972 the Teatro Nacional Popular was initiated as a section of the Instituto Nacional de Cultura, its function being to promote both experimental and popular theater throughout the country, especially at the grassroots level. Also a product of the early 1970s is the Federación Nacional de Teatro Popular del Perú, which sponsored the formation of theatrical groups in provincial cities.

During the 1940s and 1950s the Peruvian theater was dominated by three dramatists: Juan Ríos (b. 1914), Enrique Solari Swayne (b. 1915), and Sebastián Salazar Bondy. A poet and well-traveled cosmopolite, Ríos is less interested in present-day Peruvian reality than his two colleagues; he prefers to delineate the archetypal behavioral patterns exhibited by man throughout the ages. *Ayar Manko* (1952; Ayar Manko) depicts an episode from Peru's pre-Columbian past, namely, the struggle of four Inca princes for their dead father's crown. The two leading antagonists are Auka and Manko, the former emerging as a power-mad tyrant and the latter as a defender of justice who, after his brother's suicide, ascends to the throne and grants clemency to his enemies. The historical authenticity of *Ayar Manko* is enhanced by lyrical moments of Inca music and dance, which, woven into the dramatic fabric, provide a welcome contrast to the steadily mounting tension and violence.

In *Don Quijote* (1957; Don Quixote) man's struggle for immortality is embodied in Ríos's protagonist who, even on his deathbed, continues to dream of righting all wrongs. The classical myth of Prometheus underpins *El fuego* (1961; the fire), in which an army captain in an Andean republic during the early days of independence from Spain becomes a martyr to the cause of freedom under a military dictatorship. Mid-seventeenth-century Spain serves as the setting for *Los bufones* (1961; the buffoons), about the isolated, brooding King Philip IV's friendship with Sebastián de Morra, an embittered jester in his court. And *La selva* (1961; the forest), a reworking of the classical tale of Jason and the Argonauts, depicts an Indian girl who betrays her loved ones in order to free a Spanish captain from his captors.

Enrique Solari Swayne's one major drama, *Collacocha* (1959; Collacocha), has earned him a wide reputation among audiences and readers alike. A psychology professor, Solari Swayne describes in *Collacocha* the struggle of Echecopar, a civil engineer building a road through the Andes, against nature's overwhelming odds. As critics have stated, the play's fascination stems primarily from the characterization of its protagonist, who represents a unique combination of titanic energy, practicality, and idealism. The first act introduces Echecopar not only through his bombastic words and forceful actions, but also through the opinions of others who stand in awe of his capacity to inspire the Indians working on the project. At the end of the second act a cave-in caused by the overflow of Lake Collacocha obliges Echecopar to blow up a tunnel, killing more than one hundred workers, in order to save several hundred others. The third act, which takes place five years later, presents the aging Echecopar still tortured by the disaster but rejoicing over the completion of the road and the progress—a major leitmotif—it represents. *Collacocha* suffers from unconvincing rhetorical dialogue that expresses the author's message in terms too explicit for the sophisticated reader. Nevertheless, Echecopar's praise of the work ethic and his ranting against self-serving bureaucrats and class-conscious snobs are as timely today as they were in 1959.

Sebastián Salazar Bondy is usually considered the best Peruvian dramatist of his generation. Shortly after World War II he studied in France, where he came under the influence of existentialism. Many of his plays also reveal a vital concern for the adverse political and social conditions in contemporary Peru. The majority of his early dramas are grotesque satires, the most memorable being *Amor, gran laberinto* (1947; love, great labyrinth), in which the protagonist's reason is incapacitated by his amorous passion. One of Salazar Bondy's finest examples of social realism, the second phase of his oeuvre, is *No hay isla feliz* (1959; there is no happy island), which limns the disintegration of a provincial middle-class family. The idealistic Daniel and his wife Lucía open a restaurant in a town south of Lima and after twenty-five years of hard work are prosperous and respected members of the community. Their children, Pedro and Julia, however, rebel against their environment and flee to Lima, where they lead lives of dubious respectability. Daniel's dreams of an *isla feliz* vanish when the government alters the route of the Pan American Highway, the principal source of his prosperity, and Lucía dies of a sudden illness. The plot suggests that Peruvian society suffers from numerous defects, examples of which abound. Government bureaucrats ignore the legitimate concerns of the provinces; a lack of respect for traditional values as well as for individual freedom of choice has created a serious generation gap; and the subordinate role assigned to women by domineering males can only lead to lack of communication, resentment, and rebellion.

El fabricante de deudas (1962; the debt maker) best represents the final phase of Salazar Bondy's theater, that is, plays cast in the light-hearted mold he observed in French comedy. The protagonist is Luciano Obedot, a bon vivant pursued by creditors whose demands he always manages to elude. His only hope of paying his debts is the marriage of his daughter Pitusa to the Spanish Marqués de Rondavieja, who, unknown to Obedot, is a *cazador de fortunas* (fortune hunter), himself deeply in debt. The Marqués is, of course, equally ignorant of Obedot's precarious financial situation. The climax is reached when Pitusa's boyfriend brings Obedot, the Marqués, and their creditors together, resulting in the hasty dismantling of Obedot's elegant home in order to settle his debts. But the unrepentant Obedot, who despite his shortcomings stands out as an engaging personality, immediately begins to plot a new strategy to maintain his high standard of living. In this comedy of manners Salazar Bondy utilizes for the first time the Brechtian technique of having the characters momentarily abandon their roles to express their opinions of the situations in which they find themselves. The resulting impact on the audience is, as Brecht intended, intellectual rather than emotional.

Discussed earlier as one of the major writers of fiction, Mario Vargas Llosa has also published two fine dramas: *La señorita de Tacna* (1981; the señorita from Tacna) and *Kathie y el hipopótamo* (1983; Kathie and the hippopotamus). The former's two basic settings, both occupying a part of the stage simultaneously, are a modest home in Lima during the 1950s and the room of a writer (Belisario) who, from the vantage point of the year 1980, is creating a drama about events he witnessed more than two decades earlier. Thus, the first setting, where Belisario's drama takes place, is not meant to be realistic, but rather a product of his subjective, and perhaps unreliable, memory. His protagonist (the señorita from Tacna) is a spinster called Mamaé who lived with his grandparents, Pedro and Carmen, and cared for him until her death in the 1950s. Now middle-aged, Belisario feels compelled to reconstruct the life of the old woman he loved when he was a child. Mamaé was born in the second half of the nineteenth century in Tacna, a city in southern Peru occupied by the Chilean army after the War of the Pacific (1879–83). Shortly before her wedding she learned that her fiancé, a Chilean officer in the army of occupation, was having a love affair with a married woman. Shocked and offended, Mamaé burned her wedding gown and announced her resolve never to marry. Instead she became a permanent resident in the home of her cousin, Carmen, whose children affectionately nicknamed her Mamaé (for Mamá Elvira).

Although much of the action occurs in the 1950s, when the aging Mamaé, Carmen, and Pedro are living with Belisario's mother and her two brothers, a series of ingeniously devised flashbacks relates the family's gradual financial decline due to Pedro's business failures and, finally, their move to Lima. The play ends with the death of Mamaé and Belisario's reflections on the work of fiction he has created. Although *La señorita de Tacna* touches on several regional and universal themes, it emerges above all as an example of self-conscious literature, that is, a mirror reflection of the authorial consciousness in the throes of creating a work of art.

Literary concerns are also evident in *Kathie y el hipopótamo*, the setting of which is a Lima apartment decorated like a Latin Quarter garret, where Kathie (the wife of a banker) and Santiago Zavala (a journalist and part-time professor) spend two hours daily writing a novel based on Kathie's fantasies. As she describes her marriage to Johnny, a surfing addict and macho stereotype who has had sexual relations with dozens of other women, Zavala embellishes her fantasies and injects a few of his own. Kathie also describes a trip to Africa where she saw many wild animals—thus the title—in exotic surroundings. The play comes to an end when Kathie admits to an occasional extramarital affair, and Johnny, horrified at the thought of being cuckolded, commits suicide. As Vargas Llosa states in his introduction, the theme is the interrelationship between life and fiction, the latter providing an escape from everyday reality as well as an outlet for what Vargas Llosa calls the "demons" of the creative subconscious. Hilariously funny, ironic, and satirical, *Kathie y el hipopótamo* is also noteworthy for its adroit juxtapositioning of episodes and, correspondingly, for its deft manipulation of character identities.

Peru's two leading playwrights of the younger generation are Alonso Alegría (b. 1940) and Julio Ortega (b. 1942). After earning two degrees from Yale University, Alegría lectured at several institutions in the United States and in 1971 assumed the directorship of the above-mentioned Teatro Nacional Popular in Lima. His first play, *Remigio y el huaquero* (1965; Remigio and the *huaquero*), is a realistic portrait of pervasive greed and corruption, a *huaquero* being a person who illegally unearths and sells relics of the pre-Inca and Inca civilizations. Remigio, an impoverished laborer whose son finds a vase, sells the valuable artifact for a pittance to a shrewd acquaintance, who in turn is deceived by a wealthy dealer in national art treasures. Alegría's most widely acclaimed play, *El cruce sobre el Niágara* (1969; the crossing over Niagara), is based on the exploits of Jean-François Gravelet (1824–1897), a French tightrope walker known as Blondin. At the beginning both the mature Blondin and an idealistic youth named Carlo sense an existential void in their lives, Blondin having lost some of his youthful vitality, and Carlo experiencing a need to prove his valor. The latter therefore proposes to Blondin that they cross over Niagara Falls together on a tightrope, Blondin carrying Carlo on his back. With the successful completion of this feat both men achieve their goals of self-fulfillment and, at the same time, overcome their feelings of isolation and loneliness. One of Peru's best dramas, *El cruce sobre el Niágara* demonstrates man's ability to find meaning in life through action and solidarity with a fellow being.

Julio Ortega is one of Peru's best literary critics as well as a successful playwright. His early theater depicts symbolically abstract characters as vehicles for philosophical ideas, whereas his subsequent works relate more directly to Peruvian reality. Typical of the former are *Como cruzar la calle* (1965; how to cross the street), a parody on existential man's anguish over the decisions he must make, and *El intruso* (1965; the intruder), in which X's double gradually takes complete control of his life. The theme of the double is also treated in *La campana* (1965; the parish), a multidimensional allegory of the human experience. In this short dramatic piece two protagonists, Vor and Rov, are imprisoned in an enclosure with invisible walls. While

Vor tirelessly searches for an exit, even standing on Rov's shoulders in an attempt to discover an opening above, Rov is content to nap and eat one apple after another. The protagonists, as their names imply, represent not only the opposite sides of a single personality, but also the antithetical duality of all mankind. And one might speculate that the unwalled, escape-proof prison and Rov's appetite for the forbidden fruit are metaphors of the hell on earth created by sinful human beings.

Ortega's *Mesa Pelada* (1974; Mesa Pelada), an experimental documentary drama, was inspired by the capture, torture, and death of a well-known guerrilla leader at Mesa Pelada, Peru, in 1965. Almost a decade later, in 1974, General Francisco Morales Bermúdez assumed his duties as head of the liberal military junta that had ruled Peru since 1968. However, it soon became evident that he was unwilling to continue the reforms initiated by his predecessor. *Infierno peruano* (1980; Peruvian hell) reflects the disillusion that precipitated Ortega's exit from his homeland and his outrage over subsequent events. This plotless drama consists of fourteen scenes which, in their entirety, constitute a macabre metaphor of a corrupt, rigidly stratified society. The characters are presented as nameless archetypes except for Bermúdez Morales, the decadent center of power, and an Indian named Saturnino Huillca, the play's only positive element. Ortega's bitterly pessimistic portrait of Peru exhorts his compatriots to defend what they have gained and to be wary of all those in positions of authority.

THE SOUTHERN CONE

Argentina

The student of the contemporary Argentine theater finds himself confronted with a dizzying array of names, works, and trends difficult to cover satisfactorily in the space allotted here. Two of this nation's major playwrights, Griselda Gambaro and Osvaldo Dragún, have been treated above as major figures. After flourishing during the first decade of the twentieth century, Argentine theater fell into a twenty-year period of decline characterized by a plethora of mediocre realistic comedies and romantic melodramas produced primarily for commercial success. During the 1930s the so-called independent theater movement, reacting against commercial theater, attempted to revitalize the genre by introducing universal themes and experimental techniques and by emphasizing professionalism among theater personnel. The most significant independent theater groups of this period include the Teatro del Pueblo, the Teatro La Máscara (both mentioned above), and the Teatro Juan B. Justo (founded 1935), all of which provided left-wing ideological fare for intellectuals and radical working-class audiences. Although these groups enjoyed only limited success at the time, they laid the groundwork for the avant-garde forms of dramatic art that have become such an important part of the present-day literary scene.

Despite the lack of cultural exchange under the Perón government (1946–55), the independent theater flourished during the 1940s and 1950s. After 1955 the influence of Bertolt Brecht and Peter Weiss became increasingly significant, as did the revival of the *sainete*, an ideal vehicle for political satire. Since World War II most Argentine dramas have fallen into one of three broad categories: those treating universal themes of eternal human interest, usually in the European tradition; those reinterpreting, often nostalgically, the Argentine past; and those dramatizing political and social issues of immediate national concern. Of the many experimental groups active in Argentina today, the most significant is the Teatro Abierto, which opened its doors in 1981 with a program of titles by twenty-one of the nation's best playwrights.

Major dramatists of the 1930s include Samuel Eichelbaum (1894–1967), Conrado Nalé Roxlo (1898–1971), and the above-mentioned novelist Roberto Arlt. Influenced by Freud, Ibsen, and Strindberg, Eichelbaum wrote many psychological dramas, the most successful of which is *Un guapo del 900* (1940; a thug of the early 1900s). The protagonist, Ecuménico, is a local tough employed by a politician whose wife has an affair with his political rival. Out of loyalty to his employer, Ecuménico kills the rival and, despite the pleas of his mother to save himself, will probably confess his guilt and hang for his crime. *Un tal Servando Gómez* (1942; a fellow named Servando Gómez) depicts an idealistic teamster who provides refuge for a battered wife and her son after they flee for their lives from domestic violence. The theme of avarice is developed in *Dos brasas* (1955; two embers), a tragicomedy about a man, Roberto, who sues his wife Eleanor for divorce because, although she has inherited a fortune, she insists on living in poverty. Desperate to save her marriage, Eleanor signs her property over to her husband, but in the final act he ironically has taken on her characteristics and become just as pathologically miserly as she. The play ends when she demands to regain control of her fortune and he strangles her, proclaiming that their savings will remain locked in the bank forever.

Less prolific than Eichelbaum, Nalé Roxlo is known for his poetic theater frequently animated by symbolic flights of fantasy. In *La cola de la sirena* (1941; the mermaid's tail) Patricio so charms a mermaid named Alga that she submits to surgery to remove the scales imprisoning her legs. The clash between ideal dream and everyday reality emerges as the theme when Alga, no longer unique, loses her appeal to Patricio and returns to the sea. Some critics consider *Una viuda difícil* (1944; a difficult widow) as Nalé Roxlo's best creative effort. Set in the colonial period, this fanciful comedy portrays a viceroy who, on his wedding anniversary, offers to pardon a murderer if some kind-hearted woman will take him as her husband. Isabel, a clever widow, accepts the challenge, reforms her newly acquired mate, and even manages to take revenge on a suitor who had jilted her. The Faust legend and the Crusades inspired Nalé Roxlo's *El pacto de Cristina* (1945; Cristina's pact), in which the daughter (Cristina) of an innkeeper, enamored of a soldier (Gerardo), accepts the Devil's offer to win Gerardo's love and return him to her from the Holy Land. On their wedding night the Devil appears and demands as payment Cristina's first-born child, destined to become the Antichrist. Horrified and repentant, she poisons herself and, still a virgin, dies in her husband's arms.

Roberto Arlt was a product of the Teatro del Pueblo and

the leader of the independent theater movement of the 1930s. Closer to the avant-garde, experimental stage than either Eichelbaum or Nalé Roxlo, he wrote expressionistic dramas that, with their elements of cruelty, the absurd, and the grotesque, evince his deep social concerns while evolving a metaphoric vision, rather than a mimetic representation, of reality. The tragicomedy *Saverio el cruel* (1936; Saverio the cruel) contrasts a humble dairyman (Saverio) with a group of frivolous upperclass youths who, to make fun of Saverio, convince him to play the role of a colonel in a farce allegedly designed to cure Susana (one of the group) of madness. However, as the plot of the farce develops, fiction becomes reality for Susana, who first falls in love with and then shoots Saverio. Fraught with ambiguity, this play asks more questions than it answers about the characters and the enigmatic background against which they are depicted. The highly amusing farce entitled *La isla desierta* (1937; the desert island) presents a group of bored office workers who abandon their tedious routine for a few precious moments of fantasy, even though it costs them their jobs.

La fiesta del hierro (1940; the fiesta of iron), perhaps Arlt's best drama, examines the effects of man's archetypal cruelty and aggression in twentieth-century society. The setting is the Armstrong armament factory where Carlitos, Mr. Armstrong's trusted adviser, is organizing a celebration around the statue of Baal Moloc, a mythical god of war. As the guests perform a ritual of blood sacrifice to the god, their gaiety is brought to an abrupt end by the revelation that Mr. Armstrong's child, hidden inside the statue, has become the sacrificial victim. *La fiesta del hierro* evokes a Kafkaesque nightmare, Baal Moloc symbolizing the evil possessing modern man, and the armament industry, man's capacity for self-destruction. Another target of Arlt's attack is the priest, whose praise of Mr. Armstrong's enterprise represents the unholy alliance between the Church and the military-industrial complex.

One of the finest examples of Argentine tragedy is *Antígona Vélez* (1968; Antígona Vélez), by Leopoldo Marechal (discussed above as a novelist). Based on Sophocles' *Antigone*, Marechal's drama is set in nineteenth-century Argentina during the conquest of the pampa Indians. Antígona Vélez, like her Greek counterpart, defies the order of a tyrant to leave her dead brother unburied, an act that costs her her life. Marechal echoes Sophocles' gravity of tone and preserves the basic conflict between state and moral laws, but his heroine differs from her classical model in her justification of the tyrant's decree, a justification she bases on the need to preserve order. In this respect Antígona Vélez reflects Marechal's controversial political views, that is, his support of Perón and the subsequent military regimes that were obliged, in his opinion, to act dictatorially in order to save the nation from chaos.

Carlos Gorostiza (b. 1920) is considered one of Argentina's leading realists, his hallmarks being the examination of complex human relationships, usually abrasive, and the choices people are forced to make in stressful circumstances. His first and one of his best works, *El puente* (1949; *The Bridge*, 1961), adroitly delineates Argentina's rigid social structure. The antithetical settings are a street scene in a poor neighborhood and an upper-middle-class apartment, settings that become linked—thus the title—when a laborer from the poor neighborhood and an engineer who resides in the apartment are killed at a construction site where both work. Another of this author's finest works is *El pan de la locura* (1958; the bread of madness), which focuses on the existential problems of guilt and responsibility. The setting is a bakery in a low-class district of the city where sordid conditions have corrupted both the physical and moral milieux. Thus, when it becomes apparent that the bread made in the establishment is causing serious illnesses, none of the employees is willing to reveal the source of the problem. This state of affairs comes to an end with the arrival of a new assistant foreman, Mateo, who challenges the owner to improve the management of his business. When Mateo's forthrightness results in his dismissal, however, his fellow workers come to his defense, an indication of the solidarity his courage and honesty have created among them.

Additional works by Gorostiza include *Vivir aquí* (1954; living here), about a decadent family reduced to living in the servants' quarters of their once elegant manor; *Los prójimos*

(1966; *Neighbors,* in *Drama and Literature,* 9, 2, Winter 1970–71), in which witnesses of a woman's murder refuse to become involved in the judicial process; *¿A qué jugamos?* (1968; what shall we play?), a sketch of five individuals who, pretending that the end of the world is minutes away, reveal biases and violent passions that can never again be concealed; and *El lugar* (1970; the place), a representation of the absurd, beginning with an empty stage, climaxing with violent disputes among a crowd of suitcase-bearing travelers, and concluding with a lone individual, Man, in total isolation.

Marco Denevi (previously discussed in the chapter on fiction) has also excelled as a playwright. In his farce entitled *Los expedientes* (1957; the files) he satirizes the proliferating bureaucracy plaguing virtually every nation in the world today. In the initial scene an agency is created for flood victims, and when at last one lone applicant for assistance appears, the wheels of bureaucracy are set in motion, generating over the years thousands of *expedientes* that in the last lines bury the supervisor, now bored, old, and decrepit. *Falsificaciones* (1966; falsifications) consists of vignettes, most of which reinterpret myths, legends, or literary masterpieces in order to reveal basic human traits. The allegorical *Los animales en el arca* (the animals on the ark) sets forth the idea that because of the close quarters on Noah's ark, the gentlest and most beautiful animals were slain by their fellow creatures, leaving only the ugly and brutal as survivors in today's world. In another of these short dramatic pieces, *Romeo frente al cadáver de Julieta* (*Romeo Before the Corpse of Juliet*, in Gerardo Luzuriaga and Robert S. Rudder, eds., *The Orgy: Modern One-Act Plays from Latin America*, 1974), Shakespeare's hero stands before his dead sweetheart complaining that she has tried in vain to involve him in a sinister game of suicide. He then exits, and moments later two pages carry him back onto the stage with a dagger protruding from his chest.

Another major figure in contemporary Argentine theater is Agustín Cuzzani (b. 1924), whose plays combine reality, fantasy, and farce to depict man's victimization by his fellow human beings. *Una libra de carne* (1954; a pound of flesh), which was inspired by *The Merchant of Venice*, portrays a down-trodden clerk, Elías Beluver, who is tricked by his creditors into signing a contract similar to the one signed by Shakespeare's Antonio. Beluver's ultimate mutilation emerges as a metaphor of exploitation in a capitalistic society, which the author views as the modern equivalent of feudalism. Perhaps Cuzzani's most widely acclaimed comedy, *El centroforward murió al amanecer* (1955; *The Center Forward Died at Dawn*, 1970), also develops the theme of capitalistic exploitation, the victim in this case being one Cacho Garibaldo, a champion soccer player. When Cacho's soccer club goes bankrupt, he is put on the public auction block and sold to a wealthy financier who collects extraordinary human beings. Eventually Cacho, rebelling against his captivity, strangles his exploiter and is sentenced to be hanged. Brechtian in its anti-illusionistic techniques, this play is narrated by an old vagabond who has found Cacho's memoirs beneath the window of his prison cell.

Another of Cuzzani's most popular works is *Sempronio* (1957; Sempronio), which pits love against atomic power as the world's *gran motor* (driving force). A retired family man and amateur philatelist, Sempronio becomes radioactive as a result of licking stamps from Hiroshima and Nagasaki. After furnishing power for all the household appliances—his daughter plugs her radio into him and dances to rock music—as well as for a cable running through the neighborhood, Sempronio learns that the authorities are looking for the source of radioactivity in the city. Within a short time the High Commissioner and the Scholar discover the "culprit" and, after giving Sempronio's wife Olga a receipt for her husband, take him to a secret location where they intend to use him to fuel atomic weapons. Sempronio soon loses his radioactivity, however, and having been hoisted onto a truck and returned to his family, resumes his former routine. Ultimately we learn that it is Sempronio's love for his family and his fellow man, not his radioactivity, that has provided the source of his extraordinary power. Cuzzani is admired for his universality, fanciful imagination, and modern expressionistic techniques, but his didacticism occasionally detracts from the aesthetic value of his works.

Although he is a native of Spain, Juan Pérez-Carmona (b. 1930) has spent most of his life in Argentina. His theater, which is aimed at a sophisticated audience, attempts to articulate the repercussions of alienation not only in his adopted homeland, but also in all contemporary societies. *Ningún tren llega a las trece* (1963; no train arrives at one P.M.) and *Corrientes y Dorrego* (1965; Corrientes and Dorrego) both present chance meetings of strangers who share brief existentialist experiences and then separate, unaware of and indifferent to other destinies. In *La revolución de las macetas* (1960; the revolution of the *macetas*) the author treats the problem of his nation's brain drain—a *maceta* (flower pot) is a popular term for a well-trained Argentine who emigrates in search of a better life—a problem that divides families and affects individuals who find themselves torn between their responsibility to their country, to themselves, and to their fellow human beings throughout the world.

Perhaps Pérez-Carmona's best creative effort, *Piedra libre* (1970; free stone), utilizes masks, the absurd, and cruelty to define a world teetering on the edge of chaos. The setting is an apartment occupied by Miguel and María, a middle-class married couple whose games provide them with an escape from the reality they subconsciously reject. In the first of these, María, disguised as a plumber, suggests to Miguel that she is unfaithful to him; in the second game María plays the role of a cosmetics saleslady who, in a hilarious farcical episode, attempts to seduce Miguel. The couple's relations are further complicated by the arrival of Beatriz, an innocent girl from the country whose godmother had lived in the apartment previously. Miguel and María invite Beatriz to stay with them temporarily and then proceed to involve her in a series of absurd confrontations. The climax occurs when the three play hide-and-seek in the dark and Beatriz is ejected from a window onto the patio seven stories below. Miguel and María then endeavor to cover the girl's body by tossing through the window old newspapers whose headlines allude to the Nazi invasion of Poland, the Vietnam war, and other disasters of the last half-century. In its entirety the plot of *Piedra libre* seems to represent an action metaphor of the tensions, identity crises, and brutality characteristic of today's world.

In 1970 Carlos Somigliana (b. 1932), Roberto Cossa (b. 1934), Ricardo Talesnik (b. 1935), and Germán Rozenmacher (b. 1936) collaborated in the creation of *El avión negro* (the black airplane), one of Argentina's most memorable political dramas in recent years. An acerbic satire, it sketches the reactions on different social levels to the imminent arrival of an airplane carrying the long-awaited General, an allusion to Juan Perón, who did indeed return from exile three years later. What gives the play its unique flavor is the clash between the fanatical Peronists' ebullient mood of anticipation and the mounting apprehension on the part of upper-middle-class citizens, who have always detested the populist leader. The tension between these two incompatible sentiments is heightened by the injection of absurd Peronist slogans and songs fraught with thinly veiled threats to their enemies. The end result is a grotesque caricature of a society sharply divided by political ideologies and social antipathies.

Of the four authors of *El avión negro*, Cossa and Talesnik have achieved the widest reputations, both for their portraits of middle-class citizens. Cossa's *Nuestro fin de semana* (1964; our weekend) depicts three couples determined to enjoy themselves on a weekend vacation, but in the course of their dialogue it becomes evident that their gaiety is a smoke screen for a kind of vague spiritual malaise and a deep-rooted fear of solitude. Solitude is also the subject of Talesnik's *El chucho* (1976; the shivers), which examines the complex psychological reactions of a man who imagines himself to be mortally ill and finds himself incapable of communicating his anguish.

A resident of Madrid since 1977, Eduardo Pavlovsky (b. 1933) is Argentina's leading creator of psychodrama, perhaps because he is also a practicing psychiatrist. His *Somos* (1962; we are), which is written in the tradition of the theater of the absurd, presents scenes from the childhood of two individuals, one raised by a brutal and the other by an overly protective mother. *Último match* (1967; last match) portrays a boxer whose public image is determined not by his own free will but by the words and actions of his *hinchas* (fans). The influence of the theater of cruelty on Pavlovsky can be detected in several of his most popular works. In *Cacería* (1969; hunt), an early example, three former friends meet in order to dig up a treasure they buried many years before. They soon discover, however, that they intend to use their fortune for very different purposes, R. wanting to spend it for pleasure, C. for a revolutionary cause, and Pat (a priest) for the benefit of his church. A bitter quarrel ensues, and their *cacería* ends with the violent deaths of all three. Cruelty is directed against the bourgeoisie in *La mueca* (1970; the grimace), in which four hoods invade a wealthy couple's home and extract their abject confessions of egotism and hypocrisy.

Pavlovsky is probably best known for *El señor Galíndez* (1976; Mr. Galíndez), a shocking exposé of torture practiced by the Argentine government. The protagonists are three young men, Beto, Pepe, and Eduardo, whose work consists of systematically torturing the prisoners sent to them by Mr. Galíndez, their supervisor. In addition, Mr. Galíndez, who communicates with them only by phone, thus concealing his true identity, sends them two prostitutes with orders to do with them "lo que se les cante" ("whatever you want"). At first it is assumed that the whores will be required to perform their usual sexual function, but little by little the two women (and the audience) come to the horrifying realization that the preparations being made are, in reality, designed to carry out their physical torment and mutilation. The impact of this example of cruelty for the sake of cruelty—and for sexual gratification—is heightened by expressionistic lighting and sound effects as well as by the protagonists' matter-of-fact dialogue about mundane matters as they proceed with their nefarious tasks. Eduardo, who first appears as an innocent apprentice, also underscores the theme of cruelty when his final words demonstrate that he has successfully completed his apprenticeship. "And so each one of us must fight in this definitive war against those who try, under the guise of exotic ideologies, to destroy our life style, our national existence."

One of Pavlovsky's prominent contemporaries, Ricardo Halac

(b. 1935), describes the younger generation of Argentines who, disillusioned with the unstable society they have inherited, search in vain for meaningful relationships or, more often, retreat into their own private, irrational worlds. Halac's *Soledad para cuatro* (1961; solitude for four) limns a sexual encounter between two bored middle-class youths and two working-class girls, an encounter that ends with a complete breakdown in communication. *Segundo tiempo* (1976; second time) treats a similar theme, except that its protagonists are a married couple and its ending is somewhat less pessimistic. Pablo's refusal to respect María's desire for a career leads to their separation, after which a series of Freudian dreams suggests the underlying causes of their marital differences. In the final scene they become reconciled, but their relationship more than likely remains unstable.

Three of many fine playwrights of the younger generation are Roma Mahieu (b. 1940), Guillermo Gentile (b. 1942), and Ricardo Monti (b. 1945). Mahieu was born in Poland, but she has lived in Argentina since 1950. Her *Juegos a la hora de la siesta* (1976; games at the siesta hour) portrays a group of children in a park, their games serving to convey their version of the adult world, with all its norms, prejudices, and role playing. The most ominous aspect of this popular drama, however, is its depiction of the cruelty and violence perpetrated by those supposedly still at an age of innocence. In 1972 Gentile's experimental allegory *Hablemos a calzón quitado* (let's talk with our pants off) gave Argentine audiences a deeper insight into their disastrous political situation. The three leading characters are El Padre (the Father), a transvestite who assaults taxi drivers by night; Juan, his twenty-four-year-old son, whose development has never progressed beyond adolescence; and Martín, a student who befriends Juan and moves in with him and his father. The Father and Martín soon find themselves at odds over Juan's intellectual and emotional education, Martín desiring to guide his friend to maturity, and the Father preferring to keep his son in a perpetual juvenile state. The play ends ambiguously with the departure of both the Father and Martín, leaving Juan alone to face the spectators and appeal to them for counsel. To those familiar with Argentine politics during the 1970s the symbolism is obvious. The Father (*padre* and *patria*—fatherland—are closely related etymologically) represents the paternalistic and thoroughly corrupt military establishment leading the nation, Juan the politically naïve and repressed Argentine people, and Martín the enlightened minority offering the only hope of achieving a just society. The open ending suggests that in 1972 it was too soon to predict the turn toward democracy that would occur in the following decade.

Ricardo Monti has been called one of Argentina's most individual, innovative, and serious voices in the contemporary theater. His works display a mélange of surrealism and the grotesque, which he utilizes to explore national and human concerns in a manner that is both universal and profoundly Argentine. His first play, *Una noche con el señor Magnus e hijos* (1970; a night with Mr. Magnus and sons), evolves an unstable, dreamlike reality in which Magnus looms as the central, unifying figure. A symbol of the forces of totalitarianism, he browbeats his sons, murders his wife Bibi, and seduces a young woman, Julia, whose fluctuating roles exemplify the simulation to which, in Monti's view, oppressed citizens of an authoritarian state must resort. At the beginning of the play, Magnus's son Gato relates his nightmare about the gruesome slaughter of a fat rat. This grotesque, surrealistic dream sets the prevailing irrational tone and foreshadows Magnus's murder, an act of rebellion carried out by his three sons. Included also are ritualistic ceremonies that reenact key episodes such as Bibi's funeral, disrupting linear time and reinforcing the pervasive oneiric atmosphere.

Historia tendenciosa de la clase media argentina (1971; tendentious history of the Argentine middle class) is Monti's most overtly political work, consisting of a series of satirical sketches covering approximately fifty years of Argentine history. Its central character is the Old Whore, La Pola, who symbolizes the entire nation. Other grotesque figures represent prominent politicians and generals of the twentieth century as well as Mr. Hawker and Mr. Peagg, who stand for, respectively,

British and American imperialism. The play's circuslike atmosphere is generated by Mr. Peagg's grotesque act of devouring Mr. Hawker and then compelling Sr. Boñiga, a representative of the Argentine landed aristocracy, to don the mask of a cow and thus demonstrate his country's submission to the foreign exploiter.

Even more than his first two plays, Monti's *Visita* (1977; visit) plunges its spectators into a magical, abstract world totally removed from objective reality or national concerns. The protagonist, Equis (X), probably symbolic of man, journeys through the timeless realm of eternity, which ultimately turns out to be a projection of his own subconscious. Here he encounters an elderly couple, Lali and Perla, parental and god figures he must destroy in a kind of macabre ritual as a step toward gaining his existential freedom. Monti has stated that his works depict the world as a sinister place in which the quest for power is a major motivating force in human behavior. *Visita* ends ambiguously, but if Equis does indeed achieve freedom, he will also have achieved power over his own destiny.

Chile

Despite its relatively small population, Chile has produced many exceptionally fine playwrights. Indeed, two of the major figures discussed above, Egon Wolff and Jorge Díaz, are Chilean. During the early years of the twentieth century there was a flurry of activity in this nation's theater, dominated by three traditional realists: Antonio Acevedo Hernández (1886–1962), Germán Luco Cruchaga (1894–1936), and Armando Moock (1894–1942). The 1930s witnessed a decline in the genre due at least in part to the world depression and the increasing popularity of the cinema. During the following decade, however, a period of dynamic renovation began with the founding in 1941 of the Teatro Experimental de la Universidad de Chile, later to become the Instituto del Teatro de la Universidad de Chile (ITUCH). This well-directed organization established a trend away from realism and social protest, presenting both classical and modern masterpieces and introducing innovative staging techniques. It also initiated a training program for actors with emphasis on rigorous academic discipline. Two years later, in 1943, the Teatro de Ensayo de la Universidad Católica opened its doors as a forum for contemporary Chilean playwrights. For a short time after World War II dramas dealing with national issues dominated the stage, but in 1961 the founding of the Teatro Ictus initiated a period of avant-gardism that was to last until the end of the decade. Although hundreds of amateur groups were organized under Salvador Allende's socialist regime (1970–73), the overall quality of the theater was not enhanced by their obsession with the class struggle and left-wing ideology. The military coup forced many of Chile's best playwrights into exile, and those who remained were muzzled for a time by a harsh policy of censorship. Nevertheless, the situation has improved somewhat with the return to Chile of many well-known intellectuals and with the government's support of ITUCH, now referred to as the Teatro Nacional.

María Asunción Requena (b. 1915), an early innovator of the post-World War II period and an acute observer of history, was born on the pampa in southern Chile and at present resides in France. Her *Fuerte Bulnes* (1955; Fort Bulnes) utilizes Brechtian techniques to depict the courage of colonists in Magallanes, Chile's extreme southern region, during the mid-nineteenth century. The life of the first Chilean female medical doctor is treated in *El camino más largo* (1959; the longest road). Requena's most artistically conceived work is *Ayayema* (1964; Ayayema), dramatizing the moral and physical deterioration of the Alacalufe Indians of Magallanes. The title refers to this primitive tribe's god of nature, who stimulated the Indians to survive in their hostile environment until civilization robbed them of their lands and sapped their energy. Another underlying theme is the mythic struggle between good and evil, a struggle destined to end in the defeat of the now extinct Alacalufes.

Isidora Aguirre (b. 1919) is well known as a social critic and satirist of the middle class. In addition to her activities as a dramatist, she has worked as a director and a professor of theater, most recently at the University of Concepción. Her first play, *Carolina* (1955; Carolina), remains one of the most popular ever written by a Chilean. A comedy of manners, it depicts a young married woman who, while traveling on a train with her husband, remembers that she left the kitchen stove burning. After prevailing upon a neighbor she meets by chance to return to the city and turn off the burner, she learns that her husband has set a trap that will send a trunk crashing onto anyone entering their home during their absence. Aguirre and Manuel Rojas (discussed in the chapter on fiction) co-authored *Población Esperanza* (1959; Hope Village), a depiction of the marginal lives of squatters in a *callampa* (mushroom) settlement, that is, a community of impoverished families who have established their makeshift homes overnight in vacant lots without authorization. A similar setting frames *Los papeleros* (1963; the paper gatherers), about a group of alienated dispossessed who eke out a precarious existence as scavengers. The protagonist of this rapidly paced, Brechtian drama, which is replete with musical interludes, attempts to organize her fellow workers in order to improve their housing conditions, and when their employers reject their demands, she retaliates by setting fire to the wretched hovels they provide for the *papeleros*.

Another dramatist influenced by Brecht is Fernando Debesa (b. 1921), whose *Mama Rosa* (1955; Mama Rosa) reflects the breakdown of the feudal system during the first half of the twentieth century. A Chilean institution, *la mama* is a family servant, usually a girl from the country, who devotes her entire adult life to raising the children of her rich employers. In Debesa's drama Mama Rosa witnesses the financial and moral decay of the family she serves over a period of fifty years. Ultimately her "children," having squandered their wealth through dissipation, take from her the money she has saved during a lifetime of sacrifice, leaving her destitute. In *Bernardo O'Higgins* (1961; Bernardo O'Higgins) Debesa re-creates the last days of Chile's national hero who, after liberating his country from Spain, spent the remaining years of his life in Lima, where he died in 1842. Shown initially on his deathbed, O'Higgins evokes a montage of episodes from his past, revealing his human reactions to crucial moments of history.

Sergio Vodanovic (b. 1926) was born in Yugoslavia, but Chile has been his home for most of his life. After graduating with a degree in law, he studied dramatic art at Yale University in the late 1950s and since that time has remained active both as a lawyer and a dramatist. He is best known for his satirical portraits of contemporary middle-class Chilean society. In 1959 Vodanovic achieved wide recognition for his prize-winning *Deja que los perros ladren* (let the dogs bark), an attack on political corruption. The leading characters are Esteban Uribe, the Director of Public Health; his wife Carmen; and their son Octavio, an idealistic law student. In the first act, while conversing in their modest home, the family is interrupted by the arrival of the Minister, who requests that Esteban close down an opposition newspaper, *La Razón*, for violation of public health regulations. When Esteban informs his superior that the premises of the newspaper have just passed inspection, he is threatened with the loss of his job and forced to carry out the Minister's demands. In the second act, two years later, Esteban has obviously achieved financial success, but he and Carmen are not happy. The climax occurs when Esteban, realizing that Octavio, now the Minister's secretary, has become a cynical opportunist like his father, decides to resign his post and expose the Minister's corrupt practices, using the now reopened *La Razón* as his forum. At first Octavio objects to his father's "foolishness," but after the editor of *La Razón* convinces him that only youth can change the system, Octavio announces his decision to provide them with compromising letters written by the Minister and thus bring about his downfall.

Vodanovic's masterwork is *Viña: Tres comedias en traje de baño* (1964; *Viña: Three Beach Plays*, in William I. Oliver, ed., *Voices of Change in the Spanish American Theater*, 1971), a trilogy of one-acters limning Chile's rigid social stratification and the masks, role playing, and alienation characteristic of such a divided society. *El delantal blanco* (*The White Uniform*), the most amusing of the three, presents a snobbish upper-class woman with her maid on the beach at Viña del Mar, Chile's best-known summer resort. Wondering how the world would look through the eyes of a servant and confident that her breed-

ing will stand out no matter how she is dressed, the Señora
suggests that they exchange clothing. However, when the Maid
begins to treat her "servant" the way she herself has been
treated, a dispute erupts between them and the real Señora,
who despite the *delantal blanco* she is wearing insists she is
not the Maid, is carried off to a mental clinic for observation.
La gente como nosotros (*People Like Us*) develops similar themes,
its characters being two couples stranded alongside a road to
Viña del Mar after their taxi breaks down. Carolina, a stripper
in a cabaret, and Freddy, a gigolo, have never met before, but
their conversation becomes more and more intimate, revealing
much about them and their life styles. At first the Lady and
the Gentleman, middle-aged, upper-class, and married, listen
in shocked silence to the younger pair's dialogue, but gradually
they too unmask themselves, expressing all the loneliness and
frustration they have experienced during their twenty-eight
barren years of marriage.

  Las exiladas (*The Exiles*), the third drama of Vodanovic's
trilogy, equates isolation with death and nothingness through
its portrait of two wealthy women, natives of Viña del Mar,
who look askance at the increasing numbers of middle-class
vacationers streaming into the resort. Emilia, a lonely forty-
year-old spinster, brings her mother, Hortensia—confined to
a wheelchair—to an unoccupied corner of the beach. Suddenly
two young men searching for clams appear and strike up a
conversation with Emilia. The latter's complete naïveté soon
manifests itself, causing one of the youths to feign a desire to
kiss her, but instead he places a dead fish over her mouth and
disappears. Moments later, Emilia discovers that her mother
has died. After ordering their servant to throw the body into
a nearby dump, she sits down in her mother's wheelchair and
tenderly presses the dead fish against her lips, the only kiss
she has ever known.

  The political events of the 1970s provide the background
for two of Vodanovic's more recent works: *Igual que antes* (1973;
same as ever), telling of the breakup of a wealthy industrialist's
family under Salvador Allende's regime; and *¿Cuántos años tiene
un día?* (1970; how many years does a day have?), about four

television journalists who, despite the repression on the heels of the 1973 military coup, remain in Chile determined to assist in the nation's struggle for cultural survival.

His short life notwithstanding, Luis Alberto Heiremans (1928–1964) is considered one of Chile's finest modern playwrights. *Moscas sobre el mármol* (1951; flies on the marble) represents a despairing view of life, its protagonist being a man named Julián who devises a plan to kill his friend, Ernesto, because he and Julián's wife are in love. When the plan backfires, causing Julián's death, his mother rejoices because she no longer has to share him with his wife. The title suggests the absurdity of mankind (*moscas*) confronting an impenetrable world (*el mármol*). Another of Heiremans's highly acclaimed dramas, *Sigue la estrella* (1958; follow the star), re-creates the biblical tale of the three Magi, enriching its message with modern philosophical overtones. Man I, Man II, and Man III, who ultimately turn out to be Melchior, Gaspar, and Balthazar, are starving musicians following a star to the south in search of *algo* (something). Along the way they are joined by several disoriented individuals, all of whom eventually arrive at a stable bearing gifts. The play ends without mention of the Christ child, but rather with the implication that the objective of their existential quest is within reach. The theme of man's search for self-fulfillment is repeated in *Versos de ciego* (1962; verses of a blind man), a longer version of *Sigue la estrella*. In *Versos de ciego*, however, the three musicians and their companions never catch a glimpse of their goal; instead they discover mutual love and respect for one another, prompting them to pledge that their efforts will continue unabated. Critics generally agree that *Sigue la estrella* surpasses its successor in dramatic impact, the later play suffering from excessive symbolism and superfluous digressions.

Heiremans weaves everyday reality, biblical myth, and the modern theme of solitude into the dramatic fabric of his most celebrated drama, *El Abanderado* (1962; the Standardbearer). The setting is a rural community in the province of Valparaíso where an annual religious festival called the Cruz de Mayo (Cross of May) is being prepared. El Abanderado, a bandit of local fame who wears a white flowing scarf—thus his sobriquet—has just been handed over to the police by a former friend, El Tordo. The son of a brothel owner known as Pepa de Oro, El Abanderado took to crime at an early age after a childhood of neglect. Now, twenty years later, he has returned to the brothel, longing to see his mother once again. Pepa de Oro refuses to acknowledge their relationship, however, and only a young soldier, Torrealba, shows compassion for the lone prisoner before, in the final scene, he is taken away on a train to be incarcerated. *El Abanderado* is replete with biblical symbolism, the protagonist emerging as a Christ figure, El Tordo as Judas Iscariot, Torrealba as the Good Samaritan, and Pepa de Oro as a combination of Mary Magdalene and Judas.

One is tempted to believe that Landa, the protagonist of *El tony chico* (1962; the little clown), embodies Heiremans's idealism as well as his realization of life's brevity. An outsider fearful of leading a meaningless existence, Landa finds a job in a circus—a metaphor of the world—where he befriends a lonely and miserable orphan, Juanucho. The two develop an act that becomes the main attraction of the show, but soon thereafter Landa dies in an accident. His gift of love to Juanucho, however, has made his own life worthwhile and, in a sense, guaranteed him a measure of immortality. This moving tribute to human solidarity may be Heiremans's final message.

One of the younger generation's leading dramatists, Alejandro Sieveking (b. 1934), is well known for his penetrating psychological portraits and ingenious fusion of fantasy and reality. His Teatro del Ángel was an important cultural entity during the Allende regime, but after the military coup he emigrated to Costa Rica, where he continued his directing activities for a decade. Encouraged by the prospects of working again in his native land, he returned to Chile in 1984. Sieveking's first play, *Mi hermano Cristián* (1957; my brother Cristián), dramatizes the tensions within a family due to the tyranny of the elder son Cristián, who five years before was paralyzed in a shooting accident. Never allowing his brother Ariel to forget that he caused the tragedy, Cristián refuses to leave his bed and invents lies to gain sympathy for himself. The play ends on an optimistic and somewhat naïve note when Cristián, faced with the departure of Ariel and the separation of his parents, undergoes an abrupt personality change.

Ánimas de día claro (1962; souls in the light of day) is based on the Chilean superstition that the spirits of those who die without having accomplished their lifetime goals remain on earth until their desires are satisfied. The setting is a dilapidated farmhouse where five deceased sisters, all spinsters, continue to dwell, each seeking some form of self-fulfillment. The youngest, Bertina, though eighty years of age, is suddenly rejuvenated by the arrival of a handsome young man called Eulogio, who, despite rumors that the house is haunted, wants to buy the property. The two feel an increasingly strong attraction to each other until, in the final lines, they are forced to recognize that they can be united only after Eulogio's death. But the miracle of their relationship is celebrated by the sudden flowering of trees barren for many years. The poetic combination of popular myth and everyday reality makes this one of Sieveking's most memorable creations.

The 1973 military coup inspired Sieveking to write *Pequeños animales abatidos* (1974; small abject animals). A condemnation of the role played by the CIA in provoking the upheaval, this play suggests that Salvador Allende, a truly progressive leader, found himself obliged by historical circumstances to govern according to reactionary middle-class norms, these actions resulting in his downfall. The political theme is not presented in traditional form, however, but rather through the artful juxtaposition of living and dead characters swept up in rapidly changing time sequences. Also published in 1974 but very different in subject matter is *La mantis religiosa* (*The Praying Mantis*, in *Modern International Drama*, 17, 1, Fall, 1983), a thriller freighted with powerful psychological, sexual, and mythical overtones. (The mantis is an insect that feeds on other insects, often its mate, clasping its prey in forelimbs raised upward as if in prayer.) The leading characters are three sisters, Llalla, Lina, and Adela. We are led to believe that at some time in the recent past Llalla and Lina murdered their fiancés by throwing them into the den of a monstrous, demented

creature—a fourth sister and the *mantis religiosa* of the title
—who lurks behind a closed door and wails repeatedly throughout the drama. When Adela's fiancé Juan comes to call, he
inevitably meets a similar fate, but unlike the other two youths,
he is saved by the three sisters, though bleeding and half-
clothed, from the clutches of his captor. The climax occurs when
Juan berates Adela for robbing him of the most marvelous
experience of his entire life, and Adela fulfills his desire for
self-destruction by shooting him dead.

Paraguay

Paraguay is a bilingual nation that has produced dramas
in both Spanish and Guarani, the language of the Guarani
Indians. Despite a growing number of playwrights and theatrical performances, few Paraguayan works of high quality are
to be found, and Paraguayan theater lags behind most other
Spanish American countries. This situation reflects a cultural
backwardness that can be attributed at least in part to a history
of repressive dictatorial regimes. Another major problem is that
because of a lack of publishing houses, few Paraguayan plays
ever appear in print. Nevertheless, efforts have been made in
recent years to vitalize the theater. In 1942 the Ateneo Para-
guayo was founded for the purpose of developing the nation's
art, music, and drama. Six years later Roque Centurión Miranda (1900–1960) and Josefina Pla (also discussed in the chapter
on poetry) initiated the Escuela Municipal de Arte Escénico in
Asunción, the capital. And in 1969 a group of actors inspired
by the Polish director and theoretician Jerzy Grotowski formed
the Teatro Tiempoovillo, which has been acclaimed repeatedly
at international theater festivals.

An Argentine who became a Paraguayan citizen, José Arturo Alsina (b. 1897) has achieved prominence as a prolific
writer of melodramas. Typical of his work is *Intruso* (1960;
intruder), the portrait of an illegitimate son who supports his
sisters despite the scorn they heap upon him. Roque Centurión
Miranda was a respected producer during his lifetime, but he
also collaborated with Josefina Pla on plays written in both
Spanish and Guarani. Their *Desheredados* (1933; underprivi-

leged) assailed the rich who allowed impoverished peasants to fight the Chaco War (1932–35) while their own lives remained unchanged. Even more controversial at the time of its performance was these two authors' prize-winning *Aquí no pasa nada* (1945; nothing happens here), about a man who continues to love a child he thought was his own after discovering that the child is the son of his wife's lover.

Although many of her plays remain unpublished, Josefina Pla is Paraguay's most widely known dramatist. She lectured for many years at the Escuela Municipal de Arte Escénico and in addition to her dramatic works has published poetry, short stories, literary criticism, and a scholarly history of Paraguayan theater. In *Y Raquel clamó por sus hijos* (1949; and Raquel cried out for her children) Pla realistically portrays a middle-class woman condemned to poverty and abuse by the father of her illegitimate children. Her *Alcestes* (1951; Alcestis) represents a reworking of Euripides' tragicomedy, which takes place in antiquity but also alludes to the present-day world. A fine example of her drama is *Historia de un número* (1969; story of a number), a fast-paced one-act farce that sketches the life of an unnamed individual (He) who suffers from the misfortune of being born without an identifying number. Thus, he discovers in the course of his existence that he cannot purchase clothes, travel, join organizations, receive mail, or find a job. Nor is he able to make friends or marry because he is seen as an outsider by everybody except two brutal recruiters who hustle him off to the army. In the final scene, having been arrested for robbery, he appears in court where his only defense is his lifelong lack of a number. The judge corrects this deficiency, however, by granting him *para siempre* (forever) the number 131313—to be worn on a striped uniform. Pla's absurd comedy explores a major cause of alienation in today's world, namely, bureaucratic society's denial of the right to affirm one's authentic personality.

Uruguay

Prior to 1945 Uruguayan theater was dominated by Argentine playwrights and theater groups except for the late nineteenth and early twentieth centuries, when the above-mentioned Uruguayan Florencio Sánchez loomed as the major dramatist of his generation. Thus, in their discussions of the theater before World War II critics often refer to the *teatro rioplatense* (theater of the River Plate region) instead of focusing on the two nations separately. In 1939 a Uruguayan group founded the Teatro del Pueblo but had only limited success. In 1947 the Comedia Nacional was initiated by the municipal government of Montevideo, and at about this same time the Escuela Nacional de Arte Dramático was organized. In 1949 El Galpón, which was to become a major innovative force in contemporary Uruguayan theater, began producing experimental dramas, often with left-wing political overtones. Since the mid-1960s El Galpón has had its own school for actors.

Although Fernán Silva Valdés (1887–1975) earned a solid reputation as a poet in the 1920s, it was not until many years later that he achieved fame for his folkloric dramas. By far the most important of these is *Santos Vega* (1952; Santos Vega), named after a gaucho *payador* (minstrel) who, according to legend, met his only defeat in a *payada* (contest between improvising *payadores*) with the devil. In Silva Valdés's version, however, Santos Vega is portrayed not only as an irresistible Don Juan, but also as the victor in his *payada* with Satan. And when he dies under an ombu (a tree of the pampa), two of his sweethearts discover that his body has vanished; this disappearance symbolizes his transformation into a popular myth.

Discussed previously as a writer of fiction, Mario Benedetti has also excelled as a playwright. His most successful dramatic piece, *Ida y vuelta* (1963; round trip), is a Brechtian comedy in which the author plays a major onstage role in motivating the actions of his protagonists. Juan, suddenly feeling the urge to travel, departs without his wife, María, for an extended trip to Europe. Upon his return, it soon becomes evident that he has changed radically, and they agree to separate. At this point the "author" attempts to court María by assuring her that he will be everything Juan is not, but his plan backfires, precipitating her return to her husband. *Ida y vuelta* is framed by the dull life of the Uruguayan welfare state on the brink of the political and economic disaster of the late 1960s and early 1970s. (The disruptive activities of left-wing urban guerrillas known as the Tupamaros led to a military dictatorship in 1973.) Although Benedetti conveys the impression that his characters escape his control, in reality it is his own intervention that leads to Juan's departure for Europe as well as to the couple's revitalized marriage. It would seem, then, that a strong desire for change on the part of the author underlies both the setting and plot of his drama.

El reportaje (1968; the report) explores the effects of sincerity on human relations, its protagonist being a novelist (Valdés) who in an interview evokes three episodes from his past. In the first of these Valdés calls his employer an *hijo de puta* (son of a bitch); in the second Valdés's bickering parents finally agree to part; and in the third his relationship with his mistress comes to an end after he admits to having caused the suicide of a friend. Irony pervades each episode as well as the stilted foreground dialogue between the self-sufficient protagonist and his pompous critic.

Carlos Maggi (b. 1922), the leading Uruguayan dramatist of his generation, has also achieved recognition as a short-story writer and essayist. His theater presents a satirical view of modern society, especially of the middle class. In *La trastienda* (1958; the back room of the store), his first success, he relies on black humor and the grotesque to depict moments in the life of a middle-class family on the road to ruin. *El patio de la Torcaza* (1967; the patio of the Torcaza) parodies the Spanish *sainete* (a one-act melodramatic comedy), the heroine ending up as a prostitute, and her sweetheart and potential savior as her procurer, while the patio emerges as an acid metaphor of Uruguay. Many critics consider *La biblioteca* (1959; *The Library*, in William I. Oliver, ed., *Voices of Change in the Spanish American Theater,* 1971) as Maggi's best and most representative work. In the first act the young director of the library is polishing a speech he will give to introduce the secretary general, who is to arrive within the hour to lay the cornerstone of the institution's new wing. The director, however, is thwarted by a series of interruptions, some of which are a coquette seeking a job; a phone call from the director's fiancée regarding details of their wedding; a tailor demanding that the director try on his wedding suit; a patron determined to find the work of an obscure Italian engraver; and a janitor suggesting that they purchase a spittoon for the secretary general. The act ends with the latter's arrival and the harried, half-naked director's exit to greet him.

In the last two acts a total of thirty-five years pass, during which the working conditions in the library steadily worsen. Insted of constructing a new wing, the authorities have demolished parts of the old building, set up makeshift stacks, and relocated the main reading room in the dimly lit basement. The director's secretary now spends most of her time serving tea to the staff, all of whom chatter inanely about their ills and retirement benefits. Two amusing episodes involve a German patron who seeks Schopenhauer's doctoral dissertation, provoking hysterical laughter over his pronunciation of the title; and the rantings of an irate literary critic because he cannot find the works of an author he is researching for *The Alpha and Omega Review*, published at the University of Iowa. At this moment an engineer suddenly appears, throws the critic out, and informs the director that he and his staff must evacuate the building because it is being converted into offices for the "International Committee for Refugees from the Near East in the Far East." But the director remains undaunted, confident that he can find working quarters, perhaps in a warehouse, where they can all put in their time until they are eligible for retirement. And to soothe the feelings of his staff he expounds on the benefits of the seniority they have all achieved. "Seniority is the most important thing there is . . . it embalms slowly . . . . Whether one be at home or in the office, nothing matters any more. One is protected from the world and its demands. One lives marvelously, sheltered by the eighth marvel of the universe: pyramids of paper."

Like Benedetti's *Ida y vuelta*, *La biblioteca* was written on the eve of Uruguay's descent into chaos. An employee of the National Library for several years, Maggi presents this institution as a Kafkaesque metaphor of his homeland, with its

spiritual malaise and its myths of bureaucratic order and progress. At the same time he inveighs against the loss of the work
ethic, the crass materialism, and the emasculation of intellectual endeavor in Uruguay. His combination of absurd farce and
sophisticated comedy, however, goes beyond national borders,
reflecting conditions that threaten much of the Western world.
Perhaps for this reason it is considered one of Spanish America's best comedies.

A leading Uruguayan playwright of the succeeding generation is Mauricio Rosencof (b. 1934), also a journalist and
short-story writer. His prize-winning drama *Las ranas* (1961;
the frogs) realistically limns the shocking poverty, ignorance,
and brutality in the Montevideo slums. *Los caballos* (1967; the
horses), on the other hand, molds dreams and reality into a
more mature, aesthetically satisfying work of art. The setting
is a rural area of sugar-cane plantations where Segundo, his
wife Clotilde, and their two children, Lito and Anita, appear
in search of work. The ten-year-old Lito gallops happily around
on a stick, his make-believe pony, until his father finds work
for him in the fields and he tearfully abandons his plaything.
Ulpiano, an aging cane worker who has just retired, entertains
Lito with tales of his recently acquired charger on which he
yearns to fight again in the civil war. Barreto, a drunkard, and
his wife Azucena, supposedly the owners of a horse named Paco,
describe the carriage they have purchased to return to the city.
All of these fantasies are exposed, however, when Anita falls
ill, and Segundo attempts to find a means of transportation to
take her to a doctor. And, in the final lines, Anita's death suggests the emptiness of all the hopes on which her life de-
pended. The play's title emerges as a symbol of the dreams and
fantasies people come to believe in order to make their lives
more bearable.

▪ A FINAL WORD

Firm conclusions are difficult to draw from a study of this nature because it deals with such a pluralism of literary themes and styles; instead, a few broad generalizations would appear to be in order. Since 1941 Spanish American fiction has developed from traditional realism treating regional issues into one of the most vital avant-garde art forms in the world today. While seldom losing sight of the multiple problems plaguing their individual societies, many novelists and short-story writers have, in addition, discovered unbridled imagination and technical innovations as poetically vivifying elements for their creations. The result is something akin to surrealism, often labeled magical realism, a term not yet defined to the satisfaction of all critics. Some of the best fiction writers also have insisted on inventing a new language based on the spoken vernacular in order to purge their writings of the stilted, unnatural Spanish inherited from Spain. And others, disenchanted with language as a tool to mirror reality, have turned to self-conscious metafiction as a vehicle of artistic expression.

In poetry, surrealism and symbolism continue to thrive throughout most of the continent, their intense subjectivity and hallucinatory imagery offering great appeal to the Latin imagination and innovative spirit. Another important trend is toward greater directness and simplicity, characteristics not only of antipoetry, with its emphasis on irony, absurdity, and alienation, but also of revolutionary verses crying out in anguish against poverty, injustice, and political repression. Although feminism has yet to become a major issue in Spanish America, women poets of singular merit are expressing their objections to male domination.

The least recognized of the three major genres, drama has displayed surprising vitality in recent decades, having evolved from realistic commercial theater to a wide variety of experimental art forms including the theater of the absurd, the theater of cruelty, and the theater of political protest, the last often created and produced collectively. In addition, the drama has been invigorated by the use of masks and rituals, devices designed to underscore the identity crisis and the search for order in the turbulent world of today.

The vast diversity of Spanish American literature reflects the variegated experiences of developing countries that, despite their cultural similarities, reveal striking differences as well. The multilensed vision provided by the fiction, poetry, and drama of these societies offers the reader a glimpse of virtually all levels of reality, from the down-to-earth view of gritty, everyday life in a specific locale to the more universal realm of fantasy and myth. The 1980s have wreaked havoc on the economies of our southern neighbors, eroding book markets and reducing the size of theater audiences. Nevertheless, the literary scene evinces considerable evidence of health and vigor. The growing number of translations and the resultant recognition abroad of Spanish American writers would seem to indicate that their vibrant creations will continue in the mainstream of world literature for a long time to come.

SELECTED BIBLIOGRAPHY

ANTHOLOGIES OF SPANISH AMERICAN LITERATURE IN TRANSLATION

General Anthologies

Babin, María Teresa, and Stan Steiner, eds. *Borinquen: An Anthology of Puerto Rican Literature.* New York: Alfred A. Knopf, 1974.

Carpentier, Hortense, and Janet Brof, eds. *Doors and Mirrors: Fiction and Poetry from Spanish America (1920–1970).* New York: The Viking Press, 1972.

Cohen, J. M., ed. *Latin American Writing Today.* Baltimore: Penguin Books, 1967.

———. *Writers in the New Cuba.* Baltimore: Penguin Books, 1967.

Coulthard, George Robert, ed. *Caribbean Literature: An Anthology.* London: University of London Press, 1966.

Donoso, José, and William Henkin, eds. *The TriQuarterly Anthology of Contemporary Latin American Literature.* New York: E. P. Dutton, 1969. Originally a special issue of *TriQuarterly* (Fall–Winter 1968–69).

Flakoll, Darwin J., and Claribel Alegría, eds. *New Voices in Hispanic America: An Anthology.* Boston: Beacon Press, 1962.

Freemantle, Anne, ed. *Latin-American Literature Today.* New York: New American Library, 1977.

Jones, Willis Knapp, ed. *Spanish-American Literature in Translation, a Selection of Poetry, Fiction and Drama since 1888.* 2 vols. New York: Frederick Ungar, 1963.

Latin-American Writing: Essays, Fiction, Bilingual Poetry. Special issue of *Chicago Review* 27, 2 (Autumn 1975).

Rodríguez Monegal, Emir, ed. *Borzoi Anthology of Latin American Literature*. 2 vols. New York: Alfred A. Knopf, 1977.
Williams, Miller, ed. *Chile: An Anthology of New Writing*. Kent, Ohio: Kent State University Press, 1968.

Anthologies of Fiction

Brotherston, Gordon, and Mario Vargas Llosa, eds. *Seven Stories from Spanish America*. London and New York: Pergamon Press, 1968.
Carranza, Sylvia, and María Juana Cazabon, eds. *Cuban Short Stories 1959–1966*. Havana: Book Institute, 1967.
Colford, William, ed. and trans. *Classic Tales from Spanish America*. New York: Barron's Educational Service, 1962.
Franco, Jean, ed. *Short Stories in Spanish/Cuentos Hispánicos*. Baltimore: Penguin Books, 1966.
Howes, Barbara, ed. *The Eye of the Heart*. New York: Avon Books, 1973.
Mancini, Pat McNees, ed. *Contemporary Latin American Short Stories*. Greenwich, Conn.: Fawcett, 1974.
Manguel, Alberto, ed. *Other Fires: Short Fiction by Latin American Women*. New York: Crown, 1986.
Menton, Seymour, ed. *The Spanish American Short Story: A Critical Anthology*. Berkeley: University of California Press, 1980.
Torres-Rioseco, Arturo, ed. *Short Stories of Latin America*. New York: Las Américas Publishing Co., 1963.
Wagenheim, Kal, ed. *Cuentos: An Anthology of Short Stories from Puerto Rico*. New York: Schocken Books, 1978.
Yates, Donald A., ed. *Latin Blood: The Best Crime and Detective Stories of South America*. New York: Herder & Herder, 1972.

Anthologies of Poetry

Ahern, Maureen, and David Tipton, eds. *Peru: The New Poetry*. London: London Magazine Editions, 1970.
Benedetti, Mario, ed. *Unstill Life: An Introduction to the Spanish Poetry of Latin America*. Translated by Darwin J. Flakoll and Claribel Alegría. New York: Harcourt Brace & World, 1969.
Benson, Rachel, trans. *Nine Latin American Poets*. New York: Cypress Books, 1968.

Brotherston, Gordon, and Edward Dorn, eds. and trans. *Our Word: Guerrilla Poems from Latin America/Palabra de guerrillero: Poesía guerrillera de Latinoamérica*. London: Cape Goliard, 1968.

Caracciolo-Trejo, Enrique, ed. *The Penguin Book of Latin American Verse*. Baltimore: Penguin Books, 1971.

Cohen, John Michael, ed. *The Penguin Book of Spanish Verse*. Baltimore: Penguin Books, 1960.

Crow, Mary, ed. *Woman Who Has Sprouted Wings: Poems by Contemporary Latin American Women Poets*. Pittsburgh: Latin American Literary Review Press, 1984.

Garrigue, Jean, ed. *Translations by American Poets*. Athens: Ohio University Press, 1970.

Márquez, Robert, ed. *Latin American Revolutionary Poetry: A Bilingual Anthology*. New York: Monthly Review Press, 1974.

Marzán, Julio, ed. *Inventing a Word: An Anthology of Twentieth-Century Puerto Rican Poetry*. New York: Columbia University Press in association with the Center for Inter-American Relations, 1980.

Matilla, Alfredo, and Iván Silén, eds. *The Puerto Rican Poets*. New York: Bantam Books, 1972.

Paz, Octavio, and Mark Strand, eds. *New Poetry of Mexico*. New York: E. P. Dutton, 1970.

Randall, Margaret, ed. and trans. *Breaking the Silences: 20th Century Poetry by Cuban Women*. Vancouver, B.C.: Pulp Press, 1982.

Shand, William, ed. *Contemporary Argentine Poetry*. Buenos Aires: Fundación Argentina para la Poesía, 1969.

Tarn, Nathaniel, ed. *Con Cuba: An Anthology of Cuban Poetry of the Last Sixty Years*. London and New York: Cape Goliard Press in association with Grossman Publishers, 1969.

Young Poetry of the Americas. Vol. 1. Washington, D.C.: Pan American Union, 1967.

Anthologies of Drama

Colecchia, Francesca, and Julio Matas, eds. and trans. *Selected Latin American One-Act Plays*. Pittsburgh: University of Pittsburgh Press, 1973.

Luzuriaga, Gerardo, and Robert S. Rudder, eds. *The Orgy: Modern One-Act Plays from Latin America*. Los Angeles: UCLA Latin American Center, University of California, 1974.

Oliver, William I., ed. *Voices of Change in the Spanish American Theater: An Anthology.* Austin: University of Texas Press, 1971.

Woodyard, George, ed. *The Modern Stage in Latin America: Six Plays.* New York: E. P. Dutton, 1971.

WORKS OF CRITICISM, LITERARY HISTORY, AND BIBLIOGRAPHY

Adams, M. I. *Three Authors of Alienation* [María Luisa Bombal, Juan Carlos Onetti, Alejo Carpentier]. Austin: University of Texas Press, 1975.

Aldrich, Earl M., Jr. *The Modern Short Story in Peru.* Madison: University of Wisconsin Press, 1966.

Anderson Imbert, Enrique. *Spanish American Literature: A History.* Translated by John V. Falconieri. Detroit: Wayne State University Press, 1963.

Bacarisse, Salvador, ed. *Contemporary Latin American Fiction.* Edinburgh: Scottish Academic Press, 1980.

Brotherston, Gordon. *Latin American Poetry: Origins and Presence.* Cambridge, England: Cambridge University Press, 1975.

———. *The Emergence of the Latin American Novel.* Cambridge, England: Cambridge University Press, 1977.

Brushwood, John S. *Mexico in Its Novel.* Austin: University of Texas Press, 1966.

———. *The Spanish American Novel: A Twentieth-Century Survey.* Austin: University of Texas Press, 1975.

Carrera Andrade, Jorge. *Reflections on Spanish-American Poetry.* Translated by Don C. Bliss and Gabriela de C. Bliss. Albany: State University of New York Press, 1973.

Donoso, José. *The Boom in Spanish American Literature: A Personal History.* Translated by Gregory Kolovakos. New York: Columbia University Press in association with the Center for Inter-American Relations, 1977.

Fernández Moreno, César, Julio Ortega, and Ivan A. Schulman, eds. *Latin America in Its Literature.* Translated by Mary G. Berg. New York: Holmes & Meier, 1980.

Forster, Merlin H., ed. *Tradition and Renewal: Essays on Twentieth-Century Latin American Literature and Culture.* Urbana: University of Illinois Press, 1975.

Foster, David William. *Currents in the Contemporary Argentine Novel.* Columbia: University of Missouri Press, 1975.

―――. *A Dictionary of Contemporary Latin American Authors*. Tempe: Center for Latin American Studies, Arizona State University, 1975.

―――. *Studies in the Contemporary Spanish American Short Story*. Columbia: University of Missouri Press, 1979.

Foster, David William, and Virginia Ramos Foster, eds. *Modern Latin American Literature*. 2 vols. New York: Frederick Ungar, 1975.

Franco, Jean. *The Modern Culture of Latin America: Society and the Artist*. New York: F. A. Praeger, 1967.

―――. *An Introduction to Spanish-American Literature*. Cambridge, England: Cambridge University Press, 1969.

―――. *Spanish American Literature since Independence*. New York: Barnes & Noble, 1973.

Freudenthal, Juan R., and Patricia M. Freudenthal, eds. *Index to Anthologies of Latin American Literature in English Translation*. Boston: G. K. Hall, 1977.

Gallagher, D. P. *Modern Latin American Literature*. London: Oxford University Press, 1973.

Garfield, Evelyn Picon. *Women's Voices from Latin America: Interviews with Six Contemporary Authors*. Detroit: Wayne State University Press, 1985.

Guibert, Rita. *Seven Voices*. New York: Alfred A. Knopf, 1973.

Harss, Luis, and Barbara Dohmann. *Into the Mainstream*. New York: Harper & Row, 1967.

Jackson, Richard L. *Black Writers in Latin America*. Albuquerque: University of New Mexico Press, 1979.

Jones, Willis Knapp. *Behind Spanish American Footlights*. Austin: University of Texas Press, 1966.

Langford, Walter M. *The Mexican Novel Comes of Age*. Notre Dame, Ind.: University of Notre Dame Press, 1971.

Lyday, Leon F., and George W. Woodyard, eds. *Dramatists in Revolt*. Austin: University of Texas Press, 1976.

MacAdam, Alfred J. *Modern Latin-American Narratives: The Dreams of Reason*. Chicago: University of Chicago Press, 1977.

Magnarelli, Sharon. *The Lost Rib: Female Characters in the Spanish-American Novel*. Lewisburg, Pa.: Bucknell University Press, 1985.

Meehan, Thomas C. *Essays on Argentine Narrators*. Valencia, Spain: Albatros, Ediciones Hispanófila, 1982.

Menton, Seymour. *Prose Fiction of the Cuban Revolution*. Austin: University of Texas Press, 1975.

―――. *Magic Realism Rediscovered, 1918–1981*. Philadelphia: The Art Alliance Press, 1983.

Morris, Robert J. *The Contemporary Peruvian Theater.* Lubbock: Texas Tech Press, 1977.

Ortega, Julio. *Poetics of Change: The New Spanish-American Narrative.* Translated by Galen D. Greaser. Austin: University of Texas Press, 1984.

Peden, Margaret Sayers, ed. *The Latin American Short Story: A Critical History.* Boston: Twayne, 1983.

Rodman, Selden. *South America of the Poets.* Carbondale, Ill.: Southern Illinois University Press, 1972.

Schwartz, Kessel. *A New History of Spanish American Fiction.* 2 vols. Coral Gables, Fla.: University of Miami Press, 1971.

Shaw, Bradley A. *Latin American Literature in English Translation: An Annotated Bibliography.* New York: New York University Press, 1976.

———. *Latin American Literature in English 1975–1978.* New York: Center for Inter-American Relations, 1979.

Sommers, Joseph. *After the Storm: Landmarks of the Modern Mexican Novel.* Albuquerque: University of New Mexico Press, 1968.

Souza, Raymond D. *Major Cuban Novelists: Innovation and Tradition.* Columbia: University of Missouri Press, 1976.

Studies in Short Fiction 8, 1 (1971). Essays on the contemporary Spanish American short story.

The Drama Review 14, 2 (Winter 1970). Essays on Latin American theater.

Tittler, Jonathan. *Narrative Irony in the Contemporary Spanish-American Novel.* Ithaca, N.Y.: Cornell University Press, 1984.

Valenzuela, Victor M. *Contemporary Latin American Writers.* New York: Las Américas Publishing Co., 1971.

Vázquez Amaral, J. *The Contemporary Latin American Narrative.* New York: Las Américas Publishing Co., 1970.

Zyla, Wolodymyr T., and Wendell M. Aycock, eds. *Ibero-American Letters in a Comparative Perspective.* Comparative Literature Symposium, Vol. 10. Lubbock: Texas Tech Press, 1978.

INDEX

333

Index